Volume II

Wooden Planes in 19th Century America

Planemaking by the Chapins at Union Factory, 1826-1929

by

Kenneth D. Roberts

FITZWILLIAM, NEW HAMPSHIRE - 1983

Published by
Ken Roberts Publishing Co.
Fitzwilliam, NH 03447
Copyright © 1983 by Kenneth D. Roberts
Printed in the United States of America
First Edition of Volume II
ISBN 0-913602-59-0

All Rights Reserved

No part of this publication may be reproduced
or transmitted in any form or by any means,
electronic or mechanical, including
photocopy, recording or any information storage
and retrieval system, without permission
in writing from the Publisher.

Dust jacket, title page and chapter headings
designed and type-set by Jane W. Roberts
Old Time Printing, Fitzwilliam, NH

Printed by
Bond Press, Inc.
Hartford, Connecticut

Bound by
General Book Binding Co., Inc.
South Hadley, Mass.

Cover Material Skivertex-Wombati
Furnished by Whitman Products, Ltd., Johnston, RI

Imprints used on the Union Factory Planes

Planes less than 3/4 in. thickness were stamped H.CHAPIN only. Planes larger than 3/4 in. had two imprints: UNION FACTORY/WARRANTED in a semi-circular design; and a separate imprint H.CHAPIN in a straight line, located under the Union Factory imprint. There was apparently no regularity as to whether the imprints read right or left on the side. Occasionally the H.CHAPIN imprint was inadvertently inverted in relation to the Union Factory stamp. See imprint at extreme right. The imprint used by Chapin-Stephens Co. was entirely different.

Preface

When I wrote the series of articles "Wooden Planes, Some Basic Definitions", beginning in 1966, published in the *Chronicle of Early American Industries Association*, considerable information was gleaned studying the *1874 H. Chapin's Son Catalogue*, reprinted herein. In writing previous published material concerning Connecticut clocks, I had been aware of significant data in trade catalogues. After acquiring through purchase a copy of the *Chapin-Stephens Co. Catalogue No. 114*, which I published in 1975, I first became acquainted with Mrs. C. Edwin Blake, great-granddaughter of Hermon Chapin, founder of the Union Factory at Pine Meadow in 1826. Her father, Frank M. Chapin, had been president of Chapin-Stephens Co. When this firm was sold to Stanley Rule & Level Co. in 1929, fortunately Frank Chapin saved considerable records and manuscript material, some of which dated previously to the founding of this Chapin enterprise. Upon his death this collection of records went to Mrs. Blake, who subsequently turned these over to the Connecticut Historical Society at Hartford. Immediately thereafter my studies of this material began. Now, after seven years, I have pieced together this documentary evidence into this publication concerning three generations of Chapins who managed the Union Factory at Pine Meadow, Connecticut. It was here that Hermon Chapin was the first planemaker to use water power and machinery to produce wooden planes. A great industry followed in United States.

As a young boy, I was brought up at Farmington, some twenty miles south of New Hartford. Here the same Farmington River that powered the Union Factory reached its southerly point and continued to flow north and east some twenty miles into the Connecticut River. At the age of 12 in 1928 my mother drove me in her Model T Ford to Camp Pioneer, the Hartford County Boy Scout camp. We passed by the then operating factory of Chapin-Stephens and climbed west through New Hartford Center to West Hill Pond. If only I had been old enough to then comprehend that some 55 years later, I would struggle through these records. Answers to many questions could have been given.

This publication is intended to relate historical developments concerning the manufacture of wooden tools (planes, rules, levels and gauges) especially for the interests of tool collectors. The major scene where this industrial development occurred during the first half of the 19th century was here in Connecticut, where lead continued through the remainder of the century. Considerable material should be of interest to economic historians. Hopefully this will also reveal techniques and sources of documentary material for study of local history.

The text has been typeset in English Times. The footnotes have been typed and are at the end of each chapter. The photographic illustrations are listed continuously in Arabic figures. In an effort to simplify the complexity of continuous Roman numerals, the plates and table numbers for each chapter commence with I. Plates are copies of original printed or hand-written documents and tables are transcriptions of deeds, letters, etc. or summaries of data. A listing of all illustrations, plates and tables appears in the front material, indicating title, chapter and page. This information has been placed as near to the text as possible. However, in a few cases these are not in consecutive order, but any confusion as to location can be immediately corrected by reference to these front listings. An index to persons and subject matter appears on the last two pages. While the *1859 Union Factory Price List* has been reprinted entirely, pages 129-134, this has also been printed separately for use in studying the cost data on pages 129-134. It is suggested that owners may wish to make a pocket for this on the inside back cover. Sixteen photographs in color, designated A through P, of planes appear on unnumbered pages between pages 252 and 243. While these are not referred to in the text, it will be readily apparent from reading their captions as to their relevancy.

Another principal source of documentary material has been a detailed study of the artifacts made at the Union Factory. During the last ten years I have assembled a representative group of over 350 different planes made at the Union Factory to which I refer as the Chapin Collection. It is my intent to turn this over, hopefully with future additions, to the Connecticut Historical Society, where it will be maintained as a study collection. A listing of persons who have donated, traded or sold me such tools in building this collection follows this preface. Also I have listed those that have contributed documentary material. In regard to the collection, I particularly acknowledge William C. Cavallini, who sold me some 200 different Union Factory planes. Also Don and Anne Wing traded or sold me some of the very special plow and sash planes. Unless otherwise noted all tools illustrated are from my own collection.

Outstanding contributions to the text were made by John Gardner and Edward Ingraham, III with their essays on making planes. Other contributors to technical matters have been Robert D. Graham, jr, Joseph Torras and Henry Wing. Jay Gaynor, Curator of Mechanical Arts at Colonial Williamsburg Foundation has contributed work concerning the Wolcott Collection of Chapin backing planes. I am indeed very grateful to Christopher Bickford, Director at the Connecticut Historical Society, and his staff for the interest and assistance in this study. Particularly I wish to acknowledge the services of Elizabeth Abbe, Librarian, Diana McCain, Catalogue Librarian, and Ruth Blair, Manuscript Librarian. The New Hartford Historical Society loaned me materials from their collection, through coordination with Roger Jones, an authority on local history of Pine Meadow and New Hartford. Ray Townsend donated his *1882 H. Chapin's Son Catalogue*. William Taylor loaned me tools from his collection of Albert G. Tovey, a former planemaker at the Chapin-Stephens Co. Mrs. Nettie Wright Adams sold me the Solon Rust Collection and contributed material concerning his career.

Unless otherwise noted all photographs are the work of John Abbott of Keene, NH, who has made a vital contribution. I am very grateful for the services of Chris Morris of MSH Advertising also of Keene for setting the type, which was a difficult task with considerable legal and technical data to copy. Bond Press and General Book Binding Co., Inc. have accomplished their usual high standard in producing this book. Any criticsm of arrangement of the text is my responsibility, as I prepared the manuscript for offset printing. Again special thanks are made to my wife, Jane W. Roberts, for her contributions typesetting titles, design of the dust jacket and suggestions in writing this manuscript.

It has been a pleasure to share this writing with fellow collectors. Hopefully these insights will increase their appreciation of Connecticut industrial history. This work is dedicated to the 19th and early 20th century workers at the Union Factory and the three generations of Chapins who managed this firm with integrity and left a record of accomplishment.

Collection Contributors

- Fred Bair
- Kendall Bassett
- Alan Bates
- Jack Bittner
- Carl Bopp*
- James Cooley
- Richard Crane
- Joe Curtin
- William Curtis, jr.
- Francis Dorion*
- William Eviston
- Peter Gaby
- Robert Gordon
- Jack Gorlin
- Robert D. Graham, jr.
- Harvey Hanenburg
- Rolfe Hansen
- Paul Kebabian*
- Andrew MacRea
- Herman Maddocks
- J. Lee Murray, jr.
- Robert Pierce
- C. Garland Rainey
- James Rogers
- Kenneth Runkle
- Charles Schultz
- Daniel Semel
- Edward Smith
- Roger Smith *
- Bob Thieriot
- Norman Vandal

Manuscript Contributors

- Daniel Blackhurst
- John Blake
- John Dater
- William Downes
- Joseph Dziadul
- Richard Hay
- Marion Henley
- Jim Hill
- Douglas James
- Jack Kebabian
- Emil Pollak
- Henry Sawin
- Elliot Sayward
- Robert Sutter
- Chris Tahk
- Charles Watson
- William White
- Richard Wood

* Also Manuscript Contributors

Table of Contents

Preface		iii
	List of Illustrations	vi
	List of Plates	viii
	List of Tables	x
Chapter I	Introduction	1
Chapter II	Making Wooden Planes	18
Chapter III	The Union Factory, 1828 - 1860	67
Chapter IV	Other Activities of Hermon Chapin, 1835 - 1860	138
Chapter V	H. Chapin Enters the Rule Business	151
Chapter VI	Developments at the Union Hactory, 1860 - 1870	180
Chapter VII	Solon Rust	226
Chapter VIII	Union Factory Trade Catalogues, 1874 - 1882	253
Chapter IX	The Chapin Machine Company & Iron Planes	322
Chapter X	Levels & Marking Gauges	342
Chapter XI	The Union Factory, 1882 - 1900	358
Chapter XII	The Chapin-Stephens Co., 1901 - 1929	376
	Appendices	
I	The Alfred G. Tovey Collection	415
II	The Wolcott Collection at Colonial Williamsburg Foundation	419
III	The Chapin Collection of Planes	425
Index		451

List of Illustrations

Figure Number	Title	Page
1	Moulding Planes by H. Wetherel	9
2	Moulding Planes by L. Kennedy	10
3	Pitch Boards	19
4	Jack Plane: Tools & Parts	20
5	Templates for Marking Contour of Smooth Planes	21
6	Marking 2¼ in. Blank for Smooth Plane	22
7	Chiseling the Opening and Drilling with Tools	23
8	Chiseling the Escapement	24
9	Gauge for Marking the Abutment Slot	25
10	Cutting the Abutment Slot	26
11	The Wedge and Slot in the Bed	27
12	Sequence of Steps in Making a Smoothing Plane	28
13	Layout for a Moulding Plane	30
14	Marking the Bed and Breast Lines and Template	31
15	Marking the Contour of the Moulding with a Template	32
16	Shaping the Sole with Hollows and Rounds and a Scraper	33
17	Shaping the Sole with a Backing ("Mother") Plane	34
18	Cutting the Mouth with Back Saw	37
19	Cutting the Throat	38
20	Finishing the Throat and Check it with a Wedge Gauge	39
21	Finished Plane with Blank and Finished Iron	40
22	Finished Plane with Struck Moulding	41
23	Steps in Making an Iron	42
24	Planes of Francis Nicholson, John Nicholson, Cesar Chelor	46
25	Planes of Jo Fuller, H. Wetherel, D. Clark & E. Clark	47
26	Planes by Jo Fuller and Aaron Smith	48
27	Planes by Jo Fuller and Aaron Smith	49
28	Planes with imprint of Union Factory & M. & A. Copeland	68
29	Types of Full Boxing Bead Plane	69
30	Union Factory/ Warranted Slide Arm Plows	72
31	Slide Arm Plows Made by Copelands	73
32	Five Union Factory Slide Arm Plows	71
33	Handled Sash Plane with Imprint - Eagle Factory	96
34	Ogee Moulding Plane with Imprint Eagle Factory	96
35	Copeland Moulding Planes Made Previous to 1830	108
36	D. Copeland Moulding Planes Made Previous to 1830	109
37	Complex Moulding Planes with Imprint of M. Copeland	110
38	Complex Moulding Planes with Imprint of M. Copeland	111
39	H. Chapin No. 225 Slip Bead Plane	112
40	Stephens Combination Rule No. 36	175
41	Chapin-Rust Patent Plow Plane in Applewood	232
42	Solon Rust's Patterns for Making the Patent Plow Plane	234
43	No. 239-3/4 Patent Plow Plane in Applewood	233
44	Solon Rust's Tool Chest	235
45	Solon Rust's Plane-making Floats and Knives	236
46	Solon Rust's Plane-making Chisels and Knives	237
47	Parts of a Plow Plane	238
48	Parts of a Plow Plane	239
49	Template for Marking Fence Moulding	242
50	Planing Fence Moulding	242
51	Planing Edge Step in Fence	243
52	Planing Edge of Fence	243
53	Planing Fence Moulding	244
54	Threading Plow Arms, Lock Nut and Washer	244
55	Finishing Contour of Plow Handle with Special Draw Shave	245
56	Skew Dado Plane and Solon Rust's Tapered Auger	246
57	Finished Dado Plane and Position of Tapered Auger	247

Figure Number	Title	Page
58	Templates for Marking Mouth of Side Rabbet Plane	248
59	Solon Rust's Bench Plane Holding Jigs	249
60	Solon Rust's Hollow & Round Backing Planes	250
61	Solon Rust	252
62	Union Factory Levels	347
63	Marking Gauges Manufactured by E.M. Chapin	351
64	Marking Gauges Manufactured at the Union Factory	357
65	E.M. Chapin	358
66	Patent Adjustable Plow No. 239-3/4 in Applewood	364
67	Union Factory Postcard, c.1901	375
68	Union Factory Rule Shop, Preparing Stock	372
69	Union Factory Rule Shop; Making Rule Joints	372
70	Union Factory Rule Shop; Jointing Rules	373
71	Union Factory Rule Shop; Assembling and Finishing Rules	373
72	Union Factory Rule Shop; Varnishing Rules	374
73	Union Factory Level Shop; Setting Vials	374
74a	Former Philip Chapin House at Pine Meadow	367
75a	Former E.M. Chapin House at Pine Meadow	367
74b	D.H. Stephens	394
75b	Vogel's Patent Aluminum-Brass Level	408
76	Patent Dates on Vogel Aluminum-Brass Level	411
77	Rosewood, Brass Faced Square with Level	411
78	Wedge Gauges and Box	415
79	Alfred G. Tovey's Plane Vise	416
80	Alfred G. Tovey's Plane Vise	417
81	Alfred G. Tovey's Templates and Patterns	418
82	Backing Planes from the Wolcott Collection	420
83	Backing Planes from the Wolcott Collection	421
84	General Purpose Planes in Wolcott Collection	422
85	Pair of Hollow & Round Backing Planes, Wolcott Collection	423
86	Backing Planes in Wolcott Collection	424
87	No. 112 Smooth Plane with Whale Bone Handle	425
88	The Chapin Collection of Planes	426
89	The Chapin Collection of Plows and Special Bench Planes	427
90	Extra Bench Planes	428
91	Premium Long Jointer and Carriage Plane	429
92	Set of 9 Pair of Hollows & Rounds	430
93	Pairs of Snipe Bills and Side Rabbets	431
94	Miscellaneous Handled Planes	432
95	Miscellaneous Bench Planes	433
96	Handled Match Planes	434
97	Double Iron, One Block, Match Planes	435
98	Pair of Slide Arm Match Planes	436
99	Pair of Screw Arm Match Planes	437
100	Set of 14 Bead Planes	438
101	Dado Planes	439
102	Set of 9 Reverse and Back OGee Planes	440
103	Pair of Base and Bed Moulding Planes	441
104	Adjustable Sash Planes	442
105	Screw Arm Filletster Planes	443
106	Raising Planes with Adjustable Fences	444
107	Soles of Raising Planes and Crown Moulding Planes	445
108	M.Copeland Grecian Ovolo Plane	446
109	Two Early Union Factory Complex Moulding Planes	447
110	Miscellaneous Plows	448
111	Union Factory Plows	449
112	No. 160 Handled Grecian OGee with Bevel Plane	450

List of Plates

Number	Chapter	Title	Page
I	I	Three Generations of Chapins at Pine Meadow	2
II		Map of Connecticut, c.1824	4
III		Map of New Hartford and Pine Meadow	5
IIIa		Plane Imprints of H. Wetherel	9
IV		Broadside Price List of D. & M. Copeland	11
I	II	Defined Parts of a Moulding Plane	29
II		Backing Plane and Special Purpose Planes	35
I	III	Procedure for Full Boxing a Plane	69
II		H. Chapin's Work Agreements with Planemakers	92
III		Union Factory Annual Sales, 1827 - 1860	98
IV		1839 Catalogue of Union Factory - Front Cover	101
V		1853 Catalogue of Union Factory - Front Cover	102
VI		Invoice Price of Wooden Planes, 1820 - 1897	107
VII		1855 Broadside Issued by H. Chapin	114
VIIa		Front Cover 1858 Union Factory Catalogue	119
VIII		Page from Undated H. Chapin Catalogue, c.1857	119
X		Production Time to Make a Plane, 1858 Costs	128
XI		H. Chapin's 1859 Union Factory Catalogue	129
I	IV	Hermon Chapin's Business Card	138
II		Expenses for Running H. Chapin's Forge	147
III		I.S. Richardson's Agreement with H. Chapin	150
I	V	1842 Willis Thrall's Price List	159
II		Boxwood and Ivory Rule Manufactures in U.S.	160
III		Foreword to 1859 S.R. & L. Co. Catalogue	162
IV		Title Page to H. Chapin's Instruction Book	172
V		Page from Undated H. Chapin Catalogue	176
VI		S.R. & L. Co. 036 Combination Rule	
I	VI	Title Page H. Chapin's 1861 Catalogue	183
II		Phoenix Company Price List	184 -185
III		Cover to Ward Tool Co. 1870 Catalogue	187
IV		E.M. Chapin's Discharge Receipt	188
V		E.M. Chapin's 1864 U.S. Income Tax	190
VI		U.S. Internal Revenue License	191
VII		Front Cover, 1865 Union Factory Catalogue	192
VIII		Union Factory Discount Sheets, 1865	209
IX		H. Chapin's Sons 1865 Gauge Price List	210
X		Auburn Tool Co. Discount Sheet, 1865	212
XI		Ohio Tool Co. Discount Sheet, 1865	212
XII		Auburn Tool Co. Discount Sheet, 1867	213
XIII		August Howland Notice, 1867	213
XIV		Osgood & Hanna Lumber Drying Process	215
XV		Price Advance by Rule Manufacturers, 1867	216
XVI		Title Page 1669 Sargent & Co. Catalogue	219
XVII		Page 311 Sargent & Co 1869 Catalogue	220
XVIII		Page 323 Sargent & Co. 1869 Catalogue	221
XIX		Joseph Gardner & Sons 1867 Price List	222
XX		Union Factory Discount Sheets, 1869 & 1870	224
I	VII	L. DeForest 1856 Price List	228
II		Greenfield Tool Co. 1854 Price List of Plows	229
III		L. & C.H. DeForect 1860 Price List	230
IV		Patent Drawing, Chapin & Rust Plow Plane	231
V		H. Chapin's Son Announcement, July 1, 1879	241

Number	Chapter	Title	Page
I	VIII	Union Factory Price List, 1872	254
II		H. Chapin's Son's 1874 Discount Sheet	255
III		Announcement of Cash Discount, Nov.1, 1874	258
IV		Title Page to 1882 H.Chapin's Son Catalogue	297
V		Frontispiece to 1882 Catalogue	298
VI		Discount Sheet to 1882 Catalouge	307
VII		Announcement of Price Advances of Rules	311
VIII		Garland's Improvement in Hand Planes	314
IX		1870 Union Factory Lumber Want List	315
X		H.L. James Bill to H. Chapin's Son	316
XI		Advertisement in Ladd's Dicount Book	321
I	IX	1868 Advertisment, Conn. Business Directory	323
II		Chapin Machine Co. Stock Certificate	324
III		Chapin's Improved Bolt Header	325
IV		Chapin Machine Co. Factory	325
V		Letterhead of Pratt & Whitney Co.	232
VII		1878 Metallic Plane Co. Brochure	330 - 331
VIII		Illustration of Foss Patent Bench Plane	334
IX		Foos Patent Pocket Catalogue	336 - 339
X		Geo. D. Mosher's Spokeshave Patent	340
XI		Stanley Rule & Level Announcment, July 1878	341
I	X	John Staniford & Son, Level Glasses	342
II		1860 L. & C.H. DeForest Catalogue Cover	343
III		Page 12 from 1858 Union Co. Catalogue	344
IV		Page 12 from Union Factory Catalogue, c.1857	344
V		Leonard Davis Letter of Assignment	346
VI		Level Design by B.F. Neal	345
VII		Page 40 from Chapin-Stephens Co. Catalogue	348
VIII		Price List of Gauges	350
IX		Sketch of John Butler's Patent Gauge	353
X		John Marden's Drawing of Patent Gauge	355
I	XI	John H. Graham & Son List of Planes	362 - 363
II		Letterhead The H.Chapin's Son Company	365
III		Title Page to 1897 Union Factory Catalogue	368
IV		Index to 1897 Union Factory Catalogue	369
V		Discount Sheet to 1897 Catalogue	370
VI		Page 44 from Wright's Catalogue	371
I	XII	Title Page to 1902 Chapin-Stephens Catalog	384
IIA		Index to 1902 Chapin-Stephens Catalogue	385
IIB		Discount Sheet to 1902 Chapin-Stephens	386
III		Flexifold Rule, 1905 Chapin-Stephens Catalog	387
IV		Wood's Patent Level	388
V		Title Page Chapin-Stephens Catalogue #114	389
VI		Index to Chapin-Stephens Catalogue #114	390
VII		Frontispiece Catalogue #114 Union Factory	391
VIII		Foreword to Catalogue #114 Union Factory	391
IXA		Foreword to Catalogue #122 Union Factory	395
IXB		Title Page to Catalogue #122 Union Factory	396
X		1924 Price Reduction Announcement	398
XI		1925 Price Reduction Announcement	399
XII		Oct. 1,1925 Catalog #122 Price List	400 - 405
XIII		Chapin-Stephens Co. Advertising Brochure	406 - 407
XIV		Chapin-Stephens Roller Skate Brochure	410
XV		Supplement to Chapin-Stephens #122 Catalog	409

List of Tables

Number	Chapter	Title	Page
I	I	Three Generations of Chapins at Pine Meadow	2
II		Apprentice Contract of H.Chapin with the Copelands	3
III		H.Chapin Co-partnership Contract with D.Copeland	6
IV		The Kelloggs' Contract with Copeland & Chapin	13
V		Building Contract by Kelloggs with Copeland & Chapin	14
VI		Agreements by Bolles & Winship with Copeland & Chapin	15
VII		Boarding House Lease by Kelloggs to Copeland & Chapin	16
VIII		Agreement to Dissolve Partnership by Copeland & Chapin	17
I	III	Alanson Spencer's Agreement with H.Chapin	70
II		H.Chapin's Customers in 1830	75
III		Work Agreement in H.Chapin's Ledger, 1830 - 1845	76
IV		H.Chapin's Production Costs & Invoice Prices,1849 & 1858	106
V		Persons Employed at Toolmaking at New Hartford, 1850	113
VI		Inventory of H.Chapin's Assets, Nov. 1, 1857	116
VII		Inventory of Plane Lumber Stored in North Chamber	117
VIII		Agreement between Willima Warner and H.Chapin, 1857	118
X		Cost Analysis of Planes made by H.Chapin, 1849 & 1858	118
IX		Production Time Required to Make a Plane from 1858 Data	128
XI		Agreement to form H.Chapin & Sons, Oct. 1, 1860	135
I	IV	R.B. Cowles' Blacksmith Shop Inventory, April 1, 1840	139
II		Business Ventures of Hermon Chapin, 1838 - 1860	140
III		Mulberry Tree Cultivation Agreement	144
IV		New Hartford Joint Stock Co. Deed	141
V		H.Chapin's Agreement with Edward Gaines, Jan. 23, 1851	145
VII		H.Chapin's Agreement with Stephen Brignen, 1855	148
VIII		H.Chapin's Agreement with Green Woods Co., 1853	145
IX		Cost of Producing Wrought Iron at Puddleville, 1853	146
X		H.Chapin's Agreement with Ithiel Richardson, 1860	149
XI		H.Chapin's Agreement with L. & G.W. Burwell	149
I	V	Bill of Sale of Rule Equipment Sold to H.Chapin, 1835	152
II		H.Chapin's Agreement with William H.Bang, 1835	153
III		Agreement with James Goodwin to Work at Rulemaking	153
IV		Agreement with Lester Phelps to Work at Rulemaking	154
V		Price Agreed with Cramer for fitting Rule Stuff	154
VII		Agreement with William Bang with H.Chapin by N.Chapin	155
VI		Agreement with Joseph Goodwin with H.Chapin	155
VIII		Various Rule Working Agreements with H.Chapin,1839-1842	156
IX		H.Chapin's Agreement with Samuel Allen, 1845	157
X		Statement Work Agreements from H.Chapin's Ledger	157
XI		H.Chapin's Work Agreement with Edward Gaines, 1842	158
XII		Page 1 from Henry Seymour's Account Book	161
XIII		Transcription of Letter by L.C. Stephens, Oct.31,1853	164
XIV		Mortgage Loan by L.C. & D.H. Stephens, Nov. 15,1855	164
XV		H.Chapin's Typical Monthly Order of Rules	165
XVI		L.C. Stephens & Co. Attachment Served to H.Chapin	166
XVII		Abstract of L.C. Stephens' Account with H.Chapin	165
XVIII		L.C. Stephens & Co. Mortgage Loan by Chester Slade,1858	170
XIX		L.C. Stephens & Co. Mortgage Loan by Chester Slade,1860	171
XX		Product Mix of Rules Made by H.Chapin, 1839 & 1853	169
XXI		Minutes of Rule Manufacturers, May 11 and May 12, 1859	
I	VI	Inventory of Goods at Union Factory, 1860 & 1865	181
II		Distribution of 5199 Finished Planes, 1860	182
III		1860 Inventory of Planes at Union Factory	182
IV		Circular Issued Among Rule Manufacturers, 1862	183
V		Mortgage Loan of D.H.Stephens from Seth K. Priest,1862	186
VI		Deed to D.H.Stephens from Alfred Alford	184

Number	Chapter	Title	Page
VII	VI	Mortgage Loan of D.H.Stephens from Alfred Alford	184
VIII		Geo. W. Chapin Becomes Co-partner, H.Chapin & Sons	187
IX		Rule Manufacturers Agreements, 1864 & 1865	201
X		H.Chapin & Sons Stock Inventory, July 1,1865	202
XI		Middletown Tool Co. Agreement with H.Chapin & Sons	203
XII		H.Chapin & Sons Inventory of Plane Irons, 1865	204
XIII		H.Chapin's Appraisal of Plane & Rule Shop, Jan. 1865	204
XIV		H.Chapin's Property Transfers to E.M. & G.W. Chapin	205
XV		H.Chapin's Property Transfers to Philip E. Chapin	206
XVI		Agreement to Dissolve Co-partnership, H.Chapin & Sons	206
XVII		Notice of H. Chapin's Retirement	207
XVIII		Deed of Plane and Rule Shop to E.M. & G.W. Chapin	207
XIX		Agreement of Co-partnership of E.M. & G.W. Chapin	208
XXa		Inventory of Plane Starts of H.Chapin & Sons,1865	214
XXb		Joseph Gardner & Sons 1867 Price List of Exotic Wood	222
I	VII	Letter from Solon Rust to Chapin & Sons, 1864	227
II		Specification of Chapin-Rust Patent for Plane	227
III		List of Patents Granted to Solon Rust	251
I	VIII	Letter to Trade from Stephens & Co., March 1,1873	309
II		1877 Sales Quota Among Rule Manufacturers	308
III		Rule Manufacturers Report of Sales, 1877	312
IV		Articles of Agreement by Plane Manufacturers, Dec. 1885	317
I	IX	Mortgage Loan by Chapin Machine Co, Sept. 5,1874	327
II		Sale of Bailey Planes by Stanley Rule & Level Co.	329
III		Letter to E.M.Chapin from J.Pickersgill, 1876	332
IV		Inventory of Foss Patent Plane Parts	340
I	X	Agreement between John Butler and E.M.Chapin, 1873	352
II		Agreement between John A. Marden and E.M.Chapin, 1873	354
III		Letter to E.M.Chapin from John Marden, 1873	354
IV		Letter and Sketch from W.J.Lee to E.M.Chapin, 1871	356
I	XI	Total Sales at H.Chapin's Son,1st Quarter 1891 - 1897	359
II		Inventory and Appraisal of Machinery of E.M.Chapin	360
III		Articles of Association of The H.Chapin's Son Co.,1897	365
IV		Statement of Treasurer, H.Chapin's Son Co., July 1900	366
I	XII	Minutes of Directors Meeting of H.Chapin's Son Co.	377
II		Bill of Sale Delos H. Stephens to H.Chapin's Son Co.	381
III		Articles of Rule Manufacturing of Stephens & Co.	378
IV		Incorporation of Chapin-Stephens Co., Oct.1,1901	382
V		Iron Age Article concerning Chapin-Stephens Co.	382
VI		1901 Sargent & Co. Comparative List of Rules	383
VII		1902 Sargent & Co. Revised List of Rule Numbers	383
VIII		Foreword to 1901 Chapin-Stephens Co. Catalogue	388
IX		Record Dictated by Frank M. Chapin, August 13,1914	392
Xa		Transcription of F.J.Rudden Letter, Feb.7,1929	412
Xb		Warranty Deed of Chapin-Stephens Co. to Stanley Rule and Level Co., Recorded Jun 5, 1929	413

Frontispiece – The Union Factory, Office and Employees, c. 1900, Pine Meadow, Conn. [Collection of the New Hartford Historical Society]

Chapter I

Introduction

This study will principally concern three generations of Chapins working at Pine Meadow (New Hartford, Connecticut) from 1826-1929. Who were these Chapins? Where is Pine Meadow? How were they making a living? Why was this important? These are among the questions that will be presently answered. Table I presents the life tenures of these principal characters.

According to the genealogy of the Chapin family, Deacon Samuel Chapin came to Roxbury, Massachusetts from England in 1635 together with his wife and son. The succeeding four generations were born and lived at Mendon, Massachusetts. Levi, the sixth generation, was born there May 6, 1776.[1] He removed to Orange, Massachusetts, where his first son, Nathaniel, was born November 21, 1792. About 1795 Levi moved to Westmoreland, New Hampshire, purchasing an 85 acre farm with substantial standing timber.[2] His second son, Levi, jr., was born there July 2, 1796, and his third, Hermon, October 9, 1799.[3] He then moved to the adjacent town of Walpole, NH, where two other sons were born (Jonathan, March 6, 1802 and Philip, September 3, 1805).

Nathaniel served in the War of 1812. He was commissioned Captain of a company from Walpole. After the war, he and his father in 1816 leased 600 acres of timber from Sherburn Hale and started lumbering.[4] Joel Holkins of East Windsor, County of Hartford, Connecticut held the four year mortgage until March 1, 1820.[5] This was annually paid from proceeds of their timber. The Chapins developed an extensive lumber business from their saw mill at Walpole on Governor's Brook.[6] The boat service of Hall and Green, across the Connecticut River at Bellows Falls, Vermont, was hired. Their logs were floated down to Springfield, Massachusetts and Hartford, Connecticut for such projects as church buildings, canal locks and bridges.[7]

According to family tradition on such a sale trip in 1820 Hermon Chapin, after not selling all timber stock at Springfield, went further south to Hartford and sold some logs there to D. and M. Copeland, planemakers.[8] Hermon, experienced with the existing methods of working wood, was apparently fascinated with this application of planemaking and decided to make an agreement with the Copelands to apprentice to their trade. This seems remarkable considering he was then 21 years of age and probably well trained as a sawyer from his experiences working with his older brother, Nathaniel, and his father. More remarkable is that before signing a commitment with the Copelands, he came to Hartford in 1821 and achieved the following certificate:[9]

> This certifies that Hermon Chapin has attended the public School in this City, acquired a knowledge of English Grammar, Arithmetic generally and has added civility of manner to industrious and studious moral.
>
> Hartford 28th March 1821   Geo. W. Bolles

TABLE I

THREE GENERATIONS of CHAPINS at PINE MEADOW, CONNECTICUT at PLANEMAKING

I - Hermon [a; 1 & 2]
    b. Oct. 9, 1799, Westmoreland. N.H.
    m. May 28, 1828, Catherine Merrill
    d. Jan.31, 1866, Savanah, Georgia

    II. Edward Merrill Chapin, [1 - 4]
        b. Sept. 5, 1833, New Hartford, Ct.
        m.   1856
        d. Dec. 10, 1896, New Hartford, Ct.

    II. George Washington Chapin [1 - 3]
        b. Feb. 22, 1837, New Hartford, Ct.
        m.   1868,
        d. Aug. 10, 1884, Cleveland, Ohio

    II. Philip Eugene Chapin   [1 - 2]
        b. Dec. 1, 1838, New Hartford, Ct.
        m.   1866, Amelia Bushnell
        d.   1915,   Penn.

III Hermon Mills Chapin [4 - 6]
        b. Sept. 17, 1866, New Hartford, Ct.
        m. June 22, 1898
        d.   1928, New Hartford, Ct.

III Frank Mills Chapin [4 - 6]
        b. June 28, 1869, New Hartford, Ct.
        m. March 24,1891,
        d.   1942, New Hartford, Ct

Sequence of Planemaking Firms
    a. Copeland & Chapin, 1826 - 1828
    1. H.Chapin UNION FACTORY, 1828 - 1860
    2. H. Chapin & Sons, 1860 - 1865
    3. H. Chapin's Sons, 1865 - 1868
    4. H. Chapin's Son, [also known as E.M.Chapin], 1868 - 1896
    5. H. Chapin's Son & Co., 1896 - 1901
    6. Chapin-Stephens 1901 - 1929

Through insight and later discussion with his father, Hermon Chapin must has surmised a great potential and opportunity existed in planemaking. However, he first decided to supplement his limited education and achieve more formal training that would be required to perform the accounting and paper work in managing such a business. On May 1822 he signed an agreement to apprentice to this trade under the Copelands at Hartford. (See Table II)

Table II
Apprentice Contract of Hermon Chapin with D. and M. Copeland, May 20, 1822

The following is a contract existing between D. and M. Copeland on the one part and Hermon Chapin on the other.

The sd. Chapin agrees to work four years for the sd. Copelands at their Joiners Tool Manufactory for the consideration of six hundred dollars to be paid in the following manner viz,

The first year	$ 50.00
The second year	150.00
The third year	175.00
The fourth year	225.00
	$600.00

The sd. Copelands agree to learn the sd. Chapin in the trade of making Joiners Tools, so far as is practicable in the above mentioned four years, also to allow sd. Chapin in the privilege by the piece whenevery his work will admit. They also agree to board and wash for the sd. Chapin while in their employ.

The sd. Chapin further agrees to make up in labour [sic] such time as he may lose in the above mentioned four years, except that occasioned by sickness and military duty which may be deducted from his wages.

The sd. Chapin commenced his labour [sic] for the above mentioned four years on the lst of April 1822 City of Hartford, May 20th, 1822

D. and M. Copeland
Hermon Chapin

No details of his training under the Copelands are known. Concurrent with his employment, he was appointed a Corporal in the 2nd Rifle Company of the 1st Regiment of Infantry in the State of Connecticut.[10] It is certain that Hermon Chapin was an exceptionally proficient craftsman as well as demonstrating a good understanding of the business. On December 17, 1825 Daniel Copeland executed an indenture to form a co-partnership in company with Hermon Chapin according to the terms noted in Table III. This was concurrent with the termination of the firm D. and M. Copeland. It is suggested that a difference between these two brothers may have arisen due to Melvin's interests in politics.[11] Daniel Copeland must have had considerable confidence in Hermon Chapin's abilities to produce planes that he could sell with his imprint. It should be noted that he kept his co-partnership business with Chapin separate from his selling planes at Hartford. It is suggested that Hermon Chapin had discussed with Daniel Copeland the possibilities of producing planes by semi-automated processes using water powered machinery. As previously noted, Chapin was an experienced sawyer and probably realized the possibilities of at least preparing stock blanks for various sizes of bench and moulding planes while the wood was seasoning. Tremendous advances were being made using automated machinery for working wood.[12] Thomas Blanchard was granted his patent for the celebrated lathe for turning gun stocks, January 20, 1820.[13]

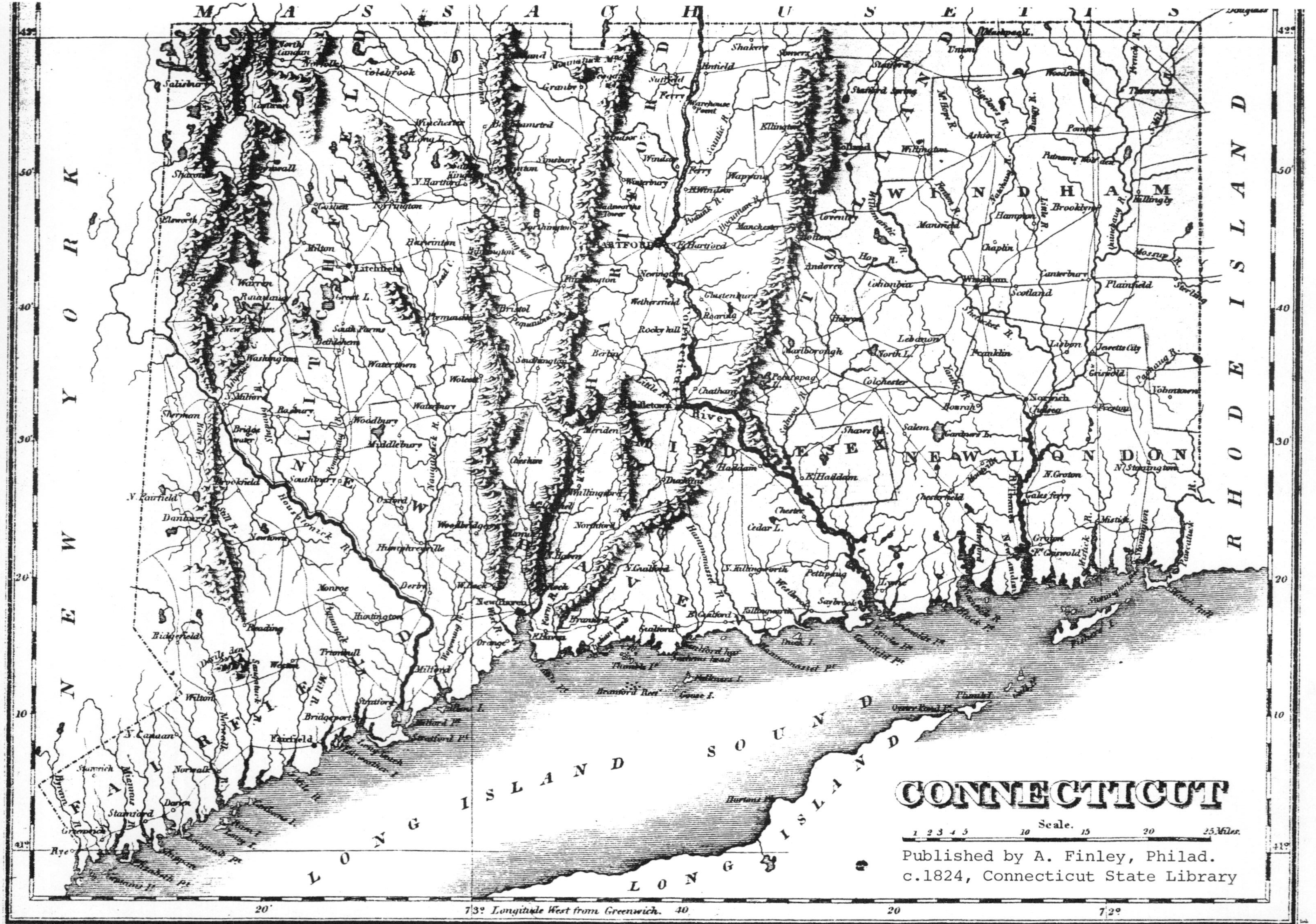

CONNECTICUT

Published by A. Finley, Philad.
c.1824, Connecticut State Library

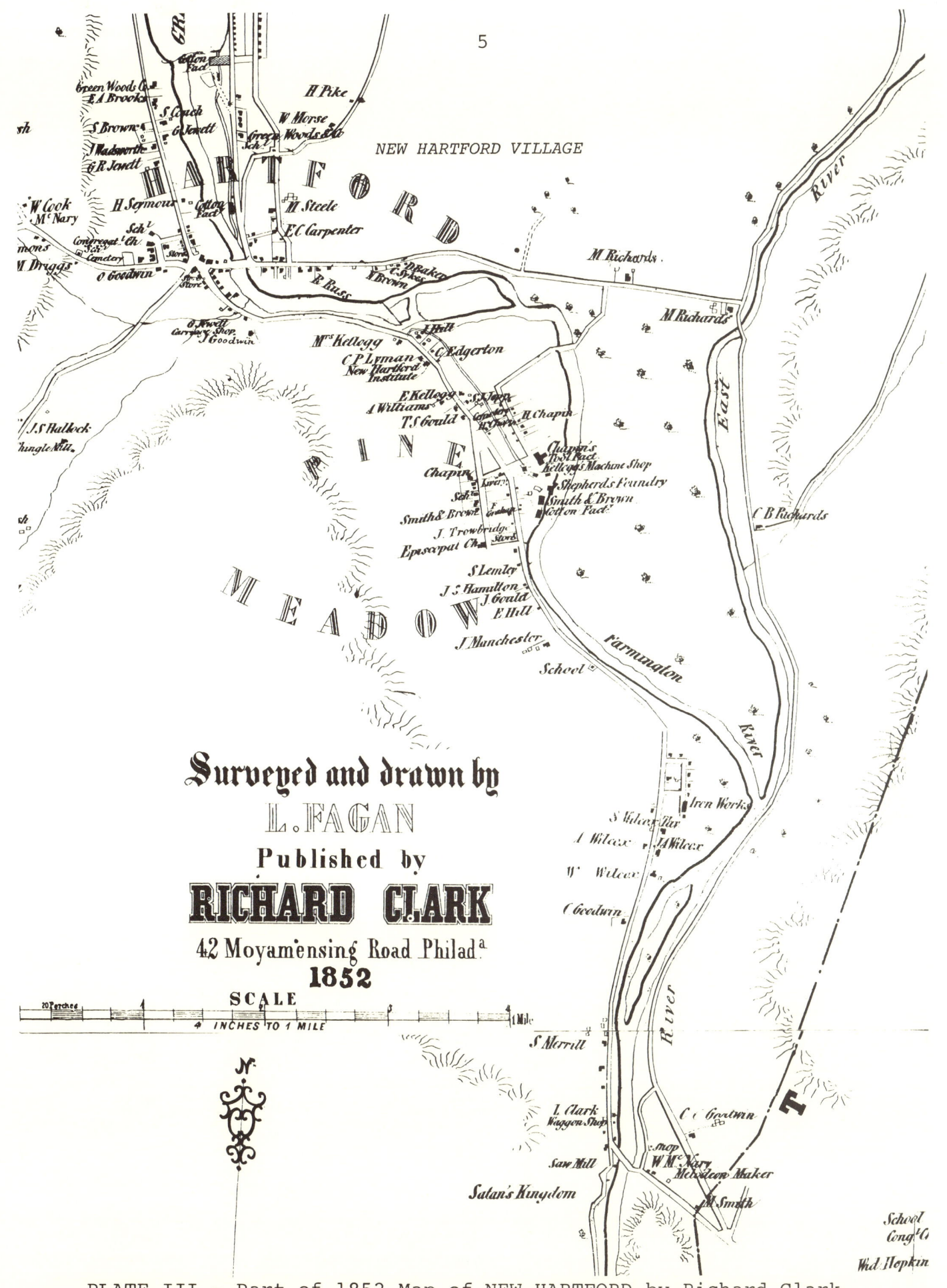

PLATE III - Part of 1852 Map of NEW HARTFORD by Richard Clark
The Town of New Hartford, Litchfield Co., Conn. in 1775 & 1852, Eileen C. Hall
[New Hartford, Conn., 1976, p. 38]

Table III
Co-partnership Contract between H. Chapin and D. Copeland, December 17, 1825

This indenture made and executed on this 17th Day of December 1825 by and between Daniel Copeland and Hermon Chapin both of the Town and County of Hartford and State of Connecticut - witnessed - that from this day said Copeland and said Chapin to enter into co-partnership, for the purpose of making and vending Joiner and Cooper tools the business to be conducted in the Country, at such place as shall be hereafter agreed upon by the parties, and on the terms and conditions herein after expressed. The said parties are to make equal advancements to the Company to provide an establishment and necessary stock for the use of said Company and to be equally interested and concerned in its profits and losses. Said Chapin agrees to devote his whole time during the continuance of said partnership to the business of the same and in consideration thereof is to receive the sum of Five Hundred Dollars each year to be paid to him by said Company. Neither of said parties shall withdraw from the capital employed by said Company except so much as he may require for necessary expenses. Said Chapin agrees during the continuance of said Co-partnership, he will, not sell any planes at wholesale, but all planes which are made by the Company shall be delivered to said Copeland at Hartford aforesaid, (except what may be sold at retail by said Chapin) - nor shall more be made than said Copeland can sell in a reasonable time and by reasonable effort and at customary prices. Said Chapin is to have no concern or interest in the business and establishment of said Copeland at Hartford. Both Parties are to have access at all times to the books and accounts of the Company and either party by giving the other six months notice may dissolve the said Co-partnership. It is further agreed between said parties that all the Joiner and Cooper Tools made by the said Company (except Bench Planes and Coopers Jointers) are to be delivered to said Copeland at forty percent discount from the present retail prices as they appear in the accompaning table. Bench planes without irons at the following prices are liable to the same discount as moulding planes

Dbl. Iron Jointer	30 in.	1.56
do Iron Jointer	26	1.42
do Iron Jointer	22	1.28
do Iron Jointer	21	1.25
do Jack Planes		.92
do Smooth Planes		.80
Single Iron Jointers	30 in.	1.37½
do Iron Jointers	26	1.25
do Iron Jointers	22	1.11
do Iron Jointers	21	1.08
do Jack Planes		.91
do Smooth Planes		.62½
Tooth Planes		.67
Single Iron Cooper Jointers		1.58
Dbl. Iron Cooper Jointers		1.07

Any articles of hardware furnished by said Copeland are to be sent to the following place of business at said Copelands expense. The business of said Company is to commence from such a day, during the coming Spring as shall be agreed upon by the said parties and the same endorsed on this instrument and from said day, said sales to said Chapin shall commence and the computation of time by said parties shall be from the same. The accounts of said Company are to be settled at the close of each year when if a balance [sic] shall be found due from said Company to said Copeland or from said Copeland to said Company, the debtor party shall allow the months interest on said balance [sic] to be paid to the other party. All tools, when delivered as foresaid to said Copeland are to be considered as sold and at the risk of said Copeland above.

Hartford December 17th, 1825 Danl. Copeland Hermon Chapin

The business to be conducted according to the foregoing instrument commenced with this first day of July one thousand eight hundred and twenty six.

Danl. Copeland
Hermon Chapin

Late in the year 1825 Hermon Chapin was sent out in search of a mill site. He was accompanied by Horace P. Deming, another planemaker at Copeland's, who subsequently became employed by H. Chapin and later also served under his son, E.M. Chapin.[14] They stopped at Jonathan Merrill's tavern, just north of Satan's Kingdom, New Hartford. There Hermon first met Catherine Merrill, his future wife. A few hundred yards north of the Merrill Inn at Kelloggville, now known as Pine Meadow, New Hartford, a woolen mill was operated from a raceway and dam across the North branch of the Farmington River. It was at this site that Hermon Chapin decided to lease property for the Copeland-Chapin plane factory.

Permission had been granted in 1732 by the Connecticut General Assembly to establish seven towns in the colony's western lands. The town of New Hartford, approximately six miles square, the most easterly in Litchfield County, was settled by 182 former residents of Hartford. It was incorporated in 1738 with settlements at Town Hill and West Hill as agricultural communities. In the early 1800's the economic interests changed from agriculture to industry and the population shifted from the hilltops to the river valley. Plate I, a map of the State of Connecticut, shows its location. New Hartford Center, then the North Village, is about 20 miles north and west of Hartford. The Albany Turnpike from Hartford ran along the west bank of the Farmington River. At Satan's Kingdom, in the southeast section, a bridge permitted crossing the river. Just north of there and south of Kelloggville, (now Pine Meadow) at the confluence of the north and east branches of the Farmington River, was an iron puddling mill, also owned by the Kelloggs. In addition to the woolen mill at Kelloggville were other mills at North Village about a mile further north. A few miles further north of this village is the town of Barkhamsted. In the southern section of this town, along the bank of the north branch of the Farmington River, Lambert Hitchcock operated his famed "Hitchcock's Mill" for mass producing painted chairs, turning and sawing material by water power from a dam on the River. Hitchcock came there from Cheshire in 1818. This district became known as Hitchcocksville, subsequently Riverton after 1866.[15] Hitchcock's manufacturing using water power for preparing his materials may have influenced Chapin to seek a mill site in that general area. In 1825 when Chapin first visited New Hartford the population was about 1700. The year after Copeland and Chapin leased the property at Pine Meadow, in 1827 the Collins Co. of Hartford, axe and edge tool manufacturers, purchased land with a saw mill and water privileges from the Farmington River at Canton, about six miles south.

While somewhat out of chronological sequence with the text, Plate II shows a section of the 1852 Map of New Hartford, published by Richard Clark. this notes the location of Satan's Kingdom, the Iron Works (Puddleville), Chapin's Tool Factory, and the north village of New Hartford.

Before continuing with Chapin's activities at Pine Meadow, the trade of planemaking as practiced in Connecticut, will be reviewed up to that date. This art of industry appears to have been initiated in New England in the southern section of Massachusetts.[16] Data concerning 18th century planemaking at Connecticut is indeed fragmentary. Recent research suggests that "A. Hide in Norwich" [Conn.] may have been the earliest working at this trade.[17] It is known that H. Wetherel brought his tool making business from Norton, Massachusetts to Chatham on the Connecticut River, c. 1790. The then flourishing boat-making trade there might have influenced this change. His business was continued there by his son, Henry, and at the town of Middletown, across the River. For some reason he added a "l" to the spelling of his last name. It is believed that he additionally imported planes from England on which he stamped his own mark. Some moulding planes made by the Wetherels at their various locations are shown in Figure 1 and their imprints in Plate III.

Twenty miles north at Hartford Leonard Kennedy, born there in 1767, noted in a list of occupations there in 1799 as a joiner, appears to be the earliest of professional planemakers working here. An advertisement in the January 11, 1809 *Hartford Courant* noted: "James H. Wells, hardware wholesale and retail, carries an assortment of Kennedy's moulding tools and planes." Incidentally the term "moulding tools" was used through the middle of the 19th century to convey what has since become known as moulding planes. Technically in geometry a plane conveys a straight, flat surface and the irregular shape of complex mouldings as planes are misnomers. However being made and used by the same groups as the straight bench planes, moulding tools have become known as moulding planes. Another advertisement in *The Connecticut Mirror* of November 26, 1810 noted the variety of shapes of Leonard Kennedy's joiner tools then available at James H. Wells' Hardware Store.[18]

Fig. 1 - Moulding Planes by H. Wetherel(1)
Upper left: H.Wetherell/Chatham, beech;   Upper right: H.Wetherel/in Norton, birch;
Lower left: H.Wetherel /Chatham, birch;   Lower right: H.Wetherll/Chatham, beech
[Collection of Don and Anne Wing]

At that date in all probability many joiners made their own tools, or at least the wooden parts of their planes. The same James Wells advertised in the *Connecticut Courant,* January 22, 1806, that he had imported for sale: "50 dozen cast steel and common plane irons" and "80 dozen soft moulding irons."[19] It was customary to purchase such irons soft and after shaping the plane stock to grind the iron to conform. Before finish grinding to final size and contour, the local blacksmith would harden and temper the iron.

PLATE III IMPRINTS of H. WETHEREL(L) on PLANES
From left to right: H.WETHEREL/IN NORTON; H.WETHERL/CHATHAM; H. WETHERELL/CHATHAM; H. WETHERELL/MIDDLETOWN

[Imprints made by Jane W. Roberts. See: *Plane Makers & Other Edge Tool Enterprises in New York State in the 19th Century,* Appendix H, p. 230

The second Hartford planemaking firm is believed to have been the brothers, Daniel and Melvin, Copeland, beginning on their own before 1820. Both were born at Sturbridge, Massachusetts, respectively 1794 and 1797. A third brother, Alfred, born 1801, also became a planemaker. The two older brothers are believed to have apprenticed at planemaking under Leonard Kennedy at Hartford. It is possible that Kennedy learned the trade from Henry Wetherel. The birth notice of George Melvin Copeland, believed to have been a son of Melvin, was witnessed by his father and Leonard Kennedy.[20]

Leonard Kennedy had two sons who probably apprenticed under him. Both had separate long careers in the planemaking busines. Samuel Lewis Kennedy (b. June 25, 1792; d.Sept. 9, 1840) made planes in New York City, 1817-1822, under his own name and latter became associated with Dyer White as Kennedy and White, 1822-1840 and for a short time in Kennedy, Barry & Way.[21] Leonard Kennedy, Jr. (b.1800; d.Dec. 14, 1879) probably had the distinction of working at planemaking at more locations than any other person. He was in business at Hartford before 1825; Utica, N.Y., 1825-1832; Rochester, N.Y., 1838; again at Hartford, 1838-1846; Milwaukee, Wisconsin, 1848-1850 and back to Hartford as an apiarist, advertising "Kennedy's Bee Hive, patented Feb. 9, 1864."[22] An advertisement in the *Connecticut Courant,* [Vol. LVII, No.2920, Thurs., January 9, 1821], which may have been Leonard Kennedy, Sr., stated:

PLANE MANUFACTORY — L. Kennedy & Co. continues to manufacture Joiners' and Cabinetmaker's Planes of every description which they will sell at wholesale and retail for cash or credit. Also Bookbinder's Cutting Presses, Ploughs, Sewing Benches, & c.

SAWS BRACES and BITS, CHISELS
steel blade squares and most other tools used by joiners and cabinet makers.

A group of moulding planes, all with the imprint, L. Kennedy/Hartford, CT., is illustrated in Figure 2.

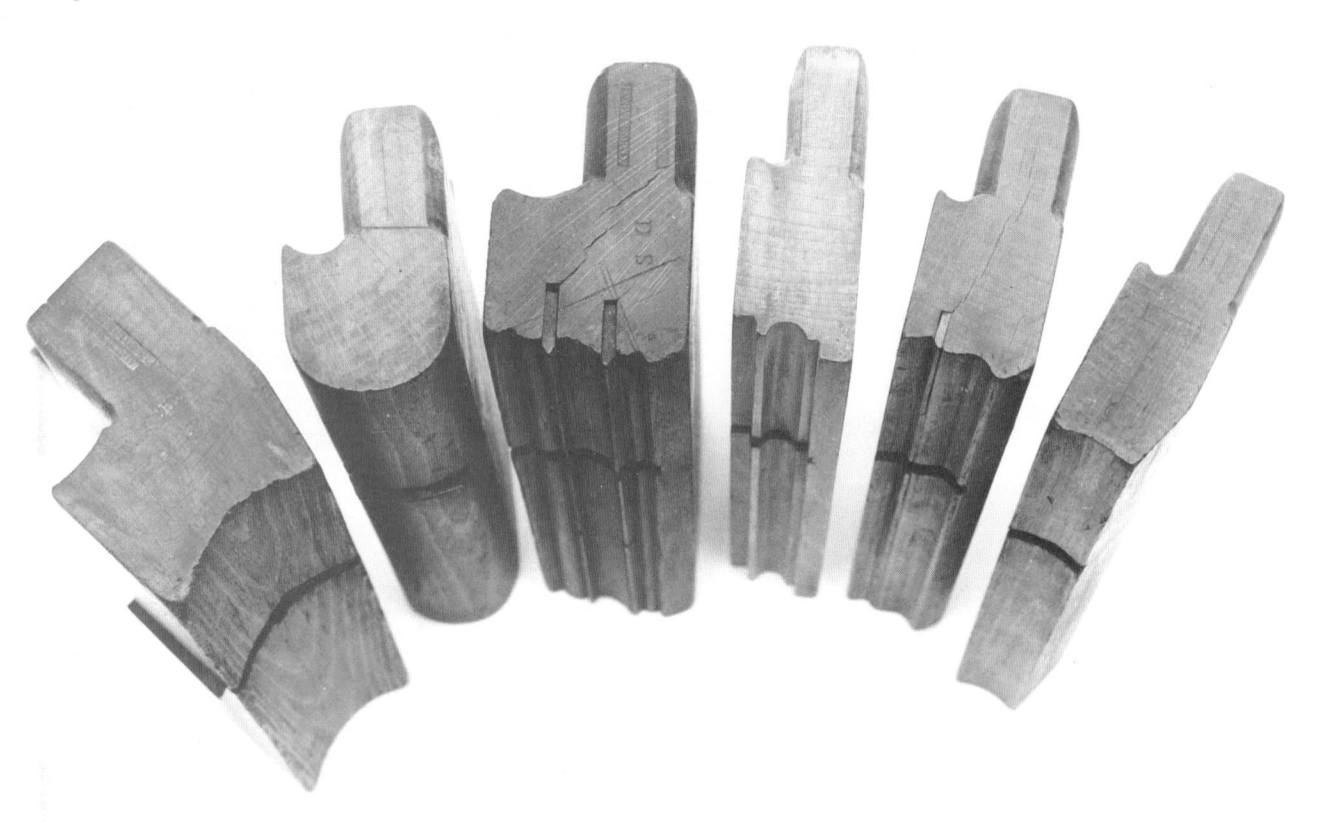

Fig. 2 - Group of Moulding Planes by Leonard Kennedy/Hartford
[Note pronounced chamfer and deep notching, characteristic of moulding planes made before 1830]

A Price List in the form of a broadside [8" x 12"] of D. and M. Copeland noted the types, sizes and prices of various bench planes and moulding tools offered by this Hartford firm. (Plate IV) While this is not dated, on the back side of one of these the Copelands penned their contract with Hermon Chapin, dated May 20, 1822. This price list was likely in effect at that date. This is believed to be the earliest extant price list of a plane firm in the United States. All of these planes were individually hand made.

Plate IV - Title to Broadside [Price List on Page 11]

JOINERS' TOOLS,

Manufactured by

D. & M. COPELAND,

HARTFORD, CONN.

Single Iron Bench Planes.

GERMAN STEEL IRONS.		CAST STEEL IRONS.	
Names.	Prices.	Names.	Prices.
Long Jointer	$1 42	Long Jointer	$1 58
Short Jointer	1 25	Short Jointer	1 42
Jack Plane	84	Jack Plane	96
Smooth Plane	75	Smooth Plane	87½
	$4 26		$4 83¼

Double Iron Bench Planes.

GERMAN STEEL IRONS.		CAST STEEL IRONS.	
Long Jointer	$1 84	Long Jointer	$2 00
Short Jointer	1 67	Short Jointer	1 84
Jack Plane	1 25	Jack Plane	1 37½
Smooth Plane	1 12½	Smooth Plane	1 25
	$5 88½		$6 46½

A.
Astragals up to ¾ in.	$0 56
Do. over ¾ in.	62½

B.
Beads up to ¾ in.	67
Do. over ¾ in.	75
Back Ogee Beads up to ¾ in.	87½
Do. Do. Do. over ¾ in.	1 00

C.
Cove and Bead up to ¾ in.	75
Do. over ¾ in.	87½
Cock Beads	56
Do. Do. double	62
Coping Plane	87½

D.
Dados, 1st rate	1 75
Do. 2d rate	1 12½

G.
Gages, Common	17
Do. Oval head	20
Do. Mortice	50
Do. Splitting	62½

H.
Hollows and Rounds, per pr.	1 12½
Table H. and Rounds, 1st rate	1 50
Do. Do. 2d rate	1 25

M.
MATCH PLANES.
Plank do.	2 42
Do. do. fence plated	2 75
Do. do. moving fence	2 75
Board Match Planes	1 75
Do. do. fence plated	2 00
Do. do. with handles	2 42
Do. do. do. fence plated	2 75
½ in. do.	1 50
do. plated	1 75

N.
Nosing, up to ¾ in.	87½
Do. over ¾ in.	1 00

P.
Plows, 1st rate, 8 irons	7 00
Do. 2d rate, 8 irons	6 00
Do. 3d rate, 8 irons	4 50
Do. 3d rate, 1 iron	3 00
Do. 4th rate, 1 iron	2 50
Philisters, common	1 50
Do. with common stop	1 75
Do. with common stop and cut	2 00
Do. with common stop, cut, and boxed	2 25
Do. with Screw Stop, cut, and boxed	3 00
Pannel Planes	1 25
Do. with cut	1 50

Q.
Quirk Ogees up to ¾ in.	75
do. do. over ¾ in.	87½
Qk. Ogee Beads up to ¾ in.	87½
do. do. over ¾ in.	1 00
Qk. Ovelos up to ¾ in.	75
do. over ¾ in.	87½
do. two fillets up to ¾ in.	87½
do. do. over ¾ in.	1 00
Qk. Ovelo Beads up to ¾ in.	1 00
do. do. over ¾ in.	1 12½
Qk. Ovelo Cove Beads up to ¾ in.	1 00
do. do. over ¾ in.	1 12½
do. do. with 2 irons	1 50

R.
Rabbet Planes up to 1 in.	62½
Do. from 1 in. to 1¼ in.	75
Do. from 1¼ in. to 1½ in.	84
Do. from 1½ in. to 1¾ in.	92
Do. from 1¾ in. to 2 in.	1 00
Do. over 2 in.	1 12½
Side Rabbets	62½
Reeding Planes	84

S.
Sash Planes, 1 iron	75
Do. 2 irons	1 12½
Do. 2 irons and boxed	1 75
Do. 2 irons and double	1 75
Do. 2 irons, double and boxed	2 25
Do. with stop on the back side	1 34
Do. double do.	2 00
Do. do. and plated do.	2 25
Do. do. boxed do.	2 50
Snipes Bills	75

T.
Tooth Plane, German Steel Iron	87½
do. Cast Steel Iron	1 00
Coopers Jointers	1 75
Do. do. dbl. irons	2 25
Do. Stock Howels	2 00
Do. do. plated	2 50
Do. Crows	75
Do. Circular Leveler	1 50
Do. do. plated	2 00

Returning to the Copeland-Chapin co-partnership, these proprietors made an agreement on December 23, 1825 with Isaac and George Kellogg to lease property adjacent to the latter's woolen mill and to use one fourth part of the water from the mill pond. The details of this transaction are noted in Table IV. Additionally the Kelloggs agreed to construct a building to contain the waterwheel and gearing. In another agreement, made the same day, a building 30 feet by 35 feet was to be constructed by the Kelloggs. This was to be a two story building with gable roof and garret, a chimney at each end, partitions, stairs, floors and windows as specified. These details are noted in Table V, which also records the gearing arrangement for running the mill from a water wheel. The building was to be completed by the middle of June 1826.

The following note was annexed to the Copeland-Chapin Co-partnership agreement of Table III:

"The business to be conducted according to the foregoing instrument commenced with this first day of July one thousand eight hundred and twenty six."
[signed] Danl. Copeland   Hermon Chapin

This marked the beginning of what became known as the UNION FACTORY. Family tradition suggested that it was so called to mark the first fifty years of the formation of the United States of America. However, it should be noted that "Union" was then a very popular word; i.e., "The Union shall be preserved," "Union forever," etc.

After organizing the shop, the next order of business was to hire two planemakers to assist H. Chapin. Indentures were agreed with Henry D. Bolles and William Winship, and both began work there in September. (See Table VI) Business through 1826 and 1827 must have been satisfactory. To expand the work force and contract for additional apprentices, Copeland and Chapin decided to rent half a house owned by the Kelloggs and establish a boarding house for their help. The details of this agreement, signed by the four parties on November 26, 1827, appear in Table VI, witnessed by William Winship.

An indication of a source of timber for making planes at the Union Factory is revealed in the following document:

"This certifies that I have assisted Charles Hayes in getting out 459 Long Jointer pieces, 468 Short Jointers and 576 Jack Plane. The timber is now in his possession and he says it is dessined [sic] for Copeland and Chapin. It is of good quality and well seasoned."
Nathaniel Hayden   Hartland [Ct.] Sept. 17, 1827

On May 28, 1828 at Canton, Hermon Chapin married Catherine Merrill of New Hartford. She was the daughter of the inn keeper where Hermon had stayed when he first came to Pine Meadow, late in 1825. They had nine children, but only three lived to adulthood. These were the 3rd, Edward Merrill Chapin; the 5th, George Washington Chapin [so named for the date of his birth]; and Philip Eugene Chapin, the 6th. (See Table I)

On October 21, 1828 Daniel Copeland agreed to sell out his half-interest in the Union Factory, water privileges, boarding house and land for $1600 to Hermon Chapin. The details of this transaction are recorded in Table VIII. Copeland removed to Huntington, Massachusetts where he subsequently made planes.[23]

Table IV
Indenture: Isaac and Geo. C. Kellogg, Daniel Copeland and Hermon Chapin
Recorded January 11, 1826 [New Hartford Land Deeds: B13, pg. 209]

This Indenture made the 23rd day of December in the year of our Lord One Thousand Eight hundred and Twenty five between Isaac Kellogg and George Kellogg of New Hartford in the County of Litchfield of the one part and Daniel Copeland and Hermon Chapin both of Hartford in the County of Hartford and in the State of Connecticut of the other part Witnesseth - That the said Isaac and George C. Kellogg for and in consideration of the yearly Rents and Convenants herein after reserved and contained on the one part of the said Copeland and Chapin, their Administrators, Executors and Assigns to be paid, observed and performed have Demised, granted and to farm, letten and by these presents do Demise, grant and to farm, let unto the said Copeland and Chapin, a certain piece or parcel of land, or Millplace lying in New Hartford aforesaid, bounded and described as follows. Namely - beginning forty feet below sd. Kellogg's Mill, or water shop, on the Southern bank of the Canal or Raceway of said Mill and crossing Sd. Canal in a line parallel to the Easterly end of the said Mill Building, thirty feet, thence crossing said Canal again, thirty feet, and above the bank forty feet to the place of beginning, with the privilege of a yard, or common and undivided passway, on all sides of the Building-Site, before described, - and also land sufficient on the Northern bank of said Canal, for the purpose of construction a small Canal of sufficient dimensions, to convey water to sd. Building Site and to connect with the head water in the main Canal, or water course which leads to the sd. Kellogg's Mill - and also the common and undivided fourth part of the water which is conveyed in the same main Canal or water course, and one fourth part of said water-course and of the Dam and Pond from which said Canal leads, together with the use in common of a road or passway to and from the premises from the Turnpike road - To have and to hold the premises above described with the privileges of appurtenances thereof, unto the said Copeland and Chapin, their Executors, administrators, assigns, from the first day of March next, for and during the term of Nine hundred and ninety nine years thence next ensuing and fully to be completed and ended; yielding and paying therefor, yearly, during said term, unto the said Isaac and Geo. C. Kellogg, their heirs and assigns the yearly rent of ten dollars, and furnishing and keeping in repair constantly, a room in the lower story, or cellar of a Building, to be errected on said Premises, about thirty feet by sixteen square, and also a room on the ground floor of said Building, of about the same dimensions, and also to furnish and keep in repair as aforesaid, a Waterwheel and main Gearing, to be built according to an agreement this day made between sd. Kelloggs and said Copeland and Chapin of the power and use of said waterwheel and gearing, said Copeland and Chapin are to have, hold and use so much at anytime, as would be sufficient to drive one run of mill stones, for common Country work and to yield and furnish unto sd. Kelloggs, their heirs and assigns as aforesaid, all the rest and residue of the powers and use of said Wheel and Gears, together with the exclusive use of the two rooms in said Building, described and aforesaid. - and in each year in which said rooms and Wheel and Gears are kept in good repair, during the whole of such year, for the use and occupancy of said Kelloggs, the said Kelloggs agree to remit the ten dollars first above written. - And in case said Copeland and Chapin, shall neglect to keep said rooms and water works in the state and condition above written for the term of four years in succession at any time, then and from thenceforth it shall and may be lawful to and for the sd. Isaac and Geo. C. Kellogg, their heirs and assigns. into the said premises to re-enter and the same to have acquired, repossess and enjoy as in his or their former, as the first estate, right and title, anything herein contained in any wise to the contrary, nothwithstanding. - And the said Daniel Copeland and Hermon Chapin, for themselves, their Executors, Administrators and Assigns, do convenant and grant to and with the said Isaac and Geo. C. Kellogg, their heirs and assigns, that they the said Copeland and Chapin, their Executors, administrators and assigns, shall and will, well and truly pay, do, and perform, or cause to be paid, done and performed unto and for the sd. Isaac and George C. Kellogg, their heirs and assigns, the yearly rents above reserved, and specified in manner and form above expressed and intended, clear of, and over and above all Taxes, notes and payments whatever, except one fourth part of the Taxes on the Building only, and one fourth part of Insurance against fire - and said Copeland and Chapin, their Executors, administrators and assigns, do further convenant with said Kelloggs, their heirs and assigns, that they will constantly and at all times, keep the said Building under a good and sufficient Insurance against fire and they also agree and convenant to make one fourth part of all the repairs of the said Dam, Canal and Raceway which may be from time to time necessary - and said Copeland and Chapin, their Executors, administrators and assigns, all further convenants as aforesaid, that no other Business shall ever be carried on in said Building or on said premises, by them or any person or persons under them, except the Business of Manufacturing Joiners Tools. In witness whereof the persons, first above named, have to these presents, Indentures, set their hands and seals, the day and year first above written.

                                                        Isaac Kellogg
                                                        Geo. C. Kellogg
                                                        Danl. Copeland
                                                        Hermon Chapin
                                                        Dec. 23, 1825

Table V
Agreement between Kelloggs and Copeland-Chapin to Construct Factory Building

This agreement made between said Isaace and Geo. C. Kellogg of New Hartford parties of the first part and Daniel Copeland and Hermon Chapin both of Hartford of the second part and all of Connecticut. Witnesseth

That said Kelloggs parties of the first part agree to build a building on a site this day leased to said Copeland and Chapin parties of the second part of the following description (to wit).

The size of the ground to be thirty by thirty five feet, the basement story to be principally of stone wall of dry masonry two feet thick and the height of said wall about twelve feet, to be supplied by eight - eight light and four twenty light windows, 7 x 9 glass (the glass to be of the cheaper sort throughout the whole). The canal or water course to be stones up to a proper level for the lower ground floor which is to be all, except over the water course, covered with such flagging stones as can be found in the neighborhood and over the Sd. water course to be a floor of planks of Chestnut. The wheel pit is to be situated in the center of Sd. building easterly and westerly and on the northerly side and to be substantially stones to the height of the blocks which receive the boxes for wheel gridirons. One door on the westerly and one on the easterly end of Sd. story and one flight of stairs and door leading to the second loft next above the wheel room. - Sd. Kelloggs to have the privilege of using such a proportion of hard bricks in the basement story as they think proper. The second story is to be made of bricks one foot thick and nine feet high in the clear between timbers and to be supplied with one outside door in the center opening into an entry out of said entry shall be one door to the right and one to the left and from the center of said entry partition. A partition shall run northerly to the opposite wall dividing the second story into two equal parts. Said partition to be made of chestnut lumber plank - from the easterly half is to be a flight of stairs with a door, the floor to be made of one thickness of Oak 1½ inches thick and tongued or matched and the next floor above to be made in the same way and both unplaned. The 2nd story to be supplied with fifteen 20 light windows of 7 x 9 glass. - The next story to be eight inches of thickness of wall and nine feet high in the clear between timbers sixteen windows of 20 lights 7 x 9 glass each and the wall to be sealed with matched pine boards.

The garrit to be floored with board with lining under and to have a portable pair of stairs made to hook up with a trap door lying horizontal. The rafters to come down nearly to the level of the garrit floor the garrit to be lighted with 20 light windows, 7 x 9 glass each. - Two chimneys, one on each gable end to be carried up with the walls - the easterly chimney to have a fireplace in the second and third stories similar to the one in the shop now occupied by the parties of the second part and each chimney to have a proper opening.

The frame is to be composed of six sticks 30 feet long 8 x 9 and three sticks 35 feet long 8 x 9 - supported by six turned pillars the joist to be placed two feet center to center 3½ x 9 inches, the rafters to be 4½ x 4½ at the lower ends and about 30 inches apart - the roof to be covered with chestnut or hemlock shingles. The timbers which support the two upper floors to be connected with iron brackets to the brick walls.

Said parties of the first part further agree to construct a water course from their bulkhead (entering from their mill) to the building above described which is to be a good and sufficient water course stoned up with rough wall of sufficient dimensions for the water wheel herein after described. Said, canal to be covered over near the mill with slabs or planks and of a flume in connection to project into the above described mill, sufficient to carry the water on to the wheel - which is to be made the same diameter as the one now in operation in sd. Kellogg Mill and the Shaft and the Flanges and arms the same with same number of buckets - the buckets to be only five feet long and the shaft to be extended (however) long enough to receive a bevel gear about forty five inches in diameter, which is to match with one about fifty inches in diameter. - Sd. small gear is to stand on an iron shaft about 3 inches square extending nearly to the 2nd floor above sd. wheel - Sd. shaft to be wrought iron and connected with a coupling box at the first floor above the wheel.

The above job to be done about the middle of June next and when done in consideration of the promises said Copeland and Chapin parties to the second half agree to pay the parties of the first half, eighteen hundred dollars in cash and the privilege this day executed, said Copeland and Chapin agree to pay Isaac and Geo. C. Kellogg five hundred dollars when sd. Kelloggs have completed their job as above written.

In writing whereof we have this twenty third day of December Ad 1825 set out hands hereunto.

                     Isaac and Geo. C. Kellogg
                     Copeland and Chapin

Table VI
H. Bolles and W. Winship Apprentice Agreements with Copeland-Chapin, November 26, 1826

1826 November 17

 This indenture witnesseth that Henry D. Bolles agrees to work for Copeland & Chapin at their Joiners Tool Manufactory in the town of New Hartford and County of Litchfield state of Connecticut four years for which the sd. Copeland & Chapin agree to pay the sd. Bolles the sum of six hundred dollars at th end of sd. four years except so much as the sd. Bolles may require for necessary expenses during sd. term.
 Copeland & Chapin further agree to board and wash for sd. Bolles during sd. four years while in their employ and to allow sd. Bolles the privilege of working by the piece when their work will admit.
 The wages of sd. Bolles to be estimated in the following manner, viz.

For the first year	$100.00
For the second "	$140.00
For the third "	$160.00
For the fourth "	$200.00
	$600.00

The sd. Bolles commenced his labours for the sd. four years on the fifth of Sept. 1826
  New Hartford Nov. 17th 1826
   Copeland & Chapin
   Henry D. Bolles

 This indenture witnesseth that William Winship agrees to work for Copeland & Chapin at their Joiners Tool Manufactory in the town of New Hartford and County of Litchfield state of Connecticut four years for which the sd. Copeland & Chapin agree to pay the sd. Winship the sum of six hundred dollars at the end of sd. four years except so much as the sd. Winship may require for necessary expenses during sd. term.
 Copeland & Chapin further agree to Board and wash for sd. Winship during sd. four years while in their employ and to allow sd. Winship the privilege of working by the piece when their work will admit.
 The wages of sd. Winship to be estimated in the following manner.

For the first year	$100.00
For the second "	$140.00
For the third "	$160.00
For the fourth "	$200.00
	$600.00

The sd. Winship commenced his labours for the sd. four years on the eighteenth of September 1826.
  New Hartford Nov. 17th 1826
   Copeland & Chapin
   Willam Winship

Table VII
Agreement between Kelloggs and Copeland-Chapin to Lease One Half Dwelling House to be Used as Boarding House - November 26, 1827

This indenture made and entered into by and between Isaac Kellogg and George C. Kellogg of New Hartford on the one part and Daniel Copeland of Hartford and Hermon Chapin of New Hartford on the other part - Witnesseth - That said Isaac and Geo. C. Kellogg have agreed to lease and do by these presents firmly and absolutely Lease and to farm Let unto the said Copeland and Chapin one common and undivided half part of a certain dwelling House, wood house and out house now occupied by Isaac Kellogg aforesaid situated in said New Hartford together with all the Garden and Land adjoining the same bounded and described as follows namely - the Garden lying north of said House and east of the Talcott Mountain Turnpike road and containing with the present fence - also the Garden east and south of said House and the lot extending south from said east mentioned garden nearly to a large pine tree standing on the said turnpike road being all the land which said Kelloggs own southerly of said dwelling house and between said turnpike road and the Farmington River, except that said Kelloggs reserve to themselves the right to take away fences which now divide the south lot aforesaid from the east and south garden and also the sole right of cutting trees on the Bank of the River and also the right to take up and carry away such part of the fruit trees and shrubs in said Gardens as they may think proper and reserving such right of way as it necessary for the use of tenter bars where they now stand - also right of way from their clothier's shop to the Well and a common right to use said Well - To have and to hold one half of the premises aforesaid unto them the said Copeland and Chapin and their heirs and assigns for the term of ten years from and after the first day of December next with the privileges and appurtenances there unto belonging - and furthermore the said Isaac and Geo. C. Kellogg do for themselves their heirs and assigns covenant and agree that neither they themselves nor any other person under them shall or will disturb or molest said Copeland and Chapin in the free use of the premises for the term aforesaid - and the said Copeland and Chapin do for themselves their heirs and assigns covenant and agree that they will pay to said Kelloggs of their heirs or assigns the annual rent of sixty dollars to be due and payable on the first day of December in each year for and during the term of ten years aforesaid - rent being due on the first day of December AD 1828 and furthermore said Copeland and Chapin covenant and agree to pay one half of the expense of the repairs of the Building aforesaid except the natural decay of the sill and outside of the said Building and to pay one half of the expense of Insuring said Building against fire and also to pay one half of the expense of keeping the fence in repair on the premises - provided that it shall happen that the said yearly rent hereby reserved shall be behind and unpaid by sixty days next after the day of payment herein specified, or if the said Copeland and Chapin or either of them shall assign over or otherwise part with this indenture or the premises hereby leased or any part thereof to any person or persons whatsoever, without consent of the said Isaac and Geo. C. Kellogg their heirs or assigns first had and obtained in writing and under their hands for that purpose, then in either of said cases it shall be lawful for said Isaac and Geo. C. Kellogg their heirs or assigns into the said premises hereby leased to re-enter and the same to have again and repossess in their first and former estate or estates.

And if the said Copeland and Chapin shall well and truly pay or cause to be paid the within specified rent and one half of the repairs (except as before excepted) and one half of the cost of Insurance against fire, which is to be obtained by said Kelloggs and shall also pay one half of the taxes charged or assessed on the said premises and shall preform and keep all and signular covenants and agreements herein on their part contained to be preformed and kept according to the true intent and meaning of this presents - then they shall and may lawfully and peaceably occupy and enjoy the said dwelling house and premises hereby demised with the parts and appurtenances thereof for the full term above written. In witness whereof the parties have hereunto interchangeably set our hand and seals at New Hartford on the 26th day of November AD 1827.

Table VIII
Agreement between Daniel Copeland and Hermon Chapin to Dissolve Co-partnership
October 21, 1828 [New Hartford Land Records: B14, p. 198]

I, Daniel Copeland of Hartford in the County of Hartford and State of Connecticut for divers good causes and consideration thereunto moving, especially for the sum of Sixteen Hundred Dollars received to my full satisfaction of Hermon Chapin of New Hartford in the County of Litchfield and State aforesaid have remised, released and forever quit-claimed, and do by these presents justly and absolutely remise and forever quit-claim unto the said Hermon Chapin to his heirs and assigns forever all such right and title as I the said Daniel Copeland have or ought to have in or to all the Real and Personal Estate belonging to the said Copeland and Chapin in common and undivided lying in said New Hartford, consisting of a Factory Building with water privileges and c., with an interest in the House and c. occupied as a Boarding House, together with all the right and title to Lands leased or conveyed to said Copeland and Chapin by Isaac and George C. Kellogg, and all the implements, tools, and machinery and stock on hand belonging to the said Copeland and Chapin, also all the debts and demands due and owing to the said Copeland and Chapin jointly from any person or persons whatsoever...To Have and to hold, the premises unto him the said Hermon Chapin...21st day of October in the year of our Lord 1828...Daniel Copeland.

Notes   Chapter I

1. *Chapin Genealogy of Deacon Samuel*, [Northampton, MA., 1862], p.232
2. *Cheshire County,[New Hampshire]Land Deeds*, Book 31, p.238
3. *Chapin Genealogy*, [Hartford, CT., 1924], Vol. I, p.11
4. *Cheshire County Land Deeds*, Book 77, p.503½
5. *ibid*, Book 78, p.58
6. *Supplement to Bellows Falls Times*, [Bellows Falls, VT., Fall 1955]
7. M. Frizzell, *A History of Walpole, NH*, [Walpole, NH., 1963], p.403
8. Oral History recorded by New Hartford Historical Society, interview with Ellie Lines Chapin, Sept. 1940. [She was wife of Frank M. Chapin.
9. Manuscript File, Connecticut Historical Society, MS 64938
10. *ibid*
11. According to the "Reminiscences of Samuel Jerome", published as a series of articles in the *Bristol Press*, [Bristol, Ct., 1880-1890], Melvin Copeland, planemaker came to Bristol while campaigning for the office of State Representative.
12. Kenneth D. and Jane W. Roberts, *Planemakers and Other Edge Tool Enterprises in New York State during the 19th Century*, pp.124-139
13. J. L. Bishop, *History of American Manufacturers, 1608-1868*, [Philadelphis, 1868], Vol. II, p.264
14. *The Winsted Times*, [Winchester, Ct., Sept. 23, 1926], Interview with Hermon M. and Frank M. Chahin, grandsons of Hermon Chapin
15. J. N. Lewis, *History of Litchfield County*, [Philadelphis, 1881], p.241
16. See Vol. I [this study], Chapter II, pp. 7-15
17. Personal communication with Emil Pollak, Dec. 10,1981
18. Library, Connecticut Historical Society, Hartford, Ct.
19. *ibid*
20. Vital Records at Hartford, CT., Vol.I, p.97
21. *op. cit.* [see 12., above], p.170
22. Geer, *1864 Hartford City Directory*, p.303
23. *History of the Connecticut Valley in Massachusetts*, [Phila., 1879], p.518

Chapter II

Making Wooden Planes

Having never made a plane, it is with some diffidence that I describe how this was done. Nevertheless, I have studied the available literature and have watched craftsman make planes. As will be noted in subsequent chapters planemaking was divided into two distinct branches; bench and moulding planes. A third division, really a special branch of moulding, was making plows, fillisters and screw arm sash planes. The latter demanded the greatest skill and therefore received the top pay.

An excellent account of the terminology and tools of this trade written by W.L. Goodman appears in *DICTIONARY of TOOLS*.[1] The important parts of a bench plane are noted on the drawing shown in Plate XVII, Vol. I, p. 82.

Beech was generally used as material. It was readily available in suitable lengths free from knots. After seasoning it was relatively stable, readily workable and reasonably wear resistant. Second growth timber was apt to be freer from knots. Other timber used was yellow birch (particularly during the 18th century, live oak (for ship building) and sometimes more exotic woods: cherry, apple, rosewood, boxwood and ebony. In order for wood to be dimensionally stable, a seasoning period of three to five years was required. Kiln drying did not begin until the middle of the 1860's.

Bench planes were made in standard cross sectional dimensions and specific lengths. After sawing a blank to proper size, the first step was to layout the mouth on the sole and define the chip evacuation cut out, comprised by the bed, front and side cheeks. This layout operation as well as subsequent procedures in removing this wood, is clearly outlined in a series of articles written by W.J. Armour and published in 1898.[2] Since this significant data is not readily available these articles on "Practical Plane Making" are reprinted in the Appendix to this Chapter.[3]

After the location of the mouth on the sole has been determined, the slope of the bed is scribed on the side using a "pitch board." This is illustrated in Fig. 3. The opposite side of this triangular gauge is used to mark and check the slope of the front by placing a bedding gauge against this side, similarly the slope of the bed may be checked. Such a bedding gauge is illustrated in the foreground of Fig. 4. This latter photograph also shows a mortised slot on the jack plane for accomodating the handle. Note that the front at the bottom of the handle is cut on an angle for a drive fit, after seating the back into this slot.[4]

Smoothing planes generally have curved sides, similar to the shape of a coffin. After cutting the evacuation chamber and the slot for the plane iron from rectilinear stock, the sides are marked with a template to indicate proper curvature to finish the plane to proper shape. (See Fig. 5)

Fig. 3 - Pitch Boards: Top, Jack Plane; Middle Smoothing Plane; Bottom, Moulding Plane

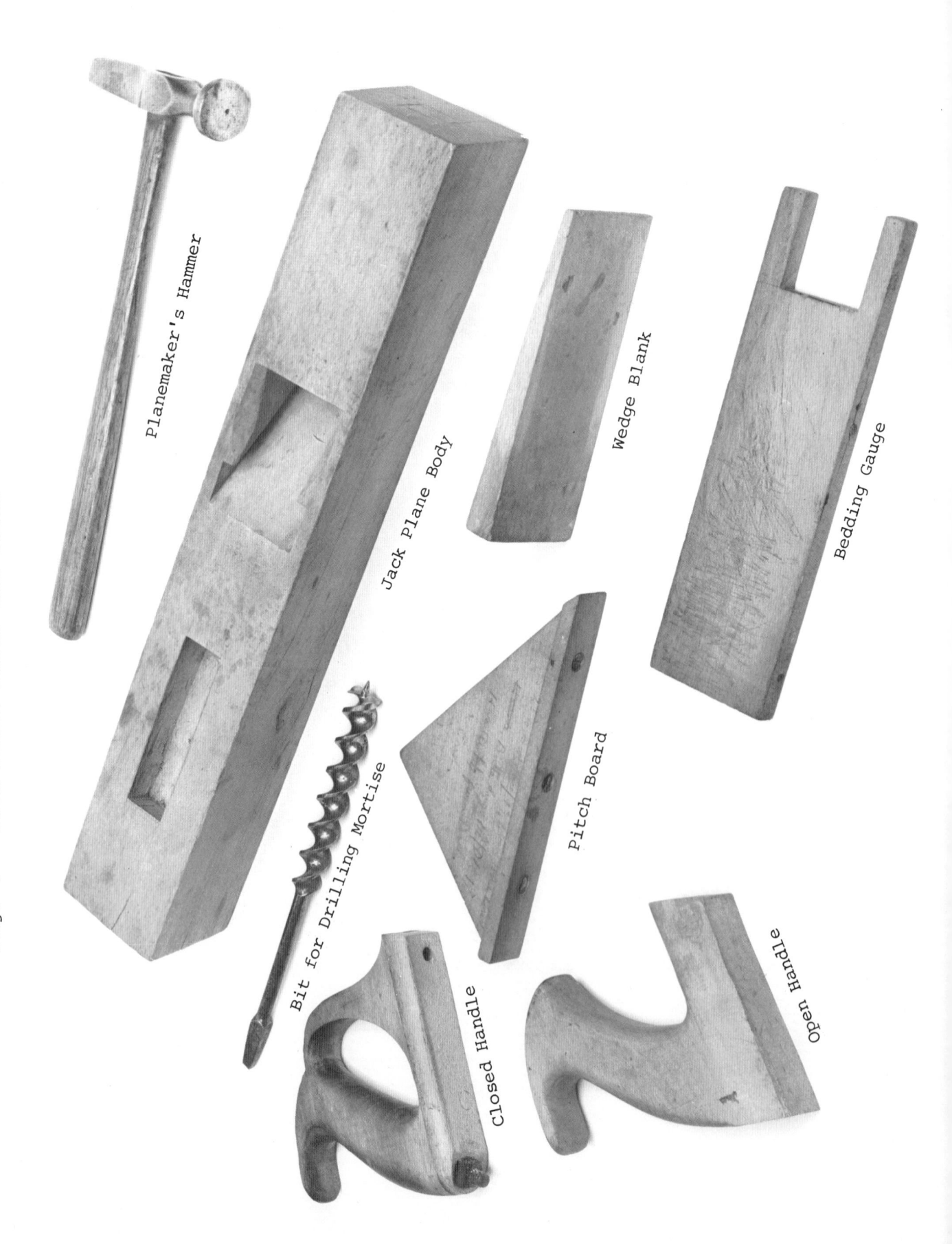

Fig. 4 - Jack Plane Parts and Tools

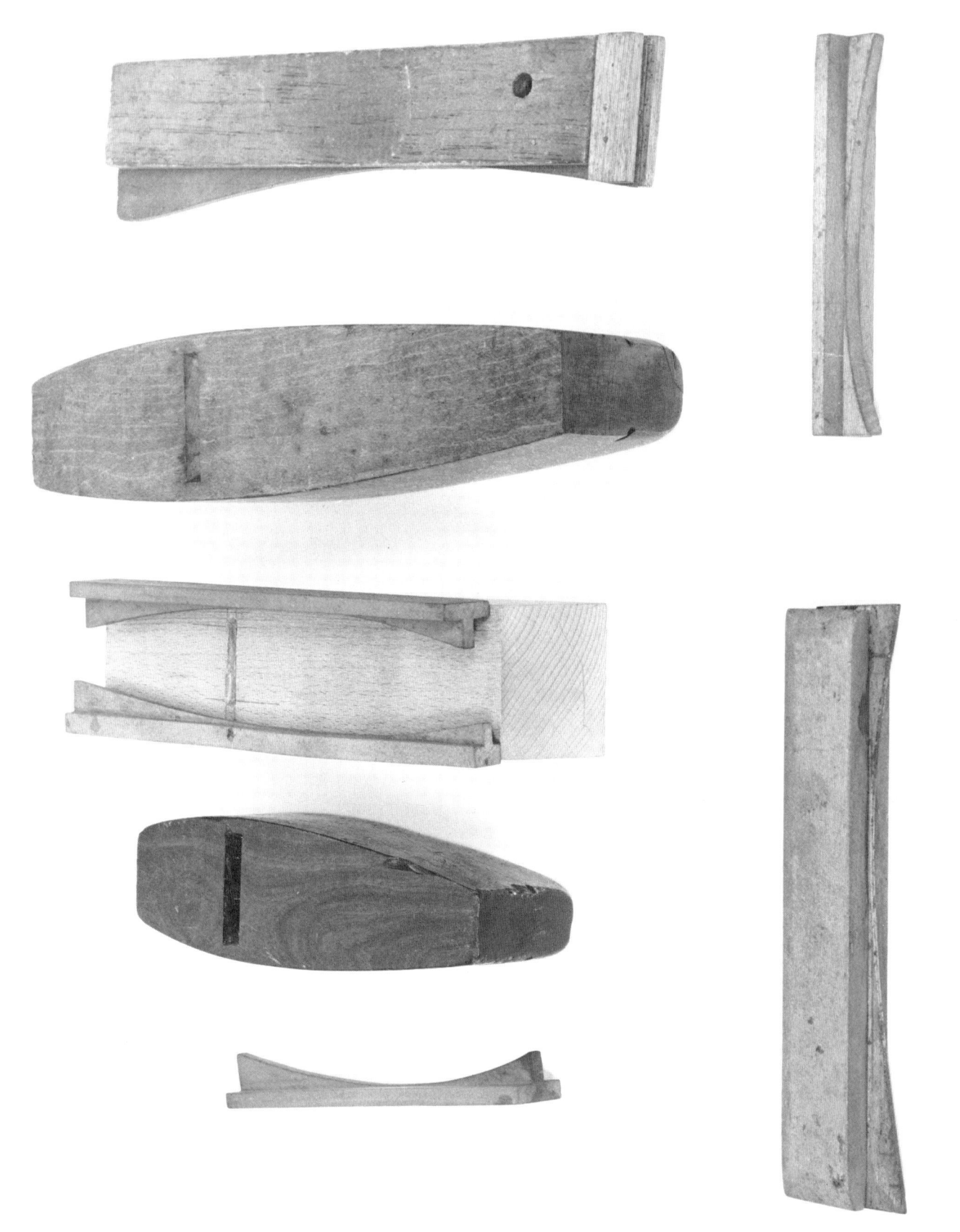

Fig. 5 - Templates for Marking Contour of Smoothing Planes

John Gardner, Curator of Small Craft at Mystic Seaport, has described his methods of making a ship builder's smoother.[5] During part of an apprenticeship during the 19th century a boatbuilder, was taught how to make planes used in this trade, as these were not readily available through purchase. The technique followed closely that used by bench planemakers, except the latter had special floats for cutting the abutment into the cheeks, which held the wedge. The following photographs, Figs. 6-12 illustrate Mr. Gardner's procedure for making such a smooth plane from beech.

- Fig. 6. The 2¼" square blank is cut to proper length (9 inches) and marked for cutting the opening.
- Fig. 7. After chiseling an opening for the mouth about ½" deep into the sole, a series of holes 3/16" diameter are drilled through the top. The material within this slot is cut out using a narrow, stiff saw.
- Fig. 8. The escapement area is cut away using a chisel.
- Fig. 9. A gauge is placed along the bed enabling a line to be marked along the cheek which defined the abutment slot for containing the wedge. A special stiff pointed saw (similar to a coping saw, but stiffer) enables a kerf to be cut on both sides, riding on the edge of the gauge, to the desired depth. This insures that both abutment cuts will be parallel for containing the wedge. Another cut is made at the back by sliding the saw on the surface of the bed. This is one of the most critical steps in the procedure.
- Fig. 10. The abutment slot is cut using a chisel and finished to a smooth surface with a float.
- Fig. 11. The wedge is made; a slot is cut in the bed to accomodate the screw on the double plane iron; the sides are shaped; and the top edges are chamferred.
- Fig. 12. The sequences of steps from right to left; layout and drill; chisel the bed and front; cut the abutment and finish the plane; double iron; wedge.

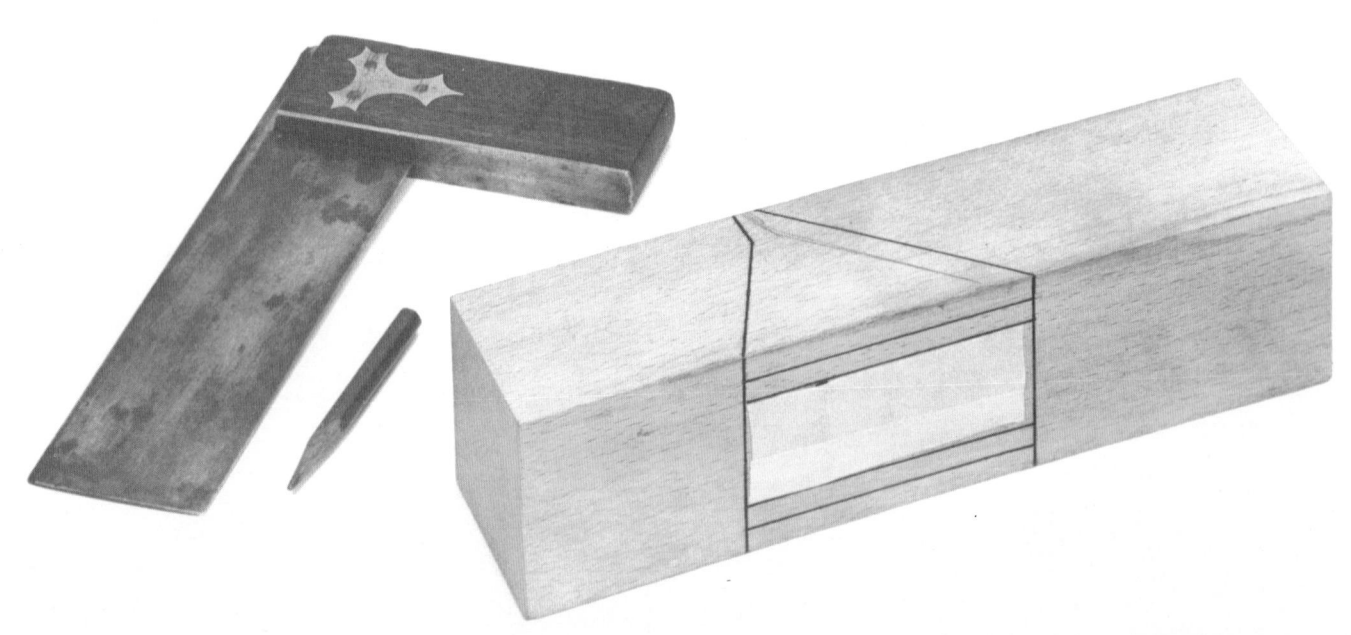

Fig. 6 - The 2½ in square blank, 9 in. long marked for opening.

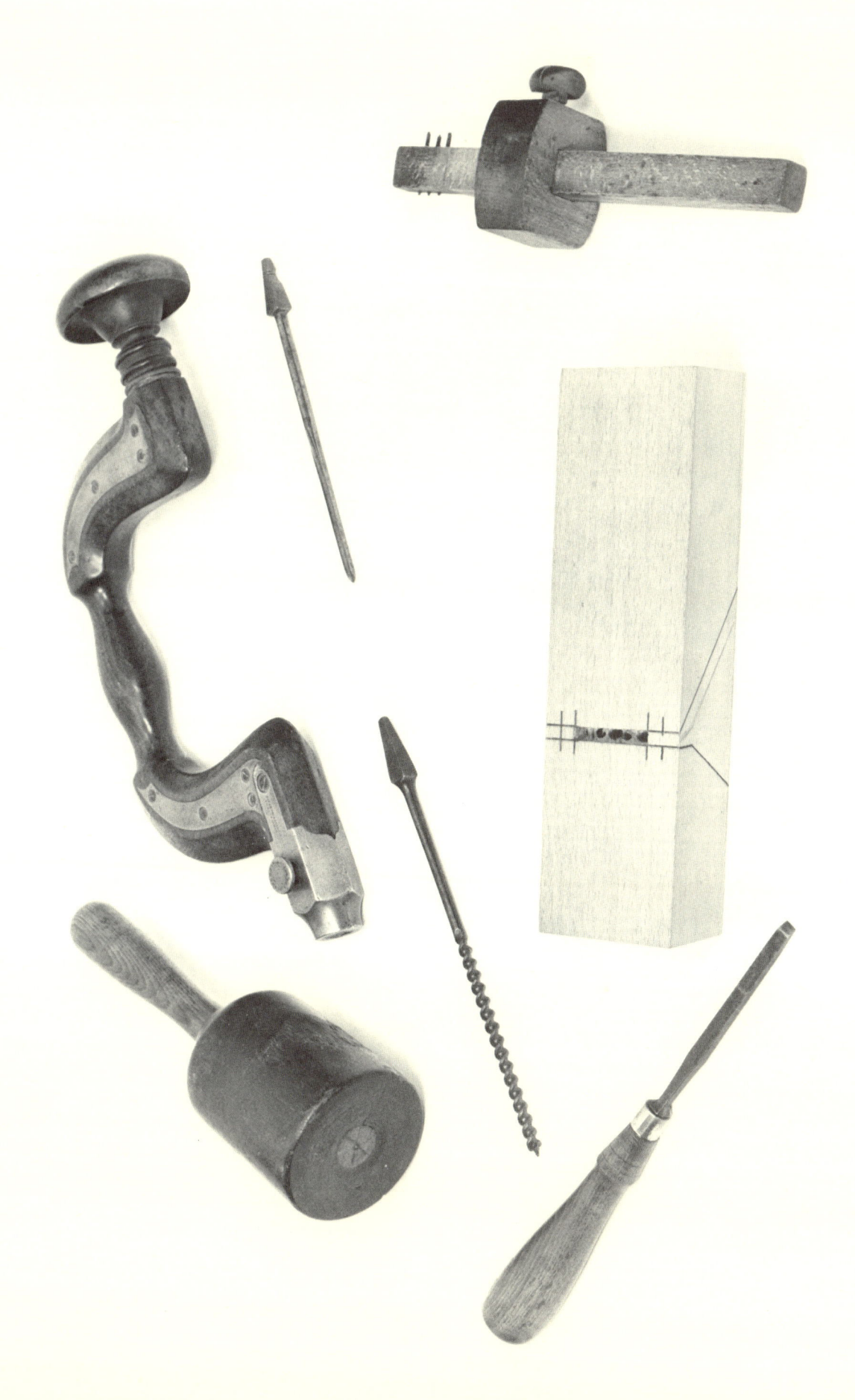

Fig. 7 - Chiseling the opening and drilling the slot.

Fig. 8 - Chiseling the escapement.

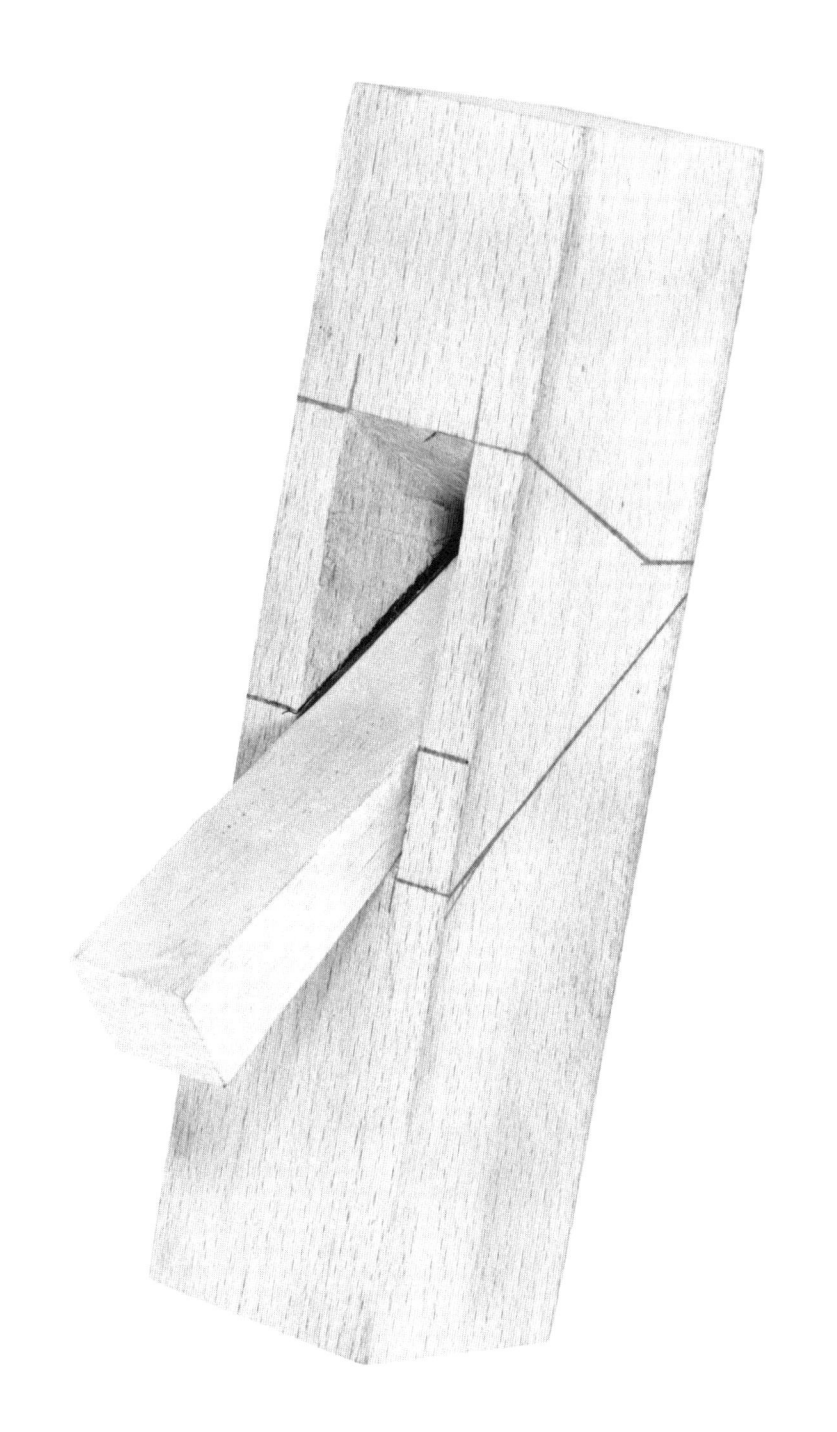

Fig. 9 - Marking the abutment slot.

Fig. 10 - Cutting the abutment slot.

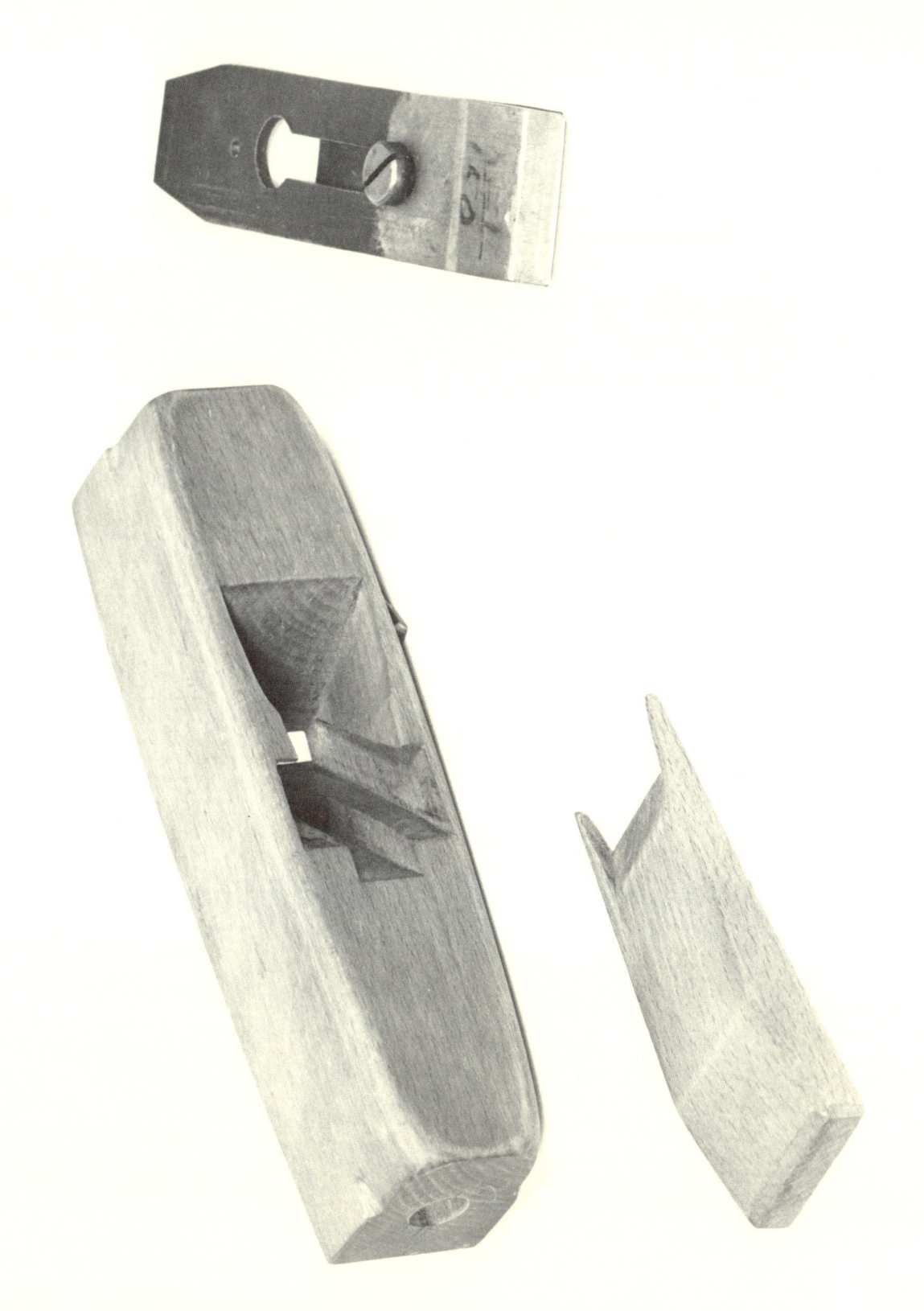

Fig. 11 - The wedge and cutting the slot in the bed.

Fig. 12 – The sequence of steps in making a smoothing plane. From Right to Left: layout and drill; chisel the bed; cut the abutment; finish the plane; double iron; wedge.

Additional sources of information on making planes are Frank Wildung's articles "Making Wooden Planes in America"[6] and Norman Vandal's article "How to make Moulding Planes."[7] There will be some further details on planemaking, particularly plow planes, in a later chapter concerning Solon Rust. Edward Ingraham of North Danville, VT makes reproductions of 18th century moulding planes in conjunction with his restoration work. Mr. Ingraham has generously contributed his procedure for making such moulding planes to this text. Following this description he has then traced the origins and styles of 18th century planemaking in southeastern New England. Those practices most certainly influenced Wetherel, which may in turn have influenced L. Kennedy and later the Copelands and finally, Hermon Chapin.

Mr. Ingraham has defined the parts of a moulding plane in Plate I. His procedure for making such a plane follows.

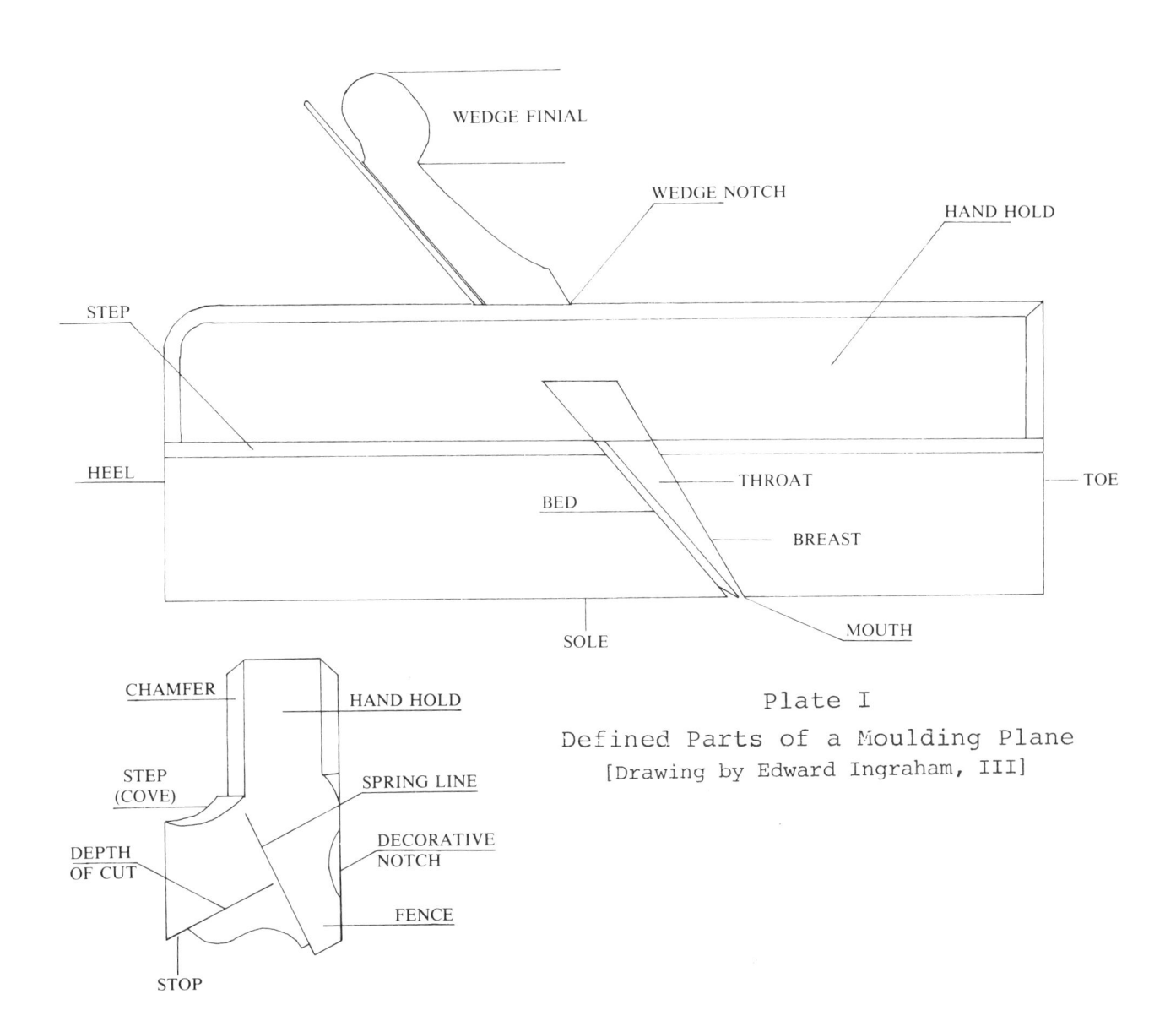

Plate I
Defined Parts of a Moulding Plane
[Drawing by Edward Ingraham, III]

I. Layout — A blank, slightly larger than 10 by 3¼ inches, and of sufficient width for the moulding, with allowance for dressing, is prepared from well seasoned wood. After this is planed square, a rabbet is cut on one side to form the hand hold. This step is generally 1½ inches deep and one third the width of the plane body. (Fig. 13) Since this proportion remains constant for a given width (i.e., stock for a ½ inch bead is the same for any other ½ inch moulding), it is possible to work up an inventory of blanks for preparing different planes.

Fig. 13 - Unmarked Blank and Marking Gauge

The bed and breast lines are first laid off on the blank. The bed line is squared across the sole, 3-¾ inches from the toe. This is followed by the mouth line, ³⁄₁₆ of an inch in front of the bed line. Using a template (Fig. 14), or a pitch board (see Fig. 3), the bed and breast angles are lightly marked on both sides of the body. A pitch board is simply a thin wooden template with a stop fastened to the base. One side is cut to the bed angle and the other to the breast; the difference always being 10°, equal to the wedge angle.[8] A plane bedded at 50° has a breast angle of 60°. After marking the bed and breast lines across the hand hold, the wedge mortise width is laid out. The mortise width is generally one third the thickness of the hand hold, and is marked out in the center. Next the fence line, slightly more than ⅓ the thickness of the hand hold, is scribed on the sole with a marking gauge. The extra width ($\frac{1}{32}$ - $\frac{1}{16}$ inch) allows the tip of the iron to be housed within the fence and prevents choking.

Fig. 14 - Layout of Throat with Gauges and Tools

Next the spring line is marked on the toe and heel. (Fig. 15) Spring permits more uniform pressure while planing along the edge of a board.[9] The spring line indicates the vertical position of the plane during use. From the spring, a line is squared, along which the depth of cut and stop are indicated. The contour of the moulding is then laid out on the toe or scribed from a template (Fig. 15)

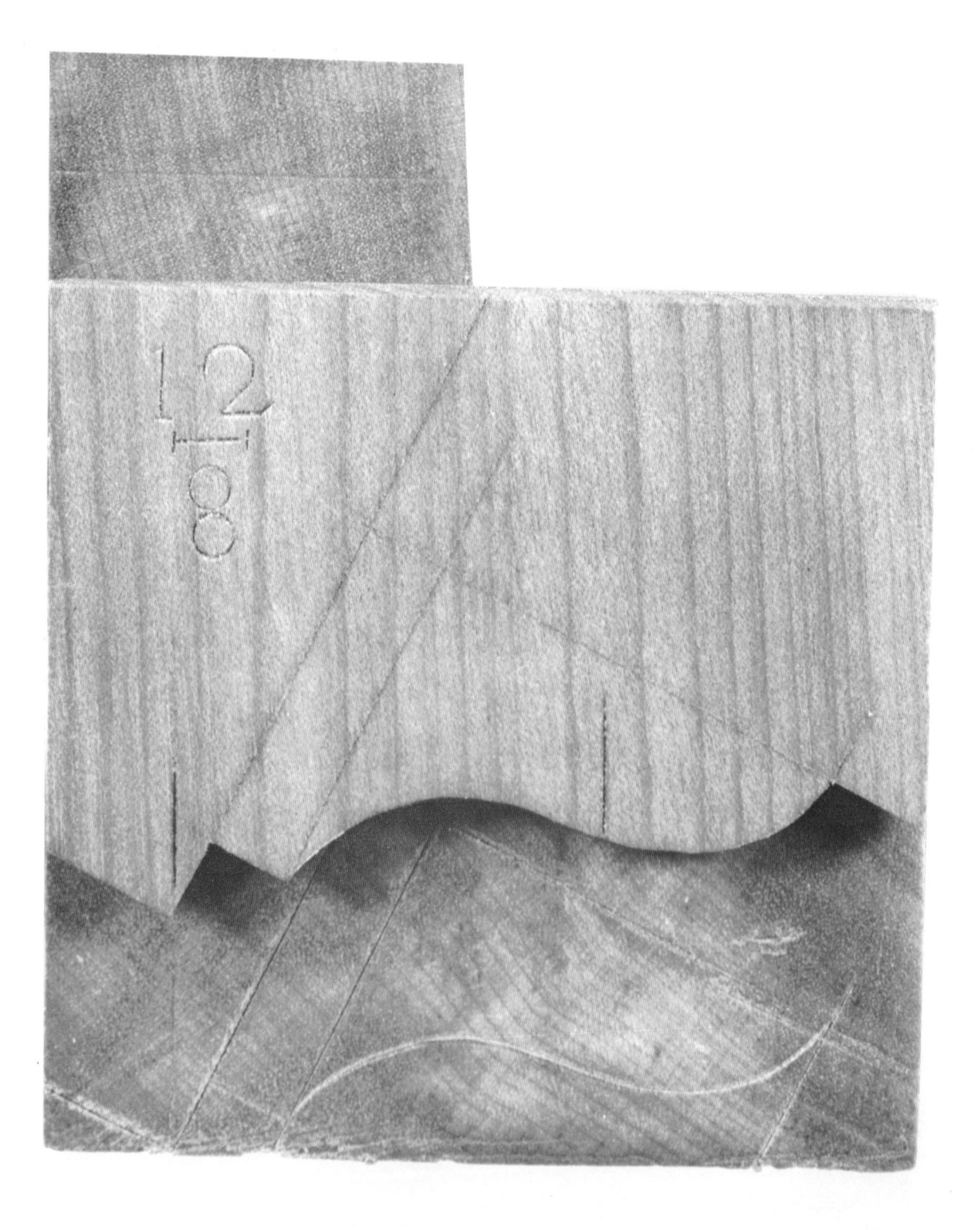

Fig. 15 - Toe End Layout with Template

II. Shaping the Sole — After securing the stock in a vise or special holding device, the material around the stop and fence is removed, using a plow and rabbet planes. The plow is again used to sink the deepest portions of the profile, the narrow grooves providing guides for subsequent planing. The profile is worked as close as possible to the lines using hollows and rounds and finished with scrapers, ground to the moulding shape. (Fig. 16)

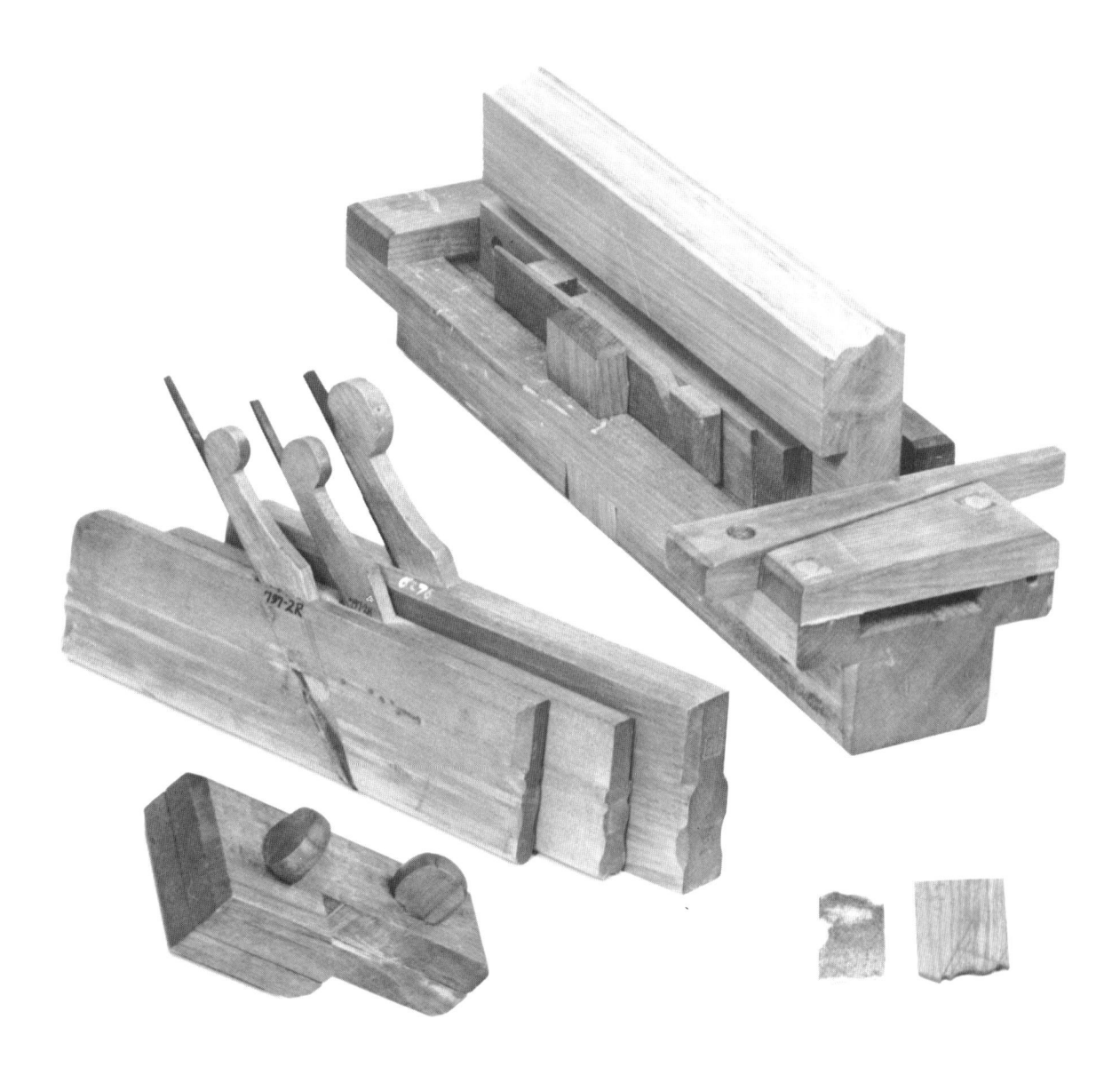

Fig. 16 - Stock in Holding Devise; Hollow & Round and Rabbet Planes for Rough Cutting Moulding Plane; Scraper for Finishing; Scraper Holder

For commonly produced shapes planes are developed called backing planes (mother planes), the exact shape of the finished moulding, that shape the sole in one operation.[10] Graduated sets of backing planes from ½ - 1½ inch sizes eliminate much of the layout on the soles and permit consistent manufacture of uniform mouldings. In combination with "special purpose" planes the availability of backing planes permits considerable diversity in the production of complex moulding tools. The use of a 1½ inch backing plane for a quirked ogee and two variation using such special purpose planes is shown in Plate II. Fig. 17 illustrates a backing plane making an ovolo door moulding plane.

After the profile is laid out on the sole, and before planing, if boxing is desired at the points of greatest wear, thin slips of boxwood or lignum vitae are inserted into dadoes, cut into the sole using a plow.

Fig. 17 - Cutting Sole of Moulding Plane with Backing Plane

35

A.

B.

C.

D.

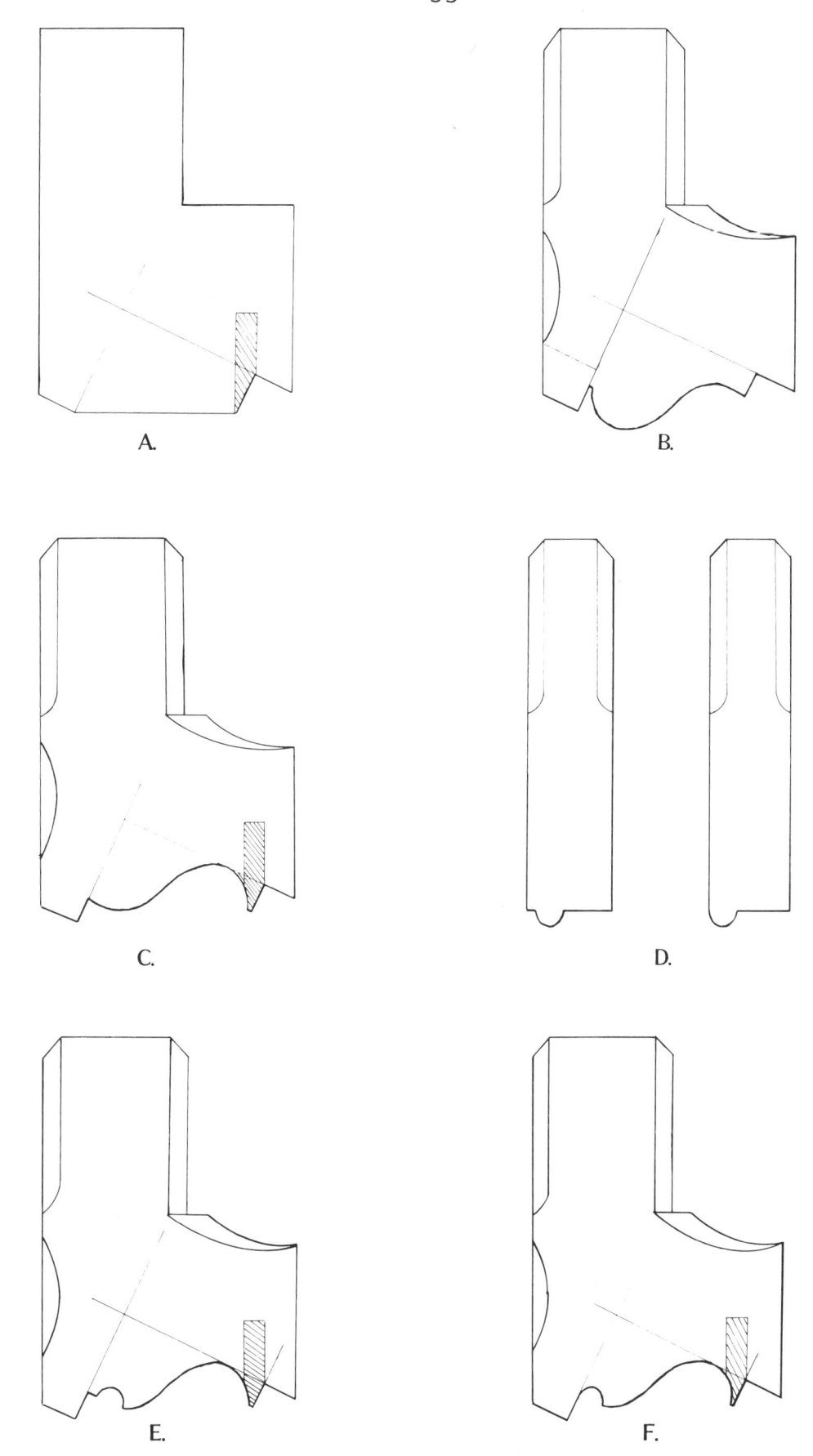

E.

F.

Plate II - Backing Plane and Special Purpose
Planes for Making 1½ inch Quirked Ogee
[Drawing by Edward Ingraham, III]

III Cutting the Troat — Securing the stock to the bench, using a back saw, two cuts along the bed and breast lines are made from the fence to the base of the hand hold. The waste stock is removed with a chisel and mallet and the throat sunk to the depth of the fence line. (Fig. 18)

IV Cutting the Wedge Mortise — Placing the stock in an upright position, a shallow mortise (¼ -½ inch) is sunk into the wedge slot. A hole is bored through to the throat using a small nose bit. A saw float is used to enlarge this cavity and the bed and breast pared with a strong narrow chisel. (Fig. 19) The sides are smoothed with a tapered float. During this operation a temporary wedge is used to test the accuracy. (Fig. 20)

V. Fitting the Iron and Wedge — A soft (annealed) plane iron blank and a wedge are fitted into the throat mortise. Care is taken to fit the bed and iron tightly at a point close to the cutting edge. Any movement of the iron during use produces chatter and ruins the moulding surface. One technique is to twist the iron slightly to force it more tightly to the bed; another is to hollow the bed slightly. The iron is marked with the profile and then filed to shape. After hardening the iron by heating in a forge and quenching, followed by tempering, it is honed to exact profile of the sole. Fig. 21 illustrates a plane with a rough wedge, a wedge pattern, a blank iron and a filed wedge shaped to the contour of the sole.

VI. Finishing — The body is dressed with a finely set smooth plane. The top chamfers are laid on with a marking gauge and then cut with a plane; while the toe and heel chamfers are cut with a chisel. The step is moulded with a round plane and notches cut with a gouge. The heel is rounded with a chisel and file. The maker's mark is stamped on the toe and the size of the moulding on the heel. Fig. 22 illustrates a finished reverse ogee plane and a sample of its "stuck" moulding.

VII Making an Iron — A wrought iron blank (3 to 4 inches wide) and a small piece of cast steel are diagonally scarf cut across adjoining edges. These are welded together in a forge by hammering at a high temperature, using borax as a flux.[11] The steel is applied to the upper surface of the iron blank. The finished blank is then trimmed and straightened. Several pieces for individual plane irons may be cut or sheared from this blank. It is easier to prepare a large composite piece from which several blanks may be cut than to attempt to fire (blacksmith) weld together individual small pieces of cast steel to wrought iron. The iron upper half of the blank is upset in order to form a tang and then drawn out over an anvil to an overall length of about seven inches. The upper portion is then thinned, allowing the cutting edge to be the thickest part. The tang is straightened and the face of the steel filed, ground and polished to insure a flawless cutting edge. This series of steps are illustrated in Fig. 23. The iron is now ready to be fitted to a plane.

Fig. 18 - Cutting Mouth and Side with Back Saw and Clearing with a Chisel.

Fig. 19 - Cutting the Throat; Drill through with bit and Clear with Chishel.

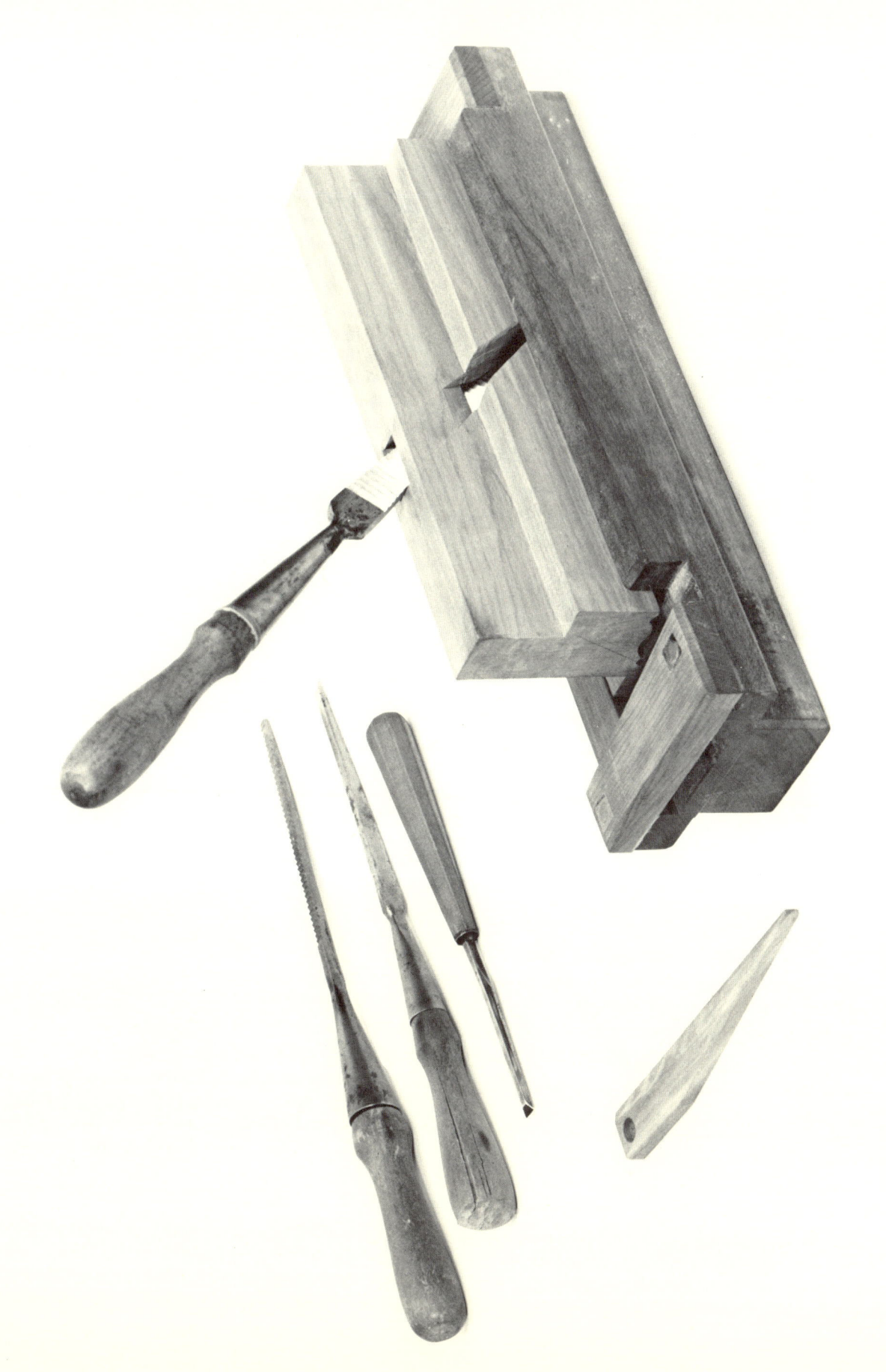

Fig. 20 - Finishing the Throat with a Float and Check with Wedge Gauge.

Fig. 21 - Finished Plane with Blank and Finished Iron and Wedge Pattern.

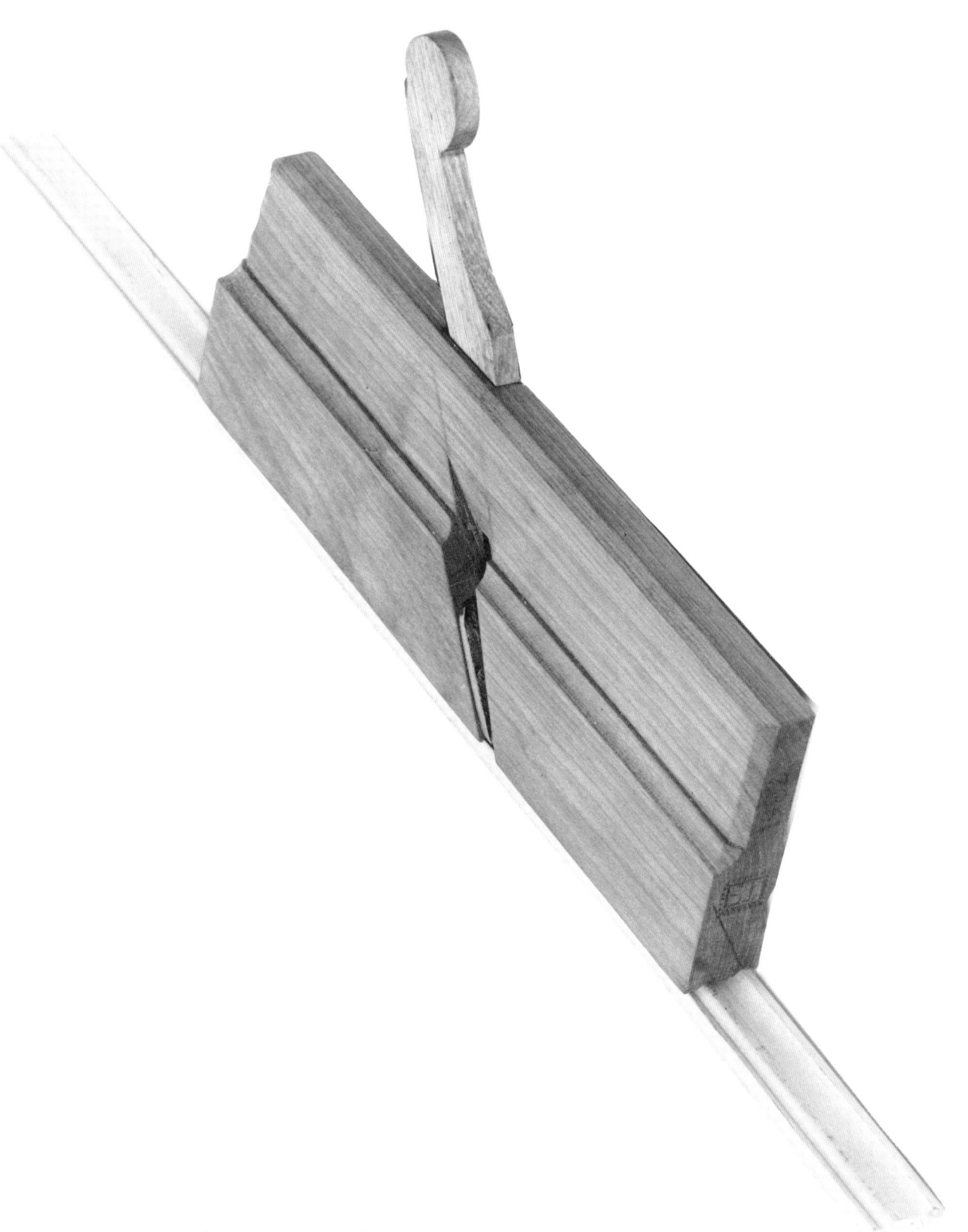

Fig. 22 - Finshed Plane with Struck Moulding.

42

Fig. 23 - Top: Steps in Making an Iron; Bottom: Moulding Layout Patterns and Scrapers

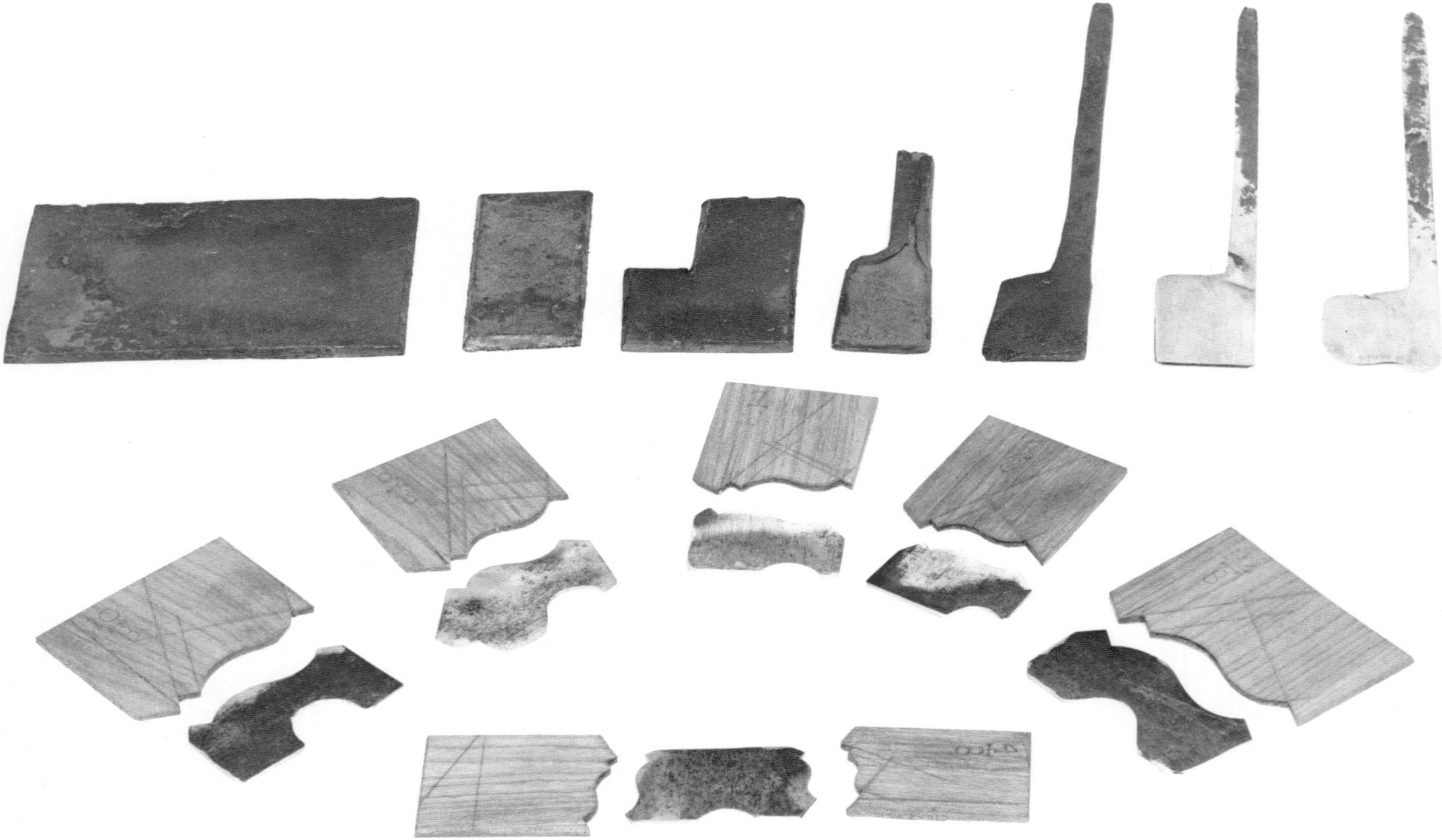

The remainder of this Chapter presents an historical essay "American Planemaking before 1820," written by Edward Ingraham, based on his observation, research and studies.

This brief examination of planemaking during the 18th and early part of the 19th centuries is focused on the development of moulding planes, rather than bench planes, for two important reasons. Since moulding planes were probably produced in greater quantities than bench planes and were subject to less wear, their survival is much greater than bench planes. Secondly, because moulding plane profiles closely followed the trends in architectural style, it is often possible to date even unsigned (not imprinted) examples from shapes alone.

The development of planemaking in America, as a trade separate from joinery, closely paralleled this craft in England. It is therefore necessary to briefly examine English practice before attempting to understand the growth of this trade in America. During the mid to late 17th century, the English economy experienced a period of rapid growth. In part this was due to the successful colonization of the American continent and the rise of London to the rank as a major world trade center. The subsequent increase in national wealth led to general improvement in the standard of living among most English people. At the same time English architecture was undergoing widespread change, as influenced by European Renaissance.[12] Guided by such books as Pallaido's *Book I,* first published in 1663, and other works by English authors, architects began embellishing buildings with classical Roman lines.[13] To meet the demands of such more sophisticated designers, English craftsmen were forced to refine their skills. As a result, specialization among the trades became more prevalent. It was during this period that the first documented English planemaker, Thomas Granford, trained as a joiner and a member of the Joiners Company of London, placed the following advertisement in *THE POST-MAN* [London, May 6-8, 1703].[14]

"Thomas Granford, living at the Sign of the 3 Plane-makers in Queen Street, near Chespside, London, maketh and selleth all sorts of Joyners and Carpenters Tooles..."

This clearly indicated his specialization as a toolmaker. Granford and his apprentice, Robert Wooding, exerted a major influence on the development of planemaking in England.[15] An additional factor that contributed to the development of tool specialists during the early 18th century was the rigidly structured system of labor. Guilds and craft organizations, long a vital part of English society, insured the passage of a high standard of craftsmanship from generation to generation.

In addition to producing planes for domestic markets, English planemakers exported their products to the colonies, principally through London merchants. Due to the high transportation costs the trade in America was limited to the larger urban centers of Boston, New York and Philadelphia. However the importation of English planes considerably influenced the stylistic development of American planes during the late 18th century.

During this same period the American colonists were not prospering nearly as well. The small populations, principally comprised of English immigrants from the farming and laboring classes, struggled to meet necessities from domestic markets. The Crown only permitted exports of goods of primary manufacture, i.e. wood products, bar and pig iron, and discouraged most forms of secondary manufacture.[16] This English policy of restricting Colonial manufacturing, greatly hampered the development of skilled American labor. The few skilled craftsmen in the Colonies during the first half of the 18th century were forced to generalize their skills to meet the demands of the populace. During this period, and for most of the 18th century, the tools used by American craftsmen were principally made by the men who used them. Through indenture apprentices were not only taught the secrets of the craft by the master, but also how to construct their tools. An indenture between Major John Dunlap, a highly skilled cabinetmaker from Goffstown, N.H., and William Huston, his apprentice, dated March 29, 1775, clearly demonstrates this tradition.

"...the Aforesaid John Dunlap is to use the utmost of his skill and Dilligence to Learn the Aforesaid William the Art and Mistrey of a cabinet-maker and Joyner that he now followeth as far as he is capable of Learning the same and at the End and Expiration of the Aforesaid time the Aforesaid John Dunlap is to Dismiss the said William from his service and help him make the Wooden part of a set of tools for the trade..."[17]

Soon after the middle of the 18th century, the American economy began to show signs of expansion. The population, now well over a million, and steadily increasing, required more domestic goods. Merchants were ignoring the laws of the Crown and traded with Europe, Africa and the West Indies, filling their coffers with foreign currency.[18] The colonists, now becoming more financially independent, sought a higher standard of living. Responding to changing American tastes, architects began designing buildings with more classical lines paying more attention to ornamentation and detail.[19] This new form was not copied directly from English works, but was however, adapted from English sources. The wide spread distribution of books on Romanesque Architecture enabled even the rural colonial carpenter to design classically styled buildings.[20]

The talents of the skilled joiner, now much in demand to provide housing and furniture, were beginning to demonstrate signs of specialization, just as they had done in England almost one hundred years earlier. Without the rigid structure of trade guilds, as had been the case in England, the specilized craft of planemaking developed at a somewhat slower pace.

The earliest documented planemaker, discovered to date in the colonies, is Deacon Francis Nicholson (b. 1683, d. 1753)[21] Nicholson lived in the rural town of Wrentham, Mass., on the Rhode Island border. Working with his son, John, and indentured servant, Caesar Chelor, Nicholson produced a large number of planes, many of which survive today.

Few, if any other American planemakers, have been identified working at this early date. This raises the question as to why Nicholson was so successful, practicing his trade in a rural out-of-the-way town. This group of southeastern Massachusetts craftsmen proved to be the exception rather than the rule, since professional planemaking in other areas did not begin to develop until the last two decades of the 18th century. The planes produced in urban shops were not altogether different from those that had been previously imported from England. The only direct transference of planemaking skill from an English source, known to the writer, were the planes made by Thomas Napier, a planemaker from Scotland who immigrated to Philadephia around 1875.[22] It can be assumed that most American planemakers simply imitated the traditional English form. Planes from Boston, New York and Philadelphia during this period were usually 9½ to 9¾ inches long, made from beech and furnished with an oval or eliptically shaped wedge. The only planes that did not resemble the traditional English style were those made in southeastern Massachusetts and northern Rhode Island. Because of its unique style, this region presents the most accurate picture of the development of planemaking in this country. The following chronology of moulding planes is based on the stylistic development from one school of planemaking in this area.

Perhaps the most characteristic feature of these planes from the southeastern Massachusetts area is that, almost without exception, they were made from yellow birch. While beech grew in abundance throughout this region, planemakers chose to ignore this traditional wood and chose birch as the primary material, until late in the 18th century. Other features that set this "school" apart from their contemporaries were the use of a relieved wedge, decorative notching and the "wedge notch." (See Plate II) This notch consisted of a small chamfer cut on the leading edge of the wedge mortice, to prevent the plane body from splitting when the wedge was driven tight. The planes of Francis and John Nicholson and Caesar Chelor illustrated in Fig. 24 clearly show the unique southeastern, Massachusetts style. All three planes support a very slightly revieved wedge and an extended chamfer on the heel and toe that was refined by later members of this school into a separate decorative notch.

Several planemakers from this area exhibit an almost identical style, including the slightly relieved wedge. Figure 25 illustrates planes made by E. Clark, Middleboro; D. Clark, Cumberland; H. Wetherel, Norton; and Jo Fuller, Providence. The remarkable similarity among these planes and the late planes of the Nicholson Group strongly suggests more than a casual relationship existed between these planemakers. Only two of these, Jo Fuller and Aaron Smith, produced a significant quantity of planes. Fuller remained in Providence, while Wetherel moved to Chatham, Connecticut. There he worked with his son, who later located the plane business at Middletown.

Fuller's earliest planes, bearing simply the large embossed stamp "JO FULLER, surrounded by a zig-zag border, were 10 inches long, constructed from birch, and supported a step, moulded with a cove. The wedge was slightly relieved and shallow decorative notches were applied to the toe and heel.[24] The second period of Fuller's planes demonstrated several small changes in design; the relief of the wedge was more pronounced and the heel was rounded slightly more than previously and he adopted a new and smaller stamp which also noted his location, "JO FULLER-IN-PROVIDENCE" (Three separate stamps). Figure 26A shows Fuller's second variation. The chamfers on the earliest and second period remain wide and flat, around $5/16$ inches, and both styles have the regional wedge notch.

During Fuller's third period, refinement of the "relieved wedge style," the work of another planemaker, Aaron Smith of Rehoboth, Mass. (b. 1769, d. 1822) comes to attention.[25] While to date research has failed to produce evidence that links these two planemakers, their identical style suggests they may have worked together at some point in their careers. Since Fuller was 22 years older, it is quite possible that Smith may have served his apprenticeship under him.

Among the changes observed in Fuller's planes include a more sharply defined relieved wedge, deeper decorative notching on the heel and slightly narrower chamfering ($3/16$ - $1/4$ of an inch). Smith's earliest planes differed only slightly with slightly sharper curvature in the wedge finial.[26] The material, length, cove step and the use of the wedge stock remained the same. Evidentaly the relieved wedge style was quite popular, as it was extensively copied by craftsmen and planemakers throughout the south eastern Massachusetts area. (See Fig. 26B & C)

The first hint of conformity to accepted standards by these two planemakers came when the narrow flat chamfers on the upper surface of the plane body were replaced with small radius chamfers. (See Fig. 27A) All the other features of their planes remained the same. The first major alteration of their style, probably dating near the turn of the century, was indicated by the reduction in length from 10 to 9½ inches and the elimination of the decorative notching. The chamfers were somewhat more rounded, while the material continued to be birch and the relieved wedge was still a prominent feature. The changes occurring in Smith's planes are clearly seen in Fig. 27B.

Towards the end of their careers both Fuller and Smith became conventional, adopting beech as material. The stylistic relieved wedge was also replaced with a more contemporary eliptical version. Smith's final design is shown in Fig. 27C. Fuller also altered his planes in similar fashion, however the wedge finial was somewhat different. A summary of the chronological changes in styles during the working careers of Jo Fuller and Aaron Smith follows.

Fig. 24 - Planes of: Francis Nicholson (left); John Nicholson (center); Caesar Chelor (right)
[Photographed by and from the collection of Edward Ingraham, III]

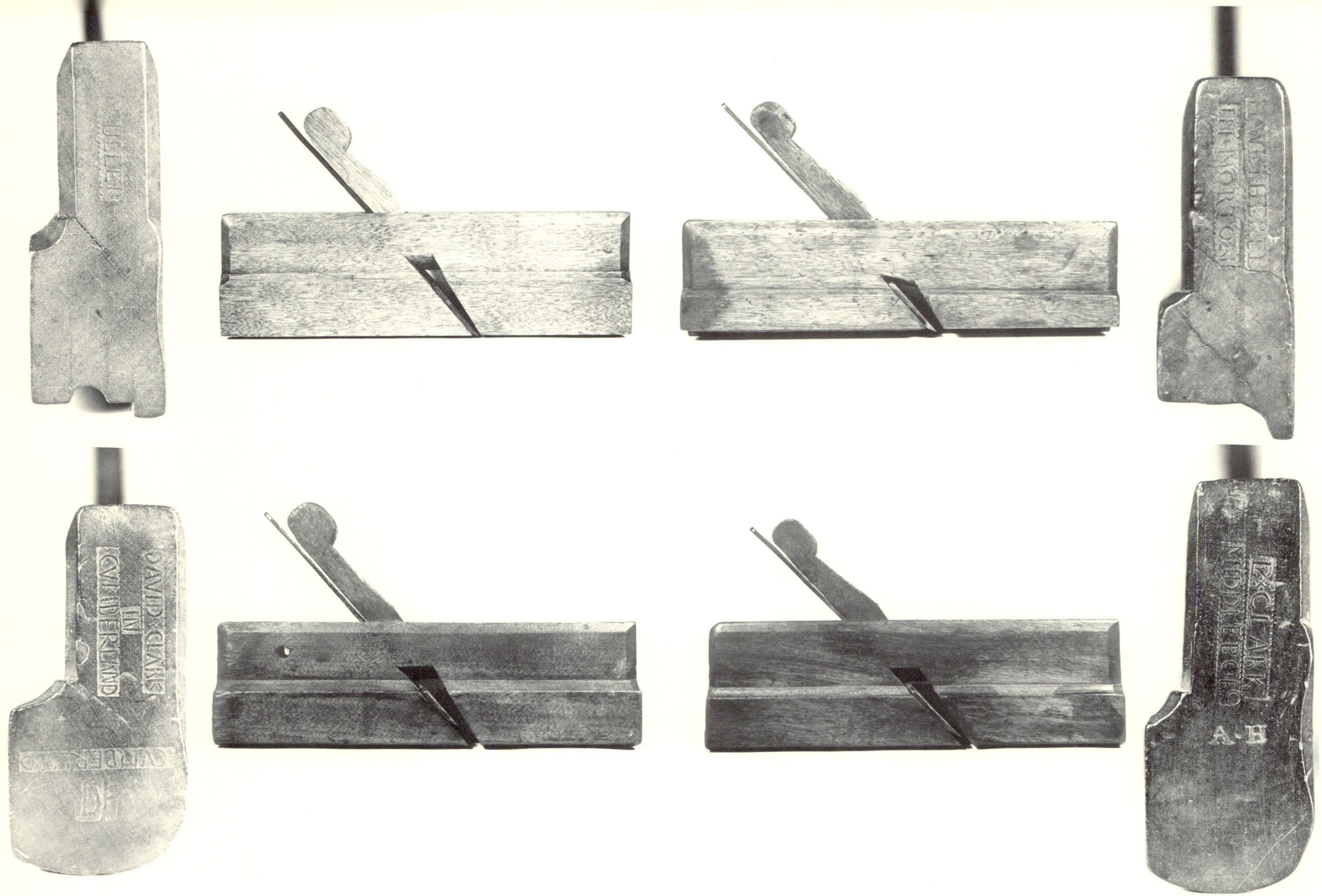

Fig. 25 - Planes of Jo Fuller (upper left); H. Wetherel (upper right); D. Clark (lower left); E. Clark (lower right).

[Photographed by and from the collection of Edward Ingraham, III]

Fig. 26 - Planes by: Joe Fuller (A); Aaron Smith (B); Joe Fuller (C)
(Left)   (Middle)   (right)

[Photographed by and from the collection of Edward Ingraham, III]

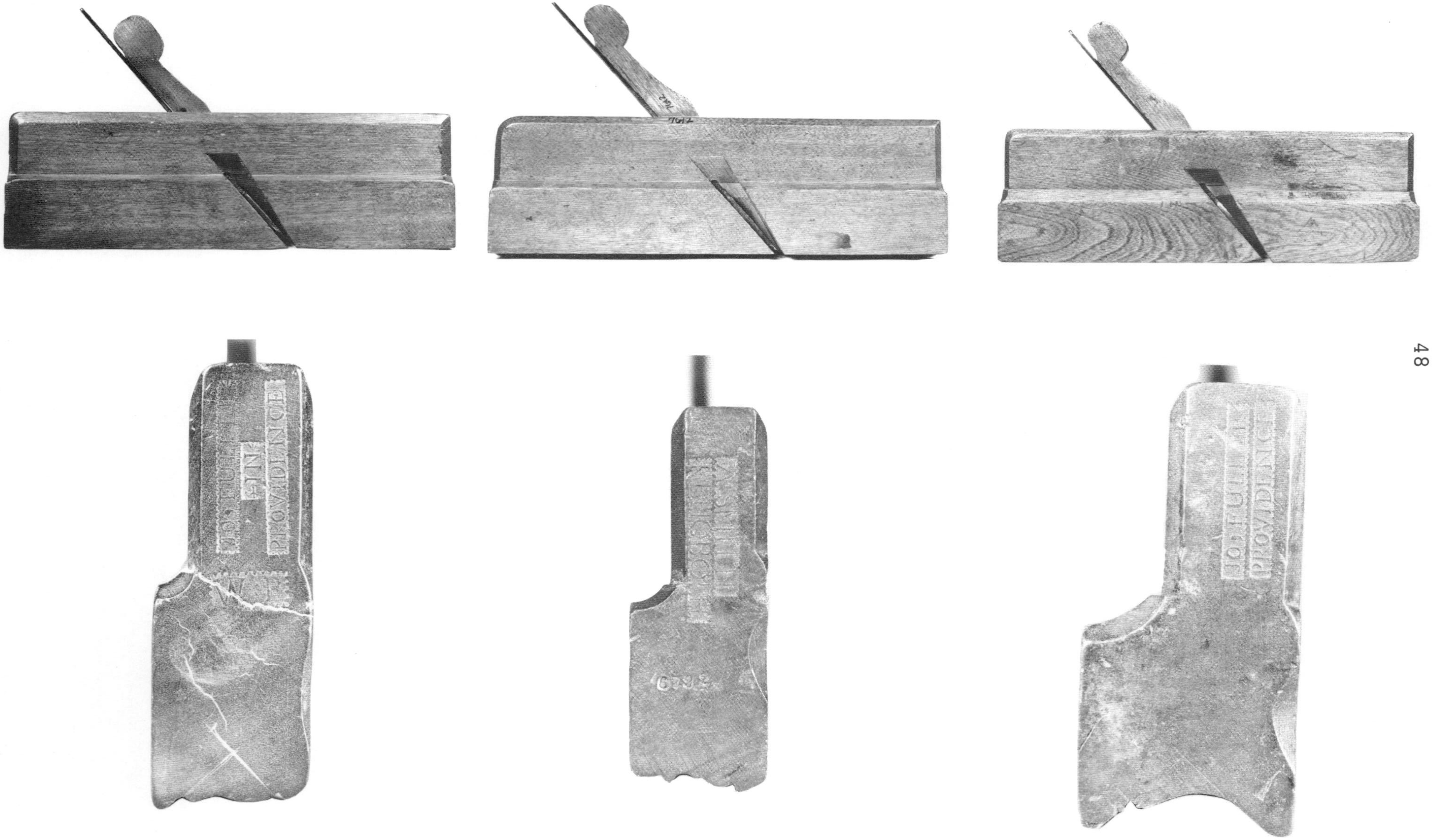

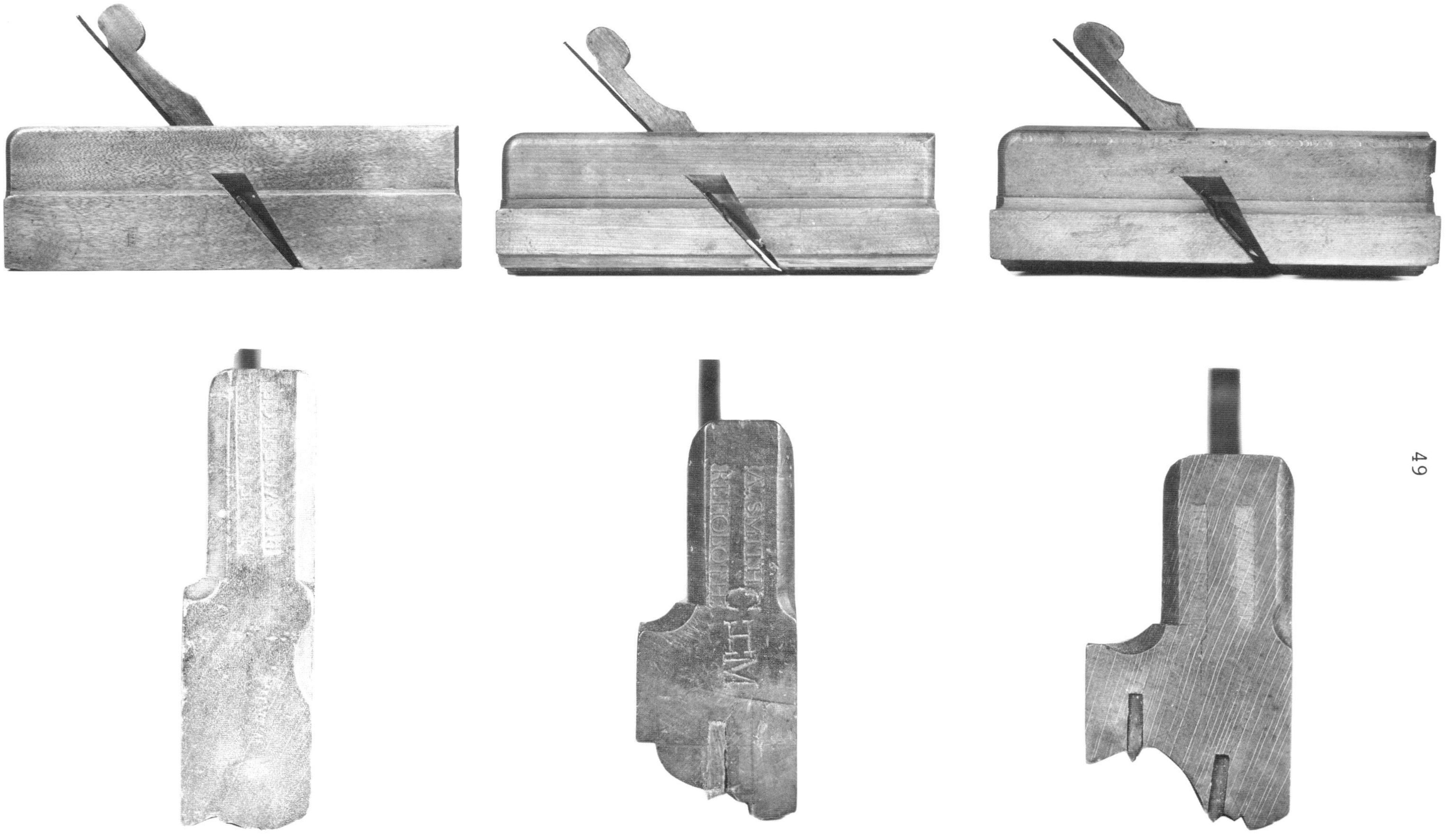

Fig. 27 - Planes by: Joe Fuller (A); Aaron Smith (B); Aaron Smith (C)
(left)   (middle)   (right)
[Photographed by and from the collection of Edward Ingraham, III]

1766-1776 FULLER — earliest planes, large stamp Jo. FULLER with zig-zag border, slightly relieved wedge, birch, 10 inchs long, cove step, wedge notch, heel approaches square, shallow notches heel and toe, wide flat chamfers (5/16″)

1776-1785 FULLER — smaller stamp JO. FULLER-IN-PROVIDENCE (three separate stamps) with zig-zag border, heel slightly rounded, relieved wedge more pronounced, all other features the same.

1785-1796 FULLER and SMITH — (Smith probably began to work on his own, around 1789 at the age of 20) Fuller's stamp the same, without the "IN." Smith's stamp, A. SMITH-REHOBOTH, large letters, (two separate stamps), 10 inch birch, narrow, flat chamfers (¼″), sharply relieved wedge, deep decorative notches on heel and toe.

1795-1800 FULLER and SMITH — Began using smaller radius chamfer on top, heel and toe, remained narrow and flat, all other features the same.

1800-1810, FULLER and SMITH — adopted the shorter length of 9½ inches, chamfers more rounded on top and on heel and toe, birch, relieved wedge, eliminated decorative notches. Smith began to use smaller stamp with indented ends.

1810-1820 FULLER and SMITH — finally adopted beech as primary material, replaced relieved wedge with eliptical shape, Smith's stamp the same, Fuller changed to a smaller version of his stamp.

1822 FULLER and SMITH — Both planemakers died.

The majority of the moulding planes made by Joseph Fuller and Aaron Smith were laid out from circular segments based on Romanesque Architecture. At the end of the 18th century the influence of Greek Revival led to a distinct change in the design of mouldings. Architects disregarded the once popular Roman shapes, which were replaced with the Grecian eliptical forms. Asher Benjamin, the author of the first American work on classical architecture clearly stated his preference for Grecian mouldings in the following excerpt from hs book:[27]

> "Although I have made some use of the Roman ovolo and ogee in all the orders, I do not generally use them in practice: the bending, or turning inward, of the upper edge of the Grecian, or quirk ovolo, when the sun shines on its surface, causes a beautiful variety of light and shade which greatly relieves it from the plane..."

The later planes of both Fuller and Smith reflect this change in architectural preference, as can be seen in the steep Grecian ovolo with astragal plane by A. Smith in Fig. 27c.

The changes seen in the planes of Joseph Fuller and Aaron Smith were by no means unique. Many other planemakers working in the southeastern Massachusetts area also altered their planes similarly during the last decade of the 18th century. Perhaps the greatest factor in the disappearance of the relieved wedge plane was the increasing competition from urban planemaking, as a result of the changing style in architecture.

Notes - Chapter II

1. R.A. Salaman, *Dictionary of Tools used in the woodworking and allied trades, 1790 - 1970,* [London, 1975], pp. 370 - 378

2. W.J. Armour, *WORK - The Illustrated Weekly Journal for Mechanics,* [London, Paris, New York Melbourne, 1898], Vol XV, No. 461, Jan. 15, p.8; No. 463, Jan. 29, pp.44-45; No. 465, Feb. 12, p.77; No. 467, Feb. 26, p.107.

3. Acknowledgement is made to Craig A. Lewis, Maroubra, Australia for bringing these articles to my attention and sending me photocopies.

4. The planemaker's hammer illustrated in Fig. 4 actually is not related to this particular work, but it is a convenient place to illustrate this special tool for tapping the end of a plane to loosen the wedge when removing an iron. The other end of this hammer functions as a screw driver for regulating the screw on a double plane iron.

5. John Gardner, *National Fisherman,* "Boatbuilder' Planes Are Many Splendored Things", Nov. 1971; "How to Make a Wooden Boatbuilder's Plane, Dec. 1971.

6. Frank Wildung, *Chronicle of EAIA,* "Making Wooden Planes in America", Part I, Vol. III, No.2, April 1955, pp. 19-20; Part II, July 1955 Vol. III, No. 3, pp. 28 - 30.

7. Norman Vandal, *Fine Woodworking,* [Newtown, CT., 1982], "How to Make a Moulding Plane", No. 37, Nov./Dec. 1982, pp. 72 - 77.

8. The four most frequent degrees of pitch were: common (45°), used in most bench, rabbet and dado planes; York (50°), the standard pitch for moulding planes for working both soft and straight grained hardwood; middle pitch, (55°); and half pitch (60°), which cut similar to a scraping action, used on dense, highly figured hardwoods.

9. The subject of spring has been discussed in detail in Vol. I, Chapter X, pp. 260 - 263. The amount of spring ranged from 20° (the later English Standard) to 35°, seen on early New England planes.

10. W.L. Goodman refers to such usage during the 18th Century as "mother planes". (*British Planemakers from 1700,* [Needham Market, England, 1978], 2nd edition, p.4). The term, backing plane, used by Armour, (see reference No. 2 above appears to this publisher as a more suitable word for such a plane used during the 19th century.

11. This practice was followed during the 18th and 19th centuries both in England and United States due to the high cost of cast steel compared to the less expensive wrought iron.

12. Martin S. Briggs, *Wren the Incomparable*, [London, 1953], pp. 27-28.

13. F.A. Praeger, *The Encyclopedia of Furniture,* [New York, 2nd Edition, 1963], p.XLI

14. M. Falkner, *Chronicle of EAIA,* Vol. 33, Dec. 1980, p. 70.

15. W.L. Goodman, *op. cit.,* p. 4.

16. Oliver Perry Chitwood, *A History of Colonial America,* [New York, 1961], p.371

17. Charles S. Parsons, *The Dunlaps and Their Furniture,* [Currier Gallery, Manchester, NH, 1970[, p. 53.

18. O.P. Chitwood, *op. cit.,* p. 387

19. Talbot Hamlin, *Greek Revival Architecture in America,* [New York, 1964], p. 10 - 11.

20. William Pain, *Practical House Carpenter*
    Abraham Swan, *British Architect*
    Other works by:
    Batty Langley
    James Gibb
    Isaac Ware
21. Donald and Anne Wing, *Catalog of the Mechanicks Workbench,* [Marion, MA, No.12], p. 15. Also see: Anne Wing "The Nicholson Family, etc." *Chronicle of EAIA,* Vol. 36, June 1983, pp. 41 - 43
22. W. L. Goodman, *op. cit.,* p. 139.
23. The only other planes known to the author that support this design feature are those made by the Dutch. Perhaps the early southeastern Massachuetts planemakers were influenced by techniques learned by their ancestors, while they were exciled in the Low Countries.
24. Fuller also used a stamp during this period with Providence misspelled "PROVIDANCE" and the large stamp "USA". The "USA" stamp would indicate that these planes were made as least as late as 1776.
25. Donald and Anne Wing, *op. cit.,* No. 8, p. 11.
26. Smith's first stamp appears in three variations; 1. "A. SMITH REHOBOTH", with a line border; 2. Same stamp, but with a decorative border; same stamp, also with decorative border, but a damaged "B".
27. Asher Benjamin, *The American Builder's Companion,* [Dover Reprint, New York, 1969], (sixth edition, 1827), p.20.

APPENDIX — PRACTICAL PLANE MAKING — I by W. J. Armour
[*WORK, The Illustrated Journal for Mechanics,* Vol. XV, No. 461, January 15, 1898, pg. 8]

Of all the tools used by carpentors, cabinet makers, coach-builders, and other workers in wood, there is none that they are more familiar with than the plane; but there has always been a mystery surrounding the method of making planes. In the columns of different journals there have been from time to time articles touching this subject, but none of those that I have seen are at all correct. In many instances the file has been made to play a very prominent part; this is quite a mistake, as in making a flat plane it is not used at all, except to file the edges of the trimming. The different planes will be dealt with in the following order: Firstly, flat planes, such as jack, try, and smooth planes; secondly, planes for moulding work, such as hollows and rounds, beads, ovolos, O.G.'s, and sash planes; thirdly, stop work, such as ploughs, fillisters, and grooving planes; fourthly, coachmaker's tools and iron planes; and fifthly, planes made to drawings or patterns.

The Jack Plane. — The wood selected should be cut from a centre plank of beech as near to the bark as can be, then it is put into a tank and steamed for about twenty-four hours, which drives out the sap and turns the wood from white to a reddish colour; this is done to assist the drying, and the sap being out of the wood it is not liable to cast. It should not be used before it is three years old; then it is cut into 17-in. lengths, which are planed up to 3 in. square. In all planes, that part which is closest to the bark is made the sole (see Fig. 1) or working part, that being the hardest part of the wood. Measure $5\tfrac{3}{4}$ in. from the fore end and strike a line A D; this is called the bed line of the mouth. Strike another line C D about $\tfrac{5}{16}$ in. from the bed line; this is called the mouth line. Then from the bed line strike the pitch of the bed (A C, Fig. 2), which is varied somewhat according to the work to be done; it is generally an angle of about 50°. Then strike a line (D E, Fig. 3) from the top of the bed line across the top of the plane; this is the top of the bed. From this line measure 1 in., then strike a line across (F G, Fig. 3); this is called the butment line. If the iron used is $2\tfrac{1}{4}$ in. wide, measure from the butment line $2\tfrac{1}{2}$ in. (it being in nearly all cases of bench planes $\tfrac{1}{4}$ in. wider than the iron used); strike a line H K, which is called the front; then strike a line B D (Fig. 2) on the side of plane from the butment line to the mouth line on the face of the plane.

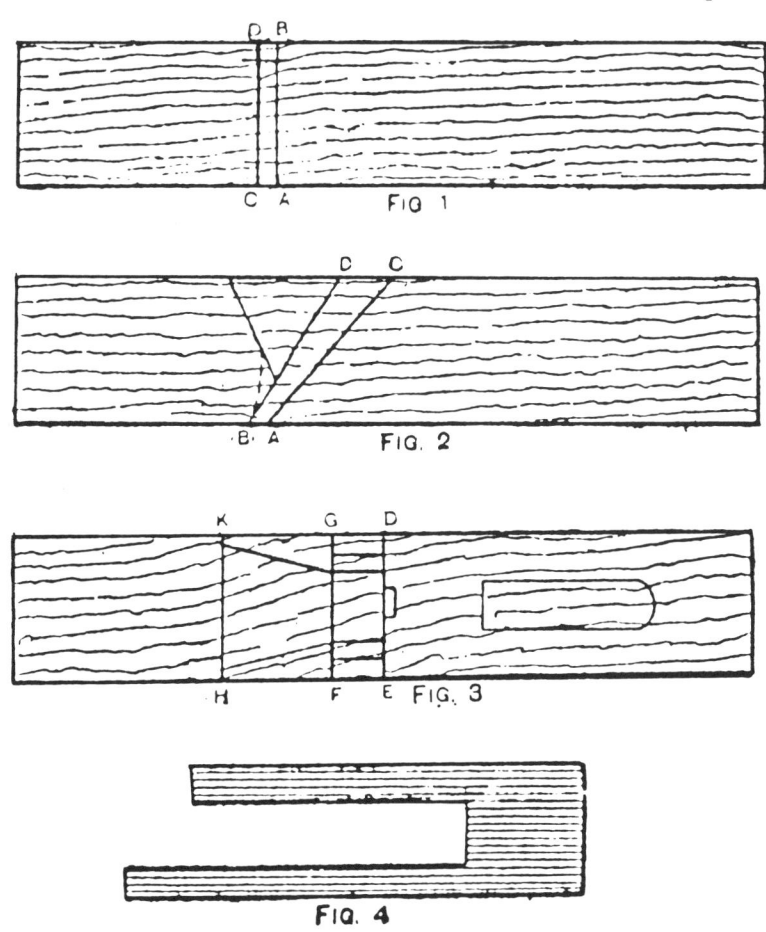

```
Fig. 1 - Sole of Jack Plane
Fig. 2 - Side View of Jack Plane
Fig. 3 - Top of Jack Plane
Fig. 4 - Sinking-down Guide
```

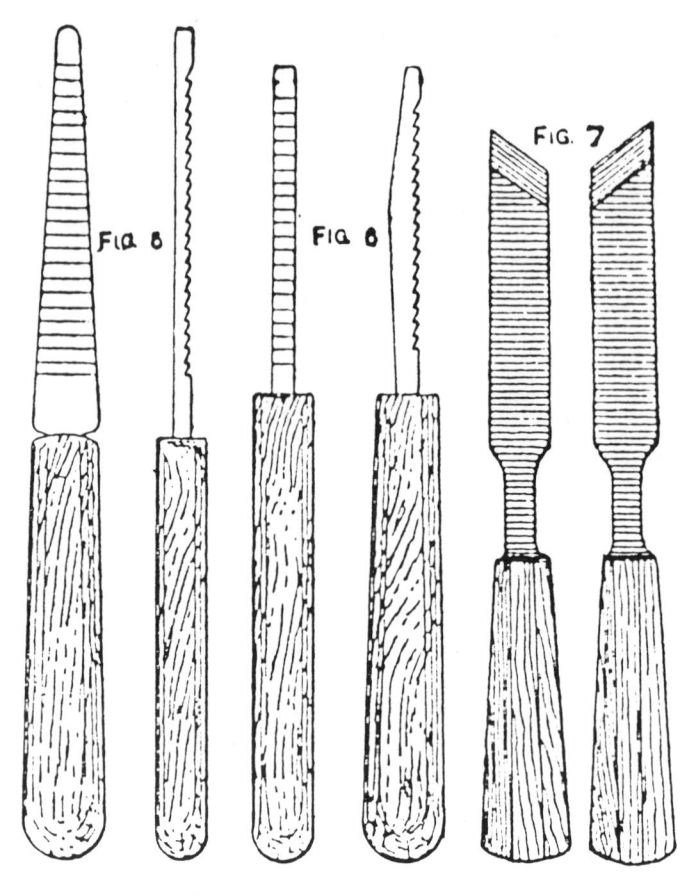

Fig. 5 - Side Float
Fig. 6 - Topping Float
Fig. 7 - Skew Chisels

Next draw a line from the front on the top of the plane to about $7/8$ in. on the side to the line running from butment to mouth; then gauge the width of iron on the face and allow $1/10$ in. wider on top; then gauge $1/4$ in. on each side of the front line of the check. Next take a chisel and mark with a slight blow to break the grain on the top from the front line to the butment line, and from there to the bed line; do the same on the other side. Next, with a very strong gauge and mallet, sink down to a level of the bed line and front line, using a guide (Fig. 4) from time to time to see that you do not go too deep; then bore with a $1/8$ in. nose-bit from the centre of the mouth on the sole in a line with the bed line, care being taken not to come below the level of the bed. Then take a small saw and cut to each side where gauged to size of iron; then with a thin chisel knock away the wood to the bottom of front; this is called the wear, and is shown by the dotted line in Fig. 2. Now we have an opening right through. Next take a thin saw and cut in through the cheeks for the wedge on each side; then a gentle tap with a small chisel will knock out the core. There is now room for the $1 1/4$ in. chisel to pare the bed; this is done by holding the chisel firmly in the right hand, bringing the shoulder on to the handle, and pressing hard on the handle, care being taken to keep the chisel quite flat. Whenever it is found that the chisel digs in, always remove the bottom portion; never commence a fresh stroke until this is done, otherwise the bed will be full of ridges. Having pared the bed, take a tool called a float and smooth the side where the wedge goes in; two varieties of float are shown in Figs. 5 and 6. Then pare the butment straight; this is done by holding a thick chisel firmly in both hands with the edge upwards. Then, having got the iron in, strike a line with the marking awl for the mouth and pare the wear.

Next take some skew chisels (Fig. 7) and clean the cheeks, front, and throat, afterwards cutting the notch hole for top iron screw. Let in the wedge, and grind and fit the irons and bed. It is important that the pressure of the wedge should be at the bottom, otherwise the iron will chatter and the top of butment will be liable to split. Then make the wedge and shoot the ends by putting in a block of wood and plane across. Next let in the toat and trim the plane edges; and, finally, glue in the toat, knock the iron and wedge in, and shoot the face, always with the irons in, otherwise the pressure on the bottom of the bed will force out the wood behind the bed, which is called backwood. If this is not done the plane will never-work easily. The foregoing instructions apply to all kinds of flat planes.

With the exception of badger planes, which are skew-mouthed to work in the corner of rebate, the whole of the setting out is on the skew (see Figs. 8, 9, and 10). The utmost care is required in the sinking down to prevent going too near the working corner, which, when finished, is worked down to a feather edge. It is better to plane the side away when finishing than to pare too closely. There are two other important points to be observed in making a badger: the first is to see that the irons are properly fitted. The method of fitting the top iron of a badger plane is as follows: first see that the cutting iron is true on the face, and that the back is ground true (it should be slightly hollow); then screw the top iron to the cutting iron and file the sides to the size of the cutting iron. Then, on a small grindstone, hollow the under part of the bevel of the top iron so that it fits perfectly to the face of the cutting iron. Grind the bevel of the top iron to a strong round bevel; this is done by rolling the bevel on the grindstone. The reason for this is that the edge should be sharp, but strong enough to resist the shaving. To break the shavings immediately they are cut by the cutting iron is the work that all top irons have to do, and the closer the top iron is to the bottom or cutting iron, the finer is the shaving. The top iron should be twisted a little so that the working corner touches the face of the cutting iron first, so that when the screw is screwed up, that, being the weakest part, will spring down, and the whole of the edge will be close down to the face of the cutting iron.

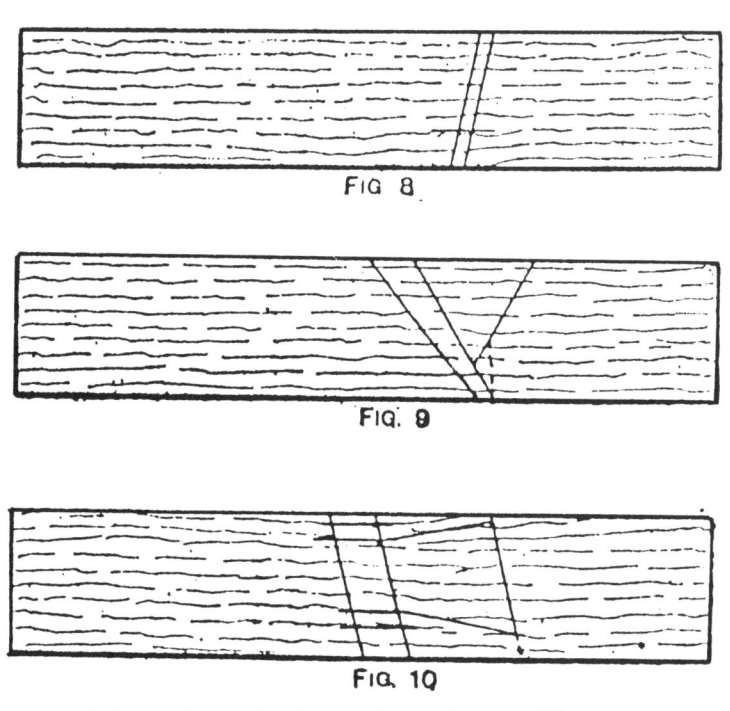

FIG 8

FIG. 9

FIG. 10

Fig. 8 - Sole of Badger Plane

Fig. 9 - Side View of Badger Plane

Fig. 10 - Top of Badger Plane

If this is not observed, the shavings will get under and the plane will choke. The second important point is the bedding; great care should be taken that too much pressure is not placed on the working corner, as it is very weak, on account of the bed coming so close to the corner; at the same time, enough pressure is required to prevent the iron from chattering.

It will be observed that the only tools used are chisels and a side float; the file is not used at all. One of the most important things is that the chisels used must on no account be sharpened on the face; if this rule is not observed, it will be impossible to pare.

PART II — [No. 463, January 29, 1898, pp. 44-45]

Moulding Planes — As a rule, all moulding planes are made 9½ in. long, and as they mostly work on the spring, they are not required to have the grain of the wood so straight as in a flat plane. Hollows, rounds, and rebate planes, however, are excepted; these should be as straight as possible, because the rebate plane, owing to its being cut through, is liable to cast if it is not straight grained; and most of the hollows and rounds begin very thin, are liable to cast if not of straight, mild, and well-seasoned wood. To make the half set of hollows and rounds, they should all be cut from one piece of wood, which should be as free from knots as possible. The sizes graduate from ½ in. to 1⅛ in. in width, and they are all 9½ in. long; the mouldings of all are parts of circles varying from ¼ in. to 6 in. in diameter. After having got all to one length and planed square to the different sizes, proceed to rebate the larger sizes. The rule in all moulding planes is to allow the handhold to be ¼ in. wider than the rebate; for instance, in a moulding plane 1¼ in. wide the rebate taken out would be ¾ in.

After this is done, measure from the fore end on the sole 3½ in. and strike the bed line; from this line measure 3/16 in. and strike the mouth line; from the bed line strike on both sides of the wood the pitch of the bed. The pitch of the bed is according to the work the planes are to do; for instance, the pitch for joiners is 50°, and for cabinet makers about 60°. The latter is called half pitch. Fig. 11 shows the pattern of pitch board used for cabinet-makers' moulding planes, and Fig. 12 the pattern of pitch board for all common and flat planes. Then from the line on top measure 1 in., strike a line, and from that line on both sides a line to the mouth line on the sole. This is the size of the mortise. Then gauge for width, which is always a third of the width of the handhold. Then gauge for the springing-on of the sole, which graduates according to the different sizes from 3/16 in. to ⅜ in. Then with a saw cut in the mouth along the bed and front line down to the springing line on the sole and through the side just to the handhold; with a small chisel push with the hand and knock the core out, and with a thin chisel sink down to a level with the springing line and the back line of mortise; then bore from the centre of the mortise to the centre of the mouth, and take a small saw float and open the mortise; pare the bed clean, and with a square float (see Fig. 5, pg. 8, No. 461) level the bed, and then stick the moulding. Always stick the hollow first and square with the back; see that it does not wind, then stick the round to it; then let in the iron and pare away to the thickness of iron for mouth, and clean and finish the mortise for the wedge, which must next be let in. File in the iron, harden and temper, grind the face straight and the back a little hollow; then, if the bed is pared a little hollow likewise, there will be no difficulty in bedding. Plane the wedge so that the pressure goes to the bottom of the mortise, and when driven home it will slightly spring on top; afterwards shoot the ends and trim.

The foregoing instructions apply to all kinds of moulding planes, the only difficulty is in setting out the different mouldings; the method of doing this will be explained further on.

Next to hollows and rounds, bead planes are mostly used as moulding planes. They are generally made in sets of nine from ⅛ in. to ⅞ in. All beads have a slip of Turkey box let in to bear the hard work of the quirk. The best beads have two slips, the second one to bear the work of the fence. The method of letting in the slip is to plough down with an ordinary plough to the depth of 1 in. and about 3/16 in. in width for the larger ones; the smaller ones are ploughed down from 1/4 in. to 3/8 in. in thickness, and all are fully boxed. The box is cut from a log about 8 in. in diameter; it is cut on the cross at an angle of about 15°, in cakes of an inch thick, and then slipped in thin pieces and let into the planes so that the working edge is half on the end way of the wood; it is afterwards glued in and allowed to dry for a day or two.

Beads are mostly slipped on the side to the 1/2 in. size; the usual way is to have the wood 1/4 in. larger than the size wanted and cut out with a saw, planed, cleaned, and put back. If this is done well it will be hard to see the joint; the object of slipping is to enable the plane to work close up to a moulding. The same rule applies to mouthing as in hollows and rounds; the moulding is stuck by a backing plane the reverse to the bead, but if this is not to be had the moulding will have to be stuck by sharp rounds called cod planes (see Fig. 15). These are planes used by plane makers for getting out mouldings to drawings, and are of various thicknesses from 1/16 in. to 3/4 in. They are seldom used by other mechanics.

All beads are the exact half circles with a quirk. It is important when filing in the iron of all beads that the bevel of iron should be filed well back, otherwise it will not cut at the side, and the shaving will choke.

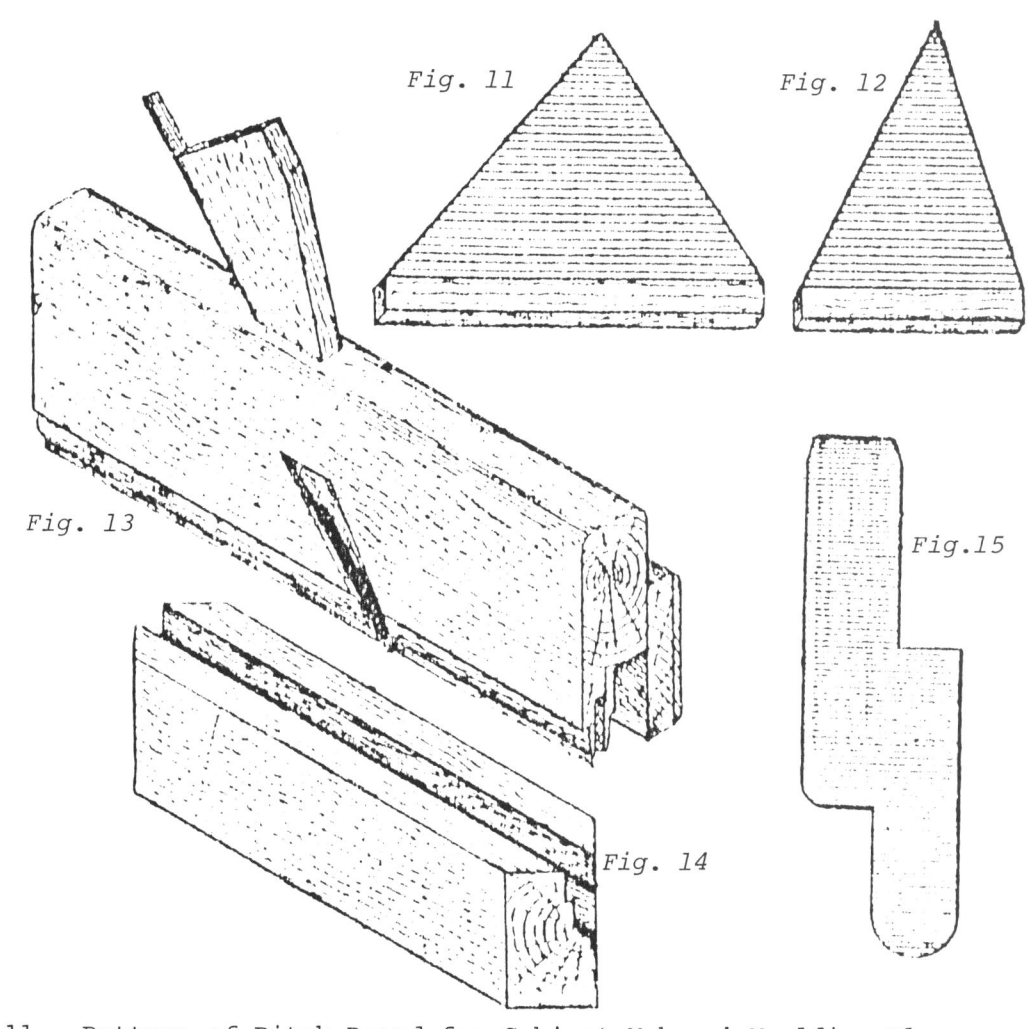

Fig. 11 - Pattern of Pitch Board for Cabinet-Makers' Moulding Planes
Fig. 12 - Pattern of Pitch Board for all Common and Flat Planes
Fig. 13 - Backing Plane for Ovolo Sash Saddle Template
Fig. 14 - Saddle Template for Ovolo Sah Bar
Fig. 15 - Cod Plane

After hollows and rounds and beads, the two next planes in common use as moulding planes are common O.G.'s and ovolos. The method of setting out these two planes will now be described, and the sizes, taken by way of example, will be ⅝ in. for an ovolo (see Fig. 16) and ½ in. for the O.G.'s (see Fig. 17); In the former instance the size of wood would be ⅝ in. Gauge a line ½ in. from the back of the plane on the sole and each end; this is the fence line. Then take the springing square S, and place the fence F of the square firmly to the back of the plane, as shown in Fig. 18; draw a line A B on the end from the back to the fence line on the fore end of the plane; then reverse the plane, and do the same on the hind end, being careful when once the spring is fixed not to alter the springing, so that each end will correspond. Next bring the long end of the springing square to the point of the fence line, and draw a line B O, which will be at right angles to the first line drawn called the springing line. Then take a pair of compasses and measure ¼ in. from the springing line down, bring the short end of the springing square to the measured point, and strike a line C D. This gives the depth of fence, and is the line of the square of the ovolo down.

All common ovolos and O.G.'s stick on the same distance as they do down. Take the compasses and measure ⅝ in. from the square of the ovolo line down, and take the short end of springing square and strike a line F O from the point measure right across, which gives the stop fence line; then measure with the compasses from the point where the fence line meets the stop line ⅝ in. along the stop line, and take the springing square to the point measure and strike a line H X; this is the line of the square of the ovolo. Then measure with the compasses a full ⅛ in. on each square line of the ovolos to give the sizes of the squares; then with the compasses strike an arc touching both points of the square. The same method is applied to common O.G.'s; should the moulding be wanted flatter or deeper, the distance on or down must be varied accordingly.

The scale boards required in setting out moulding planes are illustrated in Figs. 19, 20, 21, and 22.

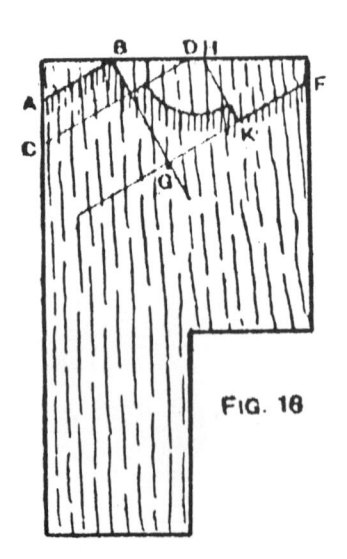

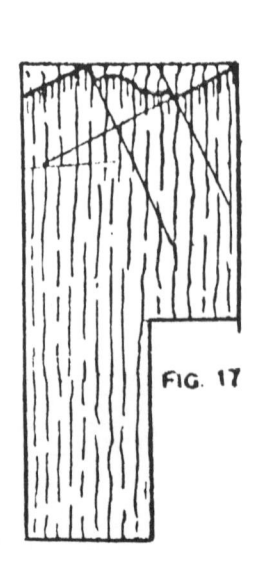

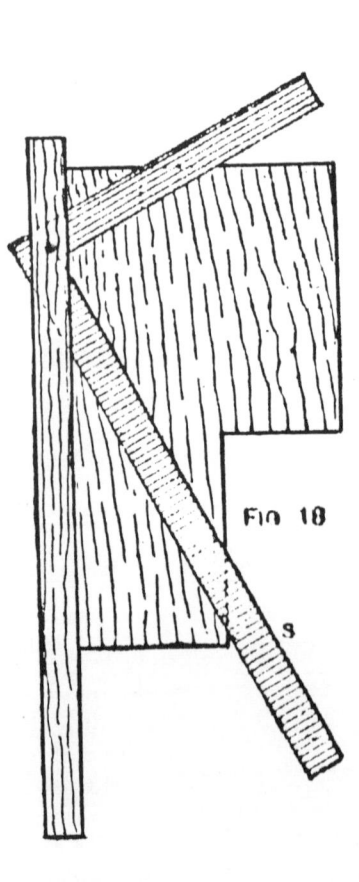

Fig. 16 Common Ovolo Scale
Fig. 17 Common O.G. Scale
Fig. 18 Springing Square with Fence to Back
of Plane to Set Out Moulding

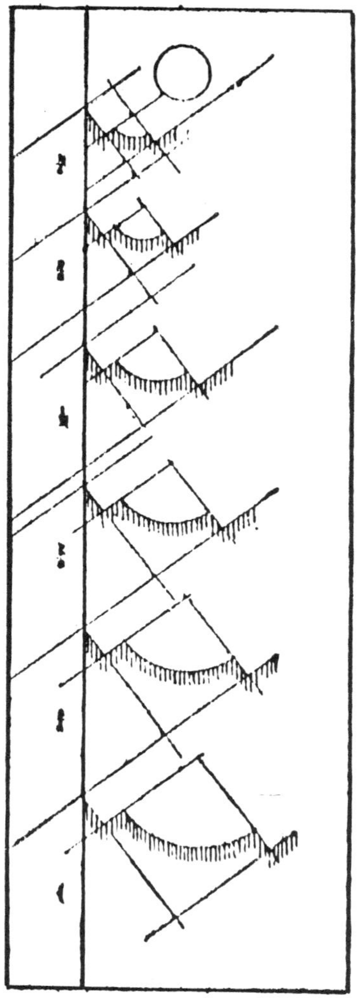

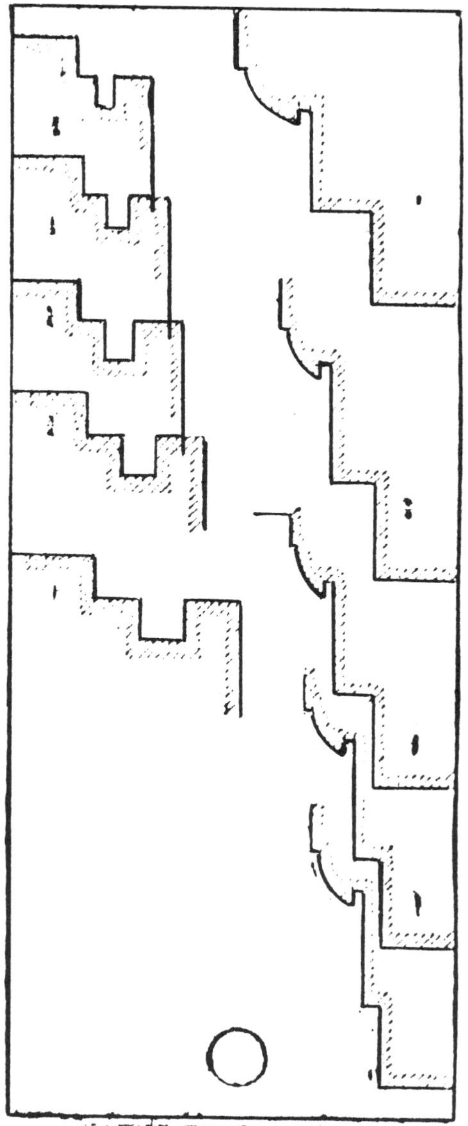

Fig. 19 - Scale Board for Common Ovolo Scales. Fig. 20 - Scale Board for Common O.G. & Scotia Scales
Fig. 21 - Scale Board for Grooving Match Scale. Fig. 22 - Scale of Boxing for Beads showing the Back Fence and Quirks

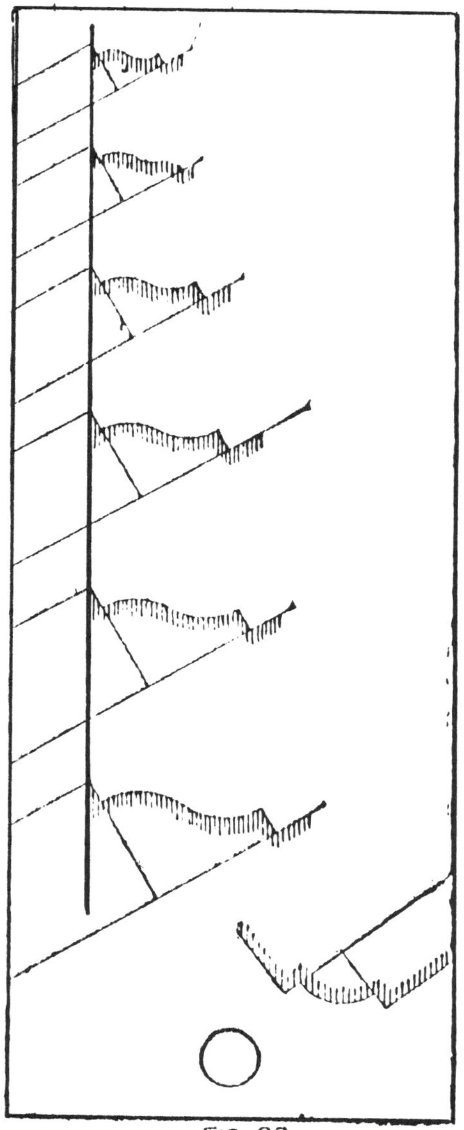

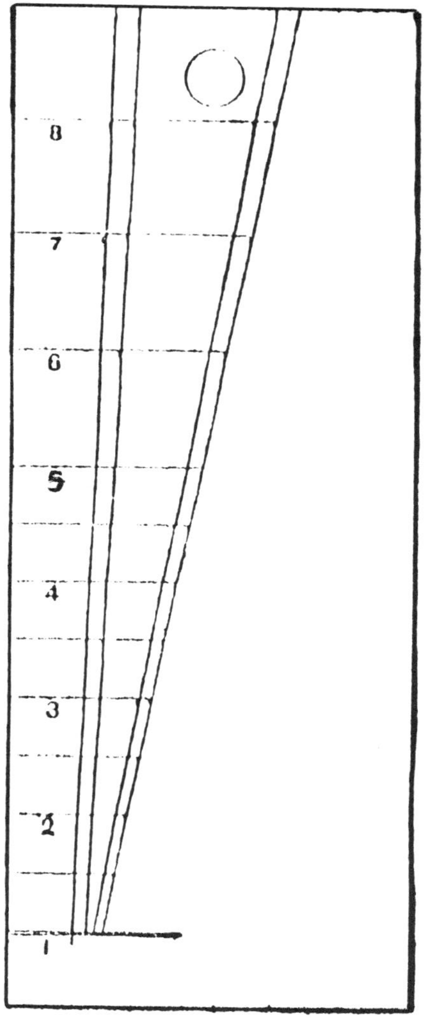

The way to make a plane to an architect's drawing, as for instance Fig. 23, will now be explained. Assuming that the size of the moulding measures 1¾ in., the size of the wood would be 2⅞ in., to allow for the stop fence and springing measure from the back. With the gauge set to 9/16 in., mark both ends and sole; then take the springing square, fix the spring required, and strike the line A C (see Fig. 24); then draw line B C from the point C; this is the fence line. From C measure along line C B a distance of 1¾ in., and draw line D E at right angle.* Next, with a rebate plane, rebate out the angles at F, G, H, and K (see Fig. 24), and plane off the springing, being very careful not to go through the line, otherwise the whole of the moulding will have to be set out again. After this is done, take a cod plane (see Fig. 15) and make the bead A (Fig. 25), then with a smaller cod plane make bead B; then with a hollow make scotia C, from time to time comparing with the drawing to see that the work is being done correctly.

The method of making a template for a ⅜ in. ovolo sash bar is as follows; The wood size is 8 in. long by 1½ in. by 2¼ in.; plane up square, and with a plough or tongueing plane (Fig. 13) plough down about ⅝ in. to the square of the moulding (see Fig. 14); then take the backing plane and plane down until it stops.

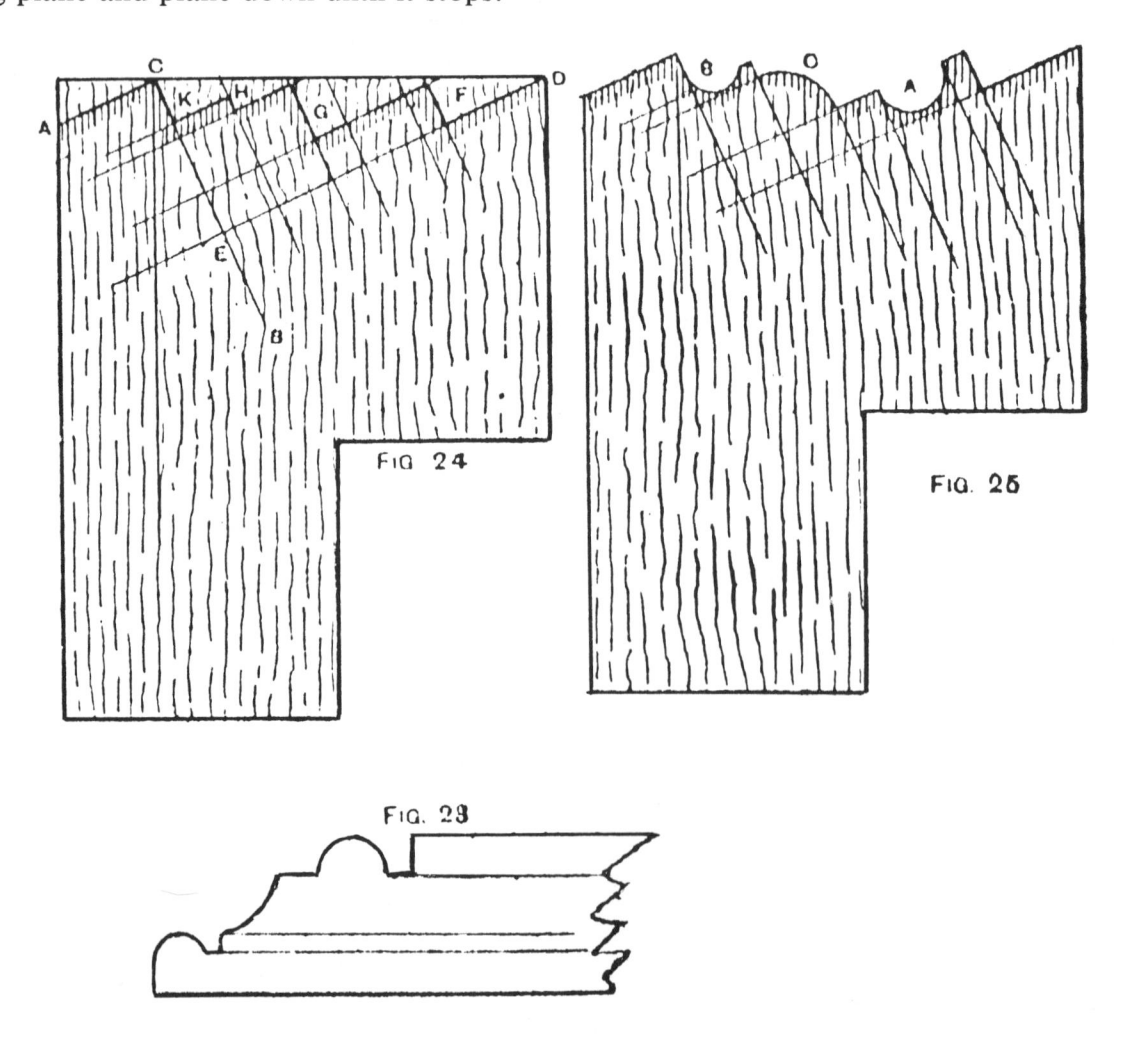

Fig. 23 — Architect's Drawing of a Moulding

Fig. 24 — Plane to Drawing showing Squares of Members of Moulding

Fig. 25 — Section of Plane to Drawing Finished

PART III — [No. 465, February 12, 1898, p. 77]

Stop Work: The Plough. — Ploughs are generally made in lots of from three to six; the reason is that the mouldings on the ends of the stems and fences are stuck together, and could not be stuck so correctly if done singly. First cut out the stems to shape as shown in Fig. 26, and plane them down in a block to the thickness of the stem hole in the plough stock; wedge them in a block with the moulding set out on the side of each one, and stick the moulding. Next cut out the fences (Fig. 27) to a size 9½ in. in length by 2⅛ in. by 2½ in., and plane up square; wedge up in a block, and stick the ends to a moulding set out on the side of each end one.

Next get out the wood for the stock (Fig. 28), and plane up 1¾ in. by 2¾ in. and 8 in. long; measure from the fore end 3 in. on the sole (Fig. 29) for the front of the mouth AB, and from this line ⅝ in. for the bed line CD. From the line CD strike the pitch of bed, and from this line measure on the top (Fig. 30) 1¼ in. and draw a line on side to mouth line; then gauge from the back ¾ in. on top and bottom, and another line ⅝ in. from this line. This is the width of the mortise for iron. Measure from each end on the side 1⅜ in., draw two lines ¾ in. apart, and carry them with the square round to the other side for the stem holes E, taking care that they are correctly drawn, otherwise the stems will be in winding. Then gauge from the sole of plough stock across the side lines of stem holes 1¼ in.; this is the bottom of stem hole; then measure ¾ in. from bottom of stem hole and gauge for the depth of stem hole; from the centre of this square with the compasses strike a semicircle. This gives the shape of stem hole. Measure from the fore end on the back 2¾ in., draw a line (FF, Fig. 31) across the back of plough stop for the stop mortise, place the barrel of stop to this line for the size of the mortise, and carry this line across the bottom and top. Then measure from the back of stock ¼ in., and gauge top and bottom; place the narrow part of stop on this line and gauge for the thickness. Gauge from the back on the sole 1 in. (GH, Fig. 29) — this is the line where the plate beds on to; and from the sole gauge ⁹⁄₁₆ in. on the side (HJ, Fig. 28) — this is the size of the rebate which is taken out for the plate. From this line gauge ⁵⁄₁₆ in. to the depth of groove for the plate. Care must be taken not to go through the line, and the plate must be in the centre of the mortise.

Having now got the stock set out, bore the stem holes with a ¾ in. centre-bit, pare with a chisel and gouge clean just a shade hollow. Then let in the stems, using the hollow plane for the top of stems, and drive in tight. Next bore the mortise with a ⅜ in. nose-bit, and rough out with a saw float; then use the side float and clean perfectly through to the lines, using a topping float or chisel for top and bed. Next let in the stop tight, screw in the thumbscrew of stop, and scribe for the top plate and shoe, which must next be let in. Then place the side brass with the slot (I, Fig. 31) on the line of stop on the side, scribe round, and let in. Then bore the slot for the side screw to work. This completes the fittings of the stock.

Next take out the rebate for the plate and groove with a grooving-plane for the plates, which are let in the groove tight. Bring the hind plate to a level with the bed line of mortise. In looking down the mortise the bottom of plate should be raised a little so as to fit into the deeper part of the groove at the bottom of the cutting iron. Having got the back plate in the proper place, bore through the holes of the plate for rivets, fit tight and rivet. Let the wedge in and bed the irons; see that the irons are all the same thickness, otherwise the same wedge will not do for all of them; fit the front plate to the iron for the size of mouth, bore for rivets, and rivet up tight. The stock must now be trimmed and cleaned ready for the stems to knock in, after they have been riveted to the fence.

Fig. 26 - Stem for Plough or Sash Fillister before Sticking with the Moulding Set Out.
Fig. 27 - Fence for Plough with Moulding Set Out on End
Fig. 28 - Side View of Plough
Fig. 29 - Sole of Plough
Fig. 30 - Top of Plough
Fig. 31 - Back of Plough Stock

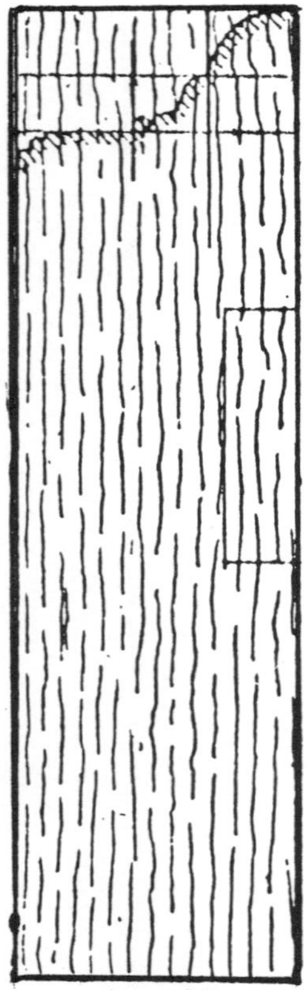

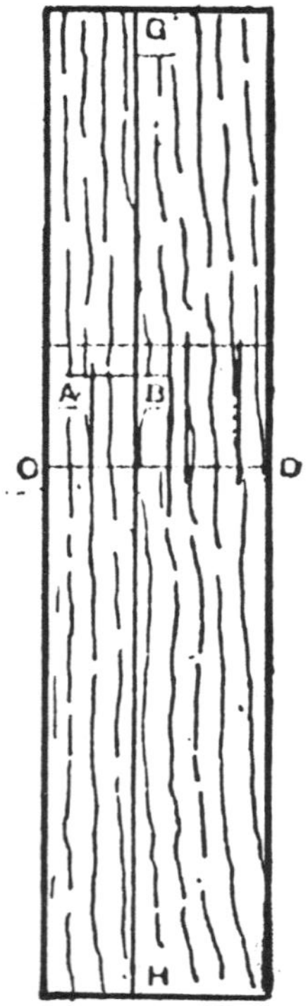

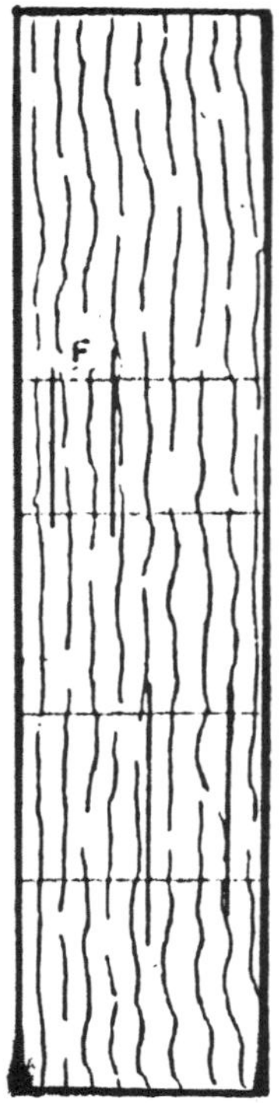

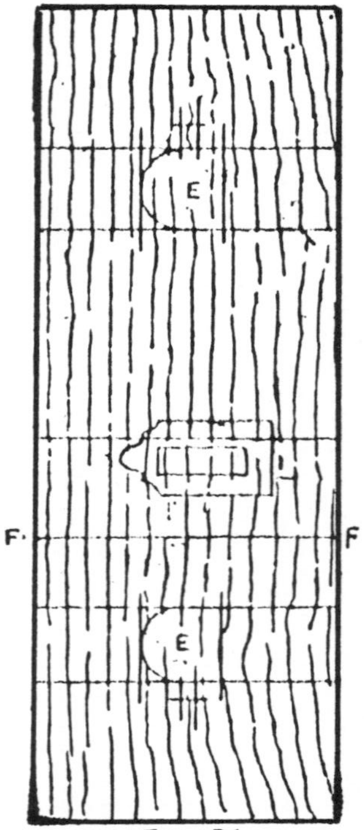

Dado Grooving Plane. — Dados are planes used to cut grooves across the grain, such as bookcase shelves, etc. Fig. 32 is a perspective view of one of these planes; Fig. 33 shows the top, Fig. 34 the side, and Fig. 35 the sole. They are made in the shape of rebate planes, with a double tooth of iron in front to cut the grain; and they have a movable stop to gauge the distance down. The ½ in. size wil be taken by way of example. Plane up square a piece of wood 9½ in. by 1⅛ in. by 3⅓ in., measure on the sole (Fig. 35) from the fore end 3⅞ in. for bed line (this is the same skew as the rebate plane), and strike the pitch AB. Next strike the mouth line CD and carry it to the top to give the size of mortise; measure from the side of plane (Fig. 33) ½ in. for the back of mortise, and, with the gauge, mark on the sole the same mark for the width of groove as in all sizes of grooving planes; the back of mortise is level with the size of the groove wanted, so that the iron fits firmly up to the back of mortise and stands straight in the plane, as the iron is to cut at each side of the groove. Halve the size on top from the back of mortise line and gauge for the width of mortise. Strike the shape of eye-hole, measure from the fore end for the tooth 2 in., and strike a line at right angles (EF, Fig. 34), as the tooth stands perpendicular; measure GH 2⅝ in. from the fore end for stop mortise and gauge for size of stop, as in a plough; then measure from the back HK ⅝ in. for the rebate for the shoe of stop.

In all dados the same size is used for the stop rebate, and all are the same distance from the sole down, ⅝ in.; the setting out is now completed. Next cut in the mouth, knock out the core, bore for mortise, clean out with floats, pare the bed, and float down true; then cut out the eye-hole and clean; let in the wedge, let in the stop, and take out the rebate. After letting in the tooth, let in the stop and scribe for shoe and top plate, which is let in flush with the bottom of rebate. In filing in the iron be sure that the tooth is a trifle fuller than the cutting iron, otherwise it will be of no use to cut the grain; then harden the irons, tooth and bed, clean the plane, and trim.

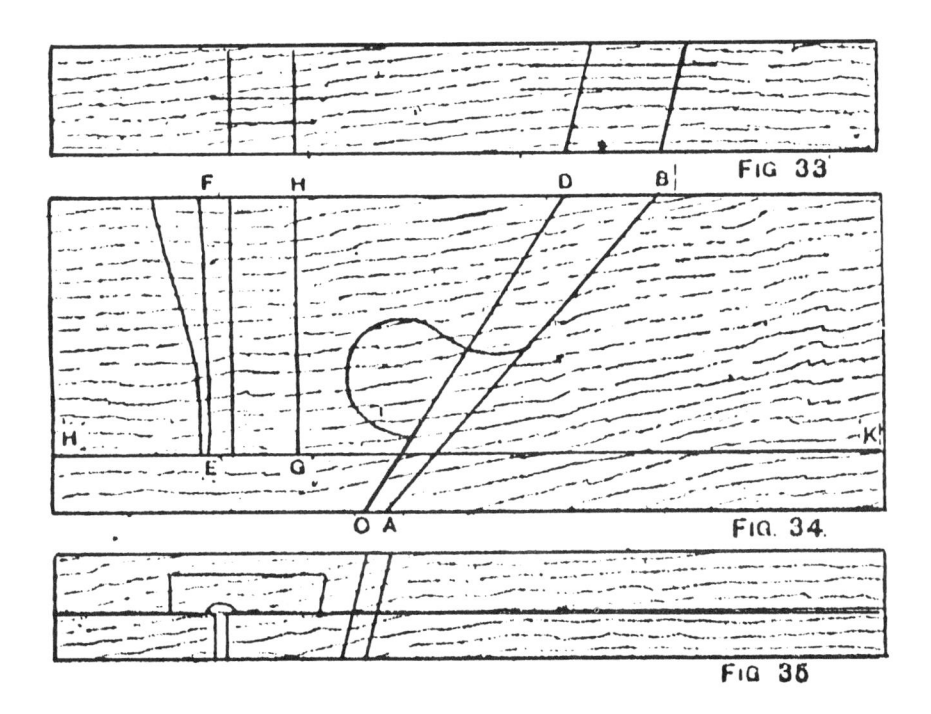

Fig. 33 - Top of Dado Grooving Plane

Fig. 34 - Side of Dado Grooving Plane

Fig. 35 - Sole of Dado Grooving Plane

PART IV — [No. 467 — February 26, 1898, p. 107]

Sash Fillister. — Next to the plough the sash fillister (Fig. 36) is the most useful, and also the most difficult to make. Views of the top, sole, and side of a sash fillister are given in Figs. 37, 38, and 39. The wood selected must be very dry and sound. The working corner is rebated out to let inthe dovetail boxing (see Fig. 40), which is put in all the best work; this dovetail

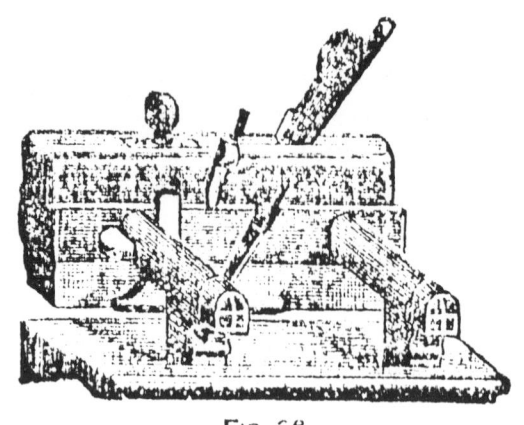

Fig. 36

Fig. 37

Fig. 39

Fig. 38

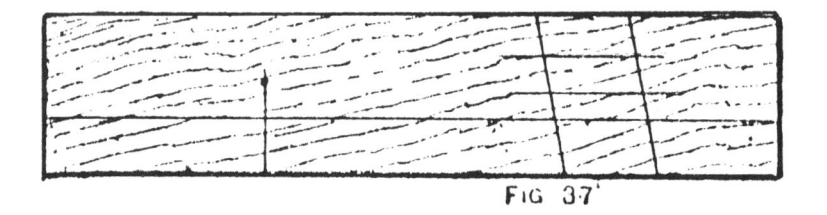

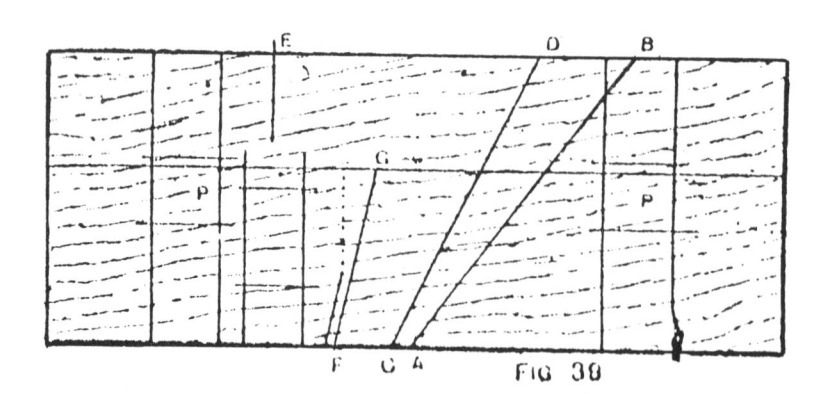

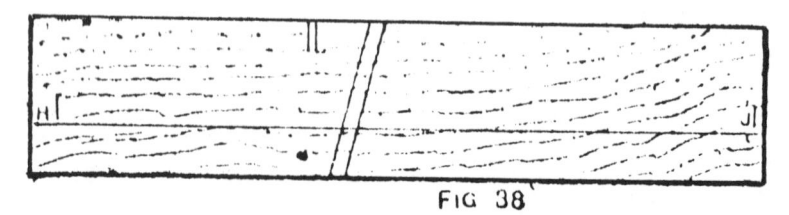

Fig. 36 - Sash Fillister   Fig. 37 - Top of Sash Fillister
Fig. 38 - Sole of Sash Fillister   Fig. 39 - Side of Sash Fillister

boxing is very fine work, and there are few plane-makers who can do it. It is absolutely necessary that it should fit in every way, as the greater part of the iron beds on to it, and, if it did not fit, it would spring when the pressure of the wedge was on it. The pattern of the dovetail boxing is varied somewhat by different manufacturers, but the London method is the one given here. In doing this work nine different planes are required; they are illustrated in Figs. 41 to 49.

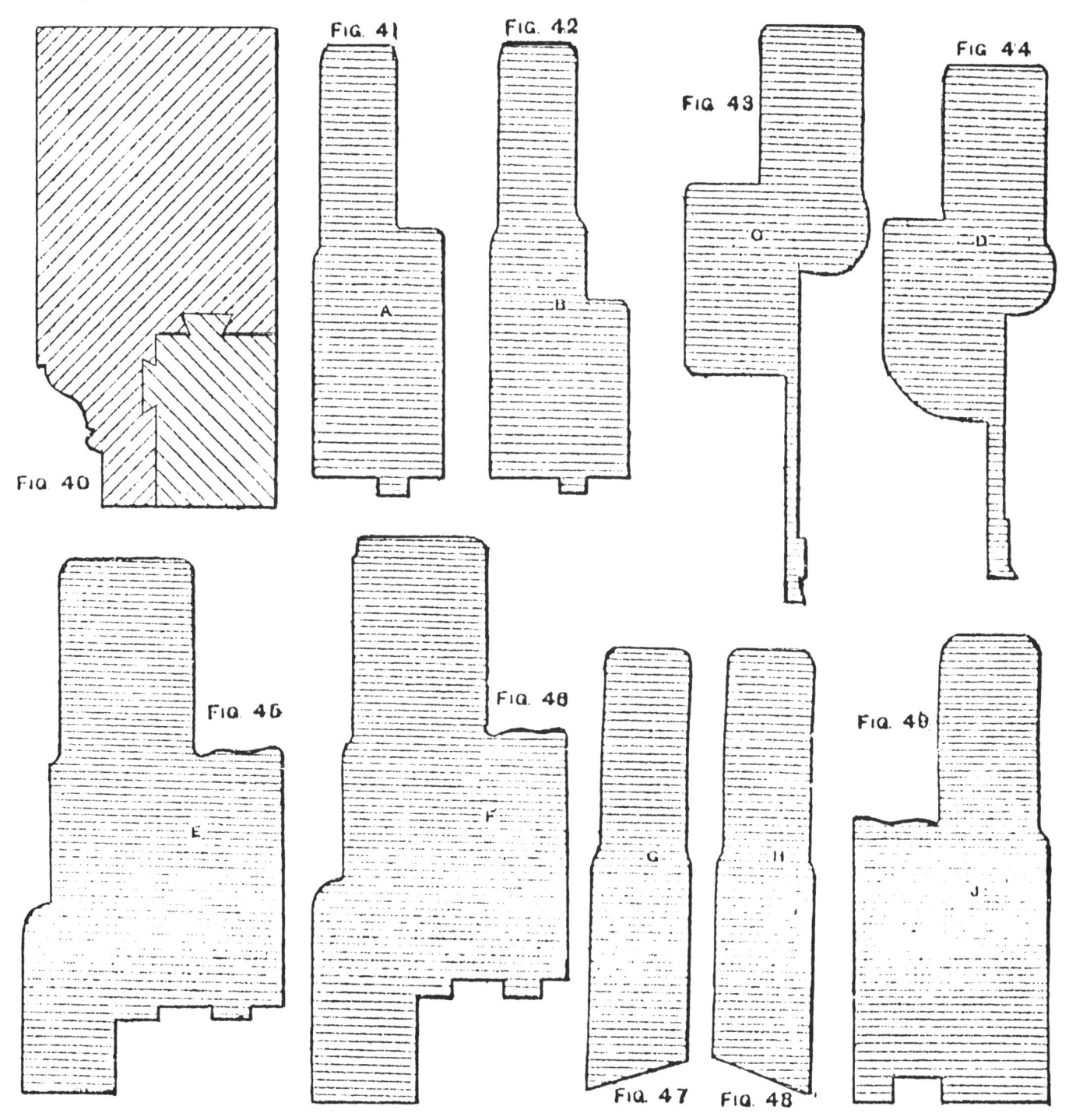

Fig. 40 - Section of Sash Fillister

Figs. 41 to 49 - Planes for Making Sash Fillister

It will be seen that the dovetail on the top is narrower and deeper than the dovetail on the side. Take the plane shown in Fig. 11, and, holding it firmly to the top of the rebate, proceed to sink down until it slopes; this makes a groove for the side dovetail. Take the plane shown in Fig. 42, and do the same to the top; this makes the groove for the top dovetail. Next take the plane shown in Fig. 43, and, holding it very firmly, with the bottom of the plane working in the bottom of groove, proceed to make the dovetail.

In the top dovetail, take the plane shown in Fig. 44, and do the same to the side dovetail; the dovetails in the stock of the plane have now been made. Next take a piece of clean Turkey box, cut diagonally, as in cutting out box for beads, so that it works half on the endway of the grain, cut off a slab 1¼ in. thick, and slip it down to the thick end of the rebate taken out of the plane. See which way the grain runs; when in the plane it should run from the hind end to the fore end. Always have the box as clean as possible, otherwise when finishing off it will chip out at mouth of iron or tooth, etc. Having got out the box, plane the sides square, so as to fit the sides of dovetail. Next take plane Fig. 45, and, with the fence working from the top of the boxwood, sink down until it stops; take plane Fig. 46, and do the same to the top of the box. The squares are now at a correct distnce from the corner. Next take plane Fig. 49 and remove the wood so as to allow of the working of the skew-side planes (Figs. 47 and 48), and make the dovetails. It is in fitting in that great skill is needed, for everything has to be quite tight; this is secured by planing down to fit with the planes shown in Figs. 43, 44, 47, 48 as required. The box should go in with a firm tap of the hammer, although not too tight, for fear of splitting the wood; then make the place for the mouth and glue in.

Having finished the dovetail boxing let the glue dry for two days, then plane up and square the four sides (the size is 8¾ in. by 3¼ in. by 1⅝ in.) and measure from fore end 4⅛ in. for the bed line AB (Fig. 39). Allow ⅛ in. for mouth, strike from the bed line the pitch and carry across the top, measure 1 in. from line on top and strike the front of mortise, gauge ⅜ in. from the side for side of mortise, and make the mortise CD ⅝ in. wide. Next set out the stem holes in the same way as for a plough, and the keys for stems in the same way PP. Meausre 2⅜ in. for stop, take the stop and put to the line and scribe for width of stop, then place the side of stop to the top of stock and scribe for centre of screw G. Next measure 3¼ in. FG for tooth and strike the pitch and mortise line for wedge; measure from the sole 2 in. and from the top ⁵⁄₁₆ in. for rebate, measure ⁹⁄₁₆ in. from the side on the sole and ¼ in. down for rebate on sole (Fig. 38). This completes the setting out of the stock. Next cut out the rebate for the hand hold, cut in the mouth and mortise the same as in a moulding plane. Make the stem holes the same way as for a plough, let in the stem, and plane the part where the fence is attached to stem down to a level of the sole of stock. Next let in the stop, taking care that it is fitted flat to the side, otherwise the shaving will get under and clog. Next bore a hole from the top for screw of stop and carry through past the mortise hole for stop for the point of screw to work in, and let in the top plate of stop; then let in the tooth, which should be very tight so as not to move when used; grind the iron and bed, the stem being ferruled, measure for the rebate on fence and stick the fence as for the plough (see p. 77, No. 465), let in the diamond burrs on top of stem, and rivet together.

---

*It is apparent that part of this article describing the setting out of the points K, H & G was omitted in the original publication. This can be clarified by examination of Fig. 24. Other editorial corrections were necessary. The spelling and style of the original English author have been maintained.

Chapter III

The Union Factory, 1828-1860

H. Chapin's Union Factory, established July 1, 1826, is believed to have been the earliest planemaking concern in the United States to utilize power driven machinery. The economic advantages of this operation will be noted in more detail as this firm developed from 1830-1850.

In order to expand his work force, Hermon Chapin made an agreement September 12, 1829 with Alanson Spencer for a year's term, with option for renewal. Spencer managed a boarding house, owned by the Kelloggs, for an average of eighteen boarders. This agreement is transcribed in Table I and provides several interesting facts about the meals, washing and discipline maintained at this boarding house, this was probably patterned after similar agreements of the times.

No planes with the imprint COPELAND & CHAPIN have yet been reported. It is believed that all planes made by H. Chapin, 1826-1830, which were sold by Daniel Copeland, had the latter imprint. After the dissolution of D&M Copeland in 1826, when Daniel formed his partnership with Chapin, Melvin formed the firm M&A Copeland with his younger brother, Alfred. The tenure of this firm is suggested to have been 1826-1830. The only Copeland listed in the 1828 Hartford Directory was Melvin, toolmaker at 110 State. Daniel was no longer in business there, probably having moved to Huntington, Mass. Alfred was then believed to have been at Pine Meadow, leasing part of Hermon Chapin's boarding house with some employees of M&A Copeland. The following excerpt from H. Chapin manuscript material dated December 24, 1829, at New Hartford substantiates this:

> "whereas Hermon Chapin is desirous to form a connection with Melvin and Alfred Copeland so far as to sell one undivided half of Bedding & house furniture in the Boarding House"

Another supporting evidence that Alfred Copeland was then living at New Hartford appears in the *Copeland Genealogy* which noted, that he was married there in 1829.

Fig. 28 illustrates three moulding planes with the imprint "UNION FACTORY/Warranted" (in semi circle) and M&A Copeland" [in a line below] the complex moulding plane at the left clearly illustrates that the "UNION FACTORY" imprint was struck after the "M&A Copeland," as it is superimposed on the latter. This plane also illustrates an early example of full boxing, which is believed to have been developed by Hermon Chapin at the Union Factory. The probable procedure for accomplishing this is shown in Plate I. Both the single spline and full boxed insets were set into the sole before shaping its contour. Various forms of full-boxing bead planes are shown in Fig. 29.

The similarity between slide arm plows with wooden screw locks, both having semicircular imprints of "UNION FACTORY/Warranted," but with the different line imprints "M&A Copeland" and "H. Chapin" are noted in Fig. 30. These are to be compared with three similar plows, illustrated in Fig. 31, with imprints of "D&M Copeland, Hartford"; "D. Copeland, Hartford" and "M. Copeland, Warranted." Five slide arm plows with imprint H. Chapin/Union Factory are illustrated in Fig. 32.

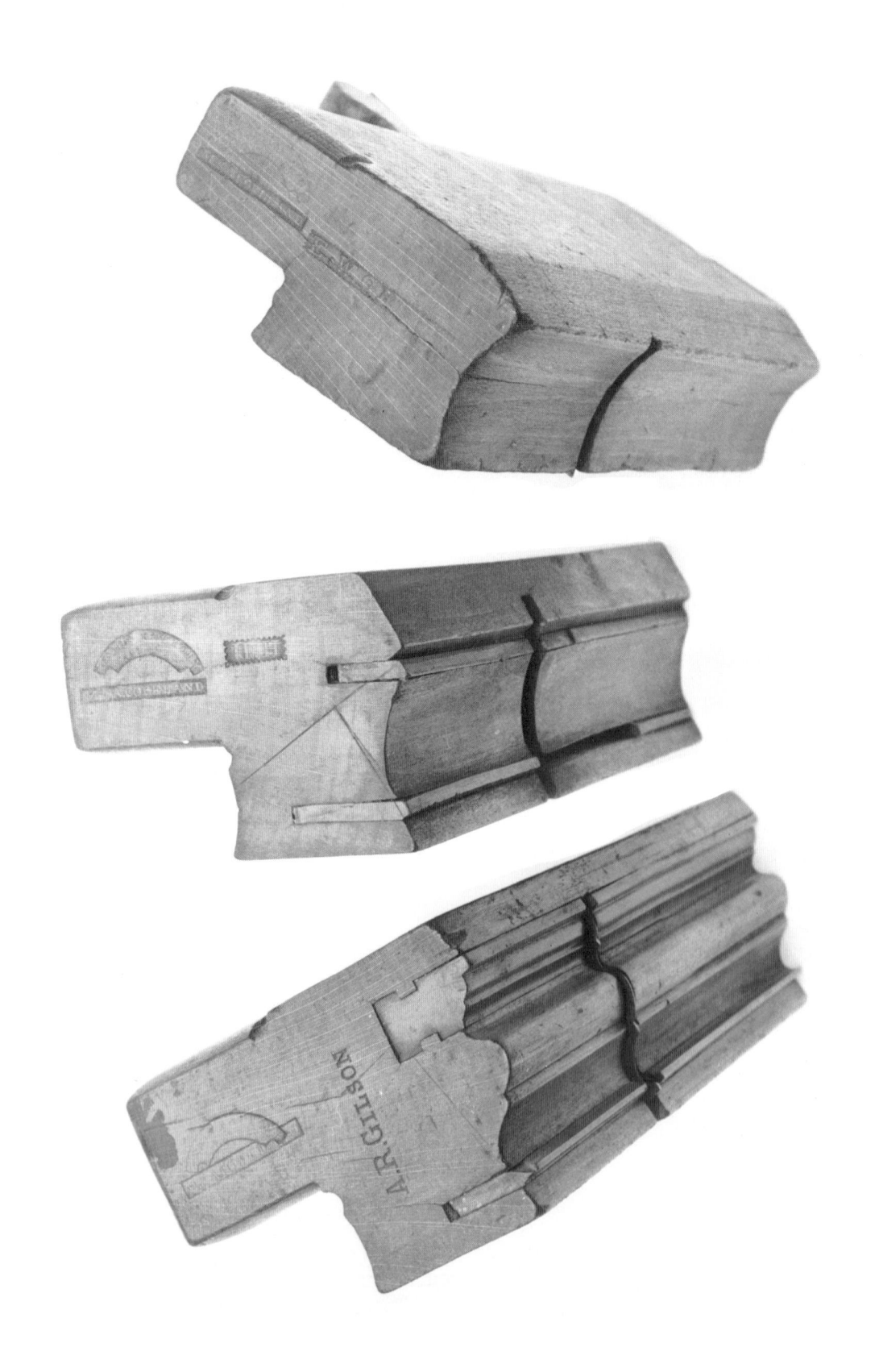

Fig. 28 - Planes with imprint: UNION FACTORY/WARRANTED and M. & A. COPELAND

Plate I - Procedure for Full Boxing a Plane

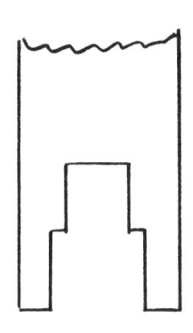

1. Cut dado in sole using circular saws.

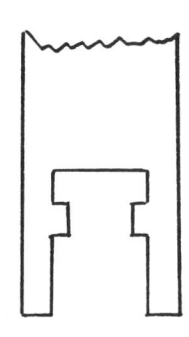

2. Remove top shoulder using miller cutter or fly cutter.

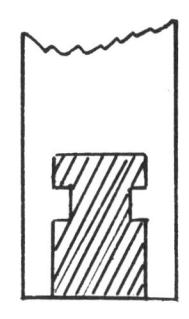

3. Push through table mounted Broach to size accurately. Fit Boxwood insert.

The tolerance of fit between the boxwood insert and slot is of the order of one thousandth of an inch. Without mechanical means it would not be possible to accomplish this degree of precision.

Fig. 29 - Types of Full Boxing Bead Planes. Union Factory Planes, except right end has imprint J. & L. Denison/ Saybrook.

Table I
Agreement Between Alanson Spencer and Hermon Chapin, September 12, 1829

This agreement made between Alanson Spencer on one part and Isaac & George C. Kellogg and Hermon Chapin on the other part all of New Hartford. Witnesseth — That said Spencer has agreed and hereby agrees to keep the boarding house belonging to said Kelloggs & Chapin one year from the 15th day of October next on these terms following; namely — he is to take said House and the land attached to it and all the stock and furniture which belongs with, and appurtances to the same — and he is to fully furnish and supply said house for eighteen constant boarders and for three or more occasionally as said Kelloggs and Chapin may want — and to furnish good comfortable lodgings and good Farmers fare with plenty of Cider for use at their meals and butter at all times with very few exceptions, fresh meat frequently, pies and cakes and puddings of various kinds generally, tea and coffee at proper times and milk and vegetables in their seasons — all of good quality and in sufficient variety, and he is to cause said house to be orderly at all times and very still after ten o'clock at night, and he shall have the right to turn away any Boarder who continues to be disorderly after suitable complaint to the employer of such disorderly Boarders, and he is to pay said Kelloggs and Chapin One Hundred and Ten Dollars per year for the rent of the premises, payable one half in six months and the other half in twelve months, and the taxes and insurance are to be paid by him — and he is to keep the glass in repair and make other small repairs which may become necessary, and he is to take the furniture &c into his possession at a fair price to be agreed upon or appraised by indifferent persons, and an account or inventory made of the same, and is to allow six percent on the amount of said inventory, and at the end of the term each article is to be returned to said Kelloggs and Chapin accounted for, and the whole of said property is to be again appraised and the difference made good by said Spencer, and he is to wash six pieces per week for each boarder included in boarding, and if more pieces are washed for any boarder per week he is to charge them as extra at 38 cents, and when boarders are absent from board and have washing done, it is to be charged as above. And said Kelloggs and Chapin agree to let said Boarding House and land appertaining to the same to said Spencer for the term of one year, and after the fifteenth day of October aforesaid, and also to give him the privilege of running the wash house and machinery belonging to it, whenever the wheel to which it is attached is at work, but not to run at for working alone, and they are to keep the house, wash house and machinery in it in repair so far as respects large repairs, but they are not to be called on for small repairs, and they agree to pay the same Spencer at the rate of one dollar and fifty cents for boarding and washing for each person boarded as aforesaid and the boarding of each person is to be charged to and paid for by the party in whose employ he is, and the account is to be kept that the amount of board for each individual with the date can be ascertained at any time, and said Kelloggs and Chapin shall get insurance on the House and furniture and charge over the amount paid on premium to said Spencer, and they are to reckon with said Spencer at the end of each quarter of the year, and said Kelloggs to pay him what may be due to him for boarding for them, and said Chapin is to pay for what is done for him as soon after the time aforesaid. When boarders are absent at one meal, it is not to be accounted, but if a boarder is absent two meals on the same day, it is to be accounted one day lost or absent board. And the said Kelloggs and Chapin agree to continue this contract for one year more, or two years from the date above, if said Spencer wishes to do so, and if said Spencer gives them notice of his wish to do so two months before the expiration of the first year — and said Kelloggs and Chapin agree that if the average number of boarders for the whole year shall not be equal to eighteen steady boarders, then they shall agree to deduct at the rate of five dollars for each years boarding for one person so wanting from the rent which is to be paid by said Spencer. In witness we have hereunto set our hands interchangeably this 12th day of September.

Hermon Chapin   Alanson Spencer

Chapin's Account Book shows entries with M&A Copeland from January 1829 — October 1830; after, only with Melvin Copeland [1831-1835] with a final single entry, July 1839. This suggests that the firm M&A Copeland dissolved in 1830, after which date H. Chapin used the entire Boarding House for his own employees. Melvin Copeland remained in Hartford until 1839, then removed to Huntington, Mass. to again combine with Daniel, as Copeland & Co. Alfred left Hartford about 1830 to go to Amherst, Mass. and subsequently also joined his brothers in the firm of Copeland & Co.

Fig. 32 - Five H. Chapin/Union Factory Slide Arm Plows.
[This style of plow, Catalogue No. 230 & 231, was made at H.Chapin's Union Factory 1828 - 1928.]

Fig. 30 - UNION FACTORY/WARRANTED SLIDE ARM PLOWS
   Top: M. & A. Copeland
Bottom: H. Chapin

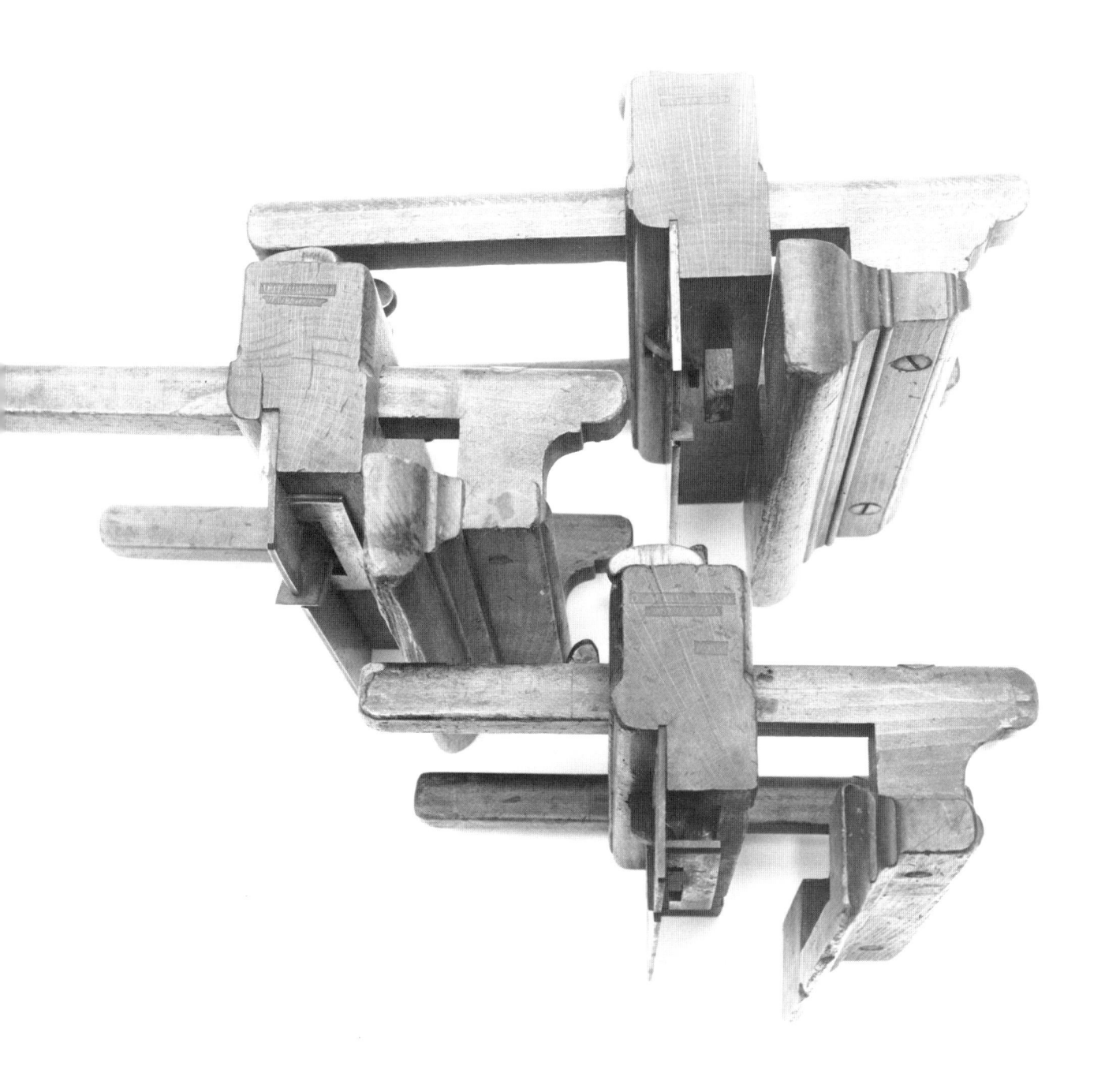

Fig. 31 - Slide Arm Plows Made by Copelands
   Top: M. Copeland
Middle: D. Copeland,   Hartford
Bottom: D. & M. Copeland, Hartford

While the majority of planes made by Hermon Chapin were for the wholesale trade, a few were sold at the Union Factory at retail. The following bill of sale is transcribed:[1]

```
                              New Hartford, January 1830
Mr. G. S. Smith
                         Bit [sic] of H. Chapin
22nd.  1 Dbl. [iron] Jointer, 22 in.      $1.92
       1 Dbl.    "   Smooth                1.25
       1 Single  "     "                    .90
Apr. 2   Sket Rabbet, 1½ in.                .75
         Gauge                              .17
May 14
       8 pair Hand Screws, 1½ in @ .20     1.60
       2 pair  Do [the same] 3/4 in. @ .20  .40
       1 Skew Rabbet, 1 in.                 .67
                                          $7.92
       In Act. of Ira A. Homer
```

Another invoice slip noted that first three above items were delivered at New Hartford to G.L. Smith by Philip Chapin [signed] January 22, 1830.[2] Philip Chapin was Hermon's younger brother, who at that date was probably assisting at the Union Factory in some supervisory capacity. While not a planemaker, he has been exposed to wood work at his father's sawmill at Walpole, NH. Later in 1830 he removed to Baltimore. Among H. Chapin's Baltimore customers noted in his Account Book, Philip was listed at 112 West Pratt Street as of January 1830.

Business with the following other Baltimore plane firms was noted in H. Chapin's Account Book:

Chapin & Ward	January 1831 — October 1834	$1780.22
Chapin & Kendall	January 1834 — April 1836	319.01
Thos. Kendall	April 1836 — July 1839	130.67
	[by bankruptcy]	13.50
Kendall & Maccubben	October 1838 — April 1839	129.52
Philip Chapin & Co.	Jan. 7, 1842 — April 1843	576.99
	after to new account book	

According to directory studies, Philip Chapin was in the following plane firms at Baltimore:[3]

Ward & Chapin	1831
Chappin [sic] & Kendall	1833
Philip Chapin	1835-36; 1842-43; 1845-55
Atkinson & Chapin	1836

After 1845 he was at business at 44 Light Street. (see Vol. I, pp. 30 & 31) Some entries noted him as Philip Chapin & Co. His card or advertisement in the 1853-54 *Matchett's Baltimore Directory* noted:[4]

```
           PHILIP CHAPIN'S
          PLANE MANUFACTORY
                 AND
              TOOL STORE
            44 LIGHT STREET
          CORNER OF BALDERSTON
       Always on Hand, Wholesale & Retail
         a large assortment of carpenters,
         carvers, coopers, cabinet, coach and
         pattern makers tools of Am. & Engl.
            manu. of best stamps & qual.
```

An indication that Philip was still doing business with Hermon as late as December 16, 1862 is revealed from a $550 note he signed on that date, due to the latter.

After 1856 he was listed as a turner and screw manufacturer and last noted in a Baltimore Directory in 1860.[5] With the developing War of the Rebellion, Philip Chapin returned to New Hartford, where he spent the rest of his life as a house carpenter. Philip Chapin does not have appeared to have been a planemaker, but undoubtedly hired such tradesmen to make planes for him while at Baltimore. It likely was Hermon Chapin's suggestion for him to go to Baltimore in 1830 to develop such business in this trade.

During the period of 1827-1830 Hermon Chapin averaged $5400 annual sales, according to his account records. This was accomplished with his two journeymen, Bolles and Winship as his only two employees. His Account Book shows the following customers with extended trade discounts in 1830.[6] (Table II)

TABLE II
H. Chapin's Customers in 1830

Customer	Address	Bench Planes	Moulding Tools
M. & A. Copeland	State St., Hartford	40%	42%
Coley & Smith	410 Chapel, New Haven		28%
T.T. Waldron	Poughkeepsie, N.Y.	35%	35%
F.H. Stevens	Hudson, NY	25%	25%
Hall & Goodwin	Bellows Falls, VT.	25%	25%
Lampson & Hale	Keene, N.H.	25%	25%
G.G. Cambell	451 Broadway, N.Y.	40%	40%
Benjamin Manning	Stanton, Virginia	25%	25%
Elijah S. Curtis	No.7 Dock Square, Boston	35%	35%
Joseph P. Horner	No.47 Market St. Philadelphia	30&35%	30&35%
Robert Hyslop	140 Pearl St., N.Y.	35%	40%
Hall	396 Grand St., NY NY	35%	35%
James S. Brown	Newburg, N.Y.	35%	35%
Cook, Wilson & Griggs	Catskil, NY	35%	35%
Hall & Hawley	Bridgeport, CT	35%	35%
Dwight & Clark	90 Madison Lane, NY	35%	
Seymour	6 Catheribe St., NY	35%	35%
Henry V. Studdiforet	Trenton, NJ	25%	25%
Philip Chapin	322 West Pratt St. Baltimore MD		
Charles Squire	112 Pond St., NY NY	40%	40%

TABLE III

INDEX OF WORK AGREEMENTS OF SEPARATE PAGE ENTRIES 1830 - 1845
ENTERED INTO HERMON CHAPIN'S LEDGER

Person Making Agreement	Tenure of Agreement	Type of Agreement	Transcription Number	Page in Ledger
H.D. Bolles	Sept.5,1830 - Sept.5,1833	Jp	I	1
William Winship	Sept.18,1830 - Sept.18,1833	Jp	II	2
William Warner	July 15,1831 - July 15,1835	Wip	III	4
Henry Brown	Aug.1,1830 - Nov.21,1833	Wip	IV	6
E.W. Barber	Sept.1,1830 - Sept.22,1834	Ap	V	8
George Robinson	Jan.27,1832 - Sept.16,1832	Ap	VI	10
Archibald Marsh	Nov.31,1831 - Nov.30,1835	Wip	VII	12
Henry Bailey	Jan.14,1832 - Jan.14,1836	Jp		14
Levi M. Bennet	Feb.15,1832 - Jan.27,1837	Ap	VIII	18
John S. Moore	Mar.12,1832 - Dec.30,1836	Ap	IX	20
Calvin Hayes	Apr.5,1832 - Apr.5,1834	Wip	X	22
William Alexander	Feb.16,1832 - Feb.16,1836	Wip		24
Henry Bailey	Dec.13,1833 - 3 years	J		26
John T. Mills	July 17,1835 - 4 years	J		28
William H. Bang	Nov. 11, 1835			30
Henry Brown	Feb. 15,1836 - 5 years	J (plows)	XI	32
John N. Fox	Feb.23,1836 - Feb.23,1848	Wip		34
George I. Dowd	Mar.7,1836 - two years	Jp	XII	36
Henry Wells	Feb.11,1836 - Feb.11,1840	Wip	XIII	38
George B. Thomas	Oct.15,1837 - Oct.19,1838	Jp	XIV	40
Asa A. Perkins	April 18,1836 - one year	Wip	XV	42
Ebenezer Goodwin	Nov.19,1835 - 2½ years +	Ar		44
Orson King	Apr.11,1836 - May 23,1839	Wip		46
Clinton Edgerton	May 31,1836 - May 3,1840	Wip	XVI	48
Mark T. Jones	June 16,1836 - June 6,1840	Wip		50
Lester Phelps	Jan.18,1837 - Jan.18,1841	Ar		53
Francis Goodwin	Dec. 26,1836 - not specified	Jp	XVII	55
Pitts Goodwin	Mar.9,1837 - Jan.31,1839	Ar		57
Albert Butler	Feb.14,1837 - 3 years	Wip	XVIII	61
William S. Davis	May 2,1837 - May 2,1840	Jip	XIX	63
Solomon Lemley	Apr.25,1837 - Apr.25,1841	Wp	XX	65

INDEX of WORK AGREEMENTS of HERMON CHAPIN'S LEDGER (CONTINUED)

Elijah White	Jan.19,137 - Jan.19,1840	Jp	XXI	67
William H. Bang	Nov.15,1837 - 3 months	Jr		68
Lucius Foot	Apr.9,1838 - Apr.9,1842	Jip		70
George Byington	Jan.2,1839 - 1 year	Wrj		72
Russel Perkins	Apr.7,1839 - 2 years	Wrj		74
William S. Nash	June 15,1841 - 3 years	Wrf		76
Joshia Allen	May 13,1841 - May 13,1844	Wrj		78
Joseph G. Goodwin	Dec.1,1841 - Dec.1,1844	Wrf	XXII	80
Samuel Allen	June 3,1845 - June 3,1848	Wrj		90

Code for Type of Work Agreement: J = Journeyman A = Apprentice W = Worker
p = planes   i = with instructions   r = rules   rj + rule joints
rf = rule framing

Among the most important sources of information concerning the operations at the Union Factory is the Work Agreement Ledger [8½" x 11", 111 pages] kept by Hermon Chapin, 1830-1865. Upon agreeing to terms of employment, including apprenticeship, it was the practice to write duplicate copies. One was held by the employee and the other kept by Hermon Chapin. Apparently after 1831 Chapin decided to keep his in this bound ledger. He then transcribed five previous agreements, made in 1830 (H.D. Bowles; William Winship; William Warner; Henry Brown; and E.W. Barber). He arranged to have these parties sign these transcriptions. Single copies of the original agreement with Winship, Brown, Barber and Hayes exist also in manuscript.[7] For some unknown reason the earliest with Calvin Hayes, April 5, 1830, was not recorded in this ledger. (a transcription of this follows, as Ia) Neither was that with Joseph Root, September 15, 1836 [transcribed herein as XXII].

With a few exceptions the first 80 pages of this Work Agreement Ledger contain agreements, usually hand written, each on separate pages and signed by the parties so agreeing. Following each agreement on the adjacent page pertinent qualifying statement or revisions were entered, or if none, the page was blank. Thirty-two of these were for planemaking, 1830-1842. Nine were for rulemaking, 1835-1841. These are listed in Table III, noting the type and tenure for each agreement. Three types of agreements were made; Viz; I, Apprenticeship, (A); II, Journeyman, (J) [usually requiring no instructions]; and III, Workman, (W) [requiring limited instructions]. Since this primary data reveals significant information concerning these work systems and this is not readily available, twenty-three of these work agreements concerning planemaking follow as transcriptions.

In a few instances agreements were noted by Hermon Chapin and not signed. Examples of these follow:

```
Dec. 23rd, 1833   Agreed with Henry Bailey to work on Bench Planes
                  for the term of three years at the following prices
                      for the first year   175 Dollars & Board
                       "   " second  "     200    "    "   "
                       "   " third   "     225    "    "   "
                  for three years            600 Dollars

May 11, 1835      Agreed with Geo. R. Stiles to work at tending
                  the Saw Mill for Seventeen dollars per Month
                  he boarding himself for the term of one year.
```

Transcription of Work Agreements with H. Chapin for Planemaking.

[The following Work Agreements for Planemaking with H. Chapin have been transcribed from his Ledger, are listed in chronological order of date agreed and are indicated by Roman numerals corresponding to the data of Table III, pages 76 & 77. Since these original agreements were all hand written, these have been transcribed in script.]

This agreement made by and between Hermon Chapin on the one part and Henry D. Bolles on the other part both of New Hartford, Connecticut Witnesseth - That the sd. H.D. Bolles agrees to work for the sd. Chapin at the business of Manufacturing Joiners Tools for the term of four years commencing on the 5th day of September 1830 thence following to the 5th day of September 1834 for the consideration of the sum of two hundred thirty dollars each year for three hundred twelve days work faithfully done as a common Journeyman's days work to be paid by the sd. Chapin to the sd. Bolles as above written. The sd. Chapin further agrees to Board or allow the sd. Bolles the common price of Board pr week for each six days work so done by the sd. Bolles. The sd. Bolles agrees not to Manufacture or sell and Joiners Tools except for and by consent of sd. Chapin during the term of four years above written. The sd. Bolles also agrees to give the sd. Chapin the privilege of furnishing him with such articles of goods as he may from time to time be in want of at as low prices as can be had of others of the same quality. In witness we have hereunto subscribed our hands this eighteenth day of Jany. 1830.

New Hartford, Connecticut
Hermon Chapin
Henry D. Bolles

Ia. - Agreement with Calvin E. Hayes, April 5, 1830

This Agreement made and entered into by and between Hermon Chapin on the one part and Calvin E. Hayes on the other part. - Witnesseth

The the sd. C.E. Hayes agrees to work for the said Chapin for the term of three years from and after the fifth day of April 1830 there following to April fifth 1833 then to be completed and fully ended for the sum of six hundred dollars to be paid in the following manner.

For the first year	175 Dollars	
" " second year	212-1/2	"
" " third year	212-1/2	"
	600 Dollars	

by the sd. Chapin together with board and washing during the sd. term while employed as above stated.

It is further agreed that the sd. Hayes is to work on Bench Planes for the first and second years and on Common or plain Moulding Tools for the third year of sd. term - Time is to be reckoned three hundred twelve days work for each year. Sd Chapin agrees to allow the sd. Hayes the privilege of working by the piece on days as the work will admit at the customary of work for day. The sd. Hayes commences labour as above agreed term on the 5th day of April 1830.

New Hartford, August 2nd 1830   Hermon Chapin
Calvin E. Hayes

II. - Agreement with William Winship, March 9, 1830

  The agreement made by and between Hermon Chapin on the one part and William Winship on the other part both of New Hartford, Connecticut.   Witnesseth -
  That the sd. Winship agrees to work for the sd. Chapin for the term of three years from and after the eighteenth day of September 1830 then following to September eighteenth 1833 and after until either party gives the other party three months notice of discontinuance sd Winship's term of labour. In consideration of which the said Chapin agrees to pay the sd. Winship the following prices for work which is all to be done in a workmanlike manner and in the most approved style.

For Screw Arm Plows	$1.00 Each
" first Rate Plows	.95 Each
" 2nd Rate Plows	.75 Each
" 3rd Rate Plows	.70 Each
" 4th Rate Plows	.55 Each
" Boxing Plow Fences	.08 Each
" Plating Plane Fences	.08 Each
" Grinding Plow Plates	.75 per Hundred

Short and Long Planes of the same price sd. Chapin To furnish screws ready turned & Fitted for use

Ten Match Planes Each pair	.34
" Do , plated	.42 each pair
" Match Planes with Arms	1.20 each pair

The sd. Chapin also agrees to give the sd. Winship in proportion to the above prices until the commencement of the above agreement as two hundred and seventy eight is to three hundred and twelve as in accordance with a former agreement now existing. In witness we have hereunto withscribed our names this ninth day of March 1830.
      Hermon Chapin
      William Winship

The above agreement is given up and made null and void from and after 4th April 1832.

III. - Agreement with William Warner, July 14, 1831

This agreement made and entered into by and between Hermon Chapin on the one part and William Warner on the other part all of New Hartford. Witnesseth - That the sd. Willian Warner agrees and does hereby agree to work for the sd. Chapin the term of four years from and after the fifteenth day of July 1831 thence following to the fifteenth day of July 1835 then to be completed and fully ended. For which the sd. Chapin agrees to pay the sd. Warner the sum of Five hundred and fifty dollars to be paid in the following manner for each year of faithful Labour -

[continued on page 80]

III. - Agreement with William Warner [continued from page 79]

```
For the first year  one hundred dollars           100
 "   "  second  "   one hundred twenty five       125
 "   "  third   "   one hundred fifty dollars     150
 "   "  fourth  "   one hundred & seventy five    175
        For the four years                        $550
```

The sd. Chapin also agrees to furnish suitable board and washing or allow him the customary price for the same. The sd. Warner is to work on such work as the sd. Chapin may wish during sd. time except so far as this that sd. Chapin agrees to learn the sd. Warner to make Bench Planes, so far as his abilities will admit. It is understood in the above agreement that three hundred and twelve days work constitute one year.

In witness we have hereunto set our hands this 14th day of July 1831.
                        Hermon Chapin
                        Wm. Warner

In addition to the written agreement it is hereby agreed that the sd. William Warner is to work by the piece on Bench Planes at the customary price by the piece he boarding himself and discounting and allowing to the sd. Chapin twelve and half percent on all work so done by the sd. Warner during sd. time within specified in consideration of which the sd. Chapin gives up all claim on the sd. Warner on account of the written agreement except so far as relates to the time which is to remain the same as within specified.
New Hartford August 10th 1832.   Hermon Chapon
                                          Wm. Warner

IV. - Agreement with Henry Brown, July 31, 1830

This agreement made and entered into by and between Hermon Chapin on the one part and Henry Brown on the other part Witnesseth - That the said Henry Brown agrees and does hereby agree to work for the said Chapin for the term of three years two months & twenty days from and after the first day of August 1830 to the twentieth day of November 1833 then to be completed and fully ended for the sum of three hundred and fifteen dollars and Board during sd. time to deduct as is customary for lost time, which the said Chapin agrees to pay in the following manner:

```
For the first 14 Months 20 Days to October 20th 1831  - $ 90-
 "   "  next  12    "             " November 20th 1832   100-
 "   "   "    12    "             " November 20th 1833   125-
                                                        $315.00
```

The said Brown further agrees to forfeit and allow to the sd. Chapin the sum of fifteen dollars if he forsakes and leaves the employ of the sd. Chapin before the expiration of the sd. time as above agreed. It is further agreed that the sd. Chapin is not to learn the sd. Brown the Trade or any part thereof except so far as is for the interest of the sd. Chapin. Also the sd. Brown is to bear his own expense of sickness, training and the like expenses customary to be paid by Masters for Apprentices.
In witness whereof we hereunto set our hands
New Hartford July 31, 1830
                                   Hermon Chapin
                                   Henry Brown

V. - Agreement with Elijah W. Barber, October 4, 1830

This indenture made and entered into by and between Hermon Chapin on the one part and Nathum B Barber and Elijah W. Barber on the other part - Witnesseth

That the sd. Nathum B. Barber and Elijah W. Barber agree that the said Elijah W. Barber shall work for the sd. Chapin as an Apprentice at the Joiner Tool Business from and after the first day of September 1830 until he is twenty two years of age which will be on the twenty second of September 1834 then to be completed and fully ended for the consideration of the sum of One hundred eight six dollars thirty eight cents to be paid in the following manner -

from Sept. 1st, 1830 to Sept. 22nd 1831	$26.38
" Sept.22nd, 1831 to Sept. 22nd 1832	$30.00
" Sept.22nd, 1832 to Sept. 22nd 1833	$30.00
" Sept.22nd, 1833 to Sept. 22nd 1834	$100.00
	$186.38

The said Chapin agrees on his part to learn the sd. E.W.Barber the trade so far as is practical in the sd. four years and the sd. E.W.Barber four days in each year as holidays and times for Military duty so far as the sd. E.W.Barber shall be by Law compelled to do the same and also to furnish equipment for the same, until he is twenty one years of age - Also to pay the sd. E.W.Barber the above named yearly sums on payments so far as the sd. E.W.Barber shall well and faithfully labour in the sd. Chapin's employ in conformity to the above agreement.

The sd. Chapin agrees to allow the sd. E.W.Barber the privilege of working by the piece as is customary in sd. Chapin's Shop. The sd. Chapin further agrees to pay the sd. E.W.Barber's Doctor and Medicine bills and expenses in sickness to the amount of twenty dollars if the same shall concern to that amount until he is twenty one years of age and none there after.   New Hartford   October 4th 1830   Hermon Chapin
                                                                Nathum B. Barber
                                                                E.W. Barber

VI. - Agreement with George Robinson, February 6, 1832

This agreement made and entered into by and between Hermon Chapin on the one part and George Robinson on the other part. Witnesseth That the sd. Robinson agrees and does hereby agree to work for the sd. Chapin from the 27th January 1832 to September 16th 1832 as an apprentice at the Joiner Tool business for the sum of Twelve dollars for each month of 26 days work done in sd. Chapins employ as above written. The sd. Robinson further agrees to be at his own expense of Board, Washing, Training and sundry other expenses customary to be paid by Masters for Apprentices. Also to make the sd. Chapin good against all loss or damage by his former Master on his the sd. Robinson's account so that the sd. Chapin shall be at no expense except the twelve dollars per Month as above written. The sd. Chapin agrees to learn the sd. Robinson the trade on the parts thereof as the sd. Robinson may wish so far as his abilities will admit during sd. time, except the making of Grooving Plows. In witness we have hereunto set our hands this 6th Day of Feby. 1832. New Hartford   Hermon Chapin
                                                George Robinson

VII. - Agreement with Archibald Marsh, August 27, 1832

The Agreement made and entered into by and between Hermon Chapin on the one part and Archibald Marsh on the other part. Witnesseth - That the said Marsh agrees and does hereby agreee to work for the sd. Chapin the term of four years from and after the 31st day of November 1831 to the 31st day of November 1835 then to be completed and fully ended. For which the sd. Chapin agrees to pay the sd. Marsh the sum of five hundred and fifty dollars to be paid in the following manner for each years faithful labour.

    For the first year One hundred dollars   100 -
    " " second " One hundred twenty five   125 -
    " " third " One hundred &fifty dollars   150 -
    " " fourth " One hundred & seventy five   175 -
                   for the four years   550 Dollars

The sd. Chapin also agrees to furnish suitable Board and Washing during sd. time or allow sd. Marsh the customary price for the same. The sd. Marsh is to work on such work as the sd. Chapin may wish during the sd. time except so far as that the sd. Chapin agrees to learn the sd. Marsh to make Bench Planes. It is understood in the above agreement that three hundred and twelve days work constitue one year. In witness we have hereunto set our hands this 18th February 1832. New Hartford   Hermon Chapin
                                                               Archibald Marsh

In addition to the within agreement it is hereby agreed that the sd. Marsh is to work by the piece on Bench Planes at the customary price by the piece he boarding himself and discounting and allowing to the sd. Chapin twelve and a half percent on the work so done to the amount of Nine Hundred dollars at the customary prices by the piece. In consideration of the above the sd. Chapin agrees to pay to the sd. Marsh the customary price for all work faithfully done to the amount of Nine Hundred dollars except the twelve and half percent as above written and also to give up all claim to the sd. Marsh on account of the within agreement when he shall have so done the sd. Nine Hundred dollars worth of work.
New Hartford August 27th 1832.   Hermon Chapin
                                                           Archibald Marsh

VIII. - Agreement with Levi M. Bemont, March 6, 1832

This agreement made and entered intoby and between Hermon Chapin on the one part and Levi M. Bemont on the other part. Witnesseth -
That the said Levi and Levi M. Bemont agree and do hereby agree that the sd. Levi M. Bemont shall work for the sd. Chapin as an apprentice at the Planemaking Business until he is twenty one years of age which will be on the 30th day of January 1837 then to be completed and fully ended in consideration of which the sd. Chapin agrees to pay to the sd. Levi M. Bemont the following sums for each years faithful labour

[continued on page 83]

VIII. - Agreement with Levi M. Bemont [Continued from page 82]

```
for 11-1/2 Months to Jany 30th 1833 to 17 years of age 22 87/100 Dollars
 "  one year     "    "  30th 1834  " 18  "   "   "  30           "
 "  one year     "    "  30th 1835  " 19  "   "   "  40           "
 "  one year     "    "  30th 1836  " 20  "   "   "  50           "
 "  one year     "    "  30th 1837  " 21  "   "   "  65           "
   The whole time Two hundred Seven 87/100 Dollars   207 87/100   "
```

The sd. Chapin also agrees to furnish suitable board and washing during sd. time for the sd. Bemont while in sd. Chapin's employ. It is further agreed that sd. Chapin is to be at no expense of sickness, Military duty and lost time on account of the sd. Levi Bemont except as above written. It is understood in the above agreement that three hundred and ten days work constitute one year. The sd. Chapin agrees to learn the sd. L.M Bemont the art or trade of Making Planes and Joiner Tools as so far is customary and practical during sd. time. Either party by giving the other party notice within two months from the date of this agreement may disolve the same and make it null and void otherwise to remain in full force to the expiration of sd. time. In witness we have hereunto set our hands this 6th day of March 1832.
New Hartford   Hermon Chapin
                                    Levi Bemont
                                    Levi M. Bemont

New Hartford Feby 2nd 1835

It is hereby agreed in addition to the within that Levi M. Bemont is to give up all his right and claim on the sd. Chapin for learning the art or trade of Plane Making as specified in the within agreement and also agree to work on such work as the sd. Chapin made wish from time to time during the time within specified. For and in consideration of which the sd. Chapin agrees to pay to the sd. Levi M. Bemont in addition to the within named price fifty dollars for the year from nineteen to twenty of age of the sd. Levi M. Bemont making in all for the sd. year one hundred dollars and also to pay in addition Sixty

Dollars for the year twenty to twenty one of the age of sd. Levi M. Bemont making in all for the last year of sd. term one hundred twenty five Dollars for each year's faithful labour - To deduct as is customary for lost time. In witness we have hereunto set our hands.   Levi Bemont
                        Hermon Chapin
                        Levi M. Bemont
Agreed to work at 15 ct. off
to pay for use of tools $5.00 Aug. 11th 1835

X. - Agreement with John S. Moore, April 7, 1832

This agreement made and entered into by and between Hermon Chapin on the one part and Allen Moore and John S. Moore on the other part. Witnesseth - That the said Allen Moore and John S. Moore agree and do hereby agree that the sd. John S. Moore shall work for the sd. Chapin as an Apprentice at the Plane Making Business until he is twenty one years of age which will be on the 30th day of December 1836 then to be complete and fully ended in consideration of which the sd. Chapin agrees to pay the sd. John S. Moore the following sums for each years faithful labour done in sd. Chapins employ

for 9-1/2 months to Dec.	30th, 1832	to 17 years of age	20 76/100 Dollars
" one year " "	30th, 1833	" 18 " " "	30 "
" one year " "	30th, 1834	" 19 " " "	40 "
" one year " "	30th, 1835	" 20 " " "	50 "
" one year " "	30th, 1836	" 21 " " "	65 "
for the whole time			205 76/100 "

The sd. Chapin also agrees to furnish suitable board and Washing during sd. time for the sd. John S. Moore while in sd. Chapins employ & It is further agreed that the sd. Chapin is to be at no expense of sickness, Military duty and lost time on the account of the sd. John S. Moore except the yearly payments and Board as above written. It is understood in the above agreement that three hundred an ten days constitute one years labour. The sd. Chapin agrees to learn the sd. John S. Moore the art or trade of making planes or Joiners Tools so far as is customary and practicable during sd. time. The sd. Chapin further agrees to allow the sd, John S. Moore Eight weeks time the coming winter to attend school he boarding himself during sd. time. Either party by giving the other party notice within two months from the date of this agreement may disolve the same and make it null and void otherwise to remain in full force until the expiration of sd. time as above written. In witness we have hereunto set our hands this 7th day of April 1832, New Hartford, Conn.

                     Hermon Chapin
                     Allen Moore
                     John S. Moore

XI. - Agreement with Calvin E. Hayes, May 26, 1832

This agreement made and entered into by and between Hermon Chapin on the one part and Calvin G. Hayes on the other part Witnesseth -
That the sd. Hayes agrees and does hereby agree to work for the sd. Chapin at the Plane Making Business for the term of two years from and after the 5th day of April 1832 thence following to the 5th day of April 1834 then to be completed and fully ended on the following terms. Viz The said Hayes is to work on Moulding Tools during the sd. time at the customary price by the piece as paid by the sd. Chapin he boarding himself during the sd. time. It is further agreed that the said Hayes is to have the privilege and necessary instruction to learn any or all the arts appertaining to sd. Moulding Plane Making except that appertaining to the making of Grooving Planes, Sd Hayes is to be at his own expense of loss of time on the account of such learning should any occur so that the sd. Chapin shall be at no expense except the time of showing on instructing sd. Hayes and the customary price by piece as above written which the sd. Chapin is to pay the sd. Hayes for all work done in a workmanlike manner. It is further agreed that the sd. Hayes can have the privilege of leaving the employ of sd. Chapin as above written at the end of one year by giving the sd. Chapin one months notice and paying to the sd. Chapin the sum of twenty dollars; Otherwise the above agreement is to remain in full force during the sd. time as above written. In witness we have hereunto set our hands this 26th day of May 1832.

                     Hermon Chapin
                     Calvin E. Hayes

XI. - Agreement with Henry Brown, February 15, 1836

This agreement made and entered into by and between Hermon Chapin on the one Part and Henry Brown on the other part, Both of New Hartford aforesaid -

Witnesseth that the said Brown agrees and does hereby agree to work for the said Chapin at the Plane Making business for the term of five years after the fifteenth day of February Eighteen hundred and thirty six to the fifteenth day of February Eighteen hundred forty one then to be completed and fully ended for which work the said Chapin is to pay to the said Brown the following Prices by the piece for all Plows and other tools the said Brown may make during said term together with a second hand which the said Brown has the Privilege to employ in the said business during the said time - Viz

for 4th Rate Plows   62cts   Box'd. or Plated   70 cts.
"   3rd Rate do.   75cts   Box'd. or Plated   83 cts.
"   2nd Rate do.   90cts   Box'd. or Plated   98 cts.
"   1st Rate do.   112cts   Box'd or Plated   115 cts.
"   2nd Rate do. Screw Arms 90cts Box'd or Plated 98 cts
"   1st Rate do.   "   " 117cts Box'd or Plated 125 cts
"   Plows Screw Arms All Boxwood Extra 137-1/2 cts

and for all other tools the said Brown may make during said time said Chapin is to allow the said Brown what is the customary price for making such tools in said Chapin's shop. Said Chapin is to allow the said Brown eight cents for turning of the arms and nuts for each screw arm Plow or do the same at his own expense. Said Brown is to furnish his own tools for himself and the workman he may employ during said time and is also to furnish a set of good screw tools for the screw arms during the said time said Chapin is to pay the said Brown for his work in part from time to time as his necessity may require and pay the balance at the end of each year for all work so done during said year. It is further agreed that either party may dissolve this agreement by giving the other party three months notice of his intent so to do and paying the sum of twenty five dollars to the party so notified - otherwise this agreement to remain in full force during the five years before written.
In witness whereof we have hereunto set our hands this fifteenth day of February aforesaid.

Henry Brown
Hermon Chapin

New Hartford - March 28th 1832
It is hereby agreed that the said Brown is to allow and pay to the said Chapin the sum of Eighty Dollars for which the sd. Chapin relinquishes his right to the sd. Browns apprenticeship and to allow him the customary price by the piece as a Journeyman's wages, he boarding himself during the sd. time within specified to work on Dbl. Smooth Planes to the full amount the sd. Chapin may have made so far as the sd. Brown shall be able to make the same. In witness we have hereunto set our hands.

Hermon Chapin
Henry Brown

XII. - Agreement with George J. Dowd, March 7, 1836

This agreement made and entered into by and between Hermon Chapin of the one part and George J. Dowd of the other part. Witnesseth - That the said Dowd agrees and does hereby agree to work for the said Chapin two years from and after the first day of April next in and according to the regulations of said Chapin shop - and the said Chapin is to pay the said Dowd for said labour well and truly performed as follows - for the first year two hundred dollars $200
                for the second year two hundred fifty dollars $250
said Chapin to furnish suitable board and washing during said time or pay said Dowd the customary price for the same.

    Said Dowd shall further have the privilege by giving said Chapin one months notice and paying said Chapin the sum of twenty five dollars to quit said Chapins employ at the expiration of one full year from the commencement of this contract his having performed one year labour as above in witness whereof we have hereunto affixed our hands at New Hartford this seventh day of March 1836.
                                          Hermon Chapin
                                          George J. Dowd

XIII. - Agreement with Henry Wells, March 9, 1836

This agreement made and entered into by and between Hermon Chapin on the one part and Henry Wells on the other part witnesseth as follows - to wit - that the said Wells agrees and does hereby agree to work for the said Chapin the term of four years from and after the eleventh day of February 1836 until the eleventh day of February eighteen hundred and forty then to be completed and fully ended - For which the said Chapin agrees to pay to the said Wells the sum of six hundred dollars to be paid in the following manner for the said Labour well and truly performed as aforesaid

    for the first year one hundred dollars $100
    for the second year one hundred and twenty five dollars $125
    for the third year one hundred and seventy five dollars $175
    for the fourth year two hundred dollars $200
    Being for the whole four years six hundred dollars $600

said Chapin agrees to furnish suitable board and Washing for said Wells during said time or to pay the said Wells the customary price for the same. said Wells to work on such work as the said Chapin may wish or direct except so far that the said Chapin agrees to learn said Wells to make bench Planes - all which being performed then this obligation is void otherwise in full force and virtue - In witness whereof we have hereunto affixed our hands at New Hartford aforesaid this ninth day of March One Thousand Eight Hundred and thirty six.
                                          Hermon Chapin
                                          Henry Wells

Henry Wells account on his contract Feby. 11, 1836

Nov. 11, 1836 Rec'd of Henry Wells on the within account the ballance of
        amount to Augt. 11, 1836 of five 47/100 Dollars $5.47
Nov. 11, 1836 Rec'd. of Henry Wells on the within contract
        twenty six dollars $26.00
Feby. 20, 1837 Rec'd. on the within Eleven Dollars $11.00
May 17, 1837 Rec'd. on the within Eleven Dollars $11.00
Nov. 13, 1837 Received on the within Nineteen 66/100 Dollars $19.66
Aug. 21, 1837 Rec'd. the amt. to be paid on the within contract
        H. Wells in full & Interest $33.31

XIII. - Agreement with Henry Wells [Continued from Page 86]

Now the conditions of this within written Agreement are as follows - that whereas the within named Henry Wells being a minor and has neither Father living nor Guardian said Wells agrees that this contract is made for and in consideration of being instructed in the art or workmanship of making bench Planes that one half of the within mentioned sums to be paid by the said Chapin for said Labour which may become due before said Wells shall have so arrived at full and lawful age and shall renew this contract by signature that the said Chapin is to pay over to the said Wells the Ballance of wages so retained and the within contract thereafter to be in full force until performed and finished. Witness our hands at New Hartford the day and year within written.
                Hermon Chapin
                Henry Wells

It is hereby agreed that the before named Henry Wells is to work by the piece during the term of the foregoing contract and that he is to pay or to allow to the aforesaid Chapin the sum of Ninety five 74/100 Dollars and Interest from this date together with the ballance of five 47/100 Dollars on book Act. up to August 11, 1836 to be abated as a compensation for instruction in the art or trade before named and for the tools heretofore sold said Wells to use in said business and the said Wells is to pay so fast as to have Seventy dollars and interest of said sum paid by the time he shall come to Lawful age to be paid in equal sums deducted from the quarterly payments for his labour and that the said tools are not to be disposed of by said Wells but remain as surety until this obligation is fulfilled being sold only to use in said business and the said Wells to be allowed for all work he may do by the piece the customery Journeymans price and paying such account or demands as sd. Chapin may have agianst him is to be paid him at the end of each quarter. New Hartford Oct. 28, 1836 Hermon Chapin
                Henry Wells

XIV. - Agreement with George B. Thomas, April 29, 1836

This agreement made and entered into by and between Hermon Chapin on the one part and George B. Thomas on the other part witnesseth as follows to wit - that the said Thomas agrees and does hereby agree to work for the said Chapin three years from and after the nineteenth day of October eighteen hundred and thirty five until the nineteenth day of October Eighteen Hundred and thirty eight then to be completed and fully ended. For which the said Chapin agrees to pay to the said Thomas the sum of six hundred Dollars to be paid as follows for each Years faithful Labour performed as aforesaid which is to be in full for said Labour -
for the first year one hundred and seventy five Dollars $175
for the second year two hundred Dollars $200
for the third year two hundred and twnety five Dollars $225
Being for the whole three years Six Hundred Dollars $600
and the said Chapin agrees to allow the said Thomas the customary price to provide his board & washing during said time and the said Thomas to be employed on making moulding Planes such as said Chapin shall direct all which being fulfilled then this obligation is Void otherwise in full force and virtue in witness whereof we have hereunto affixed our hands at New Hartford this twenty ninth day of April Eigteen Hundred and thirty six.
             Hermon Chapin
             George B. Thomas

XV. - Agreement with Asa E. Perkins, April 5, 1836

This agreement made and entered into by and between Hermon Chapin on the one part and Asa E. Perkins of the other part - Witnesseth as follows, to wit - that the said Asa E. Perkins agrees and does hereby agree to work for the said Hermon Chapin in and according to the regulations of said Chapin Shop the term of one year from and after the eleventh day of April Eighteen hundred and thirty six and board himself during said time and that the said Chapin agrees to pay the said Perkins one dollar and twenty five cents per day for the said years Labour faithfully performed as aforesaid which sum is to be paid in full for said Labour. All of which being fulfilled then this obligation is Void otherwise in full force in witness whereof we have hereunto affixed our hands at New Hartford this fifth day of April Eighteen hundred and thirty six.
            Hermon Chapin
            Asa E. Perkins

XVI. - Agreement with Clinton Edgerton, October 28, 1836

It is hereby agreed that the within named Clinton Edgerton is to work by the piece during the time of the within contract and that he is to learn only that part of the trade which is necessary to make Hollows & Rounds and he is to receive Journey Man's price according to the price in said Chapin shop for all the work he may do by the piece and the said Clinton is to pay the said Chapin the sum of fifty Dollars for his privilege and instruction in the art and also fourteen Dollars and forty one cents for a set of tools sold said Edgerton for the purpose of working at the said business making all sixty four 41/100 Dollars with interest after the date hereof to be paid in several payments in the course of Eighteen Months to be deducted from the amount of wages due him for work as asforesaid and the said tools are not to be disposed of by said Clinton until fulfillment of this contract being sold only for that purpose. The said Clinton has the privilege to work on hollows & rounds during this contract - All which being fulfilled it is considered the closing up of the within contract otherwise the former contract to remain in full force & virtue
As witness our hands at
New Hartford aforesaid October 28, 1836 Hermon Chapin
                Clinton Edgerton

```
Rec'd on the above contract Nov.31,1836  four 41/100 Dollars  $4.41
   "    "   "     "      "  March 1, 1837 eight 65/100    "   $8.65
   "    "   "     "      "  June 5, 1837  eight 41/100    "   $8.41
   "    "   " within     "  Sept. 8, 1837 eight 99/100    "   $8.99
   "    "   "     "      "  Dec. 1, 1837  six   60/100    "   $6.60
   "    "   "     "      "  March 8, 1838 nine       Dollars  $9.00
   "    "   "     "      "  June 7, 1839  eight              $8.00
   "    "   "     "      '  as Balanced
   in full for Principal & Interest        six  13/100    "   $6.13
```

XVII. - Agreement with Francis P. Goodwin, December 26, 1836

This agreement made and entered into by and between Hermon Chapin on the one part & Francis P. Goodwin on the other part witnesseth as follows - That the said Francis P. Goodwin agrees and does hereby agree to work for the said Chapin at the benchplane making business on the following conditions that the said Goodwin having in part learned the art or trade of the above business of said Chapin is to work at the Journeymans price in said Chapins shop on conditions that he is to pay to the said Chapin the sum of Eighty Seven Dollars to be paid in five payments with interest to be deducted from his quarterly payments for his work commencing with the first at this date which the said Chapin is to receive as a full compensation for all instruction and privileges in the aforesaid art and for a number of tools sold said Goodwin for the use of said occupation and the said tools are not to be sold or removed by said Goodwin until this contract is fulfilled & the said Goodwin is at all times to conform to Rules & Regulations of sd. Chapins shop as they are or may be from time to time be adopted all which being fulfilled then this obligation is void otherwise in full force as witnessed our hands at New Hartford.
Dec. 26, 1836
            Hermon Chapin
            Francis P. Goodwin

XVIII. - Agreement with Albert Butler, May 14, 1837

This agreement made and entered into by and between Hermon Chapin on one part and Albert Butler on the other part, witnesseth as follows to wit - that the said Butler is to work for the said Chapin at the Plane Making Business for the term of three years from and after the fourteenth day of February Eighteen hundred and thirty seven and the said Chapin shall give him the necessary instruction to learn him to make common moulding tools and that the said Butler is work on such tools and such kinds as said Chapin shall direct at the customary prices in said Chapin shop and that the sd. Butler is to pay to the said Chapin the sum of sixty five dollars to be paid in several payments with interest to be deducted one from each of the six first quarterly payments to said Butler for his work as aforesaid which sum of sixty five dollars is to be in full for the aforesaid instruction in the art or trade of making moulding planes as aforesaid and the said Butler is at all times to observe the Rules and Regulations of said Chapins Shop as they are or may be from time to time be adopted in witness whereof we have hereunto affixed our names this fourteenth day of May One thousand Eight Hundred and Thirty Seven at New Hartford aforesaid.
            Hermon Chapin
            Albert Butler

XIX. - Agreement with William S. Davis, August 12, 1837

This agreement made and entered into by and between Hermon Chapin on the one part and William S. Davis witnesseth that the said William agrees and does hereby agree to work for the said Chapin for the term of three years from and after the second Day of May one thousand Eight Hundred and thirty seven until the Second Day of May Eighteen hundred and forty then to be completed and fully ended to work on the plane making business on moulding planes and such kinds as said Chapin shall direct and at the customary prices for making such planes in said Chapin Shop discounting to said Chapin on all work so done twelve and a half percent from a common journeymans price, for instruction in the art or trade of planemaking as aforesaid for which the said Chapin is to pay him the balance due him for work after deducting the discount as aforesaid in quarterly payments from the commencement of said time said Davis always to faithfully perform his work and to observe all the rules and Regulations of said Chapins shop as they are or may from time to time be adopted in Witness whereby we have hereunto affixed our hands at New Hartford this twelfth day of August one thousand eight hundred and thirty seven.   William S. Davis
Nath'l Chapin
for Hermon Chapin

XX. - Agreement with Solomon Lemley, October 26, 1837

This agreement made and entered into by and between Hermon Chapin on the one part and Solomon Lemley on the other part witnesseth as follows (to wit) - That the said Lemley agrees and does hereby agree to work for the said Chapin at bench plane business for the term of four years from and after the twenty fifth day of April 1837 until the twenty fifth day of April 1841 then to be completed and fully ended for which the said Chapin agrees to pay to the said Lemley the sum of six hundred dollars to be paid in the following manner for the said labour well and faithfully preformed as aforesaid -

for the first year one hundred Dollars	$100.00
for the second year one hundred & twenty five Dollars	125.00
for the third year one hundred & seventy five Dollars	175.00
for the fourth year two hundred Dollars	200.00
Being for the whole four years six hundred Dollars	600.00

Said Chapin agrees to provide suitable board and Washing for sd. Lemley during the sd. time or pay the sd. Lemley the customary price for the same he boarding himself said Lemley to work on such work as the said Chapin shall direct except so far that the said Chapin is to Learn the said Lemley to make bench planes. Said Lemley at all time to conform to the Rules and Regulations of said Chapins Shop as they are or may be from time to time adopted all which being fulfilled then this obligation is void otherwise in full force in witness whereof we have hereunto affixed our hands at New Hartford this twenty sixth day of October 1837.   Solomon Lemley
Hermon Chapin By Nathl. Chapin

New Hartford April 24, 1840
   The within contract is annuled by mutual cansent.   Hermon Chapin
Solomon Lemley

XXI. - Agreement with Elijah White, November 2, 1837

This agreement made and entered into by and between Hermon Chapin on the one part and Elijah White on the other part witnesseth as follows - that the said White agrees and does hereby agree to work for the said Chapin at the bench plane business for the term of three years from and after the nineteenth day of June 1837 until the 19th day of June Eighteen hundred and forty then to be completed and fully ended and the said Chapin is to allow the said White the customary Journeymans prices in his shop for all planes so faithfully made to be paid in quarterly payments to said White after deducting the sum of One Hundred Twelve Dollars and fifty cents which the said White is to allow the sd. Chapin as a just consideration for instructing him in the art or trade of bench plane making together with a set of tools sold him to perform said work which sum with interest is to be paid in Eight quarterly payments to be deducted from the eight quarterly payments for work developed above. The said White to work on such parts of bench plane making as said Chapin shall direct except so far as the said Chapin is to learn him the art or trade of bench plane making. The above named tools are not to be disposed of until the fulfilling of this contract being sold only for this purpose. Said White to observe all the Rules and Regulations of said Chapins Shop as they are or may be from time to time be adopted all of which being fulfilled then this obligation is void otherwise in full force. In witness whereof we have here unto affixed our hands at New Hartford this second day of November 1837.

Elijah White
Hermon Chapin by Nath'l Chapin

XXII. - Agreement with J.M. Root, August 23, 1836

This agreement made and entered into by and between Joseph M. Root on the one part and Hermon Chapin on the other part, witnesseth as follows that the said J.M. Root agrees and does hereby agree to work for the said Hermon Chapin at the plane making business for the term of three years from and after the fifteenth day of September Eighteen hundred and thirty six until the fifteenth day of September Eighteen hundred & thirty nine then to be completed and fully ended and that the said Chapin agrees to pay the said Root for the said three years the sum of five hundred Dollars to be paid as follows, the Labour well and faithfully performed:

for the first year the sum of one hundred & twenty five Dolls. $125
" " second " " " " one hundred & seventy five Dolls. $175
" " third " " " " two hundred Dollars $200
Being for the whole three years five hundred Dollars $500

the said Chapin is also to provide suitable Board and washing for the sd. Root or pay him the customary price therefor.
The said Root is to work on such work as the said Chapin shall direct except so far that the said Chapin is to learn the sd. Root to make bench planes and the said Root at all times to conform to the Regulations of sd. Chapins shop as they are or may be from time to time adopted all which being fulfilled then this Obligation is Void otherwise in full force as witness our hands at New Hartford this twenty third day of August Eighteen hundred and thirty six.

J.M. Root
Hermon Chapin

Note the above agreement was not bound in the H. Chapin Agreement Book now at the Connectcut Historical Society but was among the papers given the New Hartford Historical Society by John Blake.

Plate II

WORK AGREEMENTS WITH PLANEMAKERS WITH HERMON CHAPIN

Union Factory, Pine Meadow, Connecticut

1830 - 1838

[Data from H.Chapin's Work Agreement Ledger
Connecticut Historical Society Collection]

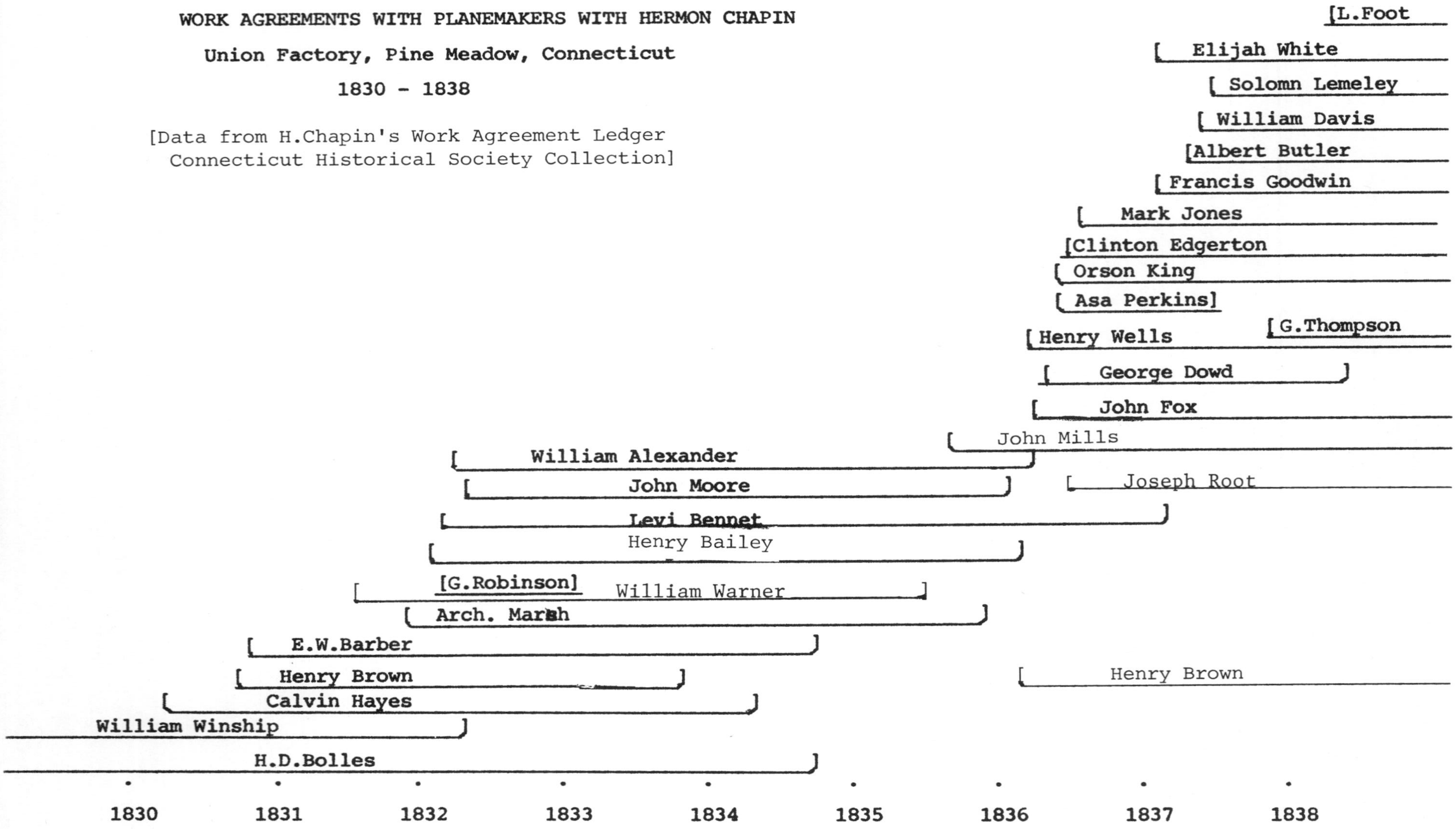

Name	1830	1831	1832	1833	1834	1835	1836	1837	1838
[L.Foot									
Elijah White									
[Solomn Lemeley									
William Davis									
[Albert Butler									
[Francis Goodwin									
Mark Jones									
[Clinton Edgerton									
Orson King									
[Asa Perkins]									
[G.Thompson									
Henry Wells									
George Dowd									
John Fox									
John Mills									
Joseph Root									
William Alexander									
John Moore									
Levi Bennet									
Henry Bailey									
[G.Robinson]									
William Warner									
Arch. Marsh									
Henry Brown									
E.W.Barber									
Henry Brown									
Calvin Hayes									
H.D.Bolles									
William Winship									

The tenure of 27 employees as planemakers, working at the Union Factory from 1830 through 1838, is shown in Plate II. The distribution of these were: 12 journeymen; 11 workmen and 4 apprentices. Two of the journeymen, Winship and Brown, were contracted at different dates to make plows. The other journeymen were directed by Chapin according to the particular requirements of the moment. Six of the workmen were assigned to make bench planes, and the other four to make moulding planes. Apprentices during their training presumably learned to make all types of planes, unless otherwise specified in their agreement. During this period about 50% of the products were bench planes. The number of employees increased accordingly; two in 1830; four in 1831; seven in 1832, nine in 1833; fourteen in 1838.

A list of prices paid for each type of plane made for H. Chapin was posted. (Unfortunately this is not extant) This included fitting the iron to the finished plane. All materials were supplied by H. Chapin. Journeymen planemakers, not requiring any instructions, were paid the full price. Those requiring instructions, were discounted according to their abilities. Even apprentices, when their abilities had been proved and the work schedule permitted, might qualify for such piece work. Employees, except apprentices, furnished their own tools. If other workmen required tools, the costs were deducted from wages. Apprentices were instructed how to make and sharpen their tools. If assigned to be paid by the piece, journeymen could hire and pay their own help, provided their work was satisfactory. Such a journeyman was known as a contractor. Workmen with the consent of H. Chapin could, as time permitted, qualify for piece work rather than agreed annual salary. The clarity, fairness and integrity of Hermon Chapin's agreements with his employees were most consistent.

In 1830 the work year was 312 days, sometimes reduced to 310 for apprentices. After 1833 it was generally 311 days. This amounted to a six day work week of 11 hours per day, Sundays free and two paid annual holidays. After 1850 the workday was reduced to ten hours. Lost time for sickness or other reasons, unless made up, was deducted from wages. During the terms of these contracts, pay was generally made by credit against Hermon Chapin's accounts. Each worker had an account pad that he took to the store to be "reckoned" through his purchases. Unless otherwise specified, Chapin furnished board and washing during the contracted term of employment.

It was customary to post "Rules and Regulations" in various factories, according to the demands of the proprietor. Unfortunately such a record is not known to have survived for the Union Factory. However, from existing regulations at other shops of that date the following are suggested:

1. Work hours will be 6 AM-12 noon; 12:30 PM-5:30 PM, as noted by the Factory Bell. All hands will adhere to these hours. Lost time will be deducted from agreed pay.
2. No gambling, nor wrestling or scuffing, nor profane language will be allowed.
3. No drinking of alcoholic beverage or smoking on the premises will be allowed.
4. All tools will be put away at the end of the day and work benches will be kept orderly.
5. The Factory will be opened only in the morning on the Sabbath and then only for the purpose of washing and shaving, preparatory for attending Church.
6. Church attendance is recommended.
7. All using the Boarding House will have lights out and remain quiet after 10 PM.

At the nearby axe factory of the Collins Manufacturing Co. at Canton, the following "Terms with Workmen" were posted as of December 1, 1834:[8]

"No man will be retained who does not always make as many as 15 axes per day, and generally more. The strikers must pick over their own coal daily and use no more borax than is absolutely necessary. All work will be inspected and no pay allowed for work that is not satisfactory to the Inspector. 26 days will be considered a month's work. The wages to be paid whenever three month's work is performed. In addition to the above stipulated wages, twenty-five cents per day will be allowed for board, every day that a man works, but never when he is not at work and said allowance for board will be paid with the wages.

We the undersigned do severally agree to work for the Collins Manufacturing Company at our several branches of the business on the foregoing terms and prices for the space of three months from the time we commence work and in case of our losing any time during the said three months we agree to make it up afterwards. And we likewise agree to conform to the rules and regulations of the establishment, it being understood that their bell hours will not exceed an average of ten hours per day. It is likewise understood that no man will be retained who cannot and does not perform a good day's work, or who is guilty of disorderly conduct, or carries spiritous liquor to the shop, or drinks them daily and habitually. If any man leaves the establishment from any cause whatever before the expiration of three months from the time he commences work, he shall not have any claim to his wages until the expiration of said three months from the time he commenced. The company will endeavor to prevent delays, accidents and detentions from occurring in the establishment, but will not be responsible in any manner for such detentions when they occur. In case a house is occupied belonging to the company, the occupant is to pay for the same quarterly $6.25, being the rate of $25 per annum and is to move out of the house within thirty days from the time he is notified so to do by the Agent of said Collins Manufacturing Company

A broadside, dated 1870, RULES & REGULATIONS of the COLLINS COMPANY, noted the following:[9]

```
The ringing of the bell indicates to time to commence and quit  work.
The bell will ring as follows:
                          MORNING           NOON           EVENING
March 1 - May  1      6:30 o'clock   12 o'clock 1 o'clock  5:30 o'clock
May   1 - Sept. 1     6:00     "     12    "     1    "    5:00     "
Sept. 1 - Oct. 1      6:30     "     12    "     1    "    5:30     "
Oct.  1 - Mar. 1      Sunrise        12    "    12:30 "    Sunset
```

An undated notice of "Prices Paid for Apprentices" at the Union Factory appeared on page 22 of H. Chapin's WORK AGREEMENT LEDGER. Since the fee paid L. Bennett [Agreement No. VII], February 15, 1837 corresponded with this rate, it may be assumed that this was about the date of this notice.

```
              Prices Paid for Apprentices
From 15 years old to 16 years old    20 Dollars
  "  16   "    "    " 17   "    "    25    "
  "  17   "    "    " 18   "    "    30    "
  "  18   "    "    " 19   "    "    40    "
  "  19   "    "    " 20   "    "    50    "
  "  20   "    "    " 21   "    "    65    "

    To furnish Board and Washing only
    311 Days work for each year or to deduct in
    proportion for lost time and Apprentice to
    be at his own expense of Board on lost time.
    Also expenses of sickness, Military duty
    and the like.  Overwork to offset against
    lost time.
```

William Winship cancelled his work contract April 4, 1832 with Hermon Chapin. He subsequently went to Springfield, Massachusetts, associating with a partner in the plane firm of Hills & Winship. After Winship left the Union Factory, Henry Brown took his place as plow plane maker, generally the top paying position in the work force. Comparison of the rate that Chapin agreed to pay Henry Brown, six years after his contract with Winship for the same work, indicates an increase of 10 to 17 per cent was made to Brown. It is interesting to note from the March 9, 1830 contract with Winship that screw arm plows were then being made at the Union Factory.

Two puzzling entries that appeared in the Work Agreement Ledger during 1835 were payments in Shillings.

"April 15th, 1835, Agreed with G.C. Ward to work Six Months at Seven Shillings per day and Board."

"April 15th, 1835, Agreed with Stephen Baldwin to work for Seven Shillings a day and Board."

A possible explanation may be that Ward and Baldwin were from England or Scotland, and not being familiar with United States currency, preferred to be paid in their native familiar money.

A significant entry in 1835 noted:

"September 1st, 1835 — Agreed with Nathaniel Chapin to work for the term of five years from this date for the first year four hundred and fifty dollars and for five hundred dollars a year after."

Apparently Hermon Chapin employed his older brother, Nathaniel, as a supervisor or overseer. Work agreements with William Davis (XIX — August 12, 1837); Solom Lemely (XX — October 26, 1837) and Elijah White (XXI — November 2, 1837) were all written and signed "Hermon Chapin by Nathaniel Chapin." It is doubtful that Nathaniel Chapin had any previous planemaking experience before hiring at the Union Factory. He had been a sawyer and probably had very broad experience with wood working. His father, Levi, died in 1833 while in Virginia as a result of an epidemic of yellow fever. He was there on business attempting to interest customers in a sawmill mechanism for which he reportedly held a patent.[10] After death his New Hampshire properties were deeded to his two other sons, Jonathan and Levi, Jr. Nathaniel sold his property at Walpole, NH and relocated in Connecticut.

It is not known how long Nathaniel was employed at the Union Factory, possibly through September 1838, according to his contract with Hermon. He apparently was a well respected citizen, as he took part in town government at New Hartford. After finishing at the Union Factory between 1839 and 1846 he may have organized a plane firm there, calling this "The Eagle Factory." A plane with this imprint and "Warranted, New Hartford, CT" may have been a product of his firm. (See Fig. 33)

In 1847 Nathaniel removed to Westfield, Massachusetts, purchasing a whip factory with a water power, which he converted into a plane factory.[11] He may have brought workers from the Union Factory with him, or hired help in Massachusetts. Some planes may have been purchased for resale from the Union Factory, An imprint with "Eagle Factory/Warranted" in a semi-circle and a line "N. Chapin & Co." below is noted in the upper left of Plate XXXII, Vol. I, p. 280. A plane with this imprint is illustrated in Fig. 34. It is not known when he ceased making planes, but he died at Westfield September 21, 1876.[12]

Imprint of Plane: Eagle Factory/Warranted   N. Chapin & Co.

Fig. 34. - Ogee Moulding
Plane with imprint: Eagle Factory
N. Chapin & Co. / Warranted

Fig. 33. - Handled Sash Plane
with imprint: Eagle Factory/ Warranted
New Hartford/ CT.

In the spring of 1835 Hermon Chapin decided to make a substantial addition to his plane factory. This was furnished with a wheel pit from which lines of circular saws could be driven. Some details of this addition are revealed from the following contract with a mason, James Egleston.[13]

"This agreement made and entered into by and between Hermon Chapin on the one part and James Egleston on the other; witnesseth that the said James Egleston agrees and does hereby agree to finish and lay a suitable outside foundation for sd. Chapin's Plane Factory about to be erected, as per draft. The whole length of the wall to be four hundred ninety-two feet, average height about three feet, sd. wall to be suitable strength for a two story Brick Building, the outside wall to be well faced, fifteen inches high on top all around sd. building with a foundation for a chimney in the center of sd. building about eight feet square. Also to dig and stone a wheel pit, sd. pit to be fifteen feet in the clear and six feet deep, more or less, with two plumb blocks for sd. wheel, not to weigh less than one ton, to be laid suitable to hand sd. wheel; one to be drilled for two bolts to hold the bearing. All sd. job to be done by the middle of May next for which the sd. Chapin agrees to pay the sd. Egleston the sum of ninety dollars when the sd. job is done, as above written. Sd. Chapin is to furnish the mortar for the sd. outside wall; sd. Egleston to furnish all the other materials for sd. job.

New Hartford, March 30, 1834   James Egleston   Hermon Chapin"

The next known addition to the plane shop was made during May 1853.

"March 16, 1853 — Agreed with William Harris to build an addition to the Plane Shop to commence about the 20th April to work by the day, self and workmen as follows:

Self	$1.25 per day and Board,	Began May 26th
Scovill	1.25 per day and Board,	Began May 26th
Andrews	1.00 per day and Board,	Began May 26th
Falell	1.00 per day and Board,	Began May 26th
Messanger	.50 per day and Board,	Began May 26th

According to H. Chapin's Account Book his annual sales at the Union Factory were: $6353 [1830]; $8495 [1831]; $10,603 [1832]; $12.244 [1833]; $9555 [1834]; and $10,754 [1835]. See Plate III. This demontrated consistent progress over his average of $5100 annual sales for the years 1827-1829. In addition to being an excellent craftsman and businessman, his mechanical ingenuity in designing machinery for semi-automated operations running from water power was a contributing factor to his financial successes. The major part of his business was to the wholesale trade for which he substantially discounted his prices. A typical account was that with Kennedy and Way of New York City. Annual sales with this concern were as follows: $83.87 [1835]; $277.94 [1836]; $97.58 [1839]; $138.94 [1840]; $181.21 [1842]; and $155.90 [1843]. Thus a great many accounts were needed to make up his total sales.

On November 7, 1835 Hermon Chapin purchased the rule business, stock and equipment from Franklin Bolles of Hartford. The entire operation was removed to the Union Factory. From that date the rule business comprised a substantial part of Chapin's total sales. This subject will be covered in detail in Chapter V.

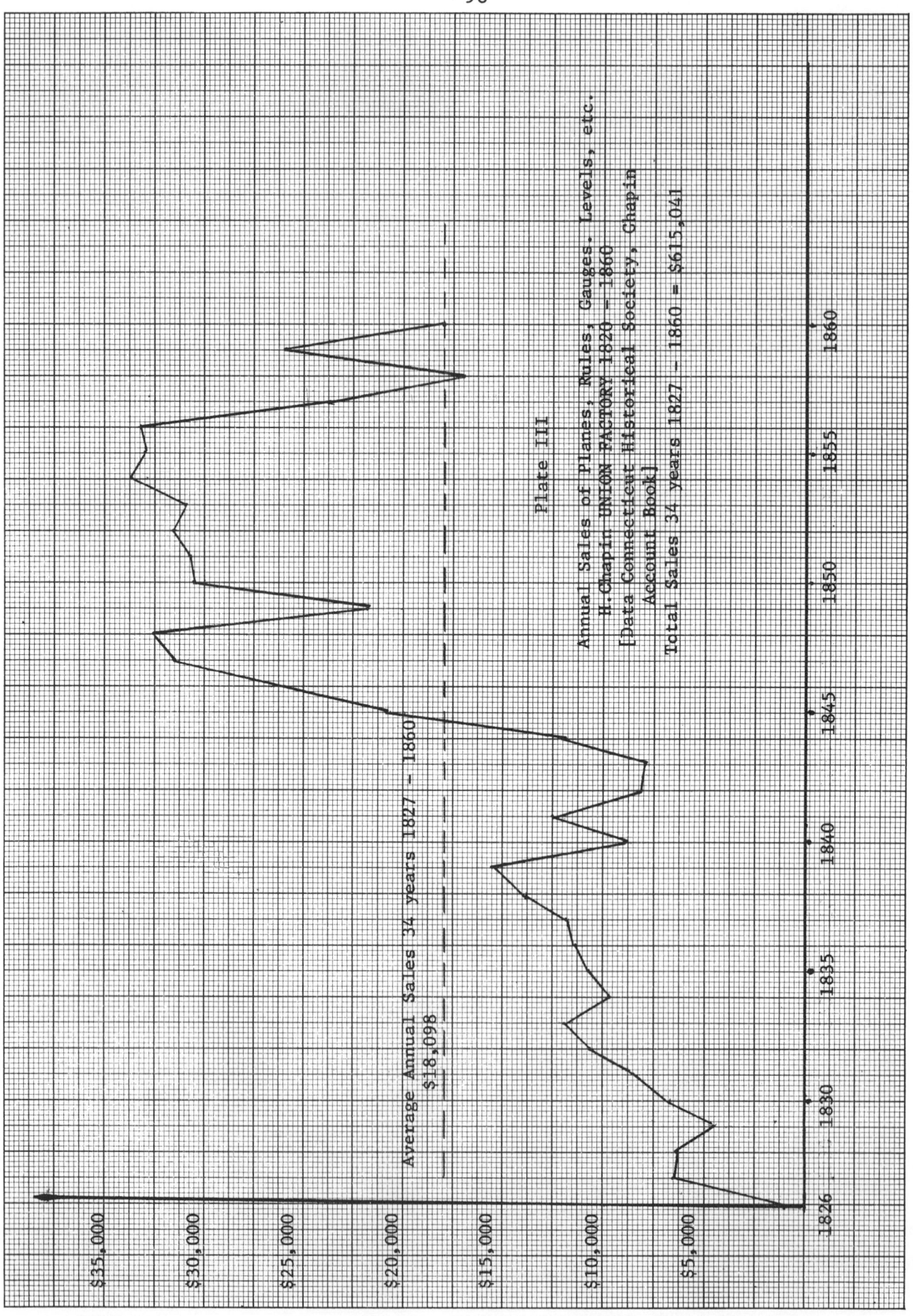

Plate III

Annual Sales of Planes, Rules, Gauges, Levels, etc.
H. Chapin UNION FACTORY 1820 - 1860
[Data Connecticut Historical Society, Chapin Account Book]

Total Sales 34 years 1827 - 1860 = $615,041

Average Annual Sales 34 years 1827 - 1860
$18,098

Hermon Chapin made an interesting agreement with Henry Brown on August 31, 1838 whereby the latter deeded his house to the former, but ran it as a boarding house for Chapin for two and a half years, but still had the option of purchasing the house back from Chapin at any time during that period for $1500. A transcription of this deed follows:

> This agreement made and entered into by and between Hermon Chapin on the one part & Henry Brown on the other part all of New Hartford, County of Litchfield, State of Cinnecticut. Witnesseth -
>
> That the said Brown has this day Deeded to the said Chapin a certain piece of Land with a dwelling house thereon now occupied by the said Brown which the said Brown agrees and does hereby agree to occupy for the term of Two and a half years from the fifteenth day of August AD 1838 for which he is to pay the said Chapin the sum of one hundred and fifty dollars a year as rent for the sd. house and premises to be paid in quarterly payments. The said Brown is to keep four Boarders for the said Chapin at customary price during the said time above, witt, if said Chapin should wish so many boarders. An the said Chapin agrees and does hereby firmly agree and bind himself to release and reduce to the said Brown free and clear of all incumbrance whatsoever the same premises and house this day deeded by said Brown to said Chapin at any time the sd. Brown shall pay or well and truly cause to be paid to the said Chapin the sum of Fifteen Hundred dollars at any time during the said two and a half years above written.
>
> Witness our hands
> New Hartford
> August 31, 1838
>
> *Hermon Chapin*
> *Henry Brown*
>
> [transcribed from files of New Hartford Historical Society]

After 1844, with the exception of the Samuel Allen agreement in 1845, the work contracts appearing in H. Chapin's LEDGER were limited to a single paragraph, often only a single sentence, and were not signed by either party. Approximately 228 of these were recorded between 1835 and 1865. Some examples of these agreements follow:

> 1844 Agreed with J. Bolles to work from May 13th at one dollar and 30 cts. by the day.
>
> Agreed with C. Edgerton to make One Thousand Single Jack Planes at 15 cts. each.
>
> Agreed March 6 with Enoch Gaines to make 1000 Dbl. Smooth CS @ 16¢ — $160.00 and 500 Dbl. Fores CS @ 21¢ — $105.00 $265 — H.C.
>
> Elisha Paine began work September 9 — agreed to work six months for ten dollars
> per month, then one year for fourteen dollars per month.

Catalogues and Invoice Prices for Rules, Planes, Gauges, etc. exist for the years 1839 and 1853.[14] The title pages of these are seen as Plates IV and V. Note that the 1853 title page indicated that "Castings, Machinery and Puddled Iron in various shapes" were also available at the Union Factory. These enterprises of H. Chapin will be discussed in Chapter IV. These two catalogues, both printed by Elihu Geer at Hartford, were the same size [approximately 5½ " x 8½ "] and for the most part had the same item numbers. Unfortunately pages 5 and 6, noting the prices of moulding planes Nos. 128 - 195, were missing from the 1839 *Catalogue*. However, these have been reconstructed, based on the relationship that the majority of 1839 prices were one and a half times those of 1853, or stating this another way, the 1853 prices were approximately two-thirds those of 1839. The catalogue pages for the 1853 are reprinted and the 1839 prices are tabulated at the extreme right column.

In analyzing these differences in prices my first thought was that mass production techniques with improved equipment had enabled H. Chapin to reduce his prices by one third in 1853 from those is 1839. While this may have been a contributing factor, detailed studies of 1849 cost data in the Chapin account records, upon which the 1853 prices were based, indicate that this price reduction was principally the result of reducing the discount from 40% in 1839 to 20% in 1853. It seems probable that lower invoice prices would increase the volume of sales, and that Hermon Chapin's decision was to lower the trade discount to accomplish this.

Cost data from H. Chapin's 1849 account records illustrate his method of calculating plane invoice prices that appeared in his 1853 *CATALOGUE*. (See Table IV) The incidental [overhead] costs were determined by adding the three costs of making, wood and iron and taking 15 per cent of this total. Two-thirds the total of these four costs was added to obtain the invoice price. (1.67 times the total of these four costs) Assuming Chapin was then content with a profit of one third his cost, which seems a reasonable figure, this is realized by discounting his invoice price by 20 per cent. (i.e., 1.67 x .8 = 1.33, which is 33% profit)

Similar reasoning will show that in 1839 by discounting 40% it was then necessary to increase the invoice price 2.22 times the cost in order to maintain a profit of one-third. (2.22 x .6 = 1.33) Plate VI shows the changes in invoice prices for the period 1822 through 1897 for various types of planes. As will be noted later when the prices were again revised for the 1859 *Catalogue,* they were increased [twice total cost] to permit a discount of one-third, which enabled the same profit of one-third. (2.0 x total cost x .667 = 1.33)

Study of these 1839 and 1853 *Catalogues* will reveal the extensive scope of plane manufacture at the Union Factory. Readers who are not familiar with the names of these plane listings should first read Chapter V in Volume I (pp. 79-140). The common simple moulding shapes, such as: astragal, quirk bead, torus, cock bead, ovalo, scotia, cavetto, etc. are seen in Plate XXIII (Vol. I, p. 107). Various complex shapes, such as: back (reverse) Ogee, Grecian Ogee, Grecian ovalo, Ovalo quirk and bead, etc. are illustrated in Plate V (Vol. I, p. 31). A bolection moulding [sometimes spelled belection] is a projected complex moulding usually having a rabbeted side, used to decorate panels, door cases and fire-place frames. H. Chapin offered this type of plane (#130) from 1839 -1861, but was not listed in 1862 or later catalogues.

The plane listings in 1839 and 1853 were considerably greater is both shape and size than those listed in the D. & M. Copeland 1822 Broadside (Plate III, Chapter I). As previously noted, the complexity of moulding shapes were fancier and more irregular in 1830 than after 1830. During the first quarter of the 19th century cabinetmakers were producing more classical mouldings, often using hollow and round planes in designing such complicated mouldings. A group of D. Copeland and M. Copeland moulding planes, probably made before 1830, illustrate such types. (Figs. 35 & 36) By 1830 the influences of American Empire and Greek Revival resulted in the simpler shapes of the Grecian Ogees and ovalos having beads, fillets, etc. Such later planes made by or for D. Copeland and M. Copeland are illustrated in Figs. 37 & 38.

CATALOGUE

AND

INVOICE PRICES

OF

RULES, PLANES, GUAGES, &C.

MANUFACTURED BY

HERMON CHAPIN,

UNION FACTORY,

NEW-HARTFORD, CONN.

ALSO, — COOPER'S TOOLS; BENCH SCREWS; HAND SCREWS; BOXWOOD MALLETS; CHALK ROLLARS; PLOW STOPS, &c., &c.
Orders for the foregoing promptly executed.
A liberal discount to Wholesale Dealers.

HARTFORD.

PRINTED BY ELIHU GEER, 26½ STATE-STREET.

1839.

Plate IV
1839 CATALOGUE of UNION FACTORY
[Collection of Connecticut Historical Society]

Plate V - 1853 CATALOGUE

CATALOGUE
AND
INVOICE PRICES
OF
RULES, PLANES, GAUGES, &c.

MANUFACTURED BY
HERMON CHAPIN.

MANUFACTURER ALSO OF
CASTINGS AND MACHINERY,
of every description,
PUDDLED IRON,
BANDS, BARS, BLOOMS, AXLE DRAFTS, CAR AXLES AND BUNTERS, CROW BARS, &c.

UNION FACTORY,
PINE MEADOW, CONN.

HARTFORD
ELIHU GEER, STATIONER AND STEAM PRINTER.
1853.

2 BOX WOOD RULES.

Invoice Numbers.		1853 Price per Dozen.	1839 Price per Dozen.
1	Two Fold Arch Joint,	$3 25	$6 25
2	do. do. Bits,	3 50	6 75
3	do. do. " Thin,	3 75	7 50
4	do. do. " Arch Tip,	5 25	10 00
5	do. do. Bound,	12 50	22 75
6	do. do. " Board Measure,	4 25	9 00
7	do. do. Bits, "	4 50	9 50
8	do. do. " Thin, "	4 75	10 50
9	do. do. " Arch Tip,	6 00	13 00
10	do. do. Bound, "	13 50	24 75
11	do. do. " Slide,	5 50	11 00
12	do. do. Bits, "	5 75	11 50
13	do. do. " Thin, "	6 00	12 50
14	do. do. " Arch Tip, "	7 25	15 00
15	do. do. Bound, "	16 00	27 50
16	do. do. " Engineers'	6 00	15 00
17	do. do. Bound, "	16 00	28 50
18	Two Fold Square Joint,	2 75	5 00
19	do. do. Bits,	3 00	5 50
20	do. do. " Thin,	3 25	6 50
21	do. do. " Arch Tip,	3 75	8 00
22	do. do. Bound,	4 00	8 50
23	do. do. " Thin,	4 25	9 50
24	do. do. Bound, "	12 50	23 00
25	do. do. " Slide,	4 75	9 50
26	do. do. Bits, "	5 00	10 00
27	do. do. " Thin, "	5 25	11 00
28	do. do. Bound, "	15 00	24 00
29	Two Fold English Joint,	2 00	3 50
30	Bench Rules, Satinwood,	2 25	4 25
31	" " Narrow,	1 50	4 00
32	Parallel " 6 inch,	2 00	6 00
33	do. " 8 "	2 50	8 50
34	do. " 10 "	2 75	11 00
35	do. " 12 "	3 00	13 50
36	Iron Monger's Calliper Rule,	6 50	15 00
37	do. " Ivory,	9 00	21 00
38	Platting Scale, 24 inch,	5 00	9 00
39	do. 12 "	2 50	7 75
40	Yard Sticks,	67	4 50
41	" " Satinwood,	2 50	4 00
42	Ship Carpenters' Bevils,	3 50	6 00
43	Shoe Makers' Size Sticks,	2 75	4 50
44	Board Sticks, 24 inch, Satinwood,	4 00	8 00
45	do. do. 36 " "	5 25	12 00
46	do. do. 36 " for Inspectors,	6 00	7 75
47	Gauging Rods, 48 inch,	5 00	9 00
48	Wantage Rods,	2 50	5 00
49	Button Gauges,	1 50	6 50
50	Watch Glass Gauges,	62½	1 00

BOX WOOD RULES.

Invoice Numbers.		1853 Price per Dozen.	1839 Price per Dozen.
51	Narrow Four Fold Arch Joint,	4 25	$ 7 50
52	Narrow Four Fold Arch Joint, Bits,	$4 50	8 00
53	do. do. do. " " Edge Plates,	5 50	9 50
54	do. do. do. " Bound	14 00	25 50
55	do. do. do. " 12 inch,	3 25	5 50
56	do. do. do. " " Edge Plates,	4 25	7 50
57	do. do. do. " Bound	10 00	16 00
58	do. do. Double Arch Joint,	6 00	11 50
59	do. do. do. do. Bits,	6 25	12 00
60	do. do. do. do. Bound	20 50	33 00
61	do. do. Square Joint,	3 25	6 00
62	do. do. do. Bits,	3 50	6 50
63	do. do. do. " Edge Plates,	4 50	8 50
64	do. do. do. 12 inch,	2 75	4 00
65	do. do. do. " Edge Plates,	3 75	6 00
66	do. do. do. 36 inch,	4 25	8 00
67	Broad Four Fold English Joint,	3 75	10 00
68	Narrow Four Fold English Joint,	2 62½	4 50
69	do. do. do. 12 inch,	2 12½	3 50
70	Broad Four Fold Square Joint,	4 75	9 50
71	do. do. do. Bits,	5 00	10 00
72	do. do. do. " Edge Plates,	6 00	12 00
73	do. do. Arch Joint,	5 75	11 00
74	do. do. do. Bits,	6 00	11 50
75	do. do. do. " Edge Plates,	7 00	18 50
76	do. do. do. Bound	16 00	30 00
77	do. do. Double Arch Joint Bits,	8 00	15 00
78	do. do. do. do. Bound	22 50	36 00
	WITH BOARD MEASURE TABLE.		
79	Broad Four Fold Square Joint Bits, Edge Plates,	7 00	15 00
80	do. do. Bound	16 00	30 00
81	do. do. Arch Joint Bits and Edge Plates,	8 00	16 50
82	do. do. do. Bound	18 00	33 50
83	do. do. Double Arch Joint Bits,	9 00	19 00
84	do. do. do.	24 00	39 00

IVORY RULES.

Invoice Numbers.		1853 Price per Dozen.	1839 Price per Dozen.
85	Narrow Four Fold Square Joint Bits and Edge Plates,	20 00	24 00
86	do. do. Arch do. do.	22 00	27 00
87	do. do. do. Bound	32 00	45 00
88	do. do. 12 inch, Edge Plates,	9 75	39 00
89	do. do. do. Bound	18 75	57 00
90	do. do. do. English Joint,	5 00	8 75
91	do. do. do. Square Joint,	6 00	10 50
92	do. Two Fold, 6 inch,	2 25	4 00
93	Broad Four Fold Square Joint Bits and Edge Plates,	24 00	31 00
94	do. do. Arch do. do.	26 00	34 00
95	do. do. Bound	36 00	52 00
96	do. do. Double Arch Joint Bits,	28 50	46 00
97	do. do. do. Bound	45 00	64 00
98	Two Fold Arch Joint Bits,	27 50	40 00
99	do. do. do. Bound	42 00	54 00

BENCH PLANES.

Invoice Numbers.		1853 Price.	1839	1839 Price per Dozen.
100	Single Smooth Plane, Common Cast Steel,	$ 42	German Steel,	$ 75
101	do. Jack do. do. do.	50	" "	85
102	do. Fore do. 21 in. " do.	65	" "	1 25
"	do. " do. 22 " " do.	75	" "	1 30
103	do. Jointer do. 26 " " do.	85	" "	1 37½
"	do. " do. 28 " " do.	95	" "	1 42
"	do. " do. 30 " " do.	1 10	" "	1 50
104	Single Smooth Plane, Best Cast Steel,	52	Cast Steel	87½
105	do. Jack do. " do.	60	" "	1 00
106	do. Fore do. 21 in. " do.	85	" "	1 50
"	do. " do. 22 " " do.	95	" "	1 58
107	do. Jointer do. 26 " " do.	1 05	" "	1 67
"	do. " do. 28 " " do.	1 15	" "	1 75
"	do. " do. 30 " " do.	1 30	" "	2 00
108	Double Smooth Plane, Common Cast Steel,	72	German Steel	1 25
109	do. Jack do. do. do.	80	" "	1 37½
110	do. Fore do. 21 in. do. do.	1 05	" "	1 75
"	do. " do. 22 " do. do.	1 15	" "	1 84
111	do. Jointer do. 26 " do. do.	1 25	" "	2 00
"	do. " do. 28 " do. do.	1 35	" "	2 08
"	do. " do. 30 " do. do.	1 50	" "	2 25
112	Double Smooth Plane, Best Cast Steel,	80	Cast Steel	1 37½
113	do. Jack do. do.	88	" "	1 50
114	do. Fore do. 21 in. do.	1 15	" "	2 00
"	do. " do. 22 " do.	1 25	" "	2 08
115	do. Jointer do. 26 " do.	1 35	" "	2 25
"	do. " do. 28 " do.	1 45	" "	2 34
"	do. " do. 30 " do.	1 60	" "	2 58
116	Single Smooth Planes, Boxwood, Best Cast Steel,	1 05		
117	Double " " do. do.	1 35		
118	Tooth Planes, do. do.	90		
119	Mitre " do. do.	60		
"	do. " Boxwood, do. do.	1 12		
120	Single Circular Planes, do. do.	65	" "	1 12½
121	Double " " do. do.	95	" "	1 50

MOULDING PLANES.

Invoice Numbers.			1853 Price.	1839 Price per Dozen.
122	Astragals,	To ¾ inch,	34	
"	do.	To 1 "	42	56¼
"	do.	To 1¼ "	50	62½
123	Beads,	To ¾ "	45	75
"	do.	To 1 "	60	75
"	do.	To 1¼ "	85	1 00
"	do. with Handles,	To 1½ "	1 75	1 25
124	Beads, Double Boxed,	To ¾ "	50	87½
"	do. do.	To 1 "	65	1 12½
"	do. do.	To 1¼ "	90	1 37½
125	Beads, Solid Box, Dovetailed,	To ¼ "	50	87½
"	do. do. do.	To ½ "	60	1 00
"	do. do. do.	To ¾ "	75	1 25
126	Base and Band Mouldings, per inch,		70	1 00
127	Bed Mouldings with Handles, do.		60	1 00

1839

116	Tooth	German Steel	1 25
117	Do.	Cast Steel	1 50
118	Mitre	German Steel	76
119	Do.	Cast Steel	86

5

MOULDING PLANES.

Invoice Numbers.		1853 Price.	1839 Price*
128	Back Ogees, To ¾ inch,	$ 40	$ 60
"	do. do. To 1 "	48	72
"	do. do. To 1¼ "	56	84
129	Back Ogees with Beads, To ¾ "	50	75
"	do. do. do. To 1 "	58	87
"	do. do. do. To 1¼ "	65	97½
130	Belections, To ¾ "	50	75
"	do. To 1 "	58	87
"	do. To 1¼ "	65	97½
131	Cock Beads,	38	57
132	do. Boxed,	42	63
133	Center Beads, To ⅜ inch,	48	72
"	do. To ¾ "	56	84
134	Center Beads, Solid Box, Dovetailed, To ⅜ "	55	82½
"	do. do. do. To ¾ "	65	97½
135	Cornice Planes, per inch,	65	97½
136	Dadoes, To 1 inch,	70	1 05
137	do. with Stop, To 1 "	80	1 20
138	do. with Side stop, To 1 "	85	1 27½
139	do. with Screw Stop, To 1 "	1 46	2 20
140	Door Planes,	65	98
141	do. do. Boxed,	75	1 12
142	Draw Planes,	45	67½
143	do. do. Boxed,	55	82½
144	do. do. Moving Fence,	70	1 05
145	do. do. do. do. Boxed,	88	1 32
146	FILLETSTERS,	90	1 35
147	do. with Stop,	1 00	1 50
148	do. with Stop and Cut,	1 15	1 75
149	do. with Stop Cut and Boxed,	1 40	2 10
150	do. with Screw Stop Cut and Boxed,	2 30	3 50
151	do. with Arms Stop and Cut,	1 65	2 50
152	do. with do. do. do. and Boxed,	1 85	2 75
153	do. with Screw Arms, Stop, Cut and Boxed.	2 12½	3 20
154	do. with " " Screw Stop, Cut and Boxed,	3 00	4 50
155	Grecian Ovolos, To ¾ inch,	48	72
"	do. To 1 "	56	84
"	do. To 1¼ "	65	97½
"	do. To 1½ "	75	1 12
156	do. with Handle, per inch,	55	82½
157	Grecian Ovolo with Fillet, To 1 inch,	58	87
"	do. do. 1¼ "	66	1 00
"	do. do. 1½ "	75	1 12½
"	do. do. 1¾ "	85	1 27½
"	do. do. Handle, per inch,	60	90
158	Grecian Ovolo, with Bead, To 1 inch,	62	93
"	do. do. 1¼ "	70	1 05
"	do. do. 1½ "	80	1 20
"	do. do. 1¾ "	90	1 35
159	do. with Handle, 2 "	1 25	1 87
"	do. do. 2½ "	1 56	2 35

6

MOULDING PLANES.

Invoice Numbers.		1853 Price.	1839 Price*
160	Grecian Ogee with Bevel or Fillet To 1 inch,	$ 58	$ 87
"	do. do. do. 1¼ "	66	1 00
"	do. do. do. 1½ "	75	1 12½
"	do. do. do. 1¾ "	85	1 27½
"	do. do. Handle, per inch,	58	87
161	Gothic Bead, with one Iron,	58	87
162	do. with two Irons, Boxed,	90	1 35
163	Halving Planes,	30	45
164	do. Plated,	40	60
165	do. Handled,	45	67½
166	do. Handled and Plated,	55	82½
167	Hollows and Rounds, No. 1 to No. 12, per pair,	62½	94
"	do. No. 13 to No. 18, "	80	1 20
"	do. No. 19 to No. 24, "	1 00	1 50
168	Table Hollows and Rounds, "	80	1 20
169	do. do. Boxed, "	1 42	2 12½
170	do. do. with Fence, "	1 40	2 10
171	MATCH PLANES, ½ inch, per pair,	1 00	1 50
172	do. Plated, ½ " "	1 20	1 80
173	do. over ½ inch to 1 " "	1 05	1 57½
174	do. Plated, to 1 " "	1 25	1 87½
175	do. with Handles, to 1¼ " "	1 95	2 90
176	do. do. Plated, to 1¼ " "	2 25	3 35
177	do. for Plank, "	1 70	2 55
178	do. do. Plated, "	2 00	3 00
179	do. do. moving Fence, "	2 10	3 15
180	do. do. do. Plated, "	2 40	3 60
181	do. do. with Arms, "	2 80	4 20
182	do. do. do. Plated, "	3 10	4 65
183	do. do. with Screw Arms, "	3 30	5 00
184	do. do. do. Plated, "	3 60	5 50
185	Nosings, with Handles,	75	1 12
186	Handrail Plane,	1 17	1 75
187	Ovolos, To ¾ inch,	42	63
"	do. 1 "	50	75
"	do. 1¼ "	58	87
188	Ovolo with Bead, To ¾ "	50	75
"	do. do. 1 "	58	87
"	do. do. 1¼ "	67	1 00
189	Panel Plane, Cast Steel,	1 05	1 57½
190	do. with Cut, do.	1 15	1 72
191	do. with moving Fence, do.	1 50	2 25
192	do. do. do. and Cut, do.	1 58	2 35
193	Qk. Ogee, To ¾ inch,	50	75
"	do. 1 "	58	87
"	do. 1¼ "	67	1 00
194	Qk Ogee with Bead, To ¾ "	55	82½
"	do. do. 1 "	62	93
"	do. do. 1¼ "	70	1 05
195	Reading Planes, To ⅜ "	56	84
"	do. do. ¾ "	62	93

*estimated [1.5×1853]

MOULDING PLANES.

Invoice Numbers.		1853 Price	1839 Price
196	Qk Ovolo, . . . To ¾ inch,	50	75
"	do. . . . . 1 "	58	87½
"	do. . . . . 1¼ "	67	1 00
197	Qk Ovolo with Bead, . ¾ "	58	87½
"	do. do. 1 "	66	1 00
"	do. do. 1¼ "	75	1 12½
198	Raising Planes, . . . per inch,	84	1 37½
199	do. Boxed, . do.	88	1 42
200	RABBET PLANES, Square, To 1 inch,	46	67
"	do. . . 1¼ "	54	80
"	do. . . 1½ "	68	87½
201	do. Double Boxed, To 1 inch,	84	1 37½
"	do. do. 1¼ "	92	1 50
"	do. do. 1½ "	1 00	1 58
202	Rabbet Planes, Skew, To 1 inch,	50	75
"	do. do. 1¼ "	56	84
"	do. do. 1½ "	64	92
"	do. do. 1¾ "	70	1 00
"	do. do. 2 "	76	1 08
"	do. do. 2¼ "	84	1 25
203	do. Box and Cut, To 1 inch,	86	1 25
"	do. do. 1¼ "	92	1 34
"	do. do. 1½ "	98	1 42
"	do. do. 1¾ "	1 04	1 50
"	do. do. 2 "	1 10	1 58
"	do. do. 2¼ "	1 16	1 75
204	Rabbet Planes with Handle and Cut, 2 inch,	1 20	1 75
205	do. and 2 Cuts, To 2½ inch,	1 50	2 12½
206	SASH PLANE, 1 Iron, Boxed,	50	87½
207	do. " Boxed,	75	1 25
208	do. 2 Irons, "	75	1 17
209	do. " Boxed,	1 00	1 50
210	do. Double, "	1 00	1 67
211	do. Boxed,	1 25	2 00
212	do. Screw Arms,	1 30	2 00
213	do. Self-regulating,	2 25	
"	do. Boxed,	1 55	2 50
"	do. Self-regulating,	2 50	
214	do. Handled, Boxed,	1 15	1 75
215	do. do. do.	1 50	2 25
"	Templets, Ganges and Prickers, each,	12½	
216	Sash Coping Plane, .	40	62½
217	do. do. Boxed,	60	84
218	Sash Filletster, Screw Arms, Screw Stop,	1 92	2 50
219	do. do.	2 65	3 50
220	Scotia, . . . To ¾ inch,	40	58
"	do. . . 1 "	48	62½
"	do. . . 1¼ "	56	75
221	Scotia with Bead, To ¾ inch,	48	67
"	do. do. 1 "	56	75
"	do. do. 1¼ "	64	87

MOULDING PLANES

Invoice Numbers.		1853 Price	1839 Prices
222	Snipe Bills, . per pair,	$ 02	1 25
223	do. full Boxed, do.	1 25	1 75
224	Side Rabbet Planes, per pair,	1 08	1 50
225	Slip Beads, To ¾ inch, "	50	87½
"	do. 1 "	65	1 12½
226	Corner dovetail Boxed, ¾ "	67	1 37½
"	do. do. 1 "	82	1 00
"	do. do. 1¼ "		1 25
227	Torus Bead, ¾ "	45	1 50

GROOVING PLOWS

228	Plows 4th Rate, 8 Irons,	3 00	4 50
229	do. do. Plated, 8 "	3 20	4 75
230	do. do. Boxed, 8 "	3 20	4 75
231	Plows 3d Rate, 8 "	3 40	5 00
232	do. do. Plated, 8 "	3 60	5 25
233	do. do. Boxed, 8 "	3 60	5 25
234	Plows 2d Rate, 8 Irons,	4 60	6 25
235	do. do. Plated, 8 "	4 80	6 50
236	do. do. Box'd, 8 "	4 80	6 50
237	Plows 2d Rate, Screw Arms, Handled 8 Irons	6 00	7 50
238	do. do. Box'd. 8 "	6 20	7 75
239	Plows 1st Rate, do. 8 "	6 50	7 75
240	do. do.Box or Rosew'd 8 "	8 00	9 00
241	2d Rate, Screw Arms 8 "	4 80	6 25
242	do. do. Box'd 8 "	5 00	6 50
243	Plows 1st Rate, Screw Arms 8 "	5 10	7 50
244	do. do. Box'd 8 "	5 30	7 75
245	Plows 1st Rate, Screw Arms, Box or Rosewood 8 Irons	6 50	8 50

GAUGES.

246	Marking Gauges per doz	85	1 75
247	do. do.	1 00	2 25
248	do. Boxwood Oval Bar do.	1 90	4 00
249	do. do. Oval Bar do.	2 10	4 75
250	Cutting Gauges per doz.	1 50	2 75
251	do. do.	1 65	3 25
252	do. Boxwood Oval Bar do.	2 65	5 00
253	do. do. Oval Bar do.	2 85	5 75
254	Mortice Gauges, plated head and bar, Box or Rosewood per doz.	12 00	7 50
255	do. Brass Slide do.	2 75	5 00
256	do. do. Plated H do.	3 25	6 50
257	do. Screw Slide do.	5 25	10 00
258	do. Rosewood Oval Bar do.	7 00	13 50
259	Pannel Gauges . per doz.	2 00	3 75
260	do. with Handles do.	2 34	4 50
261	Slitting Gauges do.	3 75	5 00
262	do. do.	5 25	8 00
263	Hand Screws ½ inch	1 75	
"	do. ¾ "	2 00	
264	do. 1 "	2 75	
265	do. 1¼ "	4 00	
266	Bench Screws 2 "	4 50	
267	do. 2½ "	8 50	
168	do. long Jaw 2½ "	9 50	
227	Torus Bead . . To ⅞ inch		75
"	Do. " " 1 "		1 00
"	Do. " " 1¼ "		1 25

Table IV

COMPARISON OF H. CHAPIN'S PLANEMAKING PRODUCTION COSTS and INVOICE PRICES, 1849 and 1858

PLANE	1849						1858					
	Making	Wood	Irons	Incidental	Total	Add 2/3 Invoice	Making	Wood	Irons	Incidental	Total	Double Invoice
#115 26" Jointer double iron	.22	.12	.375	.1075	$0.8225	$1.37 $1.35	.16	.17	.285	.125	$0.74	$1.48 $1.45
#114 22" Fore double iron	.20	.09	.34	.095	$0.725	$1.21 $1.25	.14	.15	.285	.115	$0.69	$1.38 $1.35
#113 Jack double iron	.1675	.05	.305	.0775	$0.60	$1.00 $0.88	.125	.085	.23	.09	$0.53	$1.06 $1.00
#112 Smooth double iron	.14	.025	.26	.0677	$0.4925	$0.82 $0.80	.125	.03	.23	.075	$0.46	$0.92 $0.90
#196 Quirk Ovalo 1"	.17	.035	.06	.0425	$0.30	$0.50 $0.58	.17	.03	.055	.035	$0.29	$0.58 $0.60
#123 Bead 1"	.22	.03	.06	.045	$0.355	$0.51 $0.60	.18	.025	.05	.035	$0.29	$0.58 $0.60
#200 Square Rabbit 1"	.17	.02	.08	.0475	$0.3175	$0.515 $0.46	.14	.015	.065	.035	$0.255	$0.51 $0.50
Total all above Seven Planes	$1.287	.37	$1.48	.4775	$3.615	$5.92 $5.10		.505	$1.20	.51	$3.25	$6.40
Per Cent of Total Cost	35.6	10.2	40.9	13.2	100.0		32.0	15.5	36.8	15.7	100.0	
#243 1st Rate Screw Arm Plow	$1.08	.255	$1.38	.405	$3.12	$5.20 $5.10	.90	.17	$1.05	.32	$2.44	$4.88 $5.10

Note: Above Incidental cost is overhead figured at 15% costs in 1849 and 20% in 1858

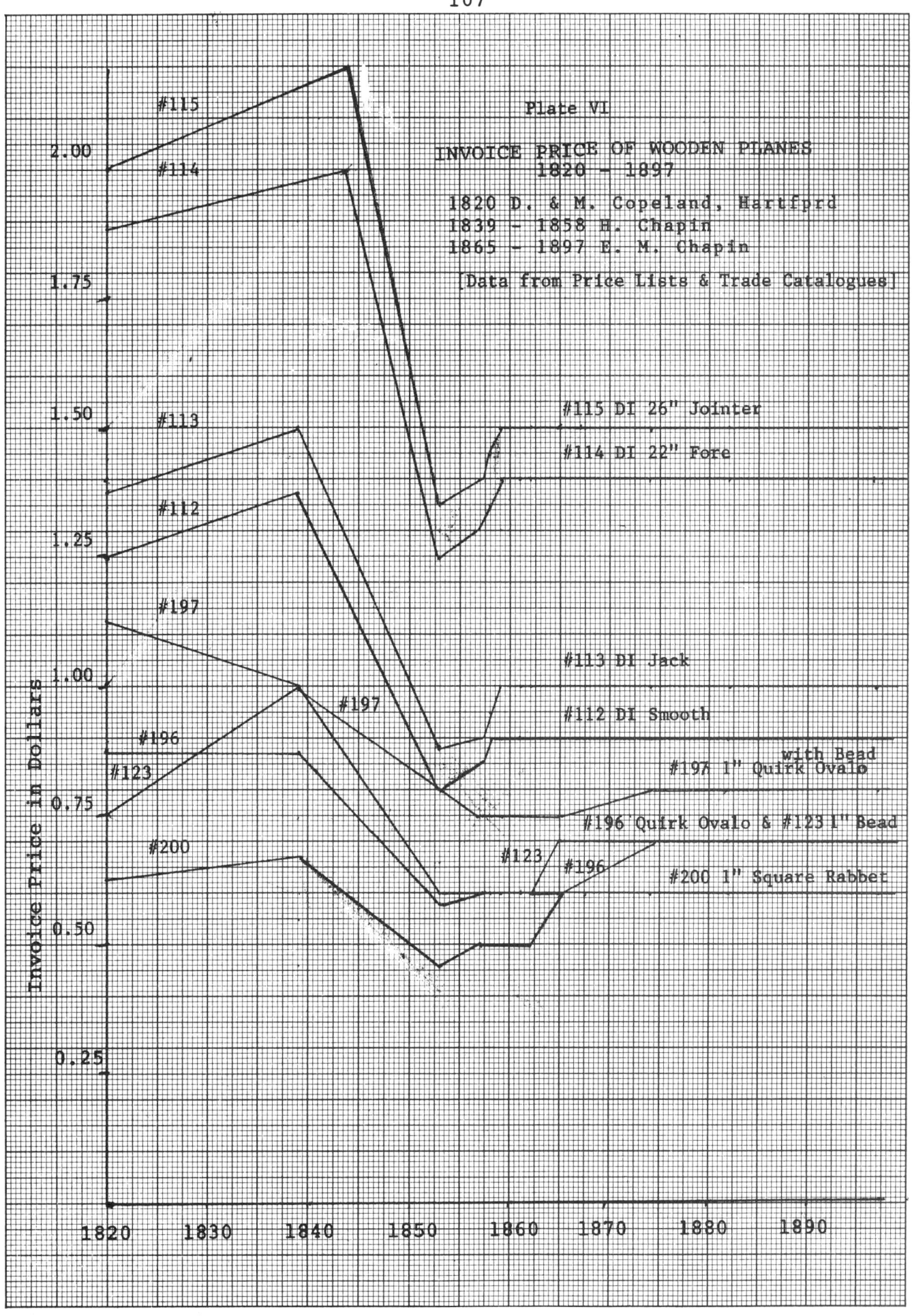

Plate VI

INVOICE PRICE OF WOODEN PLANES
1820 – 1897

1820 D. & M. Copeland, Hartford
1839 – 1858 H. Chapin
1865 – 1897 E. M. Chapin

[Data from Price Lists & Trade Catalogues]

#115 DI 26" Jointer
#114 DI 22" Fore
#113 DI Jack
#112 DI Smooth
#197 1" Quirk Ovalo with Bead
#196 Quirk Ovalo & #123 1" Bead
#200 1" Square Rabbet

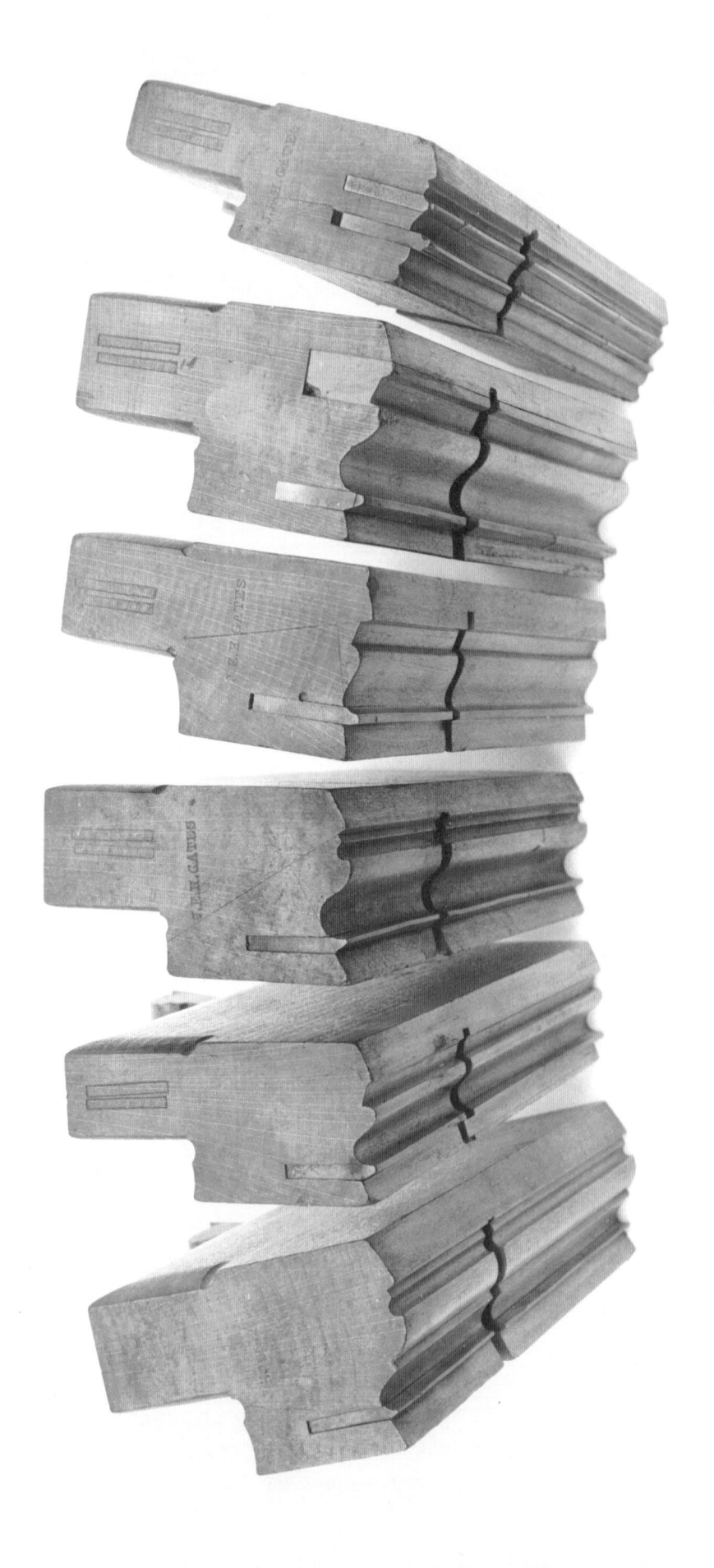

Fig. 35. — Complex Moulding Planes Made for or by D. Copeland or M. Copeland Previous to 1830

109

Fig. 36. - Moulding Planes with Imprint of D. Copeland, Manufactured Previous to 1830

Fig. 37. - Complex Moulding Planes with imprint of M. Copeland, manufactured after 1830

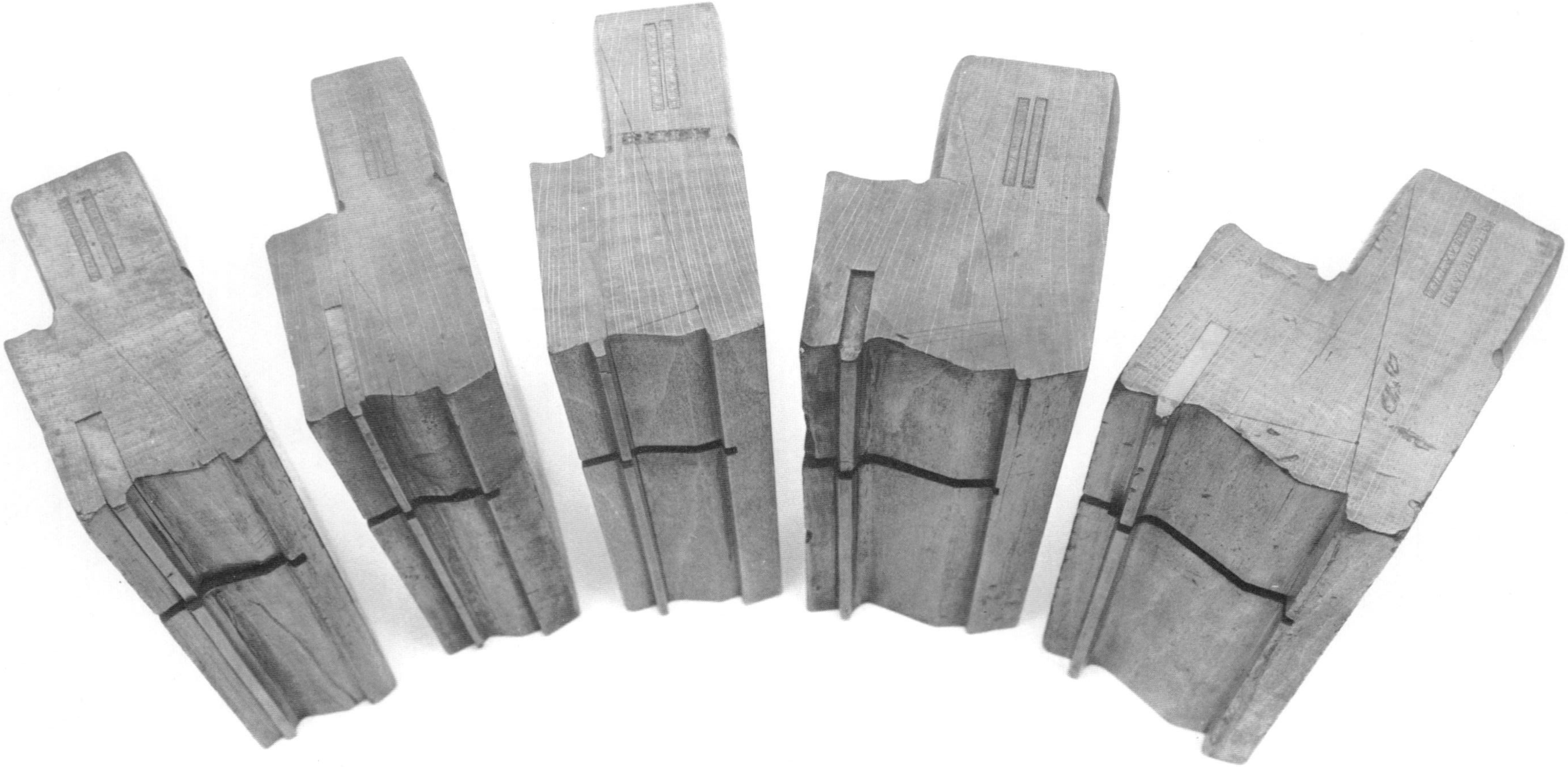

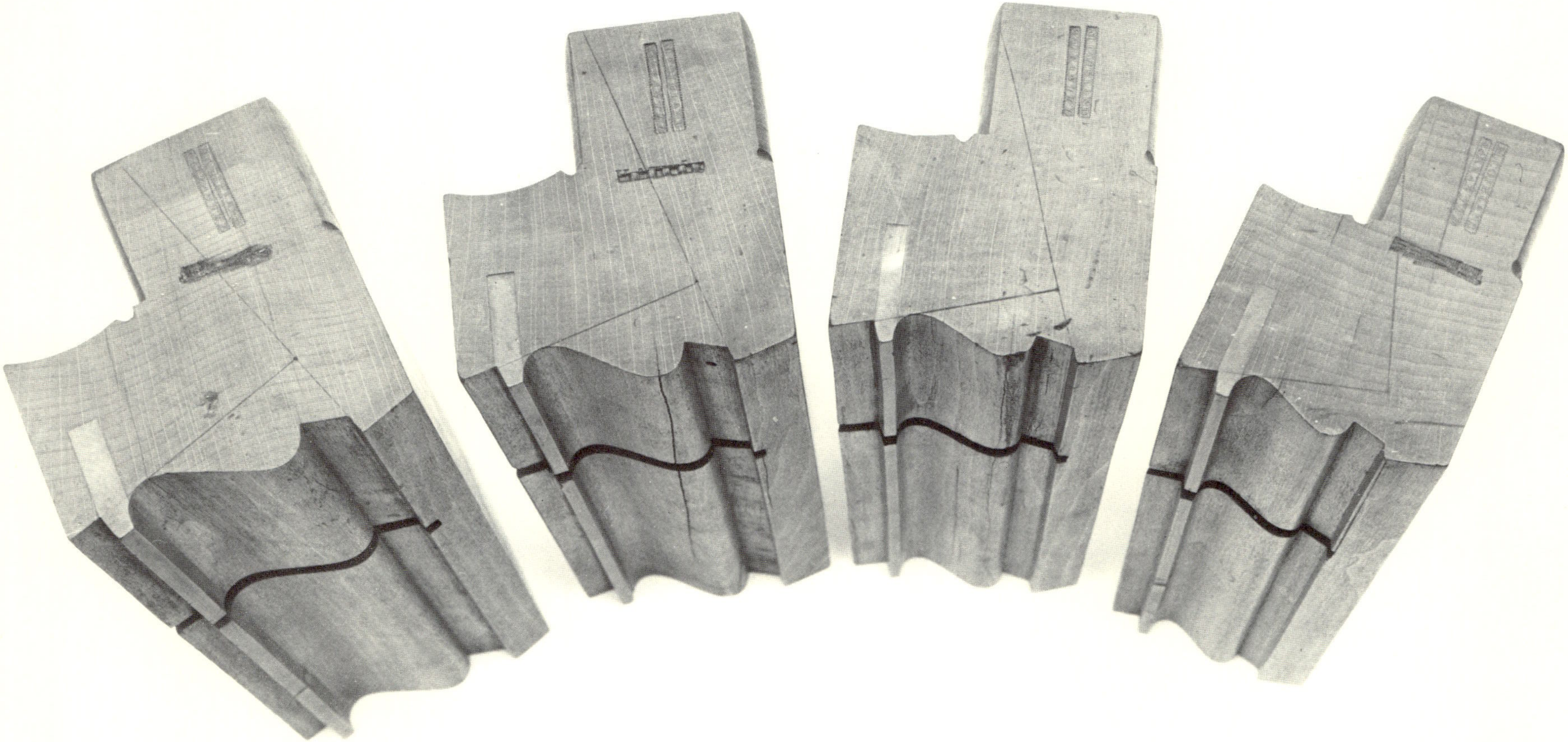

Fig. 38. - Complex Moulding Planes with imprint of M. Copeland, manufactured after 1830

Slip beads [see Vol. I, p. 112] were offered by Chapin in sizes up to 1 inch, as number 225. A ¼ inch slip bead with the H. Chapin Union Factory imprint is illustrated in Fig. 15. These were also offered 1839-1865, if not earlier, with corner dovetail boxing, according to No. 226 in Chapin catalogues.[16] While the practice of using slips was probably an English design, the fact that both Chapin and Greenfield tool Company in New England offered such planes at least through 1865 demonstrates that this style of plane was made outside of the Baltimore area, probably in considerable quantities. (See Fig. 39)

Fig. 39. - No. 225 H. Chapin/ UNION FACTORY , ¼ in. Slip Bead Plane
[Collection of Richard E. Hay]

Only two new varieties of planes were offered in 1853 that were not previously listed in 1839. These were the No. 119 Miter plane in solid boxwood and the self regulating screw arm sash plane, Nos. 212 & 213. This latter type of plane is noted in Vol. I, p. 251.[17]

Differences in the irons for bench planes are noted between 1839 and 1853. In the former the less expensive grade was made from German Steel and the best grade from "cast steel." In 1853 the less expensive grade was "common cast steel" and the more expensive "best cast steel." At that date German steel referred to shear steel, forged from faggots of blister steel without direct melting, a grade imported from Sheffield. A German immigrant by the name of Wilhelm Bertram had developed this process of forge welding steel early in the 18th century working at Tyneside.[18] This material was used by cutlers. Since his trade mark was a pair of crossed shears, such material became known as "shear steel." Cast steel, originally developed by Benjamin Huntsman working near Sheffield, involved forging ingots cast from direct melting of blister steel.[19] This process resulted in greater uniformity and was generally an improvement compared to "shear or German" steel. As improvements developed in making cast steel, the practice of forging faggots from "blister" steel became obsolete. The iron used in cast steel was imported from Sweden, some from Russia. The more refined and higher purity iron demanded high prices and was used to produce the "best" grade of cast steel. Less select iron was used for making "common" cast steel.

The first industrial United States Census of 1850 provides an insight to the operation of Hermon Chapin's Union Factory.[20] (see Vol. I, Table III, p. 23). This noted that this firm was capitalized at $28,500; had a monthly payment of $1000 for 40 hands; operated by water power; had annual sales of $30,000; consumed 10 tons of Boxwood valued at $800, $1500 of beechwood, used $5300 of plane irons, 3 tons of sheet brass [rules] and $4200 of other materials. The 1850 US Census of New Hartford provides a listing of those employed at planemaking, rulemaking and tool makers. The only other tool factory then at New Hartford was operated by William Warner, who had 5 employees. This listing is shown in Table V.

Table V

NAMES and AGES of PERSONS EMPLOYED at TOOLMAKING at NEW HARTFORD, CONNECTICUT, 1850 [Data from 1850 US CENSUS, Conn. State Library, Hartford]

NAMES and AGES of PERSONS EMPLOYED at TOOLMAKING
NEW HARTFORD, CONNECTICUT, 1850
[Data from US Census, Conn. State Library, Hartford]

PLANEMAKING	RULEMAKING	TOOL MAKING
Samuel Frazier, 29	Ashak Drake, 41	Carlos Smith, 53
James Wiswell, 26	Lorenzo Stephens, 39	Benjamin Loomis, 42
Hiram Driggs, 25	Edward Gaines, 39	William Warner, 41
James Crew, 23	Ralph Seymour, 36	Clinton Edgerton, 37
Ruel Rice, 22	William Nash, 30	Orange Marshall, 36
Eliphate Frazier, 22	Josiah Allen, 28	Horace Deming, 35
Charles Nash, 21	Warren Drake, 24	Walter Canfield, 33
	William Baldwin, 24	Enoch Gaines, 32
Total - 7	Spencer Douglas, 23	Stephen Frazier, 30
	Earl Tuttle, 22	Adna Thompson, 28
	Enoch Case, 22	Oswall Andrews, 28
	Frederick Beckwith, 22	Samuel Allen, 27
	Elmer Means, 21	William Smart, 27
	William Draper, 20	Horatio Small, 26
	Delos Stephens, 18	Charles Thompson, 26
	Hiram Loomis, 16	Everett Wilcox, 25
		Eliphalet Frazier, 25
	Total - 16	Levi Griswold, 24
		Joseph Spencer, 24
		Hiram Smith, 22
		Solon Rust, 17
		Alonzo Williams, 16
		Norman Rust, 16
		Total - 23

Average Age of 46 above = 27½ years

Note: The 1850 US Census - Products of Industry Section for New Hartford, Connecticut noted 40 male employes at H.Chapin's UNION FACTORY and 5 at WARNER & DRIGGS. These were the only tool establishments then noted at this town. This total of 45 agrees with the total of 46 listed above, as William Warner, noted as a Toolmaker was actually the principal proprietor of WARNER & DRIGGS. Hermon Chapin, then 51, was the propietor of the UNION FACTORY and not listed in the above

Those listed above at Toolmaking were probably planemakers, as well as gaugemakers and other tools, while those at rulemaking were only involved in that trade.

Hermon Chapin made an announcement July 1, 1855 that he had expanded his operation at Pine Meadow and solicitated orders for planes, etc. [Plate VII]. By that date rail facilities had come to Collinsville, about five miles south. According to his terms he then offered a 25% discount with an additional 5% for cash.

Plate VII - 1855 Broadside Issued by H.Chapin

UNION FACTORY
RULES AND PLANES.

The undersigned would respectfully present to his customers his thanks for past favors, hoping they have been mutual, and would solicit a continuance of their orders.

Having made extensive repairs and additions to his works, he is now prepared to fill orders with dispatch, and he trusts with entire satisfaction to those who may favor him with their orders the coming season.

HERMON CHAPIN,
Manufacturer, Pine Meadow, Conn.

TERMS.

25 per cent. discount on 6 months time.

5 " " less for cash.

3 " " additional discount to a purchaser of one thousand dollars worth in one season of six consecutive months.

All Goods delivered at the Collinsville Depot.

No charge for Boxes.

January 1st, 1855.

On November 1, 1857 Hermon Chapin made an inventory of his assets. This data is presented in Table VI and provides a definitive indication of the distribution of his wealth. He had acquired by purchase from the Kelloggs their foundry, machine shop, and the "old brick shop" all of which were adjacent to his plane and rule shop. Additionally he had purchased the Munson sawmill at Barkhamstead, the next town north of New Hartford. This also included a lathe and shingle mill.

The machinery in the plane and rule shop consisted of power driven circular saws for sizing stock into production blanks, but the shaping and finishing of planes was accomplished using hand tools. The brass foundry enabled production of depth stops for dado and plow planes.

The plane lumber consisted of stock, seasoning by air drying, stored in various sheds. At least three years seasoning was required. Kiln drying with hot air was not introduced until after 1865. This timber had been rived into "splits" from quarter sawn logs, cut to specific lengths and classified as this stage for ultimate end usage. A partial inventory of such material stored in the North Chamber reveals the manner of such classification. (Table VII)

From the above data is apparent that each plane was sawn from an individual "split out." However, at least two moulding planes were obtained from a split. When William Warner, who had been in business at New Hartford since 1850, discontinued his firm in 1857, he sold his lumber stock to H. Chapin according to the following agreement. (Table VIII)

The title page of Hermon Chapin's 1858 *CATALOGUE* is shown as Plate VIII. Page 7 from an undated Chapin catalogue without title page, but believed to have been earlier, possibly 1857, is shown as Plate IX. The "clock plane" noted on the top line is believed to have been similar to a conventional jack plane, only 18 inches in length, used by this trade for making shelf clock cases.

Eight pages of cost data from H. Chapin's account records follow. It was from this data that the price of each plane was figured which appeared in the 1858 and 1859 *CATALOGUES*. These were essentially the same, except in 1859 five cents was added to the invoice price of some bench planes. An estimate was entered for the cost of making, the cost of the wood blank and the cost of the plane irons. After totaling these three costs, 20 per cent was added to provide for incidental or overhead costs. Doubling the total of these four costs provided a working guide to estimate an invoice price that would enable a suitable profit after discount. With slight adjustments these invoice prices prevailed for the remainder of the 19th century.

This data provides a valuable source for determining the actual production at that date with the assumption that the average skilled planemaker then received $1.25 per day for 10 hours of labor. The relationship between the costs of a plane and the time required to make it and the number that can be made in 10 hours is shown graphically in Plate X and in Table IX.

Comparisons of production costs and data for figuring the invoice prices between 1849 and 1858 is presented in Table X. It will be noted that the making costs in 1858 had decreased for the seven listed planes by 25 cents (approximately 20%). This may have indicated some automated machinery was used by the later date making bench planes where the differences were greatest. However this reduction in cost was offset by almost the same amount of increased costs in wood. Reduced costs of the plane irons lowered the total costs for 1858, but increased sale discounts resulted in higher invoice prices. The entire July 1859 Price List of products manufactured at the Union Factory, consisting of 12 pages, is presented as Plate XI.

Edward M. Chapin, after completing his formal education at Suffield Academy in 1851 at the age of 18, entered the employment of his father's shop as superintendent. From that time on he assumed full responsibility for running the factory, his father acting in advisory capacity. Edward had spent many hours during his youth working at this factory and was undoubtedly familiar with all operations. In 1860 Hermon decided to share part ownership of the Union Factory with his sons. On October 1, 1860 he agreed to have his sons, Edward and Philip, purchase one tenth interest in the business forming a new firm of H. Chapin & Sons. The terms of this agreement are presented in Table XI. Later in 1862 he sold another tenth of the business to his other son, George, retaining seven tenths. Edward devoted full time managing the firm. Further details concerning this operation will be presented in a subsequent chapter.

Table VI

INVENTORY OF HERMON CHAPIN'S ASSETS - November 1, 1857

I. Residential or Farm Property   [$31,541.00] (29.4%)

Three lots of land in Potter County, Pennsylvania, 453 acres @ $4.25	$566.00
Richardson Lot at Barkhamsted, 26 acres [Connecticut]	$1250.00
Negro Town Land, 55 acres [New Hartford]	1100.00
Brigman House and 2 Lots	2000.00
Six Dwelling Houses & Gardens	4500.00
Mountain Land in Pine Meadow, 60 acres	1000.00
Perkins House @ $1400 [Mortgage out $800]	600.00
Lot south	375.00
Red Barn & Lot	2500.00
Meadow Lot south of Allens	1000.00
Lot south of the Dam	450.00
Park	500.00
E.M. Chapin House & Lot	1350.00
Gothic House & Lot	1350.00
E. Moses House & Lot	750.00
Lots North of the Parsonage	525.00
Lot North of F. White	450.00
Meadow Land South & rear of Church	1250.00
Case Boarding House & Barn	1400.00
Homestead, Barns and Gardens [H.Chapin's Residence]	3500.00
Geo. Seymour House	500.00
Warren Drake	350.00
Enoch Gaines	225.00
Mrs. Glasson	200.00
L. Linley	350.00
H.N. Smith	350.00
W.E. Smith	500.00
Lester Phelps	500.00
Albert Phelps	500.00
Phelps Boarding House	1000.00
2 Double House	900.00
Rye Lot	250.00

II. Industrial Land and Buildings   [$29,600.00] (27.6%)

Munson Mill, Barkhamsted, 80 acres, 2 Dwelling House, Barns, Saw Mill, Grist Mill, Lathe & Shingle Mill & Tools for the Same	8000.00
Store & Barn, Furniture,&c.	2500.00
Old Brick Shop with 2 Shares of Water Power	2500.00
Machine Shop with 2 Shares of Water Power	4500.00
Foundry, Patterns, Flasks and 2 Shares of Water Power	2000.00
Brass Foundry & Grounds	350.00
Plane & Rule Shop with 6 Shares of Water Power	9750.00

III. Industrial Machinery and Tools   [$7,450.00] (6.9%)

Machinery in the Machine Shop	3000.00
Machinery for the Plane Shop	1200.00
Tools for the same	750.00
Tools in the Finishing Room [Rules]	550.00
Machinery in Joint & Framing Rooms [Rules]	1500.00
Stoves & Pipes	200.00
Force Pump & Hose	250.00

Table VI (Continued)

IV. Industrial Stock   [$22,575.00]   (21.0%)

Lumber at Munson Mill, Barkhamsted	$175.00
Iron, Wrought & Unwrought & Old	1500.00
Brass Joints & Wire [Rule Shop]	1350.00
Plane Wood	3000.00
Lumber	200.00
Boxwood, Sawed & Unsawed	800.00
Zebra, Mahogany & Rosewood	400.00
Screw Timber	150.00
Hardware	3000.00
Planes, Gauges & Levels	5000.00
Rules	5500.00
Crow Bars	750.00
Wrought Scrap Iron	650.00
Coal	100.00

V. Personal Property   [$1,680.00]   (1.5%)

Oxen, Cows & Calves	225.00
Hogs & Poultry	50.00
Hay & Grain & Vegetables	475.00
Wood	400.00
Ploughs, Straw Cutters & C	530.00

VI. Mortgages & Bills on Account   [$14.575.00]   (13.6%)

Mortgage on Mrs. Baker	150.00
" " N. Griswold	600.00
" " G. Edgerton	125.00
" " Mrs. Guy	200.00
" " Mrs. Betts	700.00
" " J. Gould	500.00
Due from Warren Drake	200.00
Protested $ Poor Notes $3500.00	1750.00
Bills on Account Due from Merchants	10000.00
Total Assets	$107,000.00

Table VII

INVENTORY OF PLANE LUMBER STORED IN NORTH CHAMBER

End Use	Number of Splits	Length in inches*	Value in cents of each Split	Inventory Value, Dollars
Long Jointer	836	31	12	$100.32
Short Jointer	238	25	8	19.04
Jack	243	19	4	21.72
Moulding	520	21	3	15.00
Handled Match	856	15	4	34.24

[* Data from another source of H.Chapin's Records, CHS]

Table VIII

Agreement between Hermon Chapin and William Warner March 18, 1857

New Hartford, Conn. .... 1850.

M ....

[1850 Billhead of firm Warner & Driggs]

Bought of **WARNER & DRIGGS,**

Manufacturers of Bench & Moulding Planes, Grooving Plows, Bench & Hand Screws, Gauges, &c.

This agreement made by and between Hermon Chapin one the one part and William Warner on the other part. Witnesseth that the said Warner agrees to sell to the said Chapin all the Plane Wood he has and now owns at this date at the following for good sound wood as follows: -

Long Jointer Wood, Eleven cents each	.11
Fore Plane Wood, Nine cents each	.09
Jack Plane Wood, Four and a half cents each	.04½
Raising Plane Wood, Eight and a half cents, each	.08½
Moulding Plane Wood, Four and a half cents, each	.04½
Handled Match Plane Wood, Four and a half cents	.04¼

For Timber that is not well sawed, one cent less on Jointer & Fore Planes, one half cent less on other kinds.

Payable by the first of April next

Pine Meadow
March 18, 1857

Wm. Warner
Hermon Chapin

[Collection of Documents New Hartford Historical Society]

Table X

COST ANALYSIS of 1849 and 1858 PLANES MADE by H. CHAPIN
[Based on Data of Seven Planes Listed in Table IV]

	1849	1858
Cost of Making Planes	35.6%	32.0%
Cost of Wood	10.2%	15.5%
Cost of Irons	41.0%	36.8%
Overhead or Incidental Cost	13.2%	15.7%
Invoice Price	$5.92	$6.40
Wholesale Price	$4.74 (20% Disc.)	$4.48 (30% Disc)
H. Chapin's Cost	$3.615	$3.255
H. Chapin's Profit	$1.125 (31.1% Cost)	$1.225 (37.6% Cost)

PRICE LIST.   7

Miscellaneous Planes.

		Price each.
Invoice No's.		
	Clock Plane, Single, 18 inch,	$0.85
	Clock Plane, Double, 18 inch,	1.30
	Gutter Plane,	.90
	Pump Plane,	1.20

10 per cent. less discount for English Irons.

Moulding Planes.

No.	Description	Price
122	Astragals, to 3/4 inch,	.40
	do to 1 inch,	.50
	do to 1 1/4 inch,	.58
123	Beads, to 3/8 inch,	.45
	do to 1 inch,	.60
	do to 1 1/4 inch,	.85
	Beads, with Handles,	1.75
124	Beads, Double Boxed, to 3/4 inch,	.55
	do do to 1 inch,	.55
	do do to 1 1/4 inch,	.70
125	Beads, Solid Boxed, Dovetailed, to 3/4 inch,	.90
	do do do to 1 inch,	.55
	do do do to 1 1/4 inch,	.67
126	Base and Band Moulding, per inch,	.88
	do do Handle,	.70
127	Bed Moulding, Handle, do	.85
128	Back Ogees, to 3/4 inch,	.70
	do to 1 inch,	.50
	do to 1 1/4 inch,	.55
129	Back Ogees, with Bead, to 3/4 inch,	.62
	do do to 1 inch,	.55
	do do to 1 1/4 inch,	.60
130	Belections, to 3/4 inch,	.67
	do to 1 inch,	.55
	do to 1 1/4 inch,	.60
131	Cock Beads, to 3/4 inch,	.70
132	do Boxed, to 3/4 inch,	.42
133	Center Beads, to 3/4 inch,	.48
134	Center Beads, Solid Boxed, Dovetailed, to 3/4 inch,	.56
	do do do per inch,	.62
135	Cornice Planes,	.64
	Cabinet Ogee Planes,	.78
136	Dadoes,	.84
137	do with Stop, to 1 inch,	.75
138	do with Side Stop, to 1 inch,	.85
139	do with Screw Stop, to 1 inch,	.95
140	Door Planes, to 1 inch,	1.45
141	do Boxed,	.75
142	Draw Planes,	.85
143	do Boxed,	.50
144	do Moving Fence,	.60
145	do do Boxed,	.75
		.90

Plate VIII - Page 7 from Undated H. Chapin Catalogue

CATALOGUE

AND

INVOICE PRICES

OF

RULES, PLANES, GUAGES,

&c., &c., &c.,

MANUFACTURED BY

HERMON CHAPIN,

UNION FACTORY,

Pine Meadow, Conn.

1858.

WINSTED:
PRESS OF THE WINSTED HERALD.
1858.

Plate VII - Front Cover to 1858 Catalogue

1858 Inventory of Cost of Stock

Invoice No.		Making	Wood	Iron	20 pr ct Incidentals	Amount	Invoice
	Bench Planes Each						
100	Single Smooth 6 S	11	2	11	5	29	50
101	" Jack "	11	7½	11	5½	35	60
102	" Fore 21 inch "	12	13½	13	7½	46	85
"	" " 22 " "	12	14	14½	8½	49	90
103	" Jointer 26 " "	14	16	14½	9	53½	1 00
"	" " 28 " "	14	17	16	10	57	1 10
"	" " 30 " "	16	18	17½	10½	62	1 20
104	" Smooth Best C.S.	11	2½	11½	5	30	56
"	" " Handle	30	8	11½	9½	59	1 40
105	" Jack "	11	8	11½	6	36½	65
106	" Fore 21 inch "	12	14	14	8	48	90
"	" " 22 " "	12	14½	15¾	8¾	51	95
107	" Jointer 26 " "	14	16½	16	9½	56	1 [illegible]
"	" " 28 " "	14	17½	17½	10	59	1 1[illegible]
"	" " 30 " "	16	18½	19	10½	64	1 25
108	Double Smooth 6 S	12½	2½	22	7	44	80
109	" Jack "	12½	8	22	8	50½	90
110	" Fore 21 inch "	14	14	24	10	62	1 15
"	" " 22 " "	14	14½	26½	11	66	1 25
111	" Jointer 26 " "	16	16½	26½	12	71	1 35
"	" " 28 " "	16	17½	28½	12½	74½	1 45
"	" " 30 " "	18	18½	32½	14	83	1 60
112	" Smooth Best C S	12½	3	23	7½	46	90
"	" " Handle "	32	8½	23	12½	76	1 65
113	" Jack "	12½	8½	23	9	53	1 00
114	" Fore 21 inch "	14	14½	26	11	65½	1 25
"	" " 22 " "	14	15	28½	11½	69	1 35
115	" Jointer 26 " "	16	17	28½	12½	74	1 45
"	" " 28 " "	16	18	31	13	78	1 55
	" " 30 " "	18	19	35	14	86	1 70
	Miscellaneous Planes Ea						
116	Single Smooth Box or Rosewood	18	25	11½	10½	65	1 30
"	" " Handle " "	36	50	11½	19½	1 17	2 1

1858 Inventory of Cost of Stock

Invoice No.		Making $ cts	Wood	Iron	Incidental	Amount $ cts	Invoice $ cts
117	Double Smooth Box or Rosewood	23	25	23	14	84	1 70
"	" " Handle "	40	50	23	22	1.35	3 00
118	Tooth Plane	14	2½	24	8	48½	90
119	Miter "	14	2½	10	5½	32	65
"	" " Box or Rosewood	18	25	10	11	64	1 25
120	Single Circular	16	2½	11½	6	36	70
121	Double "	18	2½	23	8½	52	1 00
	Toy Smooth Single	10	1½	9	4	24½	45
	" " Double	11½	1½	20	7	40	75
	" Jack Single	10	1½	9	5	30½	55
	" " Double	11½	1½	20	8	46	85
	Block Plane Single 18 inch	12	14½	15¾	8¾	51	95
	" " Double 18 "	14	14½	28½	11	68	1 35
	Gutter "	17	7	11½	7½	53	1 05
	Pump "	37	9	11½	11½	69	1 35
	Spar "	25	23½	11½	8	47	1 00
	Moulding Planes Ea						
122	Astragals to ¾ inch	11	1½	4	2½	19	40
"	" " 1 "	13	1½	4½	3	22	50
"	" " 1¼ "	15	2	5½	3½	26	58
123	Beads " ¾ "	13	2½	4	2½	22	45
"	" " 1 "	18	2½	5	3½	29	60
"	" " 1¼ "	30	3	6	6	45	90
"	" with Handle " 1½ "	60	12	11½	12½	96	1 90
124	" Double Boxed " ¾ "	15	2½	4	3½	26	55
"	" " " 1 "	20	3½	5	4½	33	70
"	" " " 1¼ "	32	4	6	6	48	95
125	Beads Solid Boxed Dovetailed ¼	15	4	4	3½	26½	55
"	" " " ½	18	4½	4½	4	31	67
"	" " " ¾	25	6	4½	5½	41	88
126	Base & Band Moulding per inch	20	1½	5¼	4	31	70
"	" " " Handle "	20	4	6	4½	34½	85
127	Bed Moulding " "	18	4	6	4	32	70

1858 Inventory of Cost of Stock

Invoice Nos.	Moulding Planes	Each	Making dols cts	Irons	Incidental 1st cost	Amount dol cts	Amount dol cts
128	Back Ogees	to ¾ inch	14 1½	4½	3	23	50
"	" "	" 1 "	16 2	5¼	3½	27	55
"	" "	" 1¼ "	18 2½	5¾	4	31	62
129	" " with Bead	" ¾ "	16 2½	4½	3½	26½	55
"	" " " "	" 1 "	18 3	5½	4	30½	61
"	" " " "	" 1¼ "	20 3½	5¾	4¼	33½	67
130	Belections	" ¾ "	16 2½	4½	3½	26½	55
"	"	" 1 "	18 3	5½	4	30½	60
"	"	" 1¼ "	20 3½	5¾	4½	33¾	70
131	Cock Beads		10 1	4	2	17	42
132	" " Boxed		13 2	4	3	22	48
133	Center "	to ⅜ inch	15 3	4	3½	25½	56
"	" "	" ¾ "	20 3½	4	4	31½	62
134	" " Solid Boxed & Dovetailed	" ⅜ "	17 3½	4	3½	28	64
"	" " " "	" ¾ "	25 5	4	5	39	78
135	Cornice Planes	per inch	20 3½	7½	4½	35½	84
"	Cabinet Ogee	"	20 3½	7½	4½	35½	84
136	Dadoes	to 1 inch	22 3	8	5	37	78
137	" with stop	" 1 "	27 3	8	5½	43½	85
138	" " Side stop	" 1 "	27 2	11	6	46	95
139	" " Screw	" 1 "	32 2	33	10	77	1.48
140	Door Planes		25 2	4	5½	36½	75
141	" " Boxed		31 4	4	6	44	88
142	Draw "		14 2	4	3	23	50
143	" " Boxed		20 4	4	4	32	60
144	" " Mooring Fence		24 2½	8	5	39½	75
145	" " " " Boxed		30 4	8	6½	48½	90
146	Filletster		25 3½	10	6	44½	95
147	" with Stop		31 3½	15	7½	57	1.20
148	" " Scut		34 3½	17	8	62½	1.35
149	" " " & Boxed		42 6	17	10	75	1.58
150	" " Screw Stop & cut "		52 6	39	14½	1.11½	2.50
"	" " " " Solid Box & Rose		75 25	39	21	1.60	4.00
151	" " Arms Stop and cut		50 7	19	11½	87½	2.00

1858 Inventory of Cost of Stock

Invoice No.	Mouldings	Making Sto cts Wood	Irons	Incidental 15 pr ct	Amount Dollars cts	Invoice Dollars cts
152	Fillitster with arms Stop cut & Boxed	1.10 9½	19	13	1.11½	2.25
153	" " Screw " "	70 25	19	17	1.31	2.65
154	" " " Screw " "	80 25	42	22	1.69	3.70
"	" " " Solid Box or Rose	1.12 45	42	28	2.15	5.75
155	Grecian Ovolo to ¾ inch	14 3½	4	3	23½	55
"	" " " 1 "	15 3	4½	3½	25	60
"	" " " 1¼ "	17 3½	5½	4	30	65
"	" " " 1½ "	19 4	7	4½	34½	75
156	" " with Handle per inch	16 5	6	4	31	65
157	Grecian Ovolo & Fillet to 1 "	18 3	4½	4	29½	70
"	" " " " " 1¼ "	20 3½	5¾	4½	34	75
"	" " " " " 1½ "	22 4	7	5	38	80
"	" " " " " 1¾ "	24 4½	8	5½	42	90
"	" " " " with Handle per inch	17 5½	6	4	32½	75
158	Grecian Ovolo & Bead to 1 inch	20 3½	5½	4½	33½	75
"	" " " " " 1¼ "	22 4	5¾	5	36¾	80
"	" " " " " 1½ "	24 4½	7	5½	41	87
"	" " " " " 1¾ "	26 5	8	6	45	100
159	" " " " Handle 2 "	36 13	13	10	72	1.50
"	" " " " " 2½ "	45 15½	15	11	86½	2.00
160	Grecian Ogee with Bead or Fillet 1 "	17 2½	5½	4	29	65
"	" " " " " 1¼ "	18 3	5¾	4	31	70
"	" " " " " 1½ "	20 3½	7	4½	35	75
"	" " " " " 1¾ "	22 4	8	5	39	85
"	" " " " with Handle per	17 4½	6	4	31½	65
161	Gothic Bead with one bead	20 2½	5	4	31½	70
162	" " " two " Boxed	34 3½	9	5½	52	1.05
163	Halving Plane	10 1	4	2½	17½	38
164	" " Plated	14 1	5	3	23	48
165	" " with Handle	16 3	4	3½	26	56
166	" " " & Plated	20 3	5	4	32	66
167	Hollows & Rounds No 1 to 12 per pair	18 3	8	4½	33½	70
"	" " " " 13 " 18 "	23 4	11	5½	43½	85
"	" " " " 19 " 24 "	28 6	14	7	55	1.10

Inventory of Cost of Stock

Invoice No	Moulding Planes	Making D cts	Wood	Irons	Incidental 15 p ct	Amount Invoice Sole cts	D cts
168	Table Hollows & Rounds per pair	24	3	8	5—	40	90
169	" " " Boxed "	40	12	8	9	69	150
170	" " " with Fence "	38	4	9	5—	54	140
171	Match Planes to ½ inch per pair or dbl	30	3	14	7	54	105
172	" " Plated ½ " "	40	3	15	9	67	130
173	" " To 1 " "	30	4	15	7½	56½	112
174	" " Plated " 1 " "	40	4	17	9	70	137
175	" " with Handles to 1¼ inch per pair	60	9	19	13	101	190
176	" " Plated " " 1¼ " "	72	9	21	15—	118	220
177	" " for Plank "	40	12	28	12	92	185
178	" " " Plated "	54	12	32	15—	113	225
179	" " Moving Fence "	50	13	34	14½	111½	220
180	" " " Plated "	62	13	38	17	130	260
181	" " with Arms "	75	14	28	17½	134½	270
182	" " " Plated "	88	14	32	20	154	310
183	" " Screw " "	82	29	28	21	160	335
184	" " " Plated "	95	29	32	23½	179½	375
185	Nosings with Handles or two Irons	18	6	11	5—	40	85
186	Hand Rail Plane	31	7	13	8½	64½	140
187	Ovolos to ¾ inch	14	2	4	3	23	42
"	" " 1 "	15	2	4½	3½	25	50
"	" " 1¼ "	16	3½	5¾	4	28	56
188	Ovolos with Bead " ¾ "	18	3	4½	4	29½	60
"	" " " 1 "	19	3	5½	4	31½	65
"	" " " 1¼ "	21	3½	5¾	4½	35	70
189	Panel Plane Cast Steel	30	7½	13	7½	58	115
190	" " without "	37	7½	15	9	68½	140
191	" " moving Fence "	40	8	17	10	75	150
192	" " " " S Cut "	46	8	19	11	84	170
193	2R Oges to ¾ inch	15	2½	4½	3½	25½	58
"	" " To 1 "	16	3	5½	4	28½	60
"	" " " 1¼ "	17	3½	5¾	4	30	67
194	2R Oges with Bead " ¾ "	18	3½	4½	4	29	60
"	" " " " 1 "	19	3	5½	4	31½	65

Inventory of Cost of Stock

Invoice No	Moulding Planes	Each	Making Dols cts	Wood	Irons	Incidental 15 percent	Amount Dols cts		Invoice Dols cts	
194	2k Ogees with Bead	to 1¼ inch	20	3½	5¾	4½		34		75
195	Reeding Plane	" ⅜ "	20	4½	4	4		32½		65
"	" "	" ¾ "	22	5	4	4½		35½		80
196	2k Ovolo	" ¾ "	16	2½	4½	3½		26½		55
	"	" 1 "	17	3	6½	3½		29		60
	"	" 1¼ "	20	3½	5¾	4½		34		70
197	2k Ovolo with Bead	" ¾ "	21	3½	4½	4½		33½		68
"	" "	" 1 "	23	4	5½	5		37½		75
"	" "	" 1¼ "	25	4½	5¾	5		40		85
198	Raising Plane	per inch	18	3½	16	6		43½		85
	" " Dbl Iron		23	3½	30	8½		65	1	20
199	" " Boxed	"	20	4	16	6		46		90
	Extra for Cut		8		2	1		11		25
200	Rabbet Planes Square	to 1 inch	14	1½	6½	3½		26½		50
	" " "	" 1¼ "	16	2	7½	4		29½		58
	" " "	" 1½ "	18	2	9	4½		33½		68
201	" " " Dbl Boxed	" 1 "	28	5½	6½	5½		45½	1	00
"	" " " "	" 1¼ "	30	6	7½	6½		50	1	08
"	" " " "	" 1½ "	32	6	9	7		54	1	18
202	" " Skew	" 1 "	16	1½	6½	3½		27½		55
"	" " "	" 1¼ "	18	2	7½	4		31½		64
"	" " "	" 1½ "	18	2	9	4½		33½		70
"	" " "	" 1¾ "	20	2½	9½	5		37		76
"	" " "	" 2 "	20	2½	11	5		38½		85
"	" " "	" 2¼ "	20	3	12	5		40		90
203	" " " Boxed & Cut	" 1 "	30	3½	8½	6½		48½		95
"	" " " "	" 1¼ "	32	4	9½	7		52½	1	05
"	" " " "	" 1½ "	32	4	"	7		54	1	10
"	" " " "	" 1¾ "	34	4½	11½	7½		57½	1	15
"	" " " "	" 2 "	34	4½	13	8		59½	1	20
"	" " " "	" 2¼ "	34	5	14	8		61	1	25
204	" " " with Handle and cut	" 2 "	30	7	13	7½		57½	1	30
205	" " " & 2 cuts	" 2½ "	38	8	18	10		74	1	65
206	Sash Plane 1 Iron		16	2½	7	4		29½		58
207	" " " Boxed		26	6½	7	6		45		88

1858 Inventory of Cost of Stock

Invoice No	Moulding Planes Each	Making Dol cts	Wood	Irons	Incidentals 15 per ct	Amount Dol cts	Invoice Doll cts
208	Sash Plane 2 Irons	22	2½	9	5	.38½	.85
209	" " " Boxed	32	1½	9	7	.54½	1.15
210	" " Double	30	2½	13	7	.52½	1.10
211	" " " Boxed	40	1½	13	7	.68½	1.40
212	" " Screw Arms	33	15	9	8½	.65½	1.30
"	" " " Self Regulating	49	18	9	11½	.87½	2.20
213	" " " Boxed	43	19	9	10½	.81½	1.60
"	" " " " Self Reg-	59	22	9	13½	1.03½	2.50
214	" " " Handle	83	22	9	17	1.31	2.75
215	" " " " Boxed	95	26	9	19½	1.40	3.15
"	" " " " Solid Box or Wood	1 20	40	7	24	1.85	4.50
	Templets Gauges & Prickers Ea	4	½	¼	¼	.5	.12
216	Sash Coping Plane	15	1	4	3	.23	.50
217	" " Boxed	23	2½	4	4½	.34	.70
218	Sash Fillister Screw Arms	67	16	6	13½	1.02½	2.00
219	" " " Screw Stop	76	16	38	38	1.48	3.00
220	Scotia to ¾ inch	13	1½	4½	3	.22	.44
"	" 1 "	14	1½	5½	3	.24	.50
"	" 1¼ "	16	2	5¾	3½	.27	.56
221	Scotia with Bead " ¾ "	16	1½	4½	3½	.25½	.56
"	" " " 1 "	17	1½	5½	3½	.27½	.60
"	" " " 1¼ "	19	2	5¾	4	.31	.70
222	Snipe Bills per pair	30	6	8	7	.51	1.10
223	" , Half Boxed "	46	8	8	9½	.71½	1.50
224	Side Rabbet Planes	36	2	8	7	.53	1.18
225	Slip Beads to ¾ inch	17	2½	4½	3½	.27½	.60
"	" " " 1 "	22	3	5½	4½	.35	.75
226	" " Cor Dovetailed Boxed " ¾ "	24	4½	4½	3½	.36½	.75
"	" " " " 1 "	30	5	5½	6	.46½	1.00
227	Torus Beads " ¾ "	13	2½	4½	3	.23	.60

Inventory of Cost of Stock

1858

Invoice No	Grooving Plows	Each	Making Doll cts	Wood	Irons	Invoiceles	Amount Doll cts	Price ₤ s d
228	Plows 4th rate Slide or Screw Arms		50	5	75	19½	1.50	3.00
229	" " Plated " " "		58	5	77	21	1.61	3.20
230	" " Boxed " " "		58	8	75	21	1.62	3.20
231	" 3d rate " " "		62	5	77	21	1.65½	3.40
232	" " Plated " " "		71	5	79	23	1.77	3.60
233	" " Boxed " " "		70	8	77	23	1.78	3.60
234	" 2d rate " " "		76	5	105	28	2.14	4.50
235	" " Plated " " "		84	5	107	29	2.25½	4.70
236	" " Boxed " " "		84	8	105	29	2.26½	4.70
237	" " Boxwood Screw Arms Handle		112	20	99	30	2.61	5.75
238	" " " " " " Boxd		110	23	99	35	2.67	5.95
239	" 1st rate " " " "		118	23	105	37	2.83	6.25
240	" " " " " Boxwd Hds		152	67	105	49	3.73	8.50
241	" 2d Boxwd Screw Arm		80	17	99	29	2.25	4.60
242	" " " " " & Boxed		88	21	99	31	2.38	4.80
243	" 1st rate " " " "		91	17	105	32	2.44	5.10
244	" " " " " & Boxed		98	21	105	33½	2.56½	5.30
245	" " " " " Box or Rosewd		112	50	105	40	3.07	6.50

	Gauges	per dozen						
246	Marking Gauges		21	4	1	4	30	75
247	" " Oval Bar		23	4	1	4	32	85
248	" " Box or Rosewood		31	34	1	10½	81½	1.75
249	" " " Oval Bar		38	34	1	11	84	2.00
"	" " Plated Head " Bar		62	34	12	18	1.26	3.00
	Extra with Inches		8			1	9	20
250	Cutting Gauges		43	4	2	7½	56½	1.50
251	" " Oval Bar		45	4	2	7½	58½	1.60
252	" " Boxwood		61	34	2	10½	1.10½	2.75
253	" " " Oval Bar		62	34	2	14½	1.12½	3.00
254	Mortise Gauges Plated Head & Bar Box or Rosewd		89	34	2.16	75½	5.12½	12.00
255	" " Brass Slide		65	4	37	14½	1.10½	3.00
256	" " " Plated		78	4	33	17	1.32	3.50
257	" " Screw Slide "		114	4	150	39	2.97	6.50

Plate X

BASED ON 1858 COSTS at UNION FACTORY, Pine Meadow, Conn[and $1.25 daily wage for planemaker for 10 hours work.

Number of Planes made in 10 hours

Hours Required to Make One Plane

COST IN CENTS TO MAKE A PLANE

Table IX

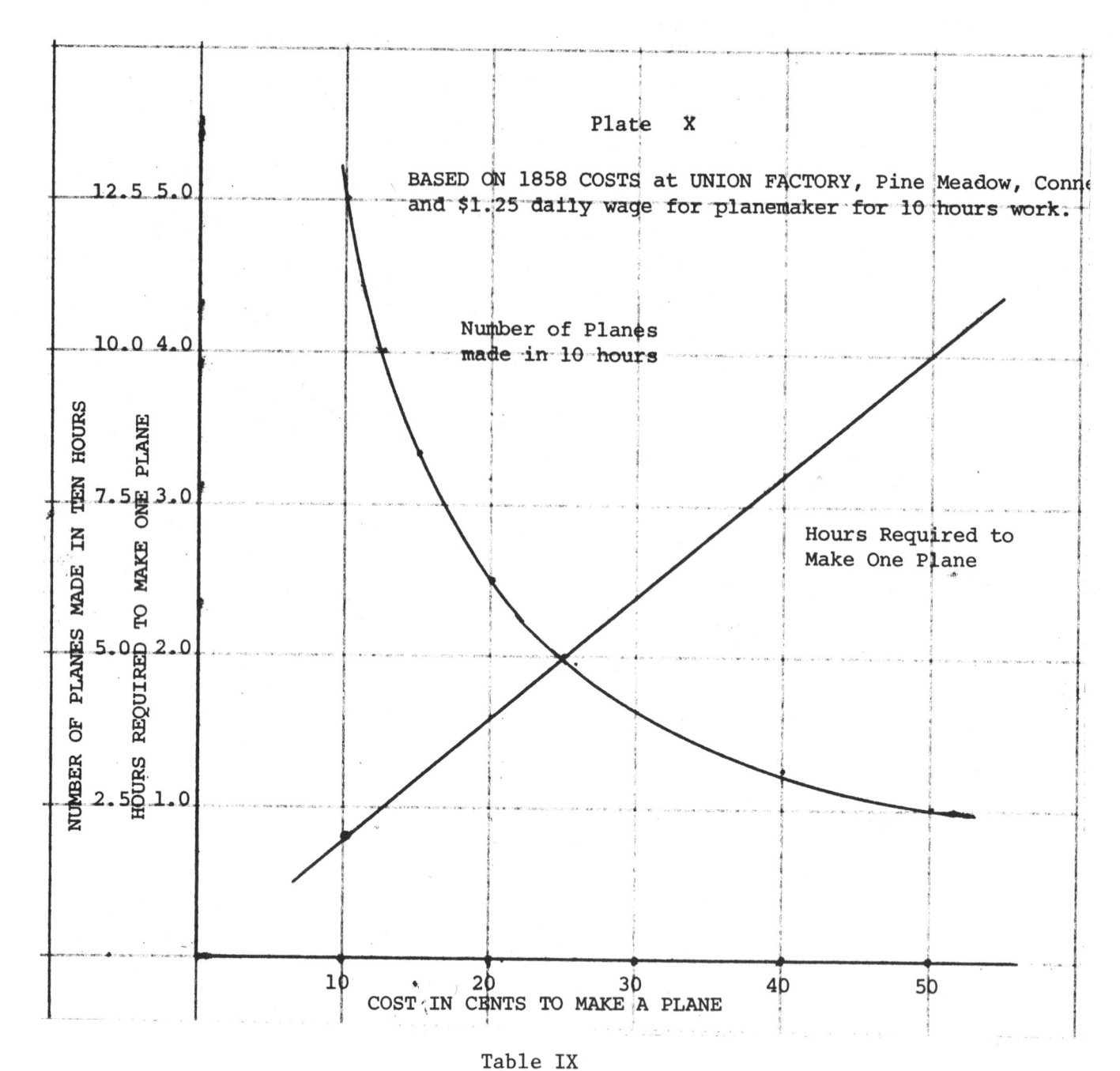

PRODUCTION TIME REQUIRED TO MAKE A PLANE AND NUMBER OF PLANES MADE IN 10 HOURS BASED ON 1858 COSTS AND AVERAGE DAILY WAGE OF $1.25

Cost in Cents to make a plane	Hours Required to make a plane	Number of Planes made in 10 hours
10	0.8 = 48 minutes	12.5
20	1.6 = 96 "	6.25
30	2.4 = 144 "	4.16
40	3.2 = 192 "	3.13
50	4.0 = 240 "	2.50

PRICE LIST

OF

RULES, PLANES, GAUGES, HAND SCREWS, BENCH SCREWS, LEVELS, &c.,

MANUFACTURED BY

HERMON CHAPIN,

Pine Meadow, Conn.

JULY, 1859.

HARTFORD:
PRESS OF CASE, LOCKWOOD AND COMPANY.
1859.

In presenting the annexed List of Prices, the subscriber would tender his thanks to his patrons and former customers for past favors; trusting that by long experience and a strict attention to their interest to merit a continuation of their orders.

All Rules are of the best and well seasoned material, made and graduated by the most approved machinery.

The Planes are of well seasoned second-growth white beech, *all rived*, thereby avoiding the twisting and warping of the Tools in the hands of the purchaser.

Although the List of Prices is on some articles advanced, *the Rule List being the same as adopted by the Convention of Rule Manufacturers, at New Haven, May 26, 1859*, the larger Discount and improved quality of the Goods, he trusts, will be entirely satisfactory to those wishing to purchase a good article.

HERMON CHAPIN.

Pine Meadow, July 1, 1859.

DISCOUNTS.

Rules, - - - - -	per cent.
Planes, - - - - -	do
Gauges, - - - - -	do
Hand and Bench Screws, - -	do
Plumb and Levels, - - -	do

TERMS.

Six Months Time.
5 per cent. less for Cash.
All Goods delivered at the Collinsville Depot.
No charge for Boxes.

PRICE LIST

OF

RULES, PLANES, GUAGES, HAND SCREWS, BENCH SCREWS, LEVELS, &c.

BOXWOOD RULES.

One Foot, Four Fold, Narrow.

			Price per doz.
No. 1, Round Joint,	-	5/8 inch,	$2.50
2, Square do		5/8 do	3.50
3, do do Edge Plates,		5/8 do	5.00
4, do do do		3/4 do	6.00
5, do do Bound,		5/8 do	11.00
6, Arch do Edge Plates,		5/8 do	4.00
7, do do do		3/4 do	5.50
8, do do Bound,		5/8 do	6.50
9, do do do		5/8 do	12.00

Two Feet, Four Fold, Narrow.

No. 10, Round Joint,	-	1 inch,	$3.00
11, Square do		1 do	4.50
12, do do Edge Plates,		1 do	6.00
13, do do do Extra,		3/4 do	7.00
14, do do Half Bound,		1 do	11.50
15, do do Bound,		1 do	14.00
16, Arch do do		1 do	5.50
17, do do Edge Plates,		1 do	7.00
18, do do Half Bound,		1 do	12.50
19, do do Bound,		1 do	16.00
20, Double Arch Joint,	-	1 do	9.00
21, do do Bound,		1 do	21.00

Two Feet, Four Fold, Broad.

No. 22, Round Joint,	-	1 3/8 inch,	$5.00
23, Square do		1 3/8 do	7.00
24, do do Edge Plates,		1 3/8 do	9.00
25, do do Half Bound,		1 3/8 do	14.00
26, do do Bound,		1 3/8 do	17.00
27, Arch do		1 3/8 do	8.50
28, do do Edge Plates,		1 3/8 do	10.50
29, do do Half Bound,		1 3/8 do	15.00
30, do do Bound,		1 3/8 do	20.00
31, Double Arch Joint,	-	1 3/8 do	12.00
32, do do Bound,		1 3/8 do	24.00
33, Arch Joint, Edge Plate, with Slide,		1 3/8 do	14.00

PRICE LIST.

BOXWOOD RULES.

Two Feet, Four Fold, Board Measure.

			Price per doz.
No. 34, Square Joint, Edge Plates,	-	1 3/8 inch,	$11.00
35, do do Bound,		1 3/8 do	16.00
36, Arch do Edge Plates,		1 3/8 do	12.50
37, do do Bound,		1 3/8 do	22.00

Two Feet, Two Fold.

No. 38, Round Joint,	-	1 1/2 inch,	$3.50
39, Square do		1 1/2 do	4.50
40, do do Bitted, Board Measure,		1 1/2 do	7.00
41, Arch do		1 1/2 do	6.00
42, do do Bitted, Extra Scales,		1 1/2 do	7.00
43, do do do Board Measure,		1 1/2 do	9.00
44, do do do Extra Scales, Thin,		1 1/2 do	8.00
45, do do Bound, do		1 1/2 do	16.00

Two Feet, Two Fold, Slide.

No. 46, Square Joint, Plain Slide,	1 1/2 inch,		$8.00
47, do do Gunter do	1 1/2 do		10.50
48, Arch do Bitted,		1 1/2 do	14.00
49, do do Bound,		1 1/2 do	24.00
50, do do Bitted, Engineers'		1 1/2 do	18.00
51, do do Bound, do		1 1/2 do	28.00
Books of Instruction for Engineers,			1.50

IVORY RULES.

One Foot, Four Fold, Narrow.

No. 52, Round Joint, Brass,	-	1/2 inch,	$8.00
53, Square do do		1/2 do	9.50
54, do do German Silver,		1/2 do	11.00
55, do do Edge Plates,		5/8 do	14.00
56, Arch do do		5/8 do	16.00
57, do do Bound,		5/8 do	27.00
58, Square do Edge Plates,		3/4 do	18.00

Two Feet, Four Fold, Narrow.

No. 59, Square Joint, Edge Plates, German Silver,	7/8 inch,		$38.00
60, Arch do do		1 do	48.00
61, do do Bound,		1 do	58.00
62, Double Arch Joint, Bound,		1 do	68.00

Two Feet, Four Fold, Broad.

No. 63, Arch Joint, Edge Plates, German Silver,	1 3/8 inch,		$64.00
64, do do Bound,		1 3/8 do	76.00
65, do do do with Slide,		1 3/8 do	84.00
66, do do do with Calliper, do		1 3/8 do	90.00
67, Double Arch Joint, Bound,		1 3/8 do	58.00

Two Fold.

No. 68, Round Joint, 6 inch, Brass,	-	1/2 inch,	$3.50
69, Arch do 12 do German Silver,		3/4 do	18.00

PRICE LIST.

CALLIPER RULES, Boxwood.

	Price per doz.
No. 70, Square Joint, Two Fold, 6 inch., 7/8 inch., Brass Case,	$7.00
71, do do do 6 do 7/8 do do	8.00
72, Arch do Four Fold, 12 do 7/8 do do	12.00
73, do do do 12 do Bound, 5/8 to 7/8 do	18.00

CALLIPER RULES, Ivory.

No. 74, Square Joint, Two Fold, 6 in, Ger. Silver, 7/8 in.,	$13.00
75, do do do 6 do do Case, 5/8 do	15.00
76, do do Four Fold, 12 do 5/8 do	30.00
77, do do do 12 do Bound, 5/8 do	38.00
78, Arch do do 12 do do 5/8 do	40.00
79, do do do 12 do do 5/8 do	46.00

MISCELLANEOUS RULES.

No. 80, Bench Rules, 24 inch, 7/8 inch,	$2.75
81, do do 1 1/4 do	3.25
82, Yard Sticks, -	1.10
83, do Brass Tipped,	3.50
84, Yard Rule, Arch Joint, Four Fold,	8.00
85, Ship Carpenters' Bevels,	6.00
86, Shoemakers' Size Sticks,	4.00
87, Board Sticks, Square and Octagon, 24 inch.,	6.50
88, do do do 36 do	9.00
89, do Walking Canes for Inspectors, 36 inch.,	10.50
90, Forwarding Sticks, 48 inch	9.00
92, Wantage Rods, -	3.50
93, Gauging Rods, 36 inch.,	7.00
94, do do 48 do	8.00
95, Three Fold Rules, 12 inch., 7/8 in.,	6.00
96, Six do 24 do Arch Joint, Edge Plates, 3/4 do	13.00

MISCELLANEOUS PLANES.

	Price each.
Toy, Smooth, Single, Cast Steel Irons, 1 1/2 inch,	$0.45
do do Double, do 1 1/2 do	.75
do Jack, Single, do 1 1/2 do	.55
do do Double, do 1 1/2 do	.85
Clock Plane, Single, 16 inch., do 2 3/8 do	.95
do do Double, 18 do do 2 3/8 do	1.30
Gutter Plane, do 2 do	.90
Pump Plane, for Chain Pump, do 1 to 1 1/2 do	1.20
Spear Plane, do 2 to 2 1/4 do	1.00
do do Double, do 2 to 2 1/4 do	1.50
Whip Plane, Steel Faced, do 1 1/4 to 1 3/4 do	1.25
Wash Board Plane, -	1.20
do do with Handle, -	1.50

1*

PRICE LIST.

COMMON BENCH PLANES, Single Irons.

	Price each.
No. 100, Smooth, Cast Steel Irons, 2 to 2 1/8 inch,	$0.55
101, Jack, do 2 to 2 1/8 do	.65
102, Fore, 21 inch, do 2 3/8 do	.90
do 22 do do 2 1/2 do	.95
103, Jointer, 26 do do 2 1/2 do	1.05
do 28 do do 2 1/2 do	1.15

EXTRA BENCH PLANES, Single Irons.

No. 104, Smooth, Cast Steel Irons, 2 to 2 1/4 inch,	$0.60
105, Jack, do 2 to 2 1/4 do	.70
106, Fore, 21 inch, do 2 3/8 do	.95
do 22 do do 2 1/2 do	1.00
107, Jointer, 26 do do 2 1/2 do	1.10
do 28 do do 2 5/8 do	1.20
do 30 do do 2 5/8 do	1.30

COMMON BENCH PLANES, Double Irons.

No. 108, Smooth, Cast Steel Irons, 2 to 2 1/8 inch,	$0.85
109, Jack, do 2 to 2 1/8 do	.95
110, Fore, 21 inch, do 2 3/8 do	1.20
do 22 do do 2 1/2 do	1.30
111, Jointer, 26 do do 2 1/2 do	1.40
do 28 do do 2 5/8 do	1.50

EXTRA BENCH PLANES, Double Irons.

No. 112, Smooth, Cast Steel Irons, 2 to 2 1/4 in.,	$0.90
do Handled, do 2 to 2 1/4 do	1.50
113, Jack, do 2 to 2 1/4 do	1.00
114, Fore, 21 inch, do 2 3/8 do	1.30
do 22 do do 2 1/2 do	1.40
115, Jointers, 26 do do 2 1/2 do	1.50
do 28 do do 2 5/8 do	1.60
do 30 do do 2 5/8 do	1.75
116, Single Smooth, Box or Rosewood, do 2 to 2 1/4 do	1.30
do Handle, do 2 to 2 1/4 do	2.50
117, Double Smooth, do 2 to 2 1/4 do	1.70
do Handle, do 2 to 2 1/4 do	2.75
118, Tooth Plane, do 2 to 2 1/4 do	.90
119, Mitre do Oval or Square, 1 3/4 to 2 do	.65
do do do Box or Rose'd, do 1 3/4 to 2 do	1.25
120, Single Circular, Smooth, do 2 to 2 1/8 do	.70
121, do Double do do 2 to 2 1/8 do	1.00

Extra Bench Planes, Double Irons, with Starts, Polished.

Smooth Plane, Extra Cast Steel Iron, 2 to 2 1/4 inch,	$1.50
do do Handle, do 2 to 2 1/4 do	2.25
Jack do do 2 to 2 1/4 do	1.75
Fore do 22 inch, do 2 3/8 & 2 1/2 do	2.25
Jointer do 28 do do 2 1/2 & 2 5/8 do	2.50
do 30 do do 2 5/8 do	2.80
do Smooth Jack, 22 inch, Fore, 28 inch, per set,	8.00

PRICE LIST.

MOULDING PLANES.

			Price each.
No. 122, Astragals,		to 3/4 inch,	$0.40
do		do	.50
do		to 1 1/4 do	.58
123, Beads,		to 3/4 do	.45
do		to 1 do	.60
do		to 1 1/4 do	.90
do	with Handles,	to 1 1/2 do	1.90
124, do	Double Boxed,	to 3/4 do	.55
do	do	to 1 do	.70
do	do	to 1 1/4 do	.95
125, do	Solid Boxed, Dovetailed,	to 1 1/2 do	.55
do	do	to 1 1/4 do	.67
do	do	to 3/4 do	.88
126, Base and Band Moulding,		per inch,	.70
127, Bed Moulding, Handle,		do	.85
128, Back Ogees,		to 3/4 inch,	.70
do		to 1 do	.50
129, do		to 1 3/4 do	.55
do	with Bead,	to 1 do	.62
do	do	to 1 3/4 do	.55
130, Belections,		to 1 1/4 do	.60
do		to 1 1/4 do	.67
131, Cock Beads,		do	.55
132, do	Boxed,	do	.60
133, Center Beads,		do	.70
134, do		to 3/8 inch,	.42
do	Solid Boxed, Dovetailed,	to 3/4 do	.56
do	do	to 3/8 do	.62
135, Cornice Planes,		per inch,	.64
Cabinet Ogee Planes,		do	.73
136, Dadoes,		to 1 inch,	.84
137, do	with Stop,	to 1 do	.84
138, do	with Side Stop,	to 1 do	.75
139, do	with Screw Stop,	to 1 do	.85
140, Door Planes, Ogee,		1/2 to 5/8 do	.95
141, do	do Bevel, Double Screw Arms,		1.45
142, Antae Caps,		to 1 inch,	.88
143, do		to 1 1/4 do	1.50
144, Antae Base,		to 1 1/2 do	1.25
145, Fluting Planes,		to 1 1/2 do	1.38
do			1.63
146, Filletster,			.60
147, do	with Stop,		.75
148, do	with Stop and Cut,		.95
149, do	with Stop, Cut and Boxed,		1.20
150, do	with Screw Stop, Cut and Boxed,		1.35
do	with Screw Stop, Cut, Solid Box or Rosewood,		1.58
			2.50
			4.00

PRICE LIST.

MOULDING PLANES.

			Price each.
No. 151, Filletser, with Arms, Stop and Cut,			2.00
152, do	with Arms, Stop, Cut and Boxed,		2.25
153, do	with Screw Arms, Stop, Cut and Boxed,		2 65
154, do	with Screw Arms, Screw Stop, Cut and Boxed,		3.70
do	with Screw Arms, Screw Stop, Cut, Solid Box or Rosewood,		5.75
155, Grecian Ovolo,		to 3/4 inch,	.55
do		to 1 do	.60
do		to 1 1/4 do	.65
do		to 1 1/2 do	.75
156, do	with Handle,	per inch,	.65
157, do	with Fillet,	to 1 inch,	.70
do	do	to 1 1/4 do	.75
do	do	to 1 1/2 do	.80
do	do	to 1 1/4 do	.90
158, do	with Bead,	per inch,	.75
do	do	to 1 inch,	.75
do	do	to 1 1/4 do	.80
do	do	to 1 3/4 do	.87
159, do	Handle,	to 2 do	1.00
do	do	to 2 1/2 do	1.50
160, Grecian Ogee, with Bevel or Fillet,			2.00
do		to 1 do	.65
do		to 1 1/4 do	.70
do		to 1 1/2 do	.75
do		to 1 1/4 do	.85
161, Gothic Bead, with one Iron	with Handle, per inch,		.65
162, do	with two Irons, Boxed,		.70
163, Halving Plane,			1.05
164, Halving Planes, Handle and Plated,			.38
165, Half Set, Hollows and Rounds, 9 pairs, 2 to 18,			.66
166, do	12 do 2 to 24,		6.75
167, Hollows and Rounds, No. 1 to 12,			10.00
do	No. 13 to 18,	per pair,	.70
do	No. 19 to 24,	do	.85
168, Table Hollows and Rounds,		do	1.10
169, do	Boxed,	do	.90
170, do	with Fence,	do	1.50
171, Match Plane,		do	1.40
172, do	Plated, to 1/2 inch., per pair or Double		1.05
173, do	do 1/2 do	do	1.30
174, do	Plated, to 1 do	do	1.12
175, do	do	do	1.37
do	with Handle, to 1 1/4 inch., per pair,		1.90
176, do	Plated, do to 1 1/4 do		2.20
177, do	for Plank, Plated,		1.85
178, do	do Plated,		2.25
179, do	Moving Fence, Plated,		2.20
180, do	do	do	2.60
181, do	Screw or Slide Arms,		2 85

PRICE LIST.

MOULDING PLANES.

No.	Description	Price each
182,	Match Plane, Screw or Slide Arms, Plated, per pair,	$3.25
183,	do Boxwood Screw Arms, do	3.35
184,	do Plated or Boxed Fence, do	3.75
	Extra, for boxing the Groove, do	.35
185,	Nosings, with Handle, or two Irons,	.85
186,	Hand Rail Plane, Ovolo and Ogee,	1.40
187,	Ovolos, to 3/4 inch,	.42
	do to 1 do	.50
	do to 1 1/4 do	.56
188,	do with Bead, to 3/4 do	.60
	do to 1 do	.65
	do to 1 1/4 do	.70
189,	Panel Plane, Cast Steel,	1.15
190,	do with Cut,	1.40
191,	do with Moving Fence,	1.50
192,	do do and Cut,	1.70
193,	Qk. Ogees, to 3/4 inch,	.55
	do to 1 1/4 do	.60
194,	do with Bead, to 3/4 do	.67
	do to 1 do	.60
	do to 1 1/4 do	.65
195,	Reeding Plane, to 1 1/4 do	.75
	do to 3/8 do	.65
196,	Qk. Ovolo, to 3/4 do	.80
	do to 1 1/4 do	.55
197,	do with Bead, to 3/4 do	.60
	do to 1 do	.70
	do to 1 1/4 do	.68
198,	Raising Planes, Boxed,	.75
199,	do do	.85
	per inch,	.85
200,	Rabbet Planes, Square, Extra for Cut,	.90
		.25
	do to 1 inch,	.50
	do to 1 1/4 do	.58
201,	do to 1 1/2 do	.68
	do Double Boxed, to 1 do	1.00
	do do to 1 1/4 do	1.08
202,	Skew, do to 1 do	.55
	do to 1 1/4 do	.64
	do to 1 1/2 do	.70
	do to 1 3/4 do	.76
	do to 2 do	.85
203,	Boxed and Cut, to 1 do	.90
	do to 2 1/4 do	.95
	do do to 1 1/4 do	1.05
	do do to 1 1/2 do	1.10
	do do to 1 3/4 do	1.15
	do do to 2 do	1.20

PRICE LIST.

MOULDING PLANES.

No.	Description	Price each
203,	Rabbet Planes, Skew, Boxed and Cut, to 2 1/4 inch,	$1.25
204,	do do Handle and Cut, to 2 do	1.30
205,	do do do two Cuts, to 2 1/2 do	1.65
206,	Sash Planes, one Iron,	.58
207,	do do Boxed,	.85
208,	do two Irons,	.85
209,	do do Boxed,	1.15
210,	do Double,	1.10
211,	do do Boxed,	1.40
212,	do Screw Arms,	1.30
	do do Boxed,	2.20
213,	do do Self Regulating,	2.50
214,	do do do Boxed,	2.75
215,	do do do Handle, Self Regulating,	3.15
	do do do Solid Box, do	4.50
216,	Templets, Guages and Prickers, each,	.12
217,	Sash Coping Plane,	.50
	do Boxed,	.70
218,	Sash Filletster, Screw Arms,	2.00
219,	do do Screw Stop,	3.00
220,	Scotia, to 3/4 inch,	.44
	do to 1 do	.50
	do to 1 1/4 do	.56
	do to 1 1/2 do	.60
221,	do with Bead, to 1 1/4 do	.70
222,	Snipe Bills, per pair,	1.10
223,	do Full Boxed,	1.50
224,	Side Rabbet Plane,	1.08
225,	Slip Beads, to 3/4 inch,	.60
226,	Corner Dovetailed, Boxed, to 1 3/4 do	.75
	do do to 1 do	1.00
227,	Torus Beads, to 3/4 do	.50

GROOVING PLOWS.

No.	Description	Price each
228,	Plows, 4th rate, Slide or Screw Arms, 8 Irons,	3.00
229,	do do Plated, do	3.20
230,	do do Boxed, do	3.20
231,	do 3d rate, Plated, do	3.40
232,	do do Boxed, do	3.60
233,	do do do do	3.60
234,	do 2d rate, Plated, do	4.50
235,	do do Boxed, do	4.70
236,	do do do do	4.70
237,	do do Handle, Boxwood Screw Arms, 8 do	5.75
238,	do do do Boxed, do	5.95
239,	do 1st rate, do do	6.25
240,	do do do Box or Rosewood, do	8.50

GROOVING PLOWS.

No.	Description				Price each.
No. 241,	Plow, 2d Rate,	Boxwood Screw Arms,		8 Irons,	$4.60
242,	do do	Boxed, do	do	8 do	4.80
243,	do 1st Rate,	do	do	8 do	5.10
244,	do do	Boxed, do	do	8 do	5.30
245,	do do	Box or Rosewood,	do	8 do	6.50

Plows with 1 Iron, $1.00 less.

GAUGES.

No.	Description	Price per doz.
No. 246,	Marking Gauges,	$0.75
247,	do Oval Bar,	.85
248,	do Box or Rosewood,	1.75
249,	do do Oval Bar,	2.00
249½,	do do Plated Head and Bar,	3.00
	EXTRA, WITH INCHES,	.20
250,	Cutting Gauges,	1.50
251,	do Oval Bar,	1.60
252,	do Boxwood,	2.75
253,	do do Oval Bar,	3.00
254,	Mortice Gauges, Plated Head and Bar, Box or Rosew'd,	12.00
255,	do Brass Slide,	3.00
256,	do do Plated,	3.50
257,	do Screw Slide, do	6.50
258,	do do Rosewood, Plated,	8.00
259,	Panel Gauges,	2.00
260,	do Oval Bar,	2.25
260½,	do do Mahogany,	3.00
261,	Slitting Gauges,	4.75
262,	do Handle,	6.75
262½,	do do with Rollers,	7.75

HAND AND BENCH SCREWS.

No.	Description	Size	Jaw	Price
	Hand or Thumb Screws for Jewellers,	⅜ inch,		$1.50
No. 263,	Hand Screws, Hickory,	½ inch,	Jaw 6 do	1.75
	do do	⅝ do	do 8 do	2.00
263½,	do do	¾ do	do 10 do	2.50
	do do	⅞ do	do 13 do	2.75
264,	do do	1 do	do 14 do	3.25
	do do	1 do	do 16 do	3.50
265,	do do	1¼ do	do 18 do	4.50
	do do	1¼ do	do 20 do	5.50
266,	Bench Screws, do	2 do		4.50
267,	do do	2½ do		7.50
268,	do do Long Jaws,	2½ do		10.00
269,	do Wrought Iron, Double Thread,	1 do		15.00
270,	do do do Collar,	1 do		16.00
271,	do do do	1⅛ do		18.00
272,	do do do Collar,	1⅛ do		19.00

HANDLES.

No.	Description	Price per doz.
No. 273,	Jack Plane Handles,	$0.85
274,	Fore do	1.45
275,	Saw Handles,	3.50
275½,	do extra,	4.00
276,	Firmer Chisel Handles, Feruled, Hickory and Apple,	.68
277,	Paring do do do	.87
278,	Socket do do	.50
279,	Auger Handles, do	.67

SCREW DRIVERS.

No.	Description	Price
No. 280,	Screw Drivers, 4 inch,	$2.50
281,	do 6 do	3.00
282,	do 8 do	3.30
283,	do 10 do	4.10
284,	do 12 do	4.60

SPIRIT LEVELS.

No.	Description	Size	Price
No. 285,	Level,	to 12 inch,	$4.00
286,	do	to 18 do	5.00
287,	do	to 28 do	6.50
288,	Plumb and Level,	to 12 do	6.50
289,	do	to 18 do	7.50
290,	do	to 28 do	9.50
291,	do Tipped,	to 12 do	17.00
292,	do do	to 18 do	18.00
293,	do do	to 28 do	22.00
294,	do do Triple Stock,	to 28 do	24.00
295,	do do Mahogany,	to 12 do	22.00
296,	do do do	to 18 do	24.00
297,	do do do	to 28 do	28.00
298,	do do do Triple Stock,	to 28 do	33.00
299,	do do Rosewood,	to 12 do	35.00
300,	do do do	to 18 do	40.00
301,	do do do Triple Stock,	to 28 do	60.00
302,	do Adjusting,	to 12 do	12.00
303,	do do	to 18 do	13.00
304,	do do	to 28 do	17.00
305,	do do Tipped,	to 12 do	24.00
306,	do do do	to 18 do	25.00
307,	do do do	to 28 do	30.00
308,	do do do Mahogany,	to 12 do	28.00
309,	do do do do	to 18 do	30.00
310,	do do do do	to 28 do	38.00
311,	Pocket Levels,		2.00
312,	do with Brass Top,		2.50

All the above Levels Polished, and with two side views.

Table XI

AGREEMENT OF October 1, 1860 to form firm of H.Chapins & Sons

This agreement made the first day of October 1860 by and betweeen Hermon Chapin, Edward M. Chapin and Philip E. Chapin all of Pine Meadow - Witnesseth   That the said parties above named have agreed and do hereby agree to become copartners in the business of manufacturing Rules,Planes,Gauges &c. as heretofor carried on by the said Hermon Chapin said copartnership to commence from and after the said first day of October 1860 and to be known by the name or firm of H.Chapin & Sons,

It is agreed that the said H.Chapin is to rent for the term of this agreement, to the said company, the Plane and Rule Shop and water power for the same, together with the Machinery, Tools, Patterns and other fixtures thereto belonging for said business also the shop now occupied by Samuel Allen for a brass foundry, with the yards and timber house in the rear of said Plane Shop. The said H.Chapin is to keep the said buildings, water power wheels and main shafting in good repair during the said time, to keep all other Machinery, Tools, Patterns and other fixtures in repair by the said Company and deliver to the said H.Chapin at the expiration of this agreement in as good repair as when received at the commencement of this agreement, also to pay to the said H.Chapin one thousand dollars each year during the term of this agreement.

It is also agreed for the purpose of carrying out this agreement that the said E.M.Chapin and P.E.Chapin are to purchase of the said H.Chapin, each one tenth part of the stock and tools aforsaid, the other eight tenths to belong to the said H.Chapin as his share in said Company, the amount of which as for inventory is Twenty thousand dollars, which is to constitute the capitol stock of said Company.

It is further agreed during the continuance of this copartnership that the said E.M.Chapin will devote his whole time and attention in the employ of said Co. for their joint interest and benefit, for which the said company is to pay him the sum of six hundred dollars annually unless otherwise agreed. If either of the other parties are employed by said company they are to be paid by said company a fair compensation for said labor so done.

It is also agreed that said parties shall and will with said company at all times during the said copartnership pay and discharge equally in proportion to their said shares between them and said company all rents, salaries and other expenses that may be required for the support and mangement of said company business and that all gains,profits and increases that shall grow out of or arise from by means of said company business shall be divided equally between the said parties in proportion to their said shares, and all losses that shall happen to said company shall be born in a like manner.

Table XI [Continued]

And it is agreed by and between the said parties that there shall be kept at all times during the continuance of said copartnership just and true Books of accounts to which each of the said parties shall at all time have free access thereto, and said business shall be managed as said parties shall from time to time agree and direct.

And also the said copartners shall once in each year or oftener if required make, yield and remit to the others a true and just account of all business transactions with and for said company. No dividends or capital shall be drawn from said company unless a true and just inventory of all the Timber, Tools, stocks and accounts shall be first made to the satisfaction of all parties, which shall be drawn at least once in five years.

The said parties hereby mutually agree that neither of them will use the company name to sign any Note or endorse any note or obligation with the company name unless it be strickly for the transaction of the company business.

Either party to this agreement may dissolve the same by giving the other parties in writing six months notice of their intention to do so.

This contract to continue during the term of ten years or during the life of all the parties, unless sooner dissolved by mutual consent.

Pine Meadow
Jan 29, 1962

Hermon Chapin
E. M. Chapin
Philip Chapin

Notes - Chapter III

1. CHS, Manuscript 74276, Box I, folder 1826-1865
2. *ibid*
3. *Directory of Baltimore Plane and Edge Tool Makers, 1796 - 1900,* Richard E. Hay, [Privately Printed, 1981], pp. 3 & 4.
4. Richard E. Hay, private communication, Jan. 22, 1977.
5. *ibid*
6. H. Chapin's Account Book, January 1830, pp. 327 - 328.
7. CHS, Manuscript H. Chapin
8. CHS, Manuscript, Collins Co.
9. *ibid*
10. M.M. Frizzel, *History of Walpole, NH, op. cit., p.404.*
11. Hamden County Register of Deeds [Mass.], Book 135, p. 470, Sept. 11, 1847.
12. *The Chapin Genealogy,* op. cit., p. 1154.
13. CHS, Manuscript 74276
14. CHS, Trade Catalogue Collection
15. This plane is the property of Richard E. Hay. It is also illustrated in his *Directory of Baltimore Plane and Edge Tool Makers, 1796 - 1900* Fig. 6, p.6.
16. Robert D. Graham, jr. has now established that such slip bead planes were designed for working the bead close to the edge.
17. Dr. Kenneth C. Barraclough, Private Communication, Jan. 24, 1983.
18. Kenneth D. Roberts, *Some 19th Century English Woodworking Tools,* [Fitzwilliam, NH, 1980, The subjects of blister, shear, German and cast steel are discussed in detail; pp. 6-9; 15-19. Also see: K.C. Barraclough, *Sheffield Steel,* [Buxton, Derbys, England, 1976], pp. 10-11.
20. Connecticut State Library, Hartford, CT, State History Section.

```
6                PRICE LIST.
            Miscellaneous Planes.
116  Single Smooth,        Box or Rosewood,     1.25
        do      Handle,       do           .    2.60
117  Double Smooth,  .  .    do       .    .    1.60
        do      Handle,  .   do       .    .    3.00
118  Tooth Plane,   .  .  .  .  .  .  .  .       .95
119  Mitre Plane,   .  .  .  .  .  .  .  .       .65
        do      Box or Rosewood,  .  .  .  .    1.25
120  Single Circular,   .  .  .  .  .  .  .      .70
121  Double Circular,   .  .  .  .  .  .  .     100
     Toy Smooth, Single,  .  .  .  .  .  .       .40
     Toy Smooth, Double,  .  .  .  .  .  .       .70
     Toy Jack, Single,   .  .  .  .  .  .  .     .50
     Toy Jack, Double,   .  .  .  .  .  .  .     .80
```

From Undated UNION FACTORY CATALOGUE, 1854-1857

Chapter IV

Other Activities of Hermon Chapin, 1835-1860

Hermon Chapin appears to have been a serious, law abiding citizen devoted to his family. Only three of his nine children survived to adulthood. (See Table I, Chapter I) The first born was the only girl. His fourth child, Hermon Terrill Chapin, drowned in the Farmington River two months before reaching the age of three.

During the period of 1835-1851 he served fourteen years as Justice of the Peace, frequently holding court as his residence in compromising and settling various disputes among residents of Litchfield County. Numerous case records and summonds survive. Among such manuscript data is the following inventory, listing the contents of a New Hartford blacksmith shop in 1840. (Table I)

Hermon Chapin, like his father Levi,[1] opposed drinking liquor. The following document attests to his sobriety.[2]

At a Meeting of the Civil Authority and Select Men of the Town of New Hartford holden at the home of John A. Shephard on Monday the 7th day of July 1839. — On Motion of Roger Mills was chosen Chairman and Hermon Chapin, Clerk — On Motion: Resolved that we have reason to fear that the Taverns in sd. Town have not in all respects observed the Laws Regulating Taverns and the sale of ardent spirits. We therefore deem it our duty to request the sd. Taverns to appear before the Civil Authority and Select Men of the sd. Town on Monday the 21st next at 6 PM at the house of John A. Shepard to show cause why their licenses should not be suspended. — On motion which the sd. Clerk of this Meeting notify sd. Taverns to appear on Monday the 21st next at 6 PM at the home of John A. Shepard. Hermon Chapin, Clerk.

Annexed to the above was the following penned note: "Pursuant to adjournment and after giving the sd. Taverns a candid hearing Resolved that we are of the opinion that the sd. Taverns have done honorably in discharge of their duty in favour of the cause of temperance. Resolved that we recommend to their rigid adherence to the Laws and the Rules of propreity in sale of ardent spirits in future."

Plate I - HERMON CHAPIN'S BUSINESS CARD

HERMON CHAPIN,
MANUFACTURER OF
RULES, PLANES, GAUGES,
LEVELS, &c., &c.,
UNION FACTORY,
Pine Meadow, Conn.

TABLE I

INVENTORY OF STOCK & TOOLS OF RICHARD B. COWLES BLACKSMITH SHOP AT NEW HARTFORD CONNECTICUT APRIL 1, 1840

Qty	Item	Amount	Qty	Item	Amount
380	Ox Shoes	23.00		Amount Brot Over	$325.28
534	Unfitted Horse Shoes	64.71	1	Slide Wrench	2.00
136	Fitted " "	22.67	2	Bitt Stocks & Bits	4.75
11-3/4 lbs.	Ox Nails @30¢	3.53	4	Wrenches	1.75
63	" Horse " @25¢	15.75	1	Churn Drill	1.00
118½	" Wagon Tire @4½¢	7.58	2	pr. Calipers	1.25
61½	" Spring Steel @8¢	4.92	1	pr. Dividers	1.25
37¼	" English Blister Steel	6.25	1	scribe	.25
			1	Hand Saw	1.00
19½	" Round Iron @6½¢	1.17	1	Buck Saw	1.25
617	" Bar Iron	30.85	1	Key Hole Saw	.37
18	Manure Forks	9.00	1	Drill Stock	.84
4	Hay "	1.50	4	Chisels	.75
1	Set Waggon Axletrees	6.50	4	Sets Shoeing Tolls	11.84
900	lbs, Buck Coal	54.00	1	Iron Saw	.46
1	Stove & Pipe	10.00	3	Anvils	46.00
43	Forging Steel Tools	7.83	3	pr. of Bellows	49.50
19	Heading "	5.63	1	Shovel	.25
4	Hand Hammers	4.00	2	Lamp Stands	.32
2	Sledges	3.25	1	Small Hand Vise	.33
1	Double Faced Hammer	.50	1	Large Lever Plate	10.00
1	Hammer	.42	1	Size Plate	7.00
4	Small Nail Hammers	1.34	1	Small Plate	2.50
4	pointing Hammers	.92	7	Jaw Corks	.56
2	Old "	.50	2	Grindstones	8.00
1	Buck Horn	5.31	1	Polishing Stand	3.00
2	Shoeing Hammers	.56	1	Desk & Boxes	1.25
2	Pointing Blocks	1.50	1	Sett of Dies	1.75
6	Cutters	1.50	2	Water Pails	1.00
1	pr. of Shears	1.68	2	Vises	13.00
22	pr. of tongs	12.98	1	Engine Lathe & tools	110.06
6	Pokers	.93			$608.56
	Swedges	13.00			
2	pr. of Spring Tongs	2.06			
		$325.28			

New Hartford, April 2, 1840 - I hereby agree receive the articles enumerated in this Inventory as full consideration for the articles Mortgaged Otis B. Armes the 14th day of Novemeber 1839.
(This was a note for $360.00 witnessed by Hermon Chapin)

Richard B. Cowles

[The above inventory was transcribed from a document in the Collection of the New Hartford Historical Society.]

During the period 1826-1860 Hermon Chapin's principal business was proprietor of the Union Factory, manufacturing woodworking tools, as can be noted from his business card of about 1857. (Plate I) As he accumulated capital he invested in land and property. (See Table VI, Chapter III). About 1838 he began to invest capital in various local business ventures.[3] Table II provides a chronological listing of these activities during the period 1838-1860. While most of these do not concern the subject of planemaking, they do provide excellent insights into the economic conditions of this time period.

TABLE II

BUSINESS VENTURES of HERMON CHAPIN, 1838 - 1860

Date	Partner	Nature of Business	Table Number
May 30, 1839	Kelloggs, et all	New Hartford Joint Stock Co. (woolen mill)	IV
April 30, 1838	Henry Brown	Mulberry Tree Cultivation[7]	III
Jan. 31, 1851	Edward Gaines	Lumber Mill, Barkhamsted	V
1851	Hiram B. Kellogg	Foundry and Machine Shop	
June 23, 1853	Stephen Brignen	Making Wrought Iron	VII
Nov. 21, 1853	Reule Rice	Cutting Wood	IX
Nov. 22, 1853	Green Woods Co.	Castings	VIII
Feb. 3, 1860	I. Richardson	Mowing Machines	X
April 20, 1860	L. & G.W. Burwell	Lumber, Shingle & Lath Mill	XI

It was from the Kellogg brothers, Isaac and George, that Hermon Chapin and Daniel Copeland leased the property that became the Union Factory in 1826. The Kelloggs had purchased about 400 acres of land, a grist mill and water privilege in 1809, comprising all the property that subsequently became Pine Meadow district of New Hartford. In fact this section was originally called Kelloggville. With others they established a woolen mill, known as New Hartford Manufacturing Company. Hermon Chapin became one of the Trustees of this firm, May 31, 1837.[4] This subsequently became the New Hartford Joint Stock Company of which Hermon Chapin was among the stockholders. (See Table IV) This factory was destroyed by fire in 1834. A cotton mill was rebuilt on the property by Smiths and Brown.[5] George Kellogg built a machine shop, associating with his son as E. Kellogg and Company, manufacturing cotton pickers. After the death of George Kellogg in 1847, his son Hiram acquired ownership, changing the firm name to H. B. Kellogg and Company. Isaac Kellogg built a foundry and machine shop at Pine Meadow, which Hermon Chapin acquired in 1852. The factory was continued under the names of Hermon Chapin and H. B. Kellogg and Company, but soon after Hermon Chapin assumed complete ownership of this firm. Among the contracts was that with the Green Wood Company for making castings (Table VIII).

Hermon Chapin made an agreement April 13, 1839 with Henry Brown, employed as a planemaker at the Union Factory, to enter the mulberry tree cultivation. (Table III) This was a scheme then sweeping the country to raise such trees for the cultivation of silk from the worms infesting such trees.

The *1853 Catalogue and Invoice Prices of the Union Factory* (Plate V, Chapter III) noted that Hermon Chapin's products in addition to woodworking tools included "Castings and Machinery of every description; Puddled Iron, bands, bars, blooms, axle drafts, car axles, bunters, crow bars, &c."

TABLE IV

NEW HARTFORD JOINT STOCK COMPANY DEED

Deed George Kellogg and Others to New Hartford Joint Stock Company Recorded May 30, 1839 [New Hartford Land Records, Book 16, page 212]

To all people to whom these presents shall come - Greeting - Know that we George Kellogg, Hermon Chapin, Sanford Brown, jr., & Isaac Kellogg of New Hartford and Jonathan Hoyt, Edward Phelps of Colebrook & Lancelot Phelps of Barkhamsted, all in the county of Litchfield, Connecticut for the consideration of Forty Thousand Dollars, received to our full satisfaction of the New Hartford Joint Stock Company of New Hartford aforesaid, do give, grant, bargain, sell & confirm unto the said New Hartford Joint Stock Co., the Woolen Factory in said New Hartford, in Pine Meadow so called, with all the Lands and Water privileges thereunto belonging with all the Dwelling Houses & other Buildings standing thereon & all the Machinery contained and used therein. An also the Cotton Factory in the North Village with all the Dwelling Houses & Land attached to the same & the Store and lot of land on which it stands & the Saw Mill & Machine Shop & all the Machinery in said Cotton Factory & all the privileges which were conveyed to Issac Kellog, Geo.C. Kellog, Sanford Brown, jr, & Hermon Chapin by Sylvester Willard & Edmund Case as Assignes or Trustees of the New Hartford Manufacturing Co. in their Deed, dated June 16 AD 1838 to which Deed reference is had for more particular description. To have and to hold the above granted & bargained premises, with the appurtances thereof unto the said New Hartford Joint Stock Company & their successors & assigns forever to them & their proper use and behoof - And also the said George C. Kellogg, Sanford Brown, jr, Hermon Chapin, Isaac Kellogg, Jonathan E. Hoyt, Edward A. Phelps & Lancelot Phelps, do for ourselves & our executors & administrators, covenant with the said Grantees & with their successors & assigns & until the ensealing of these presents, we are well seized of the premises, as a good indefeasible in fee - simple & have good right to bargain & sell the same in manner & form as is above written & the same is free from all incumbrances whatsoever - except as herein after excepted - And furthermore do by these presents we the said Grantors (each of us severally, according to the shares which we severally own in said premises) bind ourselves and our heirs forever to warrant & defend the above granted & bargained premises to then, the said New Hartford Joint Stock Co. & to their successors & assigns against all claims & demands whatsoever - Excepting only a Mortgage to the Trustees of the "Asylum-Fund" for the benefit of the Deaf & Dumb in the City of Hartford, for the sum of Ten Thousand Dollars. In witness whereof we have hereunto set our hands & seals the 29th day of April, Anno Domini 1839.

George C. Kellogg
Sanford Brown, jr.
Hermon Chapin
Isaac Kellogg

Lancelot Phelps
Jonathan Hoyt
Edw. A. Phelps

DAGUERREOTYPE of HERMON CHAPIN (1799 - 1866, married, 1828)

[The date of these daguerreotypes, pages 142 & 143, is not known, but it is suggested these may have been made for their 25th wedding anniversary, which would mean Hermon Chapin was then 54 and Catherine Chapin then 48]

DAGUERREOTYPE of CATHERINE MERRILL CHAPIN, (1805 - 1873)

[Acknowledgement is made to John Blake, great-great-grandson of Hermon Chapin for permitting the daguerreotypes to be photographed and published in this study.]

TABLE III

AGREEMENT between HERMON CHAPIN and HENRY BROWN, April 13, 1839
MULBERRY TREE CULTIVATION PROJECT

This indenture made and executed by and between Hermon Chapin and Henry Brown both of the Town of New Hartford and County of Litchfield and State of Connecticut - Witnesseth That from and after the first day of January AD 1839 the sd. Chapin and the sd. Brown do enter into a Copartnership for the purpose of cultivating, raising and selling Mulberry trees - and also for the propagation of the Silk worm and the raising and cultivating of silk and the sale of same for the equal benefit of both of the sd. parties above named - said partnership to be for the term of five years from and after the sd. first day of January AD 1839 - To be know and transact their business under the firm name of Chapin & Brown.

The sd. parties are to make equal advances to the Company to provide suitable grounds, trees, &c. for the use of sd. Company to carry on sd. business above named - and the sd. parties are to share the losses and profits over and above the expenses equal - sd. Brown is to have the care and general oversight of sd. business and agrees to devote so much of his time as it may require for the faithful management of the same, for which he is to receive the sum of one dollar and thirty four cents a day to be paid by sd. Company for all labour so performed.

Neither of said parties shall withdraw from the funds of the Company except to defray the expenses of the sd. Company - or until all demands against sd. Company are paid and an equal dividend of the balance made to the satisfaction of both parties. It is further agreed that neither party shall carry on the above named business during sd. five years above written except for the Company benefit on the equal benefit of the parties.

It is further agreed that either party advancing or paying more than the other shall be entitled and paid interest as is customary, or agreed by the parties on all balance so paid - and that no dividend shall be made until all demands by the parties on any other persons are settled and paid.

A regular Book of accounts is to be kept by the sd. Company to which both parties are at all times to have access.

It is further agreed that all accounts of the Parties shall be examined, adjusted and entered in sd. Book every three months, and annual settlements made over a year on the first of January .

Witness our hand on this thirteenth day of April AD 1839.

Hermon Chapin
Henry Brown

TABLE V

AGREEMENT between HERMON CHAPIN and EDWARD GAINES, Jan. 23, 1851

This indenture made and executed this 21st day of January, by and between Hermon Chapin on the one part and Edward Gaines on the other part, both of New Hartford, County of Litchfield and State of Connecticut.

Witnesseth from this day the said Chapin and the said Gaines do enter into a Copartnership under the name & firm of Gaines & Co. for the purpose of making & vending Lumber and such other manufacturing as from time to time may be agreed upon. The business to be carried on in the town of Barkhamsted, at the place now owned by Whitefield T. Munson, or such other place as may hereafter be agreed upon by the parties and on the terms and conditions hereafter expressed.

The said parties are to make equal advancement to the Company, to purchase the establishment, and necessary stock, Tools & machinery for the use of said Company, and to be equally interested and concerned in its profits and losses.

Said Gaines is to devote his whole time during the continuance of said partnership to the business of the same, and in consideration thereof the said Company is to pay him the sum of one dollar and fifty cents per day for such service. It is also agreed that the said Chapin is to receive on dollar and fifty cents per day for such time as he is necessarily employed by said Company. - Neither party shall withdraw from the Capital employed by said Company, except such as may be required for necessary expenses, neither shall the Company name be used but for the necessary business of the Company.

All accounts between said partners and the Company to be adjusted and interest accounts made equal once in three months.

All accounts of said Company to be kept in a fair & proper manner, and both parties are to have at all times access to the Books and accounts of the same.

This Copartnership is to continue five years from the date hereof unless sooner dissolved by mutual consent.

In witness whereof we have hereunto set our hands this 28th day of January 1857.

Hermon Chapin
Edward Gaines

TABLE VIII

AGREEMENT BETWEEN HERMON CHAPIN AND GREEN WOODS CO., Nov. 22, 1853

This Agreement made and entered into by and between the Green Woods Co. and Hermon Chapin - Witnesseth - That the said Chapin agrees to make all the castings said Co. may use for the term of one year from and after the first day of April next at the following prices, viz.

All castings for the new water wheels the Co. build; three and one half cents pr pound - All castingd for repairs and small work, four cents per pound. To be paid cash every three months. On old cast iron (delvd. at the Foundry) at one cent per pound, all of which the sd. Chapin is to have. The Co. are to take the castings at the Foundry and furnish all the Patterns except such the sd. Chapin may have on hand - All the castings are to be of good quality and made in a workman like manner.

March 22, 1853

G.A. Smith Agt.
Green Woods Co.

In 1847 D. Camp and C. C. Manchester built a puddling furnace just south of the Union Factory.[6] This converted pig iron into wrought iron. Tenement houses were constructed for the employees, forming a little village, known as "Puddletown." The expense of transporting iron from Salisbury was so great that this business did not prove a success. In 1852 it was acquired by Hermon Chapin, who continued it until 1863. The 1850 US Census (Schedule 5, Products of Industry) noted that the firm operated two furnaces, annually used 450 tons of pig iron (valued at $15,300); 1200 cords of wood (valued at $2400) and 50,000 bushels of charcoal (valued at $2500) and produced 380 tons of wrought iron worth $32,300.

On June 23, 1853 Hermon Chapin made a contract with Stephen Brignen to operate the firm. (See Table VII) A typical work week, ending May 14, 1853, is shown in Plate II. During that week 8.6 tons of wrought iron was produced, consuming 22 cords of wood at $1.75 per cord; 500 bushels of coal (18.42 tons) at $1.50 per ton. Labor varied from $3 per turn of 12 hours for puddling to $1.12 for weighing. A summary of these costs are shown in Table XII. Apparently this business was not profitable and was closed down by Hermon Chapin about 1863.

A saw and grist mill (Munson's Mill) at Barkhamsted was acquired by Hermon Chapin in the early 1850's. While this was undoubtedly used to process lumber for plane stock, building lumber was the largest product from this mill. Contracts with Edward Gaines and later with the Burwell brothers to run this mill are shown in Table V and XI.

Hermon Chapin made a contract with Ithiel S. Richardson of Boston to act as his agent for selling the New England Mower and Reaper on February 23, 1860. (Table X), also noted on Plate III.

TABLE XII
COST of PRODUCING WROUGHT IRON at PUDDLEVILLE (Week, May 14, 1853)

Item	Cost	Dollars per Ton	Dollars per 100 lbs.
Labor	$118.72	$13.79	$0.69
Fuel	66.00	7.67	0.38
Cast Iron	410.57	47.70	2.38
Total	$595.29	$69.15	$3.45

TABLE IX
AGREEMENT BETWEEN HERMON CHAPIN AND REULE RICE, November 21, 1853

This agreement made and entered into by and between Hermon Chapin on the one part and Reule Rice on the other part. Witnesseth: -
That the said Rice agrees and does by hereby agree to chop all the wood on a certain piece of land as Leased to said Chapin by Leonard Andrews as per agreement dated Nov. 18, 1853. Said wood to be chopped and well split and piled suitable for cording four feet long. All the wood on said lot to be chopped by the first of June next for which the said Chapin is to pay the said Rice Forty Five (45) cents per cord; payable for all wood chopped the first of March, the balance the first of June when said job is completed.

Reule Rice
Hermon Chapin

[Collection of Documents New Hartford Historical Society]

PLATE II - EXPENSES for RUNNING H. CHAPIN'S FORGE, WEEK OF May 14, 1853
[from H. Chapin's Account Book, Connecticut Historical Society]

H. Chapin Forge a/c

1853	Expences of running the Forge one week ending			
May 14	Charles Jaquea Melting 3 3/5 Turns at 125			4 25
	Henry Lee " 2 " " "			2 50
	John Shay " 7 3/5 " " "			9 50
	Benj. Jaquea Puddling 6 " " 305			18 30
	Stephen Brigner " 6 " " 18 30			
	Less 1 Lighting up 1 25			17 05
	Henry Hill Heating 6 Turns " 175			10 50
	Mike McGovin " 6 " " 150			9 00
	Wm H. Belcher Hammering 6 " " 200			12 00
	Nathaniel Day " 6 " " 225			13 50
	H. D. Robbins Drawgate 6 " " 112½			6 75
	John Haley " 6 " " 75			4 50
	Leeke Graham Wooding &c 6 " " 87½			5 25
	H. D. Robbins Weighing & 1 day " 112½			1 12
	D. Norton			4 50
				118 72
	Wood 22 Cords at 175			38 50
	Coal 500 Bushels " 550			27 50
	8-18-0-14 Pig Iron at $45 1/4			404 57
Allow	1-1-21 Chefferies			6 00
				595 29

Iron Made by S. Brigner 8741
"   "   " B. Jaquea 8476 } 7-13-2-25

Work by H. Shepard

TABLE VII

AGREEMENT between HERMON CHAPIN and STEPHEN BRIGNEN, June 23, 1855

This indenture made and entered into this 23rd Day of June 1855 by and between Hermon Chapin on the one part and Stephen Brignen on the other part, Witnesseth That from on and after the said 23rd day of June, the said Chapin & Brignen do enter into a copartnership for the purpose of making and vending Bar Iron and any such other iron as from time to time may be agreed upon. For which purpose the said Co. are to rent the Forge Works now owned by the said Chapin to wit, the Forge building. Coal, Iron and Wood Houses, the Office and the Hay Scale with the Yards about the same together with the Water power, Dam and Canal and all the Tools now inside in said Works, all of which they are to rent of the said Chapin during the term of this Contract for which the said Co. is to pay the said Chapin for the use and rent of the same Five Dollars per Ton of 2240 lbs. for all iron made by said Co. during the term of this said contract.

The said Chapin is to keep the natural decay of the building in repair and do all needful repairs to the Dam, also to build new Water Wheels when those now in use fail by natural decay and also to pay all Taxes on said described property.

The said parties are to be equally interested and concerned in the profits and losses of said Co., and in case either party does advance or draw from sd. Co. more than his share the interest amount is to be made equal, and the same adjusted annually.

The said Brignen is to devote his whole time to the interest of sd. Co. when said Works are in operation for which he is to receive from sd. Co. Two dollars per day. - the said Chapin is to assist in the purchase of Iron, Wood and Coal, also in sale of Iron and neither party are to charge said Co. for services except as before written, unless it be for expenses paid when absent from home on said Co. business.

Neither party shall use the Co. name but for the Co. business -
All accounts to be adjusted annually and a proper inventory of the assets made and entered on Book. All accounts of said Co. to be kept in a fair and proper manner and both parties are to have at all times access to the Books and accounts of the same.

This Copartnership is to continue during the pleasure of the parties, either party by giving the other party three months notice in writing may dissolve the same.

It is further agreed that at the dissolution of said copartnership the said Chapin is to take all the Wood, Coal and Iron remaining on hand at a fair market price, unless otherwise agreed by the parties.

In witness whereof we have hereunto set our hands this 23rd day of June 1855 at New Hartford.

Hermon Chapin
Stephen Brignen

TABLE X

AGREEMENT between HERMON CHAPIN and ITHIEL S. RICHARDSON, Feb. 3, 1860

Article of Agreement made and entered into this twenty third day of February A.D. 1860 by and between Hermon Chapin of Pine Meadow, Conn. of the first part and I.S. Richardson of Boston, Mass. by his attorney A.M. Daniels of Hartford, Conn. of the second part. To Wit: The said Hermon Chapin hereby agrees to build for the said Richardson One hundred or more Gere's Patent Mowing Machine at fifty-five Dollars each to be made of the best material and workmanship and to be delivered at their factory in Pine Meadow in complete running order on or before the 20th day of June next in consideration of which said Richardson by his Attorney A.M. Daniels agrees to send agents to said Hermon Chapin for Machines for which the said Chapin is to receive one hundred Dollars each, and from which the said Chapin is to deduct fifty-five Dollars and the remaining forty-five Dollars to be paid over to I.S. Richardson, No. 2 Emnura St., Boston, Mass.

In witness whereof we have herewith set our hands and seals the day and date above mentioned and written

In Presence of
W.G. Budling
Geo.B. Deming

Doron M. Domiely, Att.
I.S. Richardson
Hermon Chapin

Provided the said Richardson's agents take up all of the machines that said Chapin makes, if not the said Chapin has the right of selling the machine for one hundred Dollars each to his agents.

TABLE XI

AGREEMENT between HERMON CHAPIN and L. & G.W. BURWELL, April 20, 1860

This agreement made by and between Hermon Chapin on the one part and Lewis W. Burwell & G.W. Burwell on the other part. Witnesseth that the said Burwells are to take and run the Munson Grist, Shingle & Lath Mills for which they are to have one half the Saw Bills and one half the Toll received. The said Burwells are to do the sawing and grinding in a workmanlike manner, the work to be done promptly and in a way to suit and accomodate customers. Keeping the Mills & Tools in good order the term of this agreement. The wood and scraping made at the Mills to be applied to the purchase of Oil, Saw Scathen Files &c. Said Chapin to furnish all the Saws, Belting and repairs to buildings and main machinery. Said Burwells to keep a fair account of the Tolls and Saw Bills the one half of which the said Chapin is to have at any time he may call for them.

This agreement to continue during the pleasure of the parties. Either party may dissolve this agreement after one year by giving the other party three months notice in writing.

Pine Meadow
April 20, 1860

Hermon Chapin
Lewis W. Burwell
George W. Burwell

Plate III - I.S. RICHARDSON'S AGREEMENT WITH HERMON CHAPIN
March 6, 1860 to Sell New England Mowers.

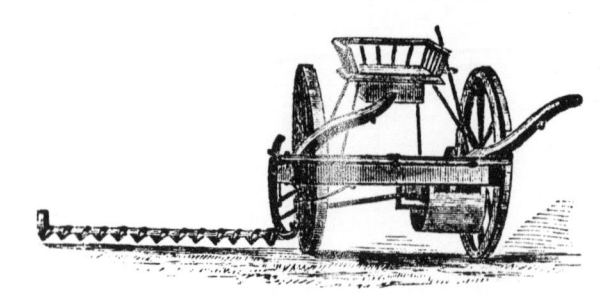

Be it Known, That I, Ithiel S. Richardson, of Boston, County of Suffolk, Mass., in consideration of the sum of *Twenty five* dollars, to me in hand paid, hereby fully authorize *Hermon Chapin* of the Town of *New Hartford* in the County of *Litchfield* and State of *Connecticut* to act as my true and lawful agent, to use, and sell to others to be used, the **New England Mower and Reaper,** in all and every part of the Town of *New Hartford*

County of *Litchfield* State of *Connecticut* for the full term of *fourteen* years from the 16th day of February, 1858, at the full sum of one hundred and twenty-five dollars ($125.00) each, and for no other price, provided he, the said *Hermon Chapin* shall purchase the said Machines from me, which I agree always to furnish.

Given under my hand and seal this *6th* day of *March* A. D. 18*60*

I S Richardson

```
Notes - Chapter IV

1. M.M. Frizzell, History of Walpole, NH, op. cit., p.404

2. Manuscript Records, Conn. Hist. Society, Ms. 74276, Box III

3. ibid, Box II

4. ibid, Box IV

5. History of Litchfield County, [Phila., 1881], p. 410

6. ibid, p. 409

7. The Great Industries of the United States,"Silk Dress-Goods",
   [Hartford, 1872], p. 773. ". . Morus multicaulis. . In 1839
   the speculation in mulberry-trees culminated, and single trees
   were sold as high as ten dollars each."
```

Chapter V

H. Chapin Enters the Rule Business

Rule making in England, like plane making, had become a highly developed industry at the end of the 18th century. London was the center of this trade, as a specialized part of instrument making. During the latter part of the 18th century this industry shifted to Birmingham. From four firms, noted in the 1770 Birmingham Directory, this industry peaked to 52 firms in 1876, and then declined to 13 by 1900.[1] Among the more prominent firms there were: John Rabone & Sons, 1825-1963 (at present still in business there as Rabone-Chesterman Ltd.); Edw. Preston & Sons, 1864-1934,[2] Thos. Bradburn, 1849-1888 (acquired by E. Preston & Sons in 1888); and L. & D. Smallwood, 1870 to present. Typical directory advertisements of these firms have been noted.[3] An account of rulemaking by J. Rabone, jr. was published in 1866.[4] This has recently been reprinted.[5]

While a few instrument makers produced rules at the important centers of Boston, Philadelphia and New York City during the late 18th century and continued through the 19th century, the first firm to employ larger production methods was Belcher Brothers of New York City.[6] Thomas Belcher is first noted in the New York City Directory of 1822 making rules at 145 Division Street. His brother, William, joined the firm in 1825. They are believed to have been English immigrants who had learned this trade there, possibly at Sheffield. While maintaining sales offices in New York City through 1877, their manufacturing was done at Camptown, NJ, near Newark, where they had established a factory in 1834.[7] A price list, originally published by Belcher Brothers & Co. in 1853, has recently been reprinted.[8]

In 1833 S. Morton Clark & Co. started a rule manufactory on the site of the old railroad depot at Brattleboro, Vermont.[9] The financial recession of 1837 caused this venture to close down. In 1838 the machinery was purchased by Edward A. Stearns, previously employed by Clark, who continued the rule business at Brattleboro.[10] After Stearn's death in 1856, Charles Mead purchased this business.[11]

Franklin Bolles & Co. had established a rule business at Hartford, Conn. sometime previous to 1835. On November 6, 1835 Hermon Chapin purchased this, moving equipment and stock to Pine Meadow. The inventory of this equipment is shown in Table I. This data shows the type of machinery then in use for making rules. Soon after, Chapin hired William H. Bang, presumably a former employee of Franklin Bolles, for the term of fifteen months to oversee and instruct hired workmen in the art of rulemaking. (Table II, Agreement No. 30). A minor, James Goodwin, hired November 11, 1835, was the first to receive training under Bang. (See Table III, Agreement No. 44)

The first apprentice hired November 15, 1845 for rulemaking was Lester Phelps. (Table IV, Agreement No. 53) About the same time an experienced rule fitter by the name of Cramer was engaged according to the agreement noted in Table V. It should be pointed out that there were two distinctly different trades involved in rulemaking: jointmaking and rule fitting. A person was apprenticed to only one of these trades, which at that date involved considerable hand work. A second apprentice, Joseph Goodwin, was hired March 9, 1837. (Table VI, Agreement No. 57)

Table I

Bill of Sale of Rule Equipment and Machinery Sold to H. Chapin

Hartford Nov. 7, 1835 Mr. Hermon Chapin Bought of

Franklin & Co, [Franklin Bolles]

2	Wood Cramps	$3.00
2	Planing & one (?) machine	7.00
2	Stamping Stone	3.00
1	Steel Stake	4.00
7	Vices	30.49
1	Brace & bits	4.50
1	Blowpipe & Lamp	.63
1 pr.	Long Divider	1.25
1	Riviting hammer	.25
1	Drill Stock	1.75
2	Hand Vices	1.00
2	Large Hammers	1.50
1	Brass Lamp Stand	.75
1	L (?) wrench	2.00
2	Cast Iron Stakes	1.83
1	Wire Gague	1.25
1	Scraping Plane	1.50
1	Splitting gague	1.00
1	Brass gague	2.50
1 pair	Large Shears	6.00
10	4 Inch Saws	18.00
3	3 Inch Saws	2.00
2	Saw arbors	3.50
1	Screw plate & tap	10.00
1	Milling Lathe	15.13
1	Sett of Slide Tools	4.00
1	Steel Spring Square	1.50
1	Small Ivory Square	1.00
	Bitting Tools	2.00
	Cramps for Joints	9.00
1 pr	Slide Tongs a number of arching tools	1.75
	Blocks for gauging & marking slides	2.00
1	Small Bow Saw	1.00
1	Double Turning Lathe	43.00
	Dies for Slides on Draw Bench	5.63
		$195.71

	account brought up	$195.71
1	Set Dies & punches	57.00
1	Punching Press	29.50
	Milling Blocks	1.00
1	Marking Machine	100.00
	Figures, Stamps, Letters (6 sets)	39.06
	Packing Board	1.75
2	Cramps for Sandpaper & polishing	1.00
1	Upright Drill	1,50
5	4 leged Stools [sic]	1.67
1 pr.	small paper shears for packing	.38
1	Lathe with drills	35.00
	Gearing for Draw Bench	4.88
		$468.45
	5½% off	23.42
		445.03
	Stock	120.25
		$565.28

Hartford Nov. 6, 1835
Rc'vd payment by Note payable
at the Pheonix Bank Sixty days.

Franklin Bolles & Co.

Table II

Agreement with William H. Bang to instruct rulemaking, November 11, 1835

This agreement made and entered into by an between Hermon Chapin on the one part and William H. Bang on the other part. Witnesseth - That the sd. Bang agrees and does hereby agree to work for the sd. Chapin for the term of fifteen months from this date then to be completed and fully ended. Sd. Bang is to work at rulemaking to oversee and to instruct workmen in sd. business for which the sd. Chapin is to pay the sd. Bang the sum of Nine Dollars and fifty cents per week for each week faithful labour so done, sd. Chapin shall pay once in three months during sd. time. Sd. Bang agrees to furnish all suitable instruction and information in regards to sd. business that he may possess. It is understood in the above agreement the the sd. Bang is to conform to the customary rules of labour in sd. Chapin's Shop and is to work eleven hours a day or as he may chose.

William H. Bang
H. Chapin

Table III

Agreement with James Goodwin to work at Rulemaking, beginning November 19, 1835

This agreement made and entered into by and between Hermon Chapin on the one part and Ebenezer Goodwin and James Goodwin on the other part. Witnesseth - The the said Ebenezer Goodwin and James M. Goodwin agree and do hereby agree that the sd. James M. Goodwin shall work for the sd. Chapin at the Rule Making business for the term of two years six months twenty two days from and after the Nineteenth day of November 1835 thence following to the eleventh day of June 1838 for which the sd. Chapin is to pay to the said J.M. Goodwin the sum of two hundred thirty dollars to be paid quarterly in the following manner for each years faithful labour so done in sd. Chapins employ

```
    For the first year fifty Dollars          $50.00
    For the second year One Hundred Dollars  $100.00
    For the following six months 22 days to   83.75
       June 11th, 1838. For the whole time  $233.75
```

The sd. Chapin also agrees to furnish suitable Board and Washing for the sd. J.M. Goodwin while in the sd. Chapins employ during the sd. term or allow him the customary price for the same in Boarding himself. Said Goodwin is to conform to the Rules and regulations which may from time to time be adopted in sd. Chapins Shop during sd. time above written. All which being fulfilled then this obligation is void otherwise in fullforce as witness our hands this Nineteenth day of May Eighteen Hundred and thirty six.

Hermon Chapin
Ebenezer Goodwin
James Goodwin

Table IV

Agreement between Hermon Chapin and Lester Phelps - Nov.15, 1836   [53]

This agreement made and entered into by and between Hermon Chapin on the one part and Lester Phelps, a minor, on the other part witnesseth as follows -   that the said Lester Phelps agrees and does hereby agree to work for the said Chapin as an apprentice at the Rule Making business until he shall arrive at the age of twenty one years which is four years from and after the eighteenth day of January 1837, and until the eighteenth day of January 1841 then to be completed and fully ended and the said Chapin is to pay the said Phelps the following sums for each years faithful labour as aforesaid -

from Nov.15,1836 to January 18,1837, two months & three days $4\frac{40}{100}$

from Jan.18,1837 to January 18,1838, one yeqr   30 Dolls.
from Jan.18,1838 to January 18,1839, one year   40 Dolls.
from Jan.18,1839 to Januray 18,1840, one year   50 Dolls.
from Jan.18,1840 to January 18,1841, one year   65 Dolls.

and the said Chapin is to provide suitable board & washing during said time while said Lester is in his employment or pay the said Lester the customary price for the same, he boarding himself. It is further agreed that the said Chapin is to be of no expense of sickness, military duty &c of the said Lester but that the sums or board above written are to be the full compensation for the above Labour, except instructing said Lester so far as is practicably in the art or trade of making Rules. It is understood that three hundred and ten days work constitute one years work or Labour and the said Lester is at all time to conform to the rules and regulations of said Chapins shop as they are or may be from time to time adopted all which being fulfilled then this obligation is Void, otherwise in full force in witness whereof we have hereunto set our names at New Hartford, Nov. 15,1836

Hermon Chapin
Lester Phelps
Samuel B. Denslow, Guardian to sd. Lester

Table V

Prices Agreed with Cramer for fitting Rule Stuff

```
Broad  4 fold         30cts. pr. Doz. Rules
New    4 fold 9 inch  28cts pr. Doz. Rules
  "    4 fold 6  "    24  "    "   "    "
  "    4 fold Eng.Joint 20 "   "   "    "
Pocket Rules          17  "    "   "    "
Common 2 fold         26  "    "   "    "
Thin   2 fold         28  "    "   "    "
or by the Month and $30 boarding himself
```

Table VI

Agreement between Hermon Chapin on the one part with Pitts Goodwin and Joseph Goodwin [minor] on the other part, 13th May 1837 (57)

". . . . that the said Joseph Goodwin shall work for the said Chapin at the Rule Making business for the term of one year ten months and twenty two days beginning on the ninth day of March 1837 and ending on the 31st of January 1839 for which the said Chapin is to pay the said Joseph Goodwin the sum of one hundred forty seven 30/100 Dollars to be paid as follows -

For the first year fifty dolloars	50.00
For the remaining ten months twenty two days	97.30
Being the whole time	$147.30 . . ."

After completing his agreed period of overseeing the rule work, William Bang on November 15, 1837 made arrangements with Nathaniel Chapin, elder brother of Hermon, then acting as superintendent at the Union Factory, to contract for a specific number of rules to be finished as outside work and delivered when completed. (Table VII, Agreement No. 69) Usually contractors worked at a particular factory with which they had contracted, but occasionally such work was accomplished on the outside and delivered when completed.

Table VII

Agreement between Hermon Chapin and William Bang by Nath. Chapin Nov.15,1837 [69]

This agreement made and entered into by and between Hermon Chapin on the one part and William H. Bang on the other part witnesseth as follows - that the said W.H.Bang agrees and does hereby agree to get out the Boxwood and make or frame Rules for said Chapin as follows -

24 Doz. Rules Narrow 4 fold Arch Joint Bits and Edge Plated Two$\frac{28}{100}$ pr doz.	$54.72
24 Doz. Rules Narrow 4 fold Arch Joint Bits and Edge Plated Two$\frac{53}{100}$ pr doz.	$60.72
24 Doz. Rules Broad 4 fold Double Arch Bits Three$\frac{9}{100}$ pr doz.	$74.16
24 Doz. Rules Broad 4 fold Arch joint Bits and Edge Plated Two$\frac{84}{100}$ pr doz.	$68.16
Making in all 96 doz. Rules at Two hundred fifty seven $\frac{76}{100}$	$257.76

Said Chapin is to furnish all the stock for said Rules and the Joints ready made at his shop in New Hartford where said Bang is to receive it and deliver the Rules free of expense to said Chapin except the above named prices and the said Bang is to perform said work in a good workmanlike manner according to the work heretofore done by said Bang in said Chapins shop and the said Bang is to perform said work commencing at this time and applying himself wholly to the prosecution of the same until said job is finished and he is to deliver at said Chapins shop so many of the aforesaid Rules as he may have finished at each succeding three months from and after this date until said work is completed at which stated times said Chapin is to pay siad Bang for all the Rules so finished and retruned, the sums or prices annexed to the several kinds above which is so far as paid to apply on the general amount to be paid by said Chapin for said Job, all which being fulfilled then this Obligation is void otherwise in full force whereof we have hereunto fixed our hands at New Hartford this fifteenth day of November 1837. *William H. Bang*
Hermon Chapin by Nathl. Chapin

In order to understand the working arrangements in hiring help for rulemaking, excerpts from several agreements, made at the Union Factory, follow. (Tables VIII and IX) After 1844 formal work agreements were discontinued and substituted by a simple statement, recorded in Chapin's ledger, indicating the tenure, type of work and pay. Examples of these later agreements appear in Table X. An unusual agreement was made on December 22, 1842 between Edward Gaines and H. Chapin whereby Gaines was to work on rules and to be paid one half in cash at the prevailing rates and the other half in some land owned by Chapin in Pennsylvania. (Table XI)

Table VIII

Various Rule Working Agreements with H. Chapin, 1839 - 1842

Agreement between H. Chapin and George L. Byington - Jan.2, 1839   [72]

". . . . sd Byington agrees to work for the sd. Chapin on Rule Joints for the term of one year from and after this date for which the sd. Chapin agrees to pay the sd. Byington One dollar 25/100 per day for the first three months and one dollar 33-1/3/100 for the next six months and one dollar 42/100 for the last three months to be paid quarterly, he boarding himself. . . .   dated Jan.2,1839 at New Hartford. . ."

Agreement between H.Chapin and Russell Perkins - June 1,1939   [74]

". . . . the said Russell Perkins agrees and does hereby agree to work for the said Chapin on making Rule Joints for the term of two years from and after the seventh day of April 1839 for which the said Chapin agrees to pay him for the said work the following prices to wit -
   for the first quarter or three months, seventy-five cents per day   75¢
   for the second quarter or three mos. eighty seven and half cts.   87½
   for the next four succeeding Quarters, one dollar per day   1.00
   for the next or seventh Quarter, one 12½/100 Dollar per day   1.12½
   for the eighth or Last Quarter, one 25/100 dollar per day   1.25
To be paid in quarterly instalments at the end of each quarter or three months succesively and board. . . . "

Agreement between H.Chapin and William S. Nash - July 15, 1841   [76]

". . . . the said Nash agrees. . .to work for the said Chapin for the term of three years after the date of July 15th, 1844. . . at framing Rules. . . for which the sd. Chapin agrees to pay the sd. Nash the customary price by the dozen for Journeymen, except discounting by twelve and a half percent on all work done by the said Nash during the first year. Said Chapin is to pay the sd. Nash once in three months as is customary in sd Chapins shop. . . . "

Agreement between H.Chapin and Josiah C. Allen - Aug.10, 1841   [78]

". . . . the sd. Allen agrees. . . to work for the said Chapin the term of three years from and after the thirteenth day of May AD 1841 to the thirteenth day of May AD 1844. . . to work on Rule Joints. . .for which the sd. Chapin agrees to pay the said Allen he Boarding himself during sd. term -
   for the first year One hundred Seventy five Dollars
   for the Second year two hundred and twenty five Dollars
   for the Third year Two hundred & Seventy five Dollars . . . . . ."

Table VIII (Continued from Page 156)

Agreement between H.Chapin and Joseph G. Goodwin - June 12, 1842   [80]

". . . . said J.G.Goodwin agrees . . . to work for the said Chapin at framing and finishing Rules for the term of three years from and after the first day of December AD 1841 to the first day of December AD 1844. . . . the said Chapin agrees on his part to pay the said Goodwin the customary price by the piece for all work well and faithfully done by the said Goodwin . . "

Table IX
Work Agreement with Samuel Allen, October 14. 1845

Agreement between H.Chapin and Samuel Allen - October 14, 1845   [90]

". . . said Samuel Allen agrees. . . to work for the said Chapin for the term of three years from and after the third day of June 1845 to the third day of June 1848. . . for which the said Chapin agrees to pay him the said Allen the following named prices to be paid once in three months, viz
    For the first year, eighteen dollars fifty cents per month
        the second year, twenty-three dollars fifty cents per month
        the third year, thirty-one dollars and fifty cents per month
which is to be in full for the labour and Board of said Allen, he boarding himself. . . .It is further agreed that the said Allen is to work on Rule joints, Packing and such other as the said Chapin may wish in said Chapin Shop during the term aforesaid. . . ."

Table X - Statement Work Agreements, H. Chapin's Ledger

Oct. 14, 1844 - ". . . Agreed with Nelson Gaines to work one year on Rules at 5 pct. discount."

July 20, 1845 - ". . . Agreed with H.A. Seymour to work one year on framing Rules & Repairing &c. Price on job will be 12½ cts. per hour."

Jan. 5, 1846 - "Agreed with Ralph Seymour to work on 68 Rules by the piece at 10% off for such time as we may agree."

June 10, 1846 - "At noon, John J. Frazier began work to work on Rules two years at 10% off, as is customary."

Sept. 15, 1847 - "John Spear began work to work two years finishing Rules &c. for the first year seventy-five cents per day for the second year One dollar per day he to board himself."

May 18, 1850 - "Solon Rust began work on Rules to work until he is 21 years old to discount 10 percent for two years and 5 percent thereafter."

August 15, 1850 - "Cyrus B. Havens began work on Rule joints at 75 cts. per day of 11 hours for one year."

Oct. 25, 1854 - "Agreed with H.H. Gilbert to make middle plate joints for pocket Rules Narrow 4 fold at two dollars per thousand. Joints to be made the average kinds as wanted and agreement to continue until the first of April."

Table XI - Work Agreement with Edward Gains

Edward Gains Agreement - November 22, 1842 [not recorded in H.Chapin's Work Ledger]

    This agreement made and entered into by and between Hermon Chapin on the one part and Edward Gains on the other part all of New Hartford, Witnesseth - That whereas the said Gains has this day bought of the said Chapin a certain peice of land in Warren County, Pa. and is thereby indebted to the said Chapin in the sum of three hundred & thirty dollars, which sum the said Gains agrees to work for the said Chapin in Labour on Rules by the piece at the price now paid by the said Chapin until the same shall amount to the sum of Six hundred & Sixty Dollars, the half to apply to the payment for said Land and the balance to be paid by said Chapin quarterly.

    It is further agreed that the said Gains is to pay interest to the said Chapin on all that may be due for said land after one year. It is understood in the above agreement that all settlements & interest amounts is to be made once in three months from this date.

Dated at New Hartford, Nov. 22, AD 1842   *Hermon Chapin*
    Edward Gains

Solomon A. Jones was first listed as a rulemaker at 206 Main Street in the Hartford 1841 Directory. Squares and marking gauges with his imprint are also extant. It is possible that Jones may have formerly worked for Franklin Bolles. Willis Thrall's first listing in a Hartford Directory was in 1842 as a map publisher, but in 1843 he was listed as a rule manufacturer. An 1862 Broadside, noting prices of his rules, stated: "Successor to S.A. Jones and Manufacturer of Boxwood and Ivory Rules." (See Plate I) In 1860 this firm became Willis Thrall & Son. They continued at Hartford in the rule business until the death of Willis Thrall June 21, 1884. His son, Edward B. Thrall, continued the firm name, selling hardware until 1896.

Plate II notes the tenure of the most important rule manufacturers in United States during the 19th century.

Henry Albert Seymour, born at New Hartford January 22, 1818, signed an agreement to work for Chapin at making rules on July 20, 1845. (See Table V) He had probably previously learned rule framing under some contractor at Chapin's factory, as this was the first agreement noted in Chapin's ledger. Seymour's account book is in the collection in the Library at the Connecticut Historical Society. The first page of this notes some 1839 and 1840 charges to Chapin for framing rules. (Table XII) He married at New Hartford in 1844, but went to Bristol in 1847 to work at the clock factory of Boardman & Wells.[12] This firm was manufacturing brass movements, but had to abandon this business due to conflicts of a patent held by Noble Jerome.[13] Seymour then went into partnership with his brother-in-law, John Churchill, manufacturing rules at Bristol about 1849, establishing the firm Seymour and Churchill. Thomas Conklin learned the rule making trade at this firm and eventually purchased this business. A. Stanley & Co. purchased this business from Conklin about 1854, removing the machinery to New Britain.[14] Conklin joined this firm and had important influence on their subsequent successful expansion. This firm merged with Hall & Knapp, level manufacturers at New Britain and in 1858 this combine became Stanley Rule & Level Co. An announcement to this effect appeared in the foreword to the *1859 Price List of the Stanley Rule & Level Co.*[15] (See Plate III) Since Seymour received his original rule training with H. Chapin, the later formation of Stanley Rule & Level Co. was related in a manner to this trade at the Union Factory.[16].

WILLIS THRALL,

SUCCESSOR TO S. A. JONES & CO.
Manufacturer of
BOX WOOD AND IVORY RULES,
HARTFORD, CONN.

WARRANTED ACCURATE, AND MADE OF WELL SEASONED AND SELECTED TURKEY BOX WOOD.

LIST OF PRICES.

	No.	per doz. $ cts.		No.	per doz. $ cts.		No.	per doz. $ cts.
Two fold Arch Joint Slide Brass Bound,	1	27.00	Four fold, Arch Jt., broad, Brass Bound,	18	27.00	Four fold, Square Jt., Small, Edge Plate,	35	8.00
" " " "	2	12.50	" Double Arch, "	19	18.00	" " " "	36	6.00
" " " "	3	12.00	" Arch Joint, " Edge Plate,	20	12.50	" " " 12 Inch,	37	5.00
" " " "	4	11.50	" " " "	21	11.25	" English, 12 "	38	4.50
Two fold Square Joint Slide,	5	11.00	Four fold " Narrow Ivory,	22	33.00	" " 12 " Ivory,	39	8.50
" " "	6	10.50	" " " Brass bound,	23	24.00	Two fold " 6 "	40	4.50
" " "	7	9.50	" " " Edge Plate,	24	10.00	" " 6 "	41	2.50
Two fold Arch Joint, with Board Measure,	8	12.00	" " " "	25	8.50	Iron Monger's Calliper Rule,	42	12.00
" " "	9	7.00	Four fold Arch Joint, small rule, Edge Plate,	26	7.50	Four fold Square Joint, 36 Inch,	43	9.00
" " "	10	6.50	" "	27	9.00	Gunter's Scales,		9.00
" " "	11	6.00	" "	28	7.00	Ship Carpenter's Bevils,		6.00
Two fold Square Joint,	12	6.50	Four fold Square Jt., Broad Edge Plate,	29	11.25	Two Feet Board Measures,		9.00
" "	13	5.50	" " "	30	10.00	" Bench Rules,		6.00
" "	14	4.50	" " Narrow, Edge Plate,	31	9.00	Shoemaker's Size Sticks,		5.00
Two fold English Joint,	15	3.50	" "	32	7.50	Yard Sticks,		6.00
Four fold Arch Joint Broad with Board Measure,			" "	33	6.00	Wantage Rods,		5.00
	16	17.00	" English Joint,	34	4.50	Guaging Rods, 4 feet,		12.00
" " " Ivory,	17	42.00				" 3 feet,		7.00

PLATED SQUARES.

4¼	6	7½	9	12	15	18	Inches.
$4.00	5.00	6.00	7.50	9.50	12.00	14.00	per doz.

SLIDING T BEVILS.

8	10	12	14	Inches.
$6.50	7.00	7.50	8.00	per doz.

Hartford April 5 on 1842

Mr Cresson

Sir You have been recommended to me to be a good agent to sell goods I am engaged in manufacturing Box wood and Ivory Rules and would be happy to send you some of my Rules on sale I could supply you with a good assortment of Rules. I make a discount of 33% off on Rules from the above prices will you receive an invoice of Rules please let me hear from you by Return of Mail

Yours Respectfully
Willis Thrall

Plate I - 1842 Price List of Willis Thrall

[Collection of John S. Kebabian]
"Reprinted by EAIA. 1976".

PLATE II - BOX-WOOD and IVORY RULE MANUFACTURERS in UNITED STATES
Prepared by Kenneth D. Roberts

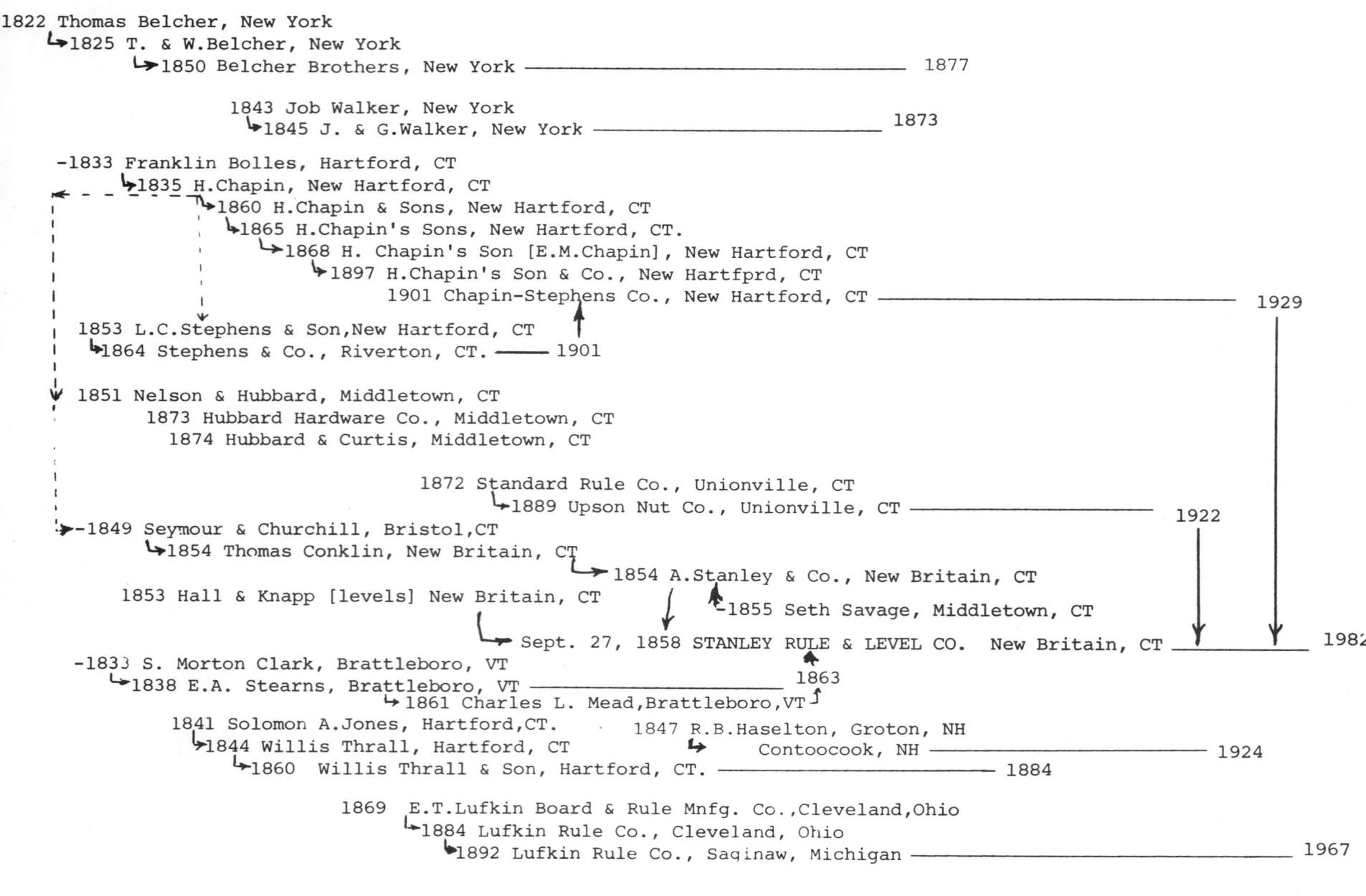

1822 Thomas Belcher, New York
↳1825 T. & W.Belcher, New York
   ↳1850 Belcher Brothers, New York ─────────────── 1877

   1843 Job Walker, New York
      ↳1845 J. & G.Walker, New York ─── 1873

-1833 Franklin Bolles, Hartford, CT
   ↳1835 H.Chapin, New Hartford, CT
      ↳1860 H.Chapin & Sons, New Hartford, CT
         ↳1865 H.Chapin's Sons, New Hartford, CT.
            ↳1868 H. Chapin's Son [E.M.Chapin], New Hartford, CT
               ↳1897 H.Chapin's Son & Co., New Hartford, CT
                  1901 Chapin-Stephens Co., New Hartford, CT ─────────────────────────────────→ 1929

1853 L.C.Stephens & Son, New Hartford, CT
   ↳1864 Stephens & Co., Riverton, CT ─── 1901 ↑

1851 Nelson & Hubbard, Middletown, CT
   1873 Hubbard Hardware Co., Middletown, CT
   1874 Hubbard & Curtis, Middletown, CT

   1872 Standard Rule Co., Unionville, CT
      ↳1889 Upson Nut Co., Unionville, CT ─────────────── 1922

-1849 Seymour & Churchill, Bristol,CT
   ↳1854 Thomas Conklin, New Britain, CT
      ↳1854 A.Stanley & Co., New Britain, CT
         ↳1855 Seth Savage, Middletown, CT
            Sept. 27, 1858 STANLEY RULE & LEVEL CO. New Britain, CT ────────────────→ 1982
                                                1863 ↑
1853 Hall & Knapp [levels] New Britain, CT

-1833 S. Morton Clark, Brattleboro, VT
   ↳1838 E.A. Stearns, Brattleboro, VT
      ↳1861 Charles L. Mead, Brattleboro,VT ↑

1841 Solomon A.Jones, Hartford,CT.   1847 R.B.Haselton, Groton, NH
   ↳1844 Willis Thrall, Hartford, CT   Contoocook, NH ─────────── 1924
      ↳1860 Willis Thrall & Son, Hartford, CT. ─── 1884

   1869 E.T.Lufkin Board & Rule Mnfg. Co.,Cleveland,Ohio
      ↳1884 Lufkin Rule Co., Cleveland, Ohio
         ↳1892 Lufkin Rule Co., Saginaw, Michigan ──────────── 1967

copyright © Kenneth D. Roberts 1982

Reprinted from *Introduction to Rule Collecting*

Table XII

Page 1 from Henry Seymour's Account Book

1839	Hermon Chapin Dr	$	Cts
Dec 17	To Framing Rules No 75 - 2.80	11	20
Dec 22	do — do 6 doz No 72 2.28	13	68
Jany 1st 1840	do — do 2 doz No 54 7.00	14	00
Jany 4th	To Making three Button Guages	—	50
" 14th	To Mending Ivory Rule for W B Spring	—	13
" 22d	To Framing Ivory Rules No 90		
	11 doz @ 1.62	18	63
Do	Do 1 & 9/12 doz No 92 .80	1	40
Feb 29th	To Framing 6 doz No 5 6.00	36	00
March 10	" 6 " No 90 1.62	9	72
March 15	To Framing 1 doz No 92 — .80	—	80
	" 4/12 " " 76 8.00	2	67
	" 12 " " 90 — 1.62	19	44
	" 10 " " 92 — .80	8	00
	" 4 " " 91 — 2.00	8	00
	" one doz Ivory Board Rule	7	00
	" 12 " No 73 — 2.18	26	16
	" 12 " " 61 — 1.24	14	88
	6 " " 62 — 1.32	7	92
	To Cleaning 35 doz Ivory Rules -3-	1	05

[Library of the Connecticut Historical Society]

Plate III - Foreword to *1859 Stanley Rule & Level Co. Catalogue*
[Library of the Connecticut Historical Society]

CIRCULAR.

Your attention is respectfully solicited to the accompanying Price List, embracing all the varieties of goods manufactured by A. STANLEY & CO., and HALL & KNAPP. In order to increase the facilities for the manufacture and sale of our goods, the above firms have united under the name of "The STANLEY RULE AND LEVEL CO.," and will continue to make the same kinds of goods as heretofore, and also any other desirable kinds that the wants of the trade may require in our line of business.

In order to avoid the inconvenience arising from different rates of discount, we have so arranged the prices in the accompanying List, as to make but one discount, and have reduced prices on all the leading kinds of goods.

Our facilities and experience enable us to furnish goods of superior quality, and on the most favorable terms ; and we invite the trade to examine our goods and prices, which can be done either at the Manufactory, or at the Warehouse, No. 52 Beekman Street, New York.

February, 1859.

Two other persons, who also had important influence on rule making at Connecticut, were Lorenzo Case Stephens (1809-1871) and his son Delos Hart Stephens (1837-1919). Lorenzo Stephens is believed to have started work for H. Chapin in 1844 as a journeyman rule contractor. There is no work agreement noted in Chapin's record book, but his account book notes Stephen's charges beginning July 1840. It is not known where Lorenzo received his rule training, possibly working with either Bolles or Jones at Hartford. Delos was born at Hartland and as soon as he was old enough was probably instructed by his father at the Union Factory. Both father and son were listed in the 1850 U.S. Census as rule makers, presumably among the 16 persons then so employed at the Union Factory (See Table V, Chapter III). In 1853, after Delos became 21, the Stephens decided to form their own rule firm. A letter written by L.C. Stephens to Hermon Chapin from Newark, New Jersey, dated October 31, 1853, requested confirmation of terms for their leasing for five years Chapin's "Old Brick Shop" to be fitted up as a rule factory. (Table XIII) Formerly this was the Kellogg Machine Shop that had been acquired by Hermon Chapin. The fact this letter was written from Newark suggests that the Stephens were then working for the Belcher Brothers and that Chapin was desirous of having them back making rules at Pine Meadow.

L.C. Stephens & Co. commenced manufacturing rules at Chapin's "Old Brick Shop" early in 1854.[17] Their lack of capital is apparent from frequent loans. Their first note of $2000 was taken from William Case and Samuel Allen of New Hartford on December 1, 1853 to be payable in two years. Their second note was from the same parties to be for $2000 payable three years after with annual interest.[18] The latter note was extended into a new note on November 15, 1855, the details of which are transcribed in Table XIV. Colateral for this note was the machinery and tools owned by the Stephens at the Brick Shop.

			Dr	L. C. Stephens	Cr			309
1844	July	103	130	57	1844	Apl	97	1 25
						July	103	129 32
			130	57				130 57
1844	July	113	1	00	1844	July	113	76 24
"	Octob	120	136	93	"	Octob	120	88 94
"	Do	134	27	25				
			165	18				165 18
1845	Jany	137	201	55	1845	Jany	137	201 55
"	April	159	289	68	"	April	159	289 68
			491	23				491 23
1845	April	183	5	11	1845	April	183	195 21
"	July	185	288	16	"	July	185	97 96
			293	17				293 17
1845	October	207	269	13	1845	October	207	256 91
1846	Jany	221	77	99	1846	Jany	221	91 21
			347	12				347 12
1846	Jany	224	97	78	1846	Jany	224	97 78
"	April	257	156	90	"	April	257	156 90
"	July	284	137	49	"	July	284	213 44
"	October	292	75	95				
			468	12				468 12
1846	October	308	34	14	1846	October	308	110 52
1847	Jany.	320	76	38	1847	January	346	125 16
"	"	346	125	16				
			235	68				235 68
"	April	370	52	16	1847	April	370	100 40
"	July	374	48	24				
			100	40				100 40

Page 309 from H. Chapin's Account Books

Accounts with L.C. Stephens, 1844 – 1847

[Library, Connecticut Historical Society]

Table XIII - Transcription of Letter by L.C. Stephens

Newark, N.J. Oct. 31, 1853

Mr Chapin

Dear Sir

I write to know if I understand the statements right in regard to Business. In the first place I understand you to say that you would put in a new wheel in your Brick Shop and fix the building so it would be suitable to work in and furnish and fix new driving shafts and warrant that the wall should not fall to do damage. And rent the shop to us, Delos and myself. for the term of five years for the Rule Business for one hundred and fifty dollars per year. And should you build a new shop that you would give us room in that equal to that of the Brick Shop with power suitable for the business and at a rent not to exceed two hundred dollars per year. In that case the Old Shop to be given up and that you will furnish shop machinery with files excepted for fifty cents per day over the price you pay the hand that does our work, or fifty cents per day if we furnish the hands. And that you will do our castings and furnish such patterns as you have without charge for the use of them. And for a year or so let us use your Ivory Machine for one cent per day. Shop to be fitted up within a few weeks. Please send a return line if we have the right understanding of the matter. If we have soon on hearing from you, we shall take steps to improve it.

Box 46A

Yours,

L.C. Stephens

Table XIV

Mortgage Loan by L.C. & D.H. Stephens from W.P. Case and Samuel Allen dated November 15, 1855. [New Hartford Land Records B19, p.309]

Know all men by these presents that we L.C. Stephens and Delos H. Stephens both of New Hartford in the County of Litchfield and State of Connecticut partners now in Co. doing business under the name and firm of L.C. Stephens & Co. for the consideration of Two thousand dollars received to our full satisfaction of William P. Case and Samuel Allen, both now of said town of New Hartford, have bargained and sold and do by these presents bargain, sell and convey unto the said Case and Allen the following described property situated in the Brick Building now occupied as a Shop by said L.C. Stephens & Co. situated in Pine Meadow and owned by Hermon Chapin, viz. all the Machinery, Benches, Belts, Shafting and Tools of every kind and description owned and used by the said L.C. Stephens & Co. by themselves or their employess in and about said Shop occupied as aforesaid in the business of Rule Making, whether said Machinery be attached to said Building or moveable together with such stock as they the said L.C. Stephens & Co. now have on hand, or may hereafter have on hand, whether the same be manufactured or in rough state. And we do hereby for ourselves, our heirs, executors, administrators and assigns agree to account and defend unto the said Case and Allen their heirs, executors and administrators all and singular the above decribed property and that we have good right to bargain and sell the same in mammer & form as is above written & that it is free from all incumbrances saving and excepting this deed. The condition of the above list of sale is that the said Stephens are indebted to the said Case & Allen by a certain promisary note of Nov.15, 1855 for the sum of seven hundred dollars payable to Case & Allen.

L.C. Stephens   *D.H. Stephens*

On August 15, 1854 L.C. Stephens & Co. made an agreement with H. Chapin to supply him with rules, stamped with the latter's name, $800 per month worth of rules of product mix appearing on H. Chapin's 1853 price list. The agreement was to run for two years. A typical order for the month of July 1855 is shown in Table XV. Due to a national recession beginning in 1855 and extending through 1857, H. Chapin was unfortunately not able to absorb this amount of contracted rules. The Stephens claimed for damages of $5000 and filed against H. Chapin at Litchfield County Superior Court. (See Table XVI) The transcript of their charges also records the terms of their original August 15, 1854 agreement. Two attachments were made to H. Chapin's property.[19] A long drawn out trial followed and by final execution, issued on March 11, 1857, H. Chapin was requred to pay $144.49 to L.C. Stephens & Co. and court costs of $95.13. This apparently left ill feeling. On December 3, 1858 H. Chapin served legal notice to L.C. Stephens & Co. "to quit possession of the Brick Shop." During the trial, and even after, H. Chapin continued to purchase rules from L.C. Stephens & Co., as can be noted from an abstract of his account book, dated May 5, 1856. (See Table XVII)

Table XV - Typical Monthly Order for Rules

[Transcribed from H.Chapin's Account Book]

```
January 12, 1855
Order L.C. Stephens & Co. for July 1855
   to be stamped H.Chapin
```

12 Doz.	No. 1		6 Doz.	No. 63	
12 "	No. 2		12 "	No. 65	
6 "	No. 3		6 "	No. 66	
2 "	No. 5		6 "	No. 77	
6 "	No. 6		6 "	No. 79	
6 "	No. 7		6 "	No. 81	
2 "	No. 8		12 "	No. 85	
6 "	No. 11		12 "	No. 86	
6 "	No. 19		2 "	No. 87	
6 "	No. 20		12 "	No. 88	
6 "	No. 21		4 "	No. 89	
4 "	No. 22		48 "	No. 90	
2 "	No. 23		12 "	No. 91	
6 "	No. 25		6 "	No. 92	
6 "	No. 54		2 "	No. 93	
12 "	No. 62		2 "	No. 94	

Table XVII

Abstract of account of Messrs L.C. Stephens & Co   May 5, 1856
          Hermon Chapin, Dr.

Cr.

Rules received in July, as per item act.	$792.65
Interest to May	28.40
Rules received in August," " " "	653.84
Interest to May	20.16
Rules received in Sept., " " " "	418.76
Interest to May	10.81
Rules received in Oct. " " " "	109.85
Interest to May	2.29
Balance of due July 1st	229.33
Interest to May	11.65
	$2297.74

Table XVI

Transcript of Attachment Served to H. Chapin by Sheriff of Litchfield County, October 22, 1855, instigated by L.C. Stephens & Co.

To the Sheriff of the County of Litchfield, his Deputy or to either of the Constables of the Town of New Hartford in said County GREETING –

By Authority of the State of Connecticut you are hereby commanded to attach to the value of Eight thousand Dollars the goods or Estate of Hermon Chapin of said town of New Hartford and summon him to appear before the Superior Court to be holden at Litchfield, within and for the County of Litchfield on the first Tuesday of Novmenber AD 1855. Then and there to answer unto Lorenzo C. Stephens and Delos Stephens, both of said New Hartford, partners in Co. under the name and firm of L.C. Stephens & Co., in a plea of the case, whereupon the plaintiffs declare and say that on the fifteenth day of August AD 1854 by a certain written agreement made by and between the plfts. and deft., the deft. agreed as follows, which agreement is in the following words to wit.

"This agreement made this fifteenth day of August 1854 between L.C. Stephens & Co. on the one part and Hermon Chapin on the other part all of Pine Meadow, Conn., Witnesseth that the said L.C. Stephens & Co. in consideration of the covenants on the part of said Chapin herein after contained doth covenant and agree to and with the said Chapin to sell to the said Chapin all the Rules, that they the said L.C. Stephens & Co. shall make to the amount of Eight Hundred Dollars a month for the term of two years from and after the date of this agreement all of which the said L.C. Stephens & Co. are to make and put up in a good workmanlike manner and ready for Market, and deliver to the said Chapin monthly at his shop at thirty four percent discount from the said Chapins present list of Prices dated 1853, all of which the said Chapin is to take at the said thirty five percent discount and pay the said L.C. Stephens & Co. monthly one half in cash and one half in a four months note payable at Bank. It is further agreed that the Rules are to be made of the usuual assortment required by the Market and in case the said Chapin wants the rules stamped with his name they are to be so done, he furnishing the stamp and the bronze labels. It is further agreed in case the said L.C. Stephens and Co. shall make more Rules than named in this agreement, and sell to other persons they are not to sell at a less rate than the said Chapin is selling at the sametime, provided also in case the said Chapin shall have the privilege if he wishes so to do to reduce the amount of his purchase as heretofore agreed half the amount the said L.C. Stephens & Co. shall sell to any other person as above. In Witness whereof we have hereunto set our hands'
Signed Hermon Chapin L.C. Stephens & Co.

(Table XVI Continued from Page 166)

and the said Agreement being so made, afterwards on the 15th day of August in consideration thereof, and that the Plfts. at the special instance and request of the deft. had then undertaken and faithfully promised to perform and fulfill said agreement in all things on his part to be done and performed and though the Plfts. have always from time to time of making said agreement well and truly kept and performed all things contained in said agreement on their part to be performed and kept according to the tenor, effect and meaning of said agreement, yet the Pltfs. say that the defendant did not perform the said agreement, nor his said promise and undertaking, but wholly omitted so to do, and perform all and singularly the promises and argument made by the Defendant in said agreement, to be by him performed in accordance with the tenor and effect thereof that is to say the deft. would not and utterly refused to pay for the Rules made and delivered to him by the Plaintiffs in accordance with said agreement and uttlerly refused to accept said rules so made by the Pfts. for the said Deft. in accordance with said agreement, all of which was in contrary to the form and effect of said agreement and his the defts. undertaking, promise and agreement and of great damage to the plaintiffs to wit - the sum of Five Thousand Dollars for the recovery of which with their just costs this suit is brought.

An the Plaintiffs further say that on the 15th day of August AD 1854 by a certain other written agreement of that date made and between the Pltfs. and defenant it was agreed the pltfs. should make and deliver at the shop of the deft. in said New Hartford Rules of the value of Eight Hundred Dollars per month if so many the pltfs. should make to be delivered by the pltfs. each and every month from and after making of said agreement for two years and the pltfs. were to make such Rules in a good workmanlike manner and of the kinds which the Market required and if the deft. requested, were to stamp the defts. name upon the same, he the deft. furnishing the stamp for the same in consideration of which agreement by the Pltfs. the defendant undertook, promised and agreed to accept such Rules and pay for the same one half in cash and one half in a Bank note to run from four months, said payment to be made monthly as the Rules were delivered, and the Pltfs. say that though they kept and performed all things them to be kept and performed by virtue of said agreement and according to the tenor & effect from time of making said agreement, the pltfs. say that the defendant did not keep and perform the said agreement nor perform his promise and undertaking of said agreement contained, but wholly neglected and omitted to perform all and singular his promises and undertakings by him in in said agreement made and proised, contrary to the tenor and effect of said agreement and to the damage of the pltfs. in the sum of Five Thousand Dollars for the recovery of which with first costs this suit is brought.

L.C. Stephens is recognized in $50 to prosecute &c.
Hereof fail not but due service & return make according to Law.
Dated at New Hartford the 22nd day of October AD 1855
    Jared B. Foster Justice of the Peace. Attachment of Property followed.

Library of the Connecticut Historical Society [Manuscript File MS 74276]

Late in 1859 the Stephens moved their equipment from the Brick Shop at Pine Meadow about a mile and a half north to the village of New Hartford, sharing space in a shop owned by Seth Priest. In order to raise capital preparatory to this move, the Stephens borrowed $1500 from Mary Moore of Hartland on May 28, 1858. This was subsequently carried by a note with Chester Slade, the details of which are presented in Table XVIII. As collateral for this note, the Stephens listed the rule machinery in their factory. This provides an excellent insight as to the equipment employed at that date. This mortgage loan was again renewed on May 14, 1860 (Table XIX) and again provides further information as to the purposes of special rule making machines.

Before continuing with historical developments of rule making at the Union Factory and also by the Stephens, a basic description of this process will be outlined. As previously noted rule makers emigrated from England to America and followed the trade as it was practiced in the mother country. The three basic types of rules: linear measure; volume measure and calculating, have been listed in *INTRODUCTION TO RULE COLLECTING*.[8] Almost any trade making products from wood, metal, ceramics or leather required measuring devices. The most common materials employed for making rules were boxwood, ivory or fabric tape. Boxwood was imported from Turkey and southern Russia. It was close grained, due to extremely slow growth rate, was relatively stable, wear resistant and had an attractive finish. Ivory from elephant tusks was imported from Africa and India. While very attractive, it was susceptible to dimensional changes. It expanded during moist weather and contracted during dry conditions.

A rule two feet long was the most common size used in the England woodworking trades. For ease in carrying about during working these were made in two-fold for the tool chest or a four-fold for the pocket. The former had a brass main joint attaching the two twelve inch legs. The later additionally had middle joints, which divided each leg folding into six inch lengths. In such folding rules the number of joints is one less than the number of folds. The designated number of folds is equal to the number of pieces being folded. Three basic types of main joints were round, square and arch, progressively more expensive in that order, but also proportionally of greater rigidity.[20] Three types of middle joints were middle plate, edge plate and arch, also progressively more expensive, but stronger. Additionally some special joints were offered. In England the ends of these rules were usually tipped for protection with an iron plate. More common practice in United States was to use brass. Protecting the outside edges with a brass pinned frame resulted in a half-bound rule; whereas continuing this protection also on the inside edges resulted in a full bound rules. Pins inserted in the inside edges, held the folded rules in alignment when folded, designated this as a "bitted" rule. In bitted unbound and half-bound rules, pieces of drilled brass were usually dovetailed into the opposite leg to prevent splitting out by the pins.

Since rule making was a highly specialized trade and most manufacturers were secretive concerning their methods, very little has been published concerning the process followed. Up until about 1850 joint making was essentially a hand operation of sawing, drilling, riveting and filing. Initially such work was performed on castings, but by 1850 machines for blanking stock from wrought metal had been developed. Such machinery was belt driven from water or steam power. In England most of the work on boxwood was done by hand sawing and planing, while these processes in America were accomplished by power circular sawing. An article written by J. Rabone, jr. of the famed Birmingham rule makers, published in 1866, described some of the techniques of marking such rules, but did not offer much information on the actual making.[4] An article published in 1872 concerning the making of rules at Stephens & Co. at Riverton, Conn. provides an insight on American practice at that time.[21]

An article written in 1910 by H.E. Drake, whose father was at that date a key employee at the Chapin-Stephens Co. at Pine Meadow, Conn., describes the practice then followed at this firm. This appears as an Appendix to this Chapter with footnotes added by this Publisher.

Returning to the subject of H. Chapin, both the 1839 and 1853 Union Factory Catalogues listed prices of 99 different sizes of many types of rules. While these same rules in 1853 were priced slightly more than half the 1839 figures, this was due to a change in wholesale discounting rather than reduced production costs. This was the same situation as with the plane prices, as previously noted in Chapter III. Approximately 80% of the product mix or rules were folding rules made from either boxwood or ivory. The remaining 20% were wooden straight rules, mostly of boxwood, for such special purposes as, log or board measure, wantage or rods, button or watch gauges, yard or bench sticks, etc. (See page 2 of Plate V, Chapter III)

The distribution of the 78 folding rules of the total 99 listed in the 1839 and 1853 Union Factory Price List (See pages 2 & 3, Plate V, Chapter III) is shown in table XX. The most frequent size was the two-foot, two-fold (33 rules) for the tool chest, followed by the two-foot, four-fold (32 rules) for the pocket.

TABLE XX

PRODUCT MIX OF FOLDING RULES MADE BY H.CHAPIN, 1839 & 1853

[Rules formerly made by Franlin Bolles, Hartford, Conn., c. 1834]

	Two-Fold Rules		Four-Fold Rules			
BOXWOOD [63]	24"	6"	36"	24"	12"	6"
Round Joint	1		1	2	1	
Square Joint	11			8	2	
Arch Joint	17			17	3	
IVORY [15]						
Round Joint					1	
Square Joint		1		1	1	1
Arch Joint	4			4	2	

Several of the two-foot, two-fold were furnished with brass slides. Two of these were further designated as "engineer." These were furnished with a logarithmic or so called "Gunter scales" for making mathematical calculations. Such rules were originally designed by J. Routledge of Bolton, England in 1811.[22] Soon thereafter Routledge wrote a book of instructions for using these rules, which was apparently copied verbatum both in England and United States for many years by numerous firms. Plate IV shows the cover of a nominal 4" x 6" hand sewn booklet of 36 pages *INSTRUCTIONS to the ENGINEERS SLIDING RULE, etc.* published in 1858 by Hermon Chapin. The text of these instructions is the same as the sixth *IMPROVED EDITION* of the same title by J. Routledge, published in London in 1823.[23] Of the other five rules listed with slides some may have been linear measuring extension scales and some may have been "Carpenter's Slides Rules," also with a Gunter scale.[24]

A page listing prices and types of rules from an undated Union Factory Catalogue, believed to have been issued in 1857, is shown as Plate V. Some ivory rules at advanced prices from the 1853 list are offered with "German silver" joints, bindings and plates. The practice of using this material, an alloy of copper, nickel and zinc, but no silver, is believed to have started in England about 1850. Belcher Brothers & Co. at New York were probably the first to make rules with this material in United States.

Table XVIII

Mortgage Loan - L.C. Stephens & Co. to Chester Slade, Recieved for Record Jan.3, 1859 [New Hartford Land Records B.21, p.508]

Know all men by these presents that we L.C. Stephens and D.H. Stephens both of New Hartford, County of Litchfield and State of Connecticut Partners in Company under the name and firm of L.C. Stephens & Co. for the consideration of fifteen hundred dollars received to our full satisfaction of Chester Slade of the Town of Barkhamsted, County and State aforesaid, have bargained sold and conveyed, and do by these presents bargain, sell and convey unto the said Chester Slade the propery now occupied by us at this time situated in the "brick shop" which shop we occupy under a lease from Hermon Chapin, said property consist of all the machinery, belts and tools in said Shop and used by us in the manufacture of rules together with all the stock on hand both of the new or material and the manufactured articles. The Machinery is described as follows, viz. For sawing Boxwood &c. one large Saw bench with 22 inch saw; on do [same] with five saws for slitting stuff &c., one planing machince, one tenoning machine, one machine for cutting stuff to a length, one power press with 50 dies & punches, two presses for foot with three dies & punches, one macine for turning rolls, one do milling head middle plates

      one do cutting rolls & drilling them
      one do drilling
      one do Driving Joints
      one do Drilling holes in head middle plates
      one do scraping heads
      one arching machine
      one machine for setting back heads
      one   do   do   do   middle joints
      one   do   do nicking middle joints
      four   do   do sawing middle joints
      one   do   do sawing for tips
      one   do   do milling tips & slitting
      one   do   do slides, bits &c.
      two   do   do nicking stuff for joints
      one   do   do slitting for bead for Patent Rule
      one   do   do pairing brass, ivory or boxwood
      one Lathe for drilling for closing pins
      Two upright Drilling Lathes
      Three Horizontal do   do
      One Arch   do
      One heavy vice for pounding tips
      One grind stone
      Four Stoves & Pipes

Five Frames for Machinery, 2 clocks, oil cans, 48 pullies & belts 7 shafts, marking machine or graduating to divide rules, one figuring machine, 3 stones for finishing, 4 sizes of figures, one set of alphabet and number of other stamps, two pieces of iron, one copying press and we do hereby for ourselves, our executors, administrators and assigns warrant and defend the above described property to the said Chester Slade his heirs and assigns against all claims and demands whatsoever,

The condition of this bill of sale is this the said Chester Slade is signer with the L.C. Stephens & Co. of a Note for the sum of fifteen hundred dollars payable to Mary Moore of Hartland in Hartford County said note payable two years after the date thereof with interest and dated May 28. 1858 . . . . . [signed July 11, 1858]

Table XIX

Mortgage Loan - L.C. Stephens & Co. from Chester Slade, Received for Record May 14, 1860 [New Hartford Land Records B.21 p.553-554]

Know all men by these presents that we L.C. Stephens and D.H. Stephens both of New Hartford, County of Litchfield abd State of Connecticut, Partners in business under the name & firm L.C. Stephens & Co. for the consideration of fifteen hundred dollars received to our full satisfaction of Chester Slade of the town of Barkhamsted, County and State aforesaid bargained, sold and confirmed unto the said Chester Slade the property owned by us at this time situated & being in the brick shop in Pine Meadow which we occupy by virtue of a lease from Hermon Chapin, said property consists of all the machine belts and tools in said shop and used by us in the manufacturing of rules together with all the stock on hand,both of the new or raw material & the manufactured articles. The machinery is describes as follows; viz., For sawing boxwood & c., one large saw bench 22 inch saw, One do with five saws for slitting stuff &c., One planing machine, One tenoning machine for cutting stuff to a length, One power press with fifty dies and punches, Two presses for foot, three dies & punches, One machine for turning rolls, One do head middle plates, One do cutting rolls and drilling therein, One do drilling, One do driving joints, One do drilling holes head middle, three do scraping heads, One arching machine, One machine for setting back heads, On do do do middle joints, One do for sawing middle joints, One do for sawing lips, One do for milling lips and slitting, One for slide bits &c., Two do for nicking stuff for joints, One do for slitting for bead for patent rule. One do for paring brass, ivory or boxwood, One lathe for drilling for closing pins, Two upright drilling lathes & Three horizonatal do, & one arch. do., one heavy vice for pounding,one grind stone, four stoves & pipes, five frames for machinery, 2 clocks, oil cans, 48 pullies & belts, one marking machine, one graduating to divide rules,one figuring Machine, three stones for finishing, four lines of figures, one set of alphabet & a number of other stamps, two pieces of iron, one copying press and we do hereby for ourselves, our executors, administrators and assigns warrant and defend the above described property to the said Chester Slade, his heirs and assigns against all claims & demands whatsoever. The condition of this bill of sale is such that the said Chester Slade is signer with & for L.C. Stephens & Co. on a note for the sum of ten hundred dollars payable to Mary Moore of Hartland, county of Hartford said note payable two years from date thereof with interest, dated May 8, 1860. Now the said Chester Slade having signed said note at the request & for the benefit of the said L.C. Stephens & Co., if they shall well and truly pay the sd. note & interest & save the sd. Chester Slade harmless from all the trouble,cost and expense on account of said note & his signing the same, then this bill of sale shall be void. otherwise to remain in full force & binding in law & equity.
In witness we have hereunto set our hands and seal this 15th day of May AD 1860.   *L.C. Stephens*   *D.H. Stephens*

> INSTRUCTIONS
>
> FOR THE
>
> ENGINEER'S
>
> IMPROVED SLIDING RULE,
>
> WITH A
>
> DESCRIPTION OF THE SEVERAL LINES UPON IT
>
> AND
>
> DIRECTIONS HOW TO FIND ANY NUMBER THEREON;
>
> TOGETHER WITH
>
> The application of those Lines to Multiplication, Division, the Rule of Three, &c., &c.
>
> THE MENSURATION OF SUPERFICES AND SOLIDS ARE LIKEWISE MADE PERFECTLY EASY; IT IS ALSO PARTICULARLY USEFUL IN WEIGHING ALL KINDS OF METALS AND OTHER BODIES.
>
> ———
>
> PUBLISHED BY
> HERMON CHAPIN,
> MANUFACTURER OF
> RULES, PLANES, GAUGES, LEVELS, &c., &c.,
> UNION FACTORY, PINE MEADOW, CONN.
> —
> 1858.

Plate IV - Title Page to Hermon Chapin's 1858
Instructions for Engineer's Improved Sliding Rule

The second page of the July 1859 H. Chapin Catalogue noted:

"Although the List of Prices on some articles advanced, **the Rule List being the same as adopted by the Convention of Rule Manufacturers at New Haven, May 26, 1859,** the larger Discount and improved quality of Goods, he trusts, will be entirely satisfactory to those wishing to purchase a good article." (See Plate IX, Chapter III, p. 1)

The first 1859 Conference of Rule Manufacturers was called to order on May 11, 1864 at the Earl House, a hotel at New York city. The participating firms were: Belcher Brothers & Co. and J. & G. H. Walker[25] of New York city, H. Chapin and L.C. Stephens & Co. of Pine Meadow, Conn., Stanley Rule & Level Co. of New Britain, Conn., and Willis Thrall of Hartford, Conn. William Belcher was elected president and George Walker as secretary. The owners of all firms attended, with T.A. Stanley representing Stanley Rule & Level Co.

The first order of business was to adopt a uniform terminology of rules to be used by all firms in future prices lists. This was recorded in the Minutes. (See Table XXI)[26] Motion by Stephens passed that an agreed uniform price list should be based on a uniform discount of 50%. A motion by Chapin that consideration be given as to what was a fair profit return resulted in a decision of 25%. Consideration of uniform prices was to be determined at the next future meeting.

Table XXI

MINUTES OF THE RULE MANUFACTURERS HELD AT NEW YORK
May 11 and May 12, 1859

At a meeting of the Rule manufacturers held at the Earl house, New York on Wednesday, May 11, 1869 the following named gentlemen were present: Mesrs. Willis Thrall, Hermon Chapin, William Belcher, Henry Belcher, Mr. Conklin, Mr. Stephens, Mr. Stanley, Geo. H. Walker, Mr. Clearman.

On motion of Hermon Chapin Esq., William Belcher, Esq. was unanimously elected President. On motion of Henry Belcher, Esq., Geo. H. Walker was also Elected Secretary.

The meeting being organized Mr. Henry Belcher moved that the rules manufactured by the aforesaid manufacturers shall be classified as follows the motion being seconded and carried unanimously.

The 2 Fold Rules shall be called as heretofore 2 Fold.
" 4   "   "   " " " " " "   4   "
" Round Jt "   " " " " "   Round Jt.
" Square " "   " " " " "   Square "
" Arch   " "   " " " " "   Arch   "
" double Arch   " " " " "   double Arch
"   "   Square   " " " " "   "   Square
" half Bound "   " " " " "   half Bound
"   Bound "   " " " " "   Bound
Rules made with Bitts " " " "   bitted or with bits

Slide Rules as follows: com. Slide, Gunters Slide & Engineers Slide.

On motion of Mr. Henry Belcher that a uniform Price List be adopted by the Members, carried. On motion of Mr. Stephens that the Price List be so arranged that a uniform discount of 50 per cent may be allowed on Box Wood & Ivory Rules, carried. On motion of Mr. Chapin that the Gentlemen Present give their opinion what they consider a fair profit on manufactured Rules. After some discussion a majority considered 25 per cent a fair profit, after which the meeting adjourned

    William Belcher, President Geo. H. Walker, Secretary

Thursday, May 12, 1859 the meeting being organized William Belcher, Esq. in the chair, Mr. Conklin moved that the Gentlemen present proceed to make a uniform price list to be adopted by all the manufacturers represented at this meeting, if approved of after careful revision, carried.

The following description of Rules named below and the prices appended were adopted preliminary to a further Revision, after which the meeting adjourned. William Belcher, President Geo. H. Walker, Secretary

At their second meeting at New Haven, Conn. on May 26, 1859 an agreed uniform price list for rules was adopted.

Belcher Brother & Co. noted in their *1860 Price List:*

"The Scale of Prices has been reduced on many of the Rules so that the whole may conform with the schedule adopted at the recent Convention of Rule Manufacturers....The Rules denominated Round Joint, being generally made of an inferior grade of Boxwood, although well seasoned, will not have the stamp of the firm upon them, but all others will be stamped "Belcher Brothers & Co., New York" and may be relied upon as genuine...."[27]

It will be noted that the 1859 H. Chapin Catalogue carried new numbers, the agreed new terminology and revised prices. This was the beginning of price fixing for rules, which continued until declared illegal in 1890 by the Sherman Anti-Trust Law. Additional data regarding the activities of Rule Manufacturers Association will follow in a later chapter. At the date of their first conference the probable order of size of the firms attending from largest to smallest was: Belcher Brothers & Co., H. Chapin, J. & G.H. Walker, Stanley Rule & Level Co., L. Stephens & Co., and Willis Thrall & Son.

The outstanding rule making talents of Lorenzo Case Stephens are apparent from U.S. Patent No. 19, 105 for a Carpenter's Rule. Actually, as the patent stated this was for a combination tool.

"...I claim as new and desire to secure Letters Patent as an improved article of manufacture — A measuring rule made as set forth, viz. — having a movable blade and spirit level attached thereto as described, the whole constituting an instrument which may be used either as a rule, square, bevel, plumb, indicator, etc....L.C. Stephens..."[28]

This became known as **Stephens Combination Rule No. 036.**[29] Fig. 40 illustrates this rule as manufactured by Stephens & Co. at Riverton, CT (1863-1901) and also later versions by their successors, Chapin-Stephens (1901-1929) and Stanley Rule & Level Co. (1929-1941). Perhaps the best description of this rule appeared in a circular issued by Stanley Rule & Level Co., c. 1940.[30] Other earlier descriptions have been published.[31] Generally this was made in boxwood with a brass joint and binding. Rare examples are known made in ebony, at least one of which was bound in German silver.[32] These rules are very popular among present tool collectors. The last known advertisement of this rule appeared on page 28 of the *Stanley Rule & Level Co. Catalogue No. 139,* March 15, 1941. (Plate VI) Those rules made by the Stanley firm appear to be the most rare, as they were manufactured for the shortest period.

Data from the 1860 U.S. Census (Schedule 5, Products of Industry) provides an insight to the size of L.C. Stephens & Co., then at New Hartford. This firm was reported to have been capitalized at $10,000, manufacturing a variety of rules, as well as a combination rule of great value [described in the previous paragraph]. Materials used annually included 10 tons of boxwood, valued at $1200; $300 of ivory; $3500 of brass and sundries at $1000. There were 45 employees with an average monthly payroll of $1450. This is equivalent to $32 per month per employee ($1.20 per day for a 27 working day month). The annual production was 86,400 rules, which sold for $37,000.

Fig. 40. – Stephens Combination Rule No. 36. Upper left: Stephens & Co., Riverton, CT.; Upper Right: Chapin-Stephens Co., New Hartford, CT.; Lower middle: Stanley Rule & Level Co., New Britain, CT.

Plate V - Undated H.Chapin Catalogue, c.1854 - 1857

PRICE LIST.   5

Invoice No's. / Price per doz.

Boxwood Rules.—Broad Four Fold.

76	Arch Joint, Bound,	$14.50
	do Half Bound,	11.50
77	Double Arch Joint, Bits,	8.00
78	do Bound,	20.00
	do Half Bound,	17.00

WITH BOARD OR LUMBER MEASURE.

79	Square Joint, Edge Plates,	7.50
80	do Bound,	14.50
81	Arch Joint, Edge Plates,	8.00
82	do Bound,	15.50
83	Double Arch Joint, Bits,	9.00
84	do Bound,	21.00

Ivory Rules.—Narrow Four Fold.

85	Square Joint, Edge Plates,	24.00
	do do German Silver,	26.00
86	Arch Joint, Edge Plates,	25.00
	do do German Silver,	27.50
87	do Bound,	34.00
	do do German Silver,	40.00
88	do 12 inch, Edge Plates,	10.00
	do do do German Silver,	12.00
89	do do Bound,	16.50
	do do do German Silver,	20.00
90	Round Joint, do	5.00
	do do German Silver,	6.00
91	Square Joint, do	6.00
	do do German Silver,	7.25
92	do do Edge Plates,	7.00
	do do do German Silver,	8.25

Ivory Rules.—Broad Four Fold.

93	Square Joint, Edge Plates,	30.00
	do do German Silver,	34.00
94	Arch Joint, Edge Plates,	32.00
	do do German Silver,	36.00
95	do Bound,	38.00
	do do German Silver,	46.00
96	Double Arch Joint,	33.00
	do German Silver,	39.00
97	do Bound,	45.00
	do do German Silver,	54.00
98	Two Fold Round Joints, 6 inch,	2.50
	do do do German Silver,	3.00
99	do Arch Joints, 12 inch,	12.00
	do do do German Silver,	14.00

1*

Plate VI - No. 036 Boxwood Combination Rule, etc.

Nos. 32, 36 and 36½ can be furnished English and Metric; when ordering add EM to the number. No. 136 can be furnished with caliper graduated English on top Metric on under side (No. 136 EM) or with Metric on both sides (No. 136M).

BOXWOOD COMBINATION RULE
RULE—LEVEL—PLUMB—TRY SQUARE—CLINOMETER

Used by miners, carpenters, machinists, engineers and others as a Slope Level or Clinometer to determine *the Degree of Slope and the Pitch to the Foot* of an inclined plane; to lay out angles; to measure the distance to an inaccessible object; also used as a pocket level, plumb, rule, try square and with a straight edge as a parallel rule. Rule is graduated in inches in 8ths, 10ths, 12ths, 16ths and 24ths. Steel Blade, nickel plated, is numbered to show degree of angles and pitch to the foot; also graduated inches in 8ths.

One Foot—Two Fold—1⅝ Inches Wide—Brass Bound

No.	Weight Each Lbs.	Price Per Doz.
036	⅜	$50.40

No. 036 Packed 1 in a Box; All Others 6 in a Box

STANLEY TRADE MARK

28

From *Stanley Rule & Level Co. Catalogue No. 138*, March 15, 1941

Notes - Chapter V

1. See Check List of Birmingham Rule Firms: *1892 John Rabone & Sons Rule & Level Catalogue*, [Reprint by Ken Roberts Publishing Co., 1982], pp.85-87

2. See Documentary, *Edw. Preston & Sons 1901 Catalogue,* [Reprint by Ken Roberts Publishing Co., 1979], p. 1

3. *op. cit.*, [Reprint *1892 J.Rabone & Sons Catalogue*] See note No. 1, p. 88

4. *Birmingham & The Midland Hardware District,* Article written by J.Rabone, jr., [Birmingham, 1866], pp. 628 - 637

5. *op. cit.*, [Reprint *1892 J.Rabone & Sons Catalogue*] See note No. 1, p.83

6. See Documentary, *1860 Belcher Brothers & Co. Catalogue*, [Reprint by Ken Roberts Oublishing Co.], inside front cover

7. Personal communication with Alexander Farnum. See "Carpenters' and Engineers' Slide Rules" by Kenneth D. Roberts, *Chronicle of EAIA*, V.36, March 1983, p. 1

8. *Introduction to Rule Collecting*, [Ken Roberts Publishing Co., 1982], Plate IX

9. Private Communication with Paul B. Kebabian quoting Mary R. Cabot, *Annals of Brattleboro* [Vermont], V.1, p. 414

10. *ibid*, p. 415

11. *ibid*, p. 415, In 1862 Stanley Rule and Level Co. of New Britain, Conn. purchased Mead's interests, continuing the firm there until 1867, when the equipment was removed to New Britain. Mead came to Stanley Rule & Level Co. and brought many of the workmen from Brattleboro with him.

12. *Bristol, Connecticut*, [Hartford, Conn., 1907], p. 483

13. K.D. Roberts, *The Contributions of Joseph Ives to Connecticut Clock Technogy, 1810 - 1862,* [Bristol, Conn., 1970], p. 243

14. J.D. Van Slyck, *New England Manufacturers and Manufactories,* [Boston, 1879], Vol. 2, p. 743

15. Reprinted by Ken Roberts Publishing Co., 1975

16. See Plate II, this Chapter

17. *op. cit., History of Litchfield County*, p. 241

18. New Hartford Land Records, B.19, p. 299, recorded Nov. 21, 1854

19. *ibid*, B.19, p. 307, $3000 attachment; B.19, p. 317, $5000 attachment

20. *Stanley Tools, Catalogue No. 34,* [New Britain, Conn., 1912], p. 4

21. *The Great Industries of the United States*, [Hartford, 1871], Rules, (describes rule making at Stephens & Co.), pp. 739 - 744

22. K.D. Roberts, "Carpenter's and Engineer's Slide Rules, Part I, *Chronicle of EAIA,* Vol. 36, March 1936, p. 3

23. *ibid*, p. 3. See also *Instructions for Improved Slide Rule as arranged by J. Routledge*, J.Rabone & Sons [Birmingham, England, 1867], Reprint by Ken Roberts Publishing Co., 1983

24. J.Rabone & Sons, *The Carpenters' Slide Rule, Its History and Use,* third edition, [Birmingham, 1880] Reprint by Ken Roberts Publishing Co., 1983

25. Job Walker, believed to have been an immigrant from England, was first listed in the 1843 New York City Directory as a Rule maker at Hester St. In 1845 he was joined by his brother, George H. Walker at 61 Elizabeth St. and the firm became J. & G.H. Walker, which continued until 1873. See Plate II.

Footnotes continued Chapter V

26. Also see *1860 Belecher Brothers & Co. Price List of Boxwood and Ivory Rules,* [Reprinted by Ken Roberts Publishing Co., 1982], inside back cover

27. *ibid,* p. 3

28. Also see *U.S. Patent Gazette,* 1859, p. 1o4

29. K.D. Roberts. "The L.C. Stephens Patent Combination Rule, Square, Level and Plumb", *Chronicle of EAIA,* Vol. 35, No. 2, June 1982, p. 29

30. *ibid,* back cover

31. *op. cit. Introduction to Rule Collecting,* Plate XII
    Original from *Hardware Trade Report,* [New York, 1872]; also see *Chapin-Stephens Catalogue No. 114.* p. 21 (Reprint, K.Roberts Pub. Co., 1975]

32. *op. cit.,* Reference No. 29 above

APPENDIX TO CHAPTER V — Rule Manufacturing by H.E. Drake*

One of the most peculiar and interesting, as well as the least known of the industries of this country, is the making of rules. By rules I mean measuring instruments of wood or ivory with one or more joints. Little does a person think that whether he picks up a cheap rule in a five and ten cents store in Boston or an ivory rule in a first class hardware store in Galveston, they are both made within a radius of fifteen miles in western Connecticut. There are only three factories in existence in America which make them.[1] These supplemented by some in Germany supply the world.[2] These are in order of size: The Stanley Rule and Level Co. of New Britain; the Chapin-Stephens Co. of Pine Meadow and the Upson Nut Co. of Unionville. The second named concern is to be the basis of my article, has a capacity of about five thousand rules a day. The secrecy with which the work is carried on, as well as the few concerns manufacturing, is due to the fact that the machinery, most of which is automatic can not be bought, therefore must be invented and constructed at great expense within the shop itself.

Since the Spanish-American War the boxwood of which every rule is made is no longer profitably bought in the West Indies, but must come from the north coast of South America.[3] This is shipped in logs about fifteen feet long to New York by boat and then by rail to the factory. It must be handled by crane, as the weight of a single log is enormous. This wood is chosen for its fine grain, hardness and capability of taking a fine finish. The boxwood logs are piled loosely to allow free circulation of air in timber sheds to start the process of curing. When about half dry the logs are rolled in great chutes to the cross cut saws and cut up into six inch lengths. From there a belt carries them to a splitting saw and then to sizing saws. The pieces slightly larger than the finished product are piled in a brick kiln, where for weeks stifling hot air is forced through them by huge fans. Now they are ready to "burr," that is take down to the required size. The work is now inspected and any dark colored grain thrown out. It is next slotted for the tips, joints and binding, if it has the latter.

The ivory is imported in sticks about a foot long and three inches square, and after being sun cured,[4] is prepared the same way as the boxwood, but with greater care, owing to its brittleness.

The making of the joints may be said to be the most interesting part, with the exception of marking, in the whole process. The sheet brass for the joints, which must be a certain percent mixture,[5] comes in huge rolls weighing one fourth ton each.[6] This is cut and sheared by a machine into strips about eight feet by two inches, for joints; and one foot by six inches for binding, other sizes and thickness being used in other cases. Now it is ready for the presses.

The dies and punches of these presses are considered so valuable that they are kept in a stone vault. Without them the company is lost. They are very hard to keep in repair. The presses punch out the tips, plates and binding from the sheets of brass. The plates are countersunk, milled and scraped to make the pin hold and joint work easy. The soft iron pins are made from wire coils by automatic machines. The rolls are also the product of a single process. The machine takes large brass wire from rolls and drills, turns down and cuts it off with mechanical precision. Now the joint may be "driven up." A roll, two plates, another roll, two more plates, another roll and a pin comprise the most common joint. These are driven together into a joint by air pressure. The tips are sunk and squared by a turret roller. Now the work is ready to be put together.

German silver[7] and ivory, and brass and boxwood are in most cases drilled, countersunk and riveted in one operation, and delivered to the power files, which in turn deliver them to the scrapers who finish them ready for inspection. After they are "passed" they go to the marking room. The graduations on a rule are not stamped on as one would expect, but scratched on by accurate little hardened steel knives, thus eliminating the denting of the brass work. the machines which do this are worth their weight in silver at least. Many years and men are needed to build one machine, as they must be absolutely without fault. Linseed oil and lampblack are rubbed over it, giving the dark color to the lines and figures. After this is rubbed off they are shellacked, rubbed down, re-shellacked and after another inspection are ready for the market.

```
Notes by the Publisher to Rule Manufacturing by H.E. Drake
```

1. At the date of this writing, Dec. 20, 1910, two other firms, Lufkin Rule Co. of Saginaw, Michigan and R.B. Haselton of Contoocook, N.H. were making wooden rules (maple and hickory) for lumber measuring, but not folding rules. After 1920 Lufkin began making boxwood folding rules.

2. The writer, H.E. Drake, was obviously not aware of the large number of rules manufactured then at Birmingham, England at that date.

3. This statement is quentionable. While mahogany and rosewood came from the West Indies and South America, boxwood principally came from southern Russia and Turkey. It grew in a dry climate at the rate of 2½ inches diameter increase in 10 years, thus had a very dense structure.

4. Often ivory was stored in the cupola of the building to expose it to sun light, thus bleaching out stains. See Chapter XII.

5. Leaded high brass (66% copper; 0.5% lead, balance zinc)

6. This appears to be in error. At that date an ingot from which the strip was rolled was limited to about 125 pounds. There was no way to continuously join coild together. It is quite possible that the author meant to state that a single order delivered at the factory was 500 pounds.

7. German silver, now commonly known as nickel silver contains nominally 66% Copper; 17% nickel, balance zinc. Its color resembles silver.

* This article was written, December 20, 1910, by Harold E. Drake, then a student at Worcester Polytechnic Institute. At that date his father, Wilbur Drake was Superintendent at the Rule Shop of Chapin-Stephens Co. Grateful acknowledgement is made to his surviving relatives for use of this data in this publication.

Chapter VI

Developments at the Union Factory, 1860-1870

Before formation of the firm H. Chapin & Sons in 1860, an inventory of the stock, materials in process, finished goods and hand tools was made. The value of these goods was $20,000. (See Table I) Previously in 1857 H. Chapin had evaluated the plane and rule shop with water power at $12,000 and the fixed machinery at $4000. (See Table VI, Chapter II, Part II) Therefore the entire value of the establishment in starting the new firm in 1860 was of the order of $36,000. The listing of approximately 5,200 finished planes totaled about $2,600. (Table II) The large inventory of plane irons (Table III) almost equaled the value of the finished planes. These inventories indicate that bench planes, comprising about 40% of the total, were the most important products.

H. Chapin & Sons issued a 12 page catalogue in 1861 and 1862, similar in most respects to the 1859 Price List of H. Chapin. Rules continued to be sold at the 1859 Convention Listing (see Table IV). The title page to this 1861 Catalogue is shown as Plate I.

At New Hartford in 1861 Delos H. Stephens acquired sole ownership of the firm previously owned jointly with his father. The firm name was then changed to Stephens & Co. Delos arranged a $3000 Mortgage Loan from Seth Priest, using the firm's machinery as collateral. (Table V) The details of this loan provide a useful record of the machinery then at use for making rules. Delos had been issued U.S. Letters Patent #88,094, dated March 1869, for an Improved Rule Clamp. There can be no doubt as to his inventive genius.[1] Unfortunately his lack of understanding business matters kept him in constant debt.

Early in 1864 Delos Stephens purchased the former Phoenix plane shop of Alfred Alford. (Table VI) This was located along the North Branch of the Farmington River at a district of Barkhamsted, then known as Hitchcockville. Originally Alford had sold this property to Lambert Hitchcock in 1818, when the latter, formerly from Cheshire, Conn. came there to make chairs.[2] After a fire and insolvency of Hitchcock, Alfred with his brother Arba, continued to make chairs there until 1853.[3] Alfred then acquired sole ownership and fitted the building up as a plane manufactory.[4] A price list of planes made at the Phoenix Factory is shown as Plate II. While this is undated, it must be between 1853 and 1864. In financing the sale of this property to Stephens, Alford held a $2000 mortgage for which the plane machinery then at this site was offered as collateral. (Table VII) This data provides an excellent insight as to the machinery in use at that date for making planes. Stephens did not make any planes and this machinery was subsequently sold at auction to the brothers George and Horace J. Ward.[5] The title page to their 1870 trade catalogue is shown as Plate III. This firm was apparently not a financial success and was discontinued in 1873. L.H. Stephens purchased their factory building, moved it across the street and set it up as a barn in back of his residence.[6] In moving to this district of Barkhamsted in 1854 Stephens preferred the name of Riverton, which continues at the present date.

On January 29, 1862 Hermon Chapin decided to include his other son, George Washington Chapin, with the firm H. Chapin & Sons, giving him a tenth interest, reducing his by the same amount. (See Table VIII). This gave George and equal share with Edward and Philip. (See Chapter III, Table XI) George had been in co-partnership with his father, managing a sea island cotton plantation in Georgia.[7]

Table I

INVENTORY OF GOODS AT UNION FACTORY

	H.Chapin, 1860		H.Chapin & Sons, 1865	
I. Timber				
Plane Starts	$2299.57		$4307.18	
Planes & Levels	1382.80			
Boxwood	517.59			
Rules			326.56	
Bench Screws			1908.66	
Miscellaneous	836.91		445.63	
Levels	71.17		488.89	
Total	$5108.04	25.5%	$7476.92	23.3%
II. Materials				
Plane Irons	$2586.66		$1516.19	
Level Glasses	41.14		204.07	
Ivory	68.69		553.92	
Sand & Emory Paper	137.61		45.95	
Hardware	96.43		398.86	
Total	$2930.53	14.1%	$2719.01	8.5%
III. Stock in Proces				
Planes	$197.64		$1720.85	
Rules	1486.54		3394.04	
Levels	45.18			
Wood Screws	183.82			
Total	$1913.18	9.6%	$5114.89	16.0%
IV. Equipment				
Hand Tools	$507.02		$472.19	
Files	208.27		308.50	
Total	$715.29	3.5%	$780.69	2.4%
V. Finished Goods				
Planes	$2009.91*		$5409.26	
Rules	4195.56		4147.83	
Gauges	365.65		314.57	
Handles	295.09			
Bench Screws	560.85		492.88	
Levels	725.92		709.05	
Total	$8152.98	40.8%	$11073.59	34.5%
VI. Unpaid Finished Goods on Consignment				
	$1199.27	6.0%	$4892.06	15.3
Total	$20,000.00	100.0%	$32,057.16	100.0%

*Note: An error was made in computation and the correct figure should have been $3129.16, 60% of cost, not 40%. The distribution of planes in 1860 was 28% Bench and 71.6% Moulding, while in 1865 was 36% Bench and 64% Moulding.

Table II

DISTRIBUTION of 5199 FINISHED PLANES
H.CHAPIN & SONS INVENTORY 1860

I. 1296 Single Iron Bench Planes (24.9%)

        365 Smooth   (7.0%)
        331 Jack   (6.4%)
        283 Fore   (5.4%)
         38 Jointer   (0.7%)
        279 Special   (5.4%) [Toy, Gutter, Raising, Mitre, Toothing, Pannel, Door]

II. 598 Double Iron Bench Planes (11.5%)

        221 Smooth   (4.3%)
        104 Jack   (2.0%)
        219 Fore   (4.3%)
         33 Jointer   (0.6%)
         21 Special   (0.4%)

III. 876 Simple Moulding (16.8%) [Bead, Astragal, Reed, Center Bead]

IV. 821 Complex Moulding (15.8%) [OG, Belection, Ovallo, Grecian Ovallo, etc.]

V. 257 Dado   (4.9%)

VI. 49 Filletser   (1.0%)

VII. 346 Rabbet   (6.7%)

VIII. 261 Hollow & Rounds (5.0%) [Pairs]

IX. 358 Match   (6.9%) [Pairs or Double]

X. 202 Sash   (3.9%)

XI. 135 Plows   (2.6%)

Table III

H.CHAPIN'S UNION FACTORY 1860 INVENTORY OF PLANE IRONS
[totaling $2,586.86]

	Number of Irons	Cost in Dollars	Cost per iron	
I.	6939 Single Irons for Bench Planes totaling $913.82			(35.3%)
	3664 Baldwin	416.47	$0.128	
	2205 Casey, Clark Co.	277.42	.126	
	525 Butcher	85.55	.163	
	540 Special	133.88		
II.	4495 Double Iron for Bench Planes totaling $1101.35			(42.6%)
	2147 Baldwin	501.26	.233	
	1980 Casey, Clark Co.	491.31	.248	
	368 Butcher	108.78	.296	
III.	10,658 Moulding totaling $571.69			(22.1%)
	7673 Moulding	358.65	.048	
	906 skew rabbet	66.64	.074	
	516 square rabbet	30.15	.058	
	1077 match	79.05	.073	
	486 plow	37.20	.077	

PRICE LIST

OF

RULES, PLANES, GAUGES,

HAND SCREWS, BENCH SCREWS,

LEVELS, &c.,

MANUFACTURED BY

H. CHAPIN & SONS,

UNION FACTORY,

Pine Meadow, Conn.

JANUARY, 1861.

HARTFORD:
PRESS OF CASE, LOCKWOOD AND COMPANY.
1861.

Plate I

Table IV - Circular Issued Among Rule Manufacturers, 1862

We the undersigned Rule Manufacturers hereby agree not to sell Rules at prices less than the following discounts from the Convention List of 1859, viz: from Boxwood Rules a discount of 50 per cent; from Ivory Rules and goods under the denomination of Miscellaneous articles, a discount of 40 per cent on a credit in no case, either directly or indirectly, to exceed Six months; but for prompt Cash payment Ten per cent may be allowed. These to be our lowest rates to first class buyers, except in certain cases at our discretion, we may allow a further discount of _five_ _per_ _cent_ _from_ _the_ _net_ _Six_ _months_ _rate_, in which case not more than five per cent will be allowed for cash. Given under our hands and Seals this 15th day of July 1862.

Belcher Brothers   Stephens & Co.
J. & G.H. Walker   Willis Thrall & Son
H. Chapin & Sons   Stanley Rule & Level Co.

[Transcription of Circular issued to Rule Manufacturers, Libraey CHS]

Table VI

Deed to Delos H. Stevens from Alfred Alford of Phoenix Co. Mill
Barkhamsted Land Records [B18,p.362] Signed Feb.11, 1864

Know you that I Alfred Alford of the Town of Barkhamsted County of Litchfield and State of Connecticut for the consideration of Three Thousand & fifty dollars received to my full satisfaction of Delos H. Stephens of the town of New Hartford in said County & State Do give, grant, bargain, sell and confirm unto the said Delos H. Stephens a certain piece or parcel of land lying & being in the town of Barkhamsted & bounded as follows (viz) North on land in the possession of M. L. Vanostrum in part & part on a line running easterly & westerly between the land of Wm. Gabriel & George Ransom, Easterly on the Farmington River Turnpike Road, Southerly on the Sanely Brook Turnpike Road in part & part on the Ransom Bridge (so-called) & westerly on highway containing about one acre & a half more or less together with a Brick Factory and all other buildings standing on the same also including the water power dam, floom race & all the wheels, shafts, machinery & fixtures constructed therewith & belong there to also all the patterns, old machines and tools which have been in use & which were purchased by the Grantor of the Phoenix Company by their deed dated October 23rd 1861 and now on the premises & reserving one half of the timber house for six months & the lower room in the yellow building for sixty days from this date. . . .

Table VII

Mortgage Loan of $2000 from Alfred Alford to Delos H. Stephens
February 16, 1864 Barkhansted Land Records [B18, p.363]

Property same as described in [B18, p.362] ". . . . and all the machinery & fixtures connected therewith & belonging therewith including water wheel & the gearing & shafting attached to the same, also three Turning Lathes, one Groove Head Lathe, seven screw taps & augers to match, seven boxes for cutting screws to match the above taps, New Plaining machine, one whip saw, two boxing lathes, seven circular saws now hung with frames & carriage, one polishing machine with nine polishing wheels to fit, one pair of shaves to cut iron, one power press, one screw engine lathe, five filing vices, one large iron vice & all the shafting now on the premises & to include the new wheel first gear and nine shafts which the Grantor may put into the Factory. . . ."

[The above machinery was probably that used by the Phoenix Company in making planes during the period 1853 - 1864.]

Plate II - Title to Price List of Phoenix Company

PLANES, GAUGES, HAND AND BENCH SCREWS,
MANUFACTURED BY THE
PHOENIX COMPANY, HITCHCOCKVILLE, CONN.
Orders respectfully solicited and promptly attended to.

[Price List to Above Caption Reprinted on Page 185]

Plate II - (continued from Page 184)

BENCH PLANES.

Invoice Number.	Price
1 Single Smooth Planes, common Cast Steel,	$ .42
2 do. Jack do. do. do.	.50
3 do. Fore do. 21 in. do. do.	.65
" do. " do. 22 " do. do.	.75
4 do. Jointer do. 26 " do. do.	.85
" do. " do. 28 " do. do.	.95
" do. " do. 30 " do. do.	1.10
5 Single Smooth Planes, best Cast Steel,	.52
6 do. Jack do. do. do.	.60
7 do. Fore do. 21 in. do. do.	.85
" do. " do. 22 " do. do.	.95
8 do. Jointer do. 26 " do. do.	1.05
" do. do. do. 28 " do. do.	1.15
" do. do. do. 30 " do. do.	1.30
9 Double Smooth Plane, common Cast Steel,	.72
10 do. Jack do. do. do.	.80
11 do. Fore do. 21 in. do. do.	1.05
" do. " do. 22 " do. do.	1.15
12 do. Jointer do. 26 " do. do.	1.25
" do. " do. 28 " do. do.	1.35
" do. " do. 30 " do. do.	1.50
13 Double Smooth Planes, best Cast Steel,	.80
14 do. Jack do. do. do.	.88
15 do. Fore do. 21 in. do. do.	1.15
" do. " do. 22 " do. do.	1.25
16 do. Jointer do. 26 " do. do.	1.35
" do. " do. 28 " do. do.	1.45
" do. " do. 30 " do. do.	1.60
28 Mitre Planes, best Cast Steel,	.60

MOULDING PLANES.

32 Beads,- To ¾ inch	.45
" do. To 1 "	.60
" do. To 1¼ "	.85
33 Beads Double Boxed, To ¾ inch,	.50
" do. do. To 1 "	.65
" do. do. To 1¼ "	.90
34 Beads Solid Boxed Dovetailed, To ¼ inch,	.50
" do. do. do. To ½ "	.60
" do. do. do. To ¾ "	.75
42 Center Beads, To ⅜ inch,	.48
" do. To ¾ "	.56
43 Center Beads Solid Boxed Dovetailed, To ⅜ in.	.55
" do. do. do. To ¾ "	.65
45 Dadoes, To 1 inch,	.70
46 do. with Stop, To 1 "	.80
47 do. with Side Stop, To 1 "	.85
48 do. with Screw Stop To 1 "	.146
55 Filletsters,	.90
56 do. with Stop,	1.00
57 do. with Stop and Cut	1.15
58 do. with Stop, Cut and Boxed,	1.40
59 do. with Screw Stop, Cut and Boxed,	2.30
60 do. with Arms, Stop and Cut,	1.65
61 do. with Arms, Stop, Cut and Boxed,	1.85
62 do. Screw Arms, Stop, Cut and Boxed,	2.12½
63 do. S. Arms, Screw Stop, Cut & Boxed,	3.00
64 Grecian Ovolos, To ¾ inch,	.48
" do. To 1 "	.56
" do. To 1¼ "	.65
" do. To 1½ "	.75
68 Grecian Ovolo with Bead, To 1 inch,	.62
" do. do. To 1¼ "	.70
" do. do. To 1½ "	.80
" do. do. To 1¾ "	.90
70 Grecian Ogee with Bevel or Fillet, To 1 inch,	.58
" do. do. do. To 1¼ "	.66
" do. do. do. To 1½ "	.75
" do. do. do. To 1¾ "	.85
78 Hollows and Rounds, No. 1 to No. 12, per pair,	.62½
" do. do. No. 13 to No. 18, do.	.80
" do. do. No. 19 to No. 24, do.	1.00
82 Match Planes, ½ inch, per pair,	1.00
83 do. Plated, ½ " "	1.20
84 do. Over ½ inch to 1 " "	1.05
85 do. Plated, to 1 " "	1.25
86 do. with Handles, to 1¼ " "	1.95
87 do. do. Plated, to 1¼ " "	2.25
88 do. For Plank, "	1.70
89 do. do. Plated, "	2.00
90 do. Moving Fence, "	2.10
91 do. do. Plated, "	2.40
92 do. With Arms, "	2.80
93 do. do. Plated, "	3.10
94 do. with Screw Arms, "	3.30
95 do. do. Plated, "	3.60

MOULDING PLANES, Continued.

Invoice Nos.	Price
104 Qk Ogee, To ¾ inch,	.50
" do. 1 "	.58
" do. 1¼ "	.67
107 Qk Ovolo, To ¾ inch,	.50
" do. 1 "	.58
" do. 1¼ "	.67
109 Raising Planes, per inch,	.84
110 do. Boxed, do.	.88
111 Rabbet Planes, Square, To 1 inch,	.46
" do. do. 1¼ "	.54
" do. do. 1½ "	.68
113 Rabbet Planes, Skew, To 1 inch,	.50
" do. do. To 1¼ "	.56
" do. do. To 1½ "	.64
" do. do. To 1¾ "	.70
" do. do. To 2 "	.76
" do. do. To 2¼ "	.84
114 do. do. Boxed and Cut, To 1 inch,	.86
" do. do. do. 1¼ "	.92
" do. do. do. 1½ "	.98
" do. do. do. 1¾ "	1.04
" do. do. do. 2 "	1.10
" do. do. do. 2¼ "	1.16
115 Rabbet Planes, with Handle and Cut, 2 "	1.20
116 do. do. and 2 Cuts, 2½ "	1.50
119 Sash Planes, 2 Irons.	.75
120 do. do. Boxed,	1.00
121 do. Double,	1.00
122 do. Double Boxed,	1.25
123 do. Screw Arms,	1.30
124 do. do. Boxed,	1.55
125 do. Handled,	1.15
126 do. do. Boxed,	1.50
127 Sash Coping Plane,	.40
128 do. do. Boxed,	.60
129 Sash Filletster, Screw Arms,	1.92
130 do. do. Screw Stop,	2.65
131 Scotia, To ¾ inch,	.40
" do. 1 "	.48
" do. 1¼ "	.56
135 Side Rabbet Planes, per pair,	1.08

GROOVING PLOWS.

139 Plows, 4th Rate, 8 Irons,	3.00
140 do. do. Plated, 8 "	3.20
141 do. do. Boxed, 8 "	3.20
142 Plows, 3d Rate, 8 "	3.40
143 do. do. Plated, 8 "	3.60
144 do. do. Boxed, 8 "	3.60
145 Plows, 2d Rate, 8 "	4.60
146 do. do. Plated, 8 "	4.80
147 do. do. Boxed, 8 "	4.80
148 Plows, 2d Rate, Screw Arms, Hand'ld, 8 "	6.00
149 do. do. do. do. Boxed, 8 "	6.20
150 Plows, 1st Rate, do. do. do. 8 "	6.50
151 do. do. do. Handled, Box [or Rosewood, 8 "	8.00
152 do. 2d Rate, Screw Arms. 8 "	4.80
153 do. do. do. Boxed, 8 "	5.00
154 Plows, 1st Rate, Screw Arms, 8 "	5.10
155 do. do. do. Boxed, 8 "	5.30
156 Plows, 1st Rate, do. Box or Rosew'd, 8 "	6.50

GAUGES.

157 Marking Gauges, per doz.	.85
158 do. Oval Bar, "	1.00
161 Cutting Gauges. "	1.50
162 do. Oval Bar, "	1.65
165 Mortise Gauges, Plated Head and Bar, [Box or Rosewood, "	12.00
166 do. Brass Slide, "	2.75
167 do. do. Plated, "	3.25
168 do. Screw Slide, do. "	5.25
170 Pannel Gauges, per doz.	2.00
171 do Oval Bar, do.	2.34
172 Slitting Gauges, do.	3.75
173 do. with Handles, do.	5.25

HAND AND BENCH SCREWS.

174 Hand Screws, ¾ inch, per doz.	2.00
175 do. 1 " per doz.	2.75
176 do. 1¼ " per doz.	4.00
177 Bench Screws, 2 " per doz.	4.50
178 do. 2¼ " per doz.	8.50

Reprinted for EAIA 1978   Collection of John S. Kebabian

Table V

Mortgage Loan - Delos H. Stephens to Seth K. Priest Received Feb, 24, 1862
Recorded New Hartford Land Records B.22 p.529-530

To all persons to whom these presents shall come - Greeting. Know ye that I Delos H. Stephens of New Hartford, County of Litchfield & State of Connecticut, for the consideration of three thousand dollars received to my full satisfaction of Seth K. Preist of said town, county and state, have bargained & sold & by these presents do bargain, sell assign & set over to him the said Priest, his heirs & assigns to his & their own proper use & behoof forever the following described property situated & being in the shop now occupied by me hiterto jointly with the said Priest & located in said town the same being a shop or factory for the manufacture of rules, viz. in the lower room of said shop, one twenty-two inch saw for cutting logs, five small saws & saw bed for slitting up stuff, one cutting off machine, one planing machine for wood, one shaft iron, seven foot long, one iron shaft, eight foot long, both inch and a half. Eight iron pullies, two of which are twenty inches, four sixteen inches, one twelve inches & one eight inches in diameter. One leather belt five inches wide wide & twenty feet long, one leather belt twenty eight feet long, three inches broad, one four inches wide & twelve feet long, one do three inches wide & seven feet long, two do one & a half inches wide & seven feet long. In the second story in the joint room, so called, one roll machine, one large power press and dies, one joint machine, one milling machine, two drilling lathes, one small turning lathe, three scraping tools , one machine for sciriving brass, two iron shafts six feet long, 1 do 5 feet, 1 do 8 feet and all one inch + a half in diameters, one 4 inch cottom belt 40 feet, two leather belts 3 inch wide & 12 feet long, one cotton belt 3 inches wide & 18 feet long, four belts one inch & 10 feet long, 1 do 1½ wide & 7 feet long, 1 do 12 feet, 1 do 7 feet, 1 do 10 feet, 5 thirteen inch iron pullies, 3 do 9 inch, 1 do 12 inch, 3 do 21 inch, 1 do 30 inch.
In south east room second story one tenoning machine, one nicking machine, one tip machine, one machine for scriving middle joints. one drilling lathe, 3 sixteen inch iron pullies, 5 iron 9 inch do, one iron 16 inch groove pully, 2 do 13 inch, 2 do 6 inch, 1 shaft 11 feet, 1 do 6 feet, 2 do 2½ feet, 1 do 1 inch 2 feet long, 1 three inch leather belt 12 feet, one 1½ do 9 feet, 1 do 16 feet, 1 do 12 feet, 2 do 10 feet, one round belt 30 feet, 2 do 8 feet. - In the machine room, one lathe 8 feet long for iron, one power planer, 5 feet bed, one upright drill for iron, one lathe chuck, one fluting tool, 3 shafts iron, 4 feet long, 1½ inch, one 3 inch leather belt 20 feet, on do 30 feet, one i inch do 20 feet - five 1½ inch do 12 feet, one 2½ inch do 24 feet, one 1½ inch do 18 feet - two 21 inch iron pullies, 5 twelve inch Do, 4 cone pullies, one 30 inch iron pulley. In the finishing room - 1 marking machine, 1 figuring machine. In the varnishing room, 1 drilling machine. In the framing room, 3 story, - one tenoning machine, 3 upright small lathes, 1 arching press, one machine for cutting rules to a length, 3 small horizonatl drilling lathes, 1 set back machine, 1 burring machine, 1 small sawing machine, 1 slide do do, one machine for splitting & milling tips, 3 machines for sawing middle joints, one machine for nicking middle joints, 1 tip machine, 2 nicking machines for head, 1 set back machine, 1 drop, 1 vice & block for tips, one iron 1½ inch shaft 11 feet, 4 do do 5 feet - sixteen 16 inch iron pullies, 6 thirteen inch do, seven 9 inch do, 3 one inch leather belts 12 feet, - one 1½ inch do 12 feet, thirteen 1½ inch do 8 feet, four feet 8 feet each - And I do hereby covenant & defend all & singular the aforesaid property & bind myself & heirs to him the said Priest. . . .

Plate III - WARD TOOL CO. Price List, 1870 [Conn. Hist. Soc.]

PRICE LIST

OF

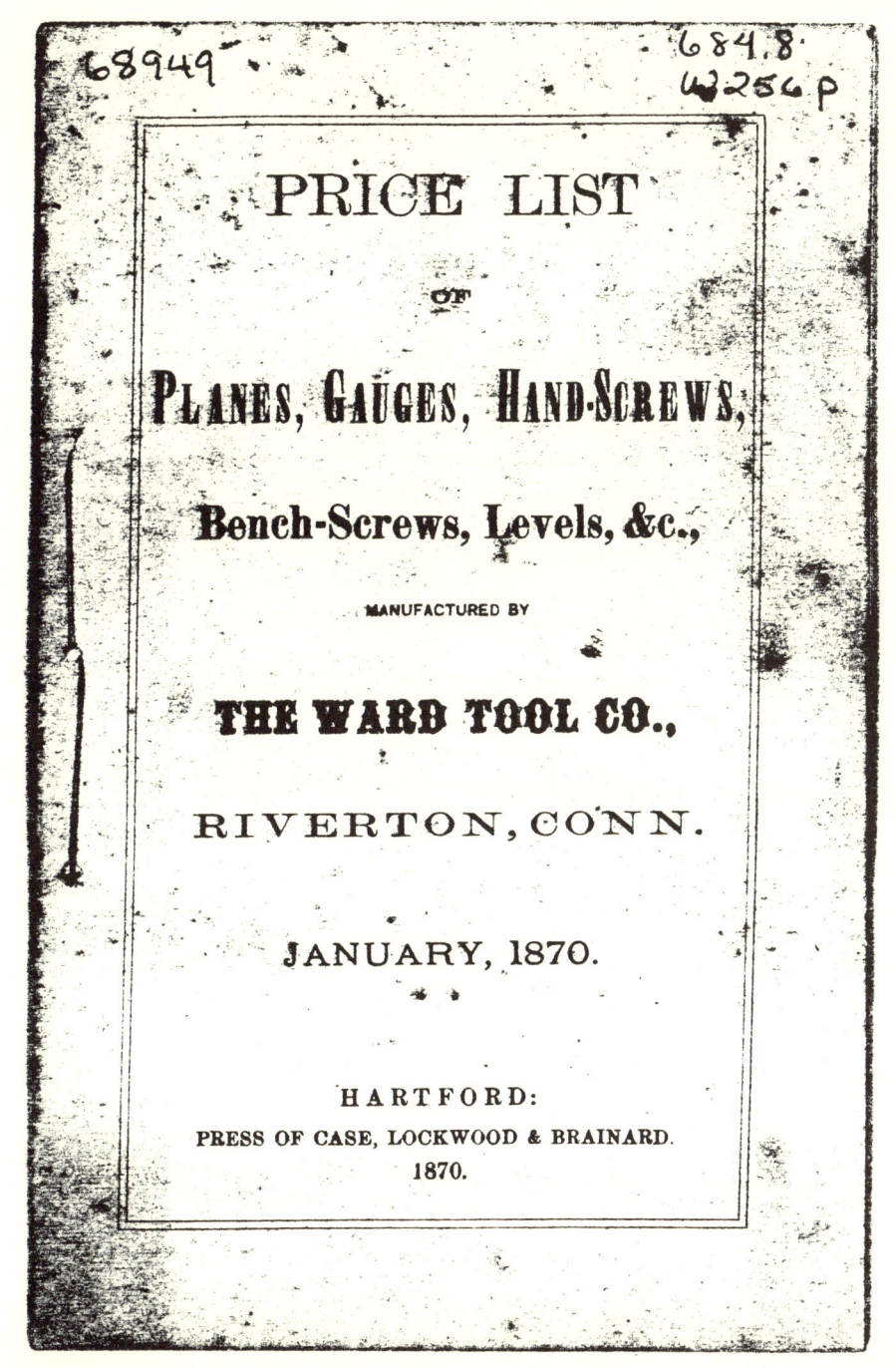

Planes, Gauges, Hand-Screws,

Bench-Screws, Levels, &c.,

MANUFACTURED BY

THE WARD TOOL CO.,

RIVERTON, CONN.

JANUARY, 1870.

HARTFORD:
PRESS OF CASE, LOCKWOOD & BRAINARD.
1870.

Table VIII

Agreement to elect Geo. W. Chapin as a Copartner in H.Chapin & Sons
August 12, 1862

Pine Meadow - August 12, 1862

It is hereby agreed in addition to and in alteration of the within agreement that Geo. W. Chapin is to have One Tenth Share and Hermon Chapin is to have only Seven Tenths Shares as within stipulated and agreed. This said alteration and addition is to date from the commencement and date of this within agreement.
Said agreement being dated Jan. 29th, 1862.

Hermon Chapin   E.M. Chapin   Geo. W. Chapin   Philip E. Chapin

Edward M. Chapin was 26 years old when he assumed full responsibility managing the new firm of H. Chapin's Sons. He had married Mary Pike of Canton in 1856. He was drafted into the service of the United States on October 23, 1863, but discharged in consideration of $300 payment. (See Plate IV) United States Internal Revenue was collected during the Civil War. A copy of E.M. Chapin's Tax Return for the year 1864 is shown as Plate V. Internal Revenue Licenses were issued each year during the War for carrying out business. (Plate VI)

Plate IV - Discharge Receipt from Service in United States

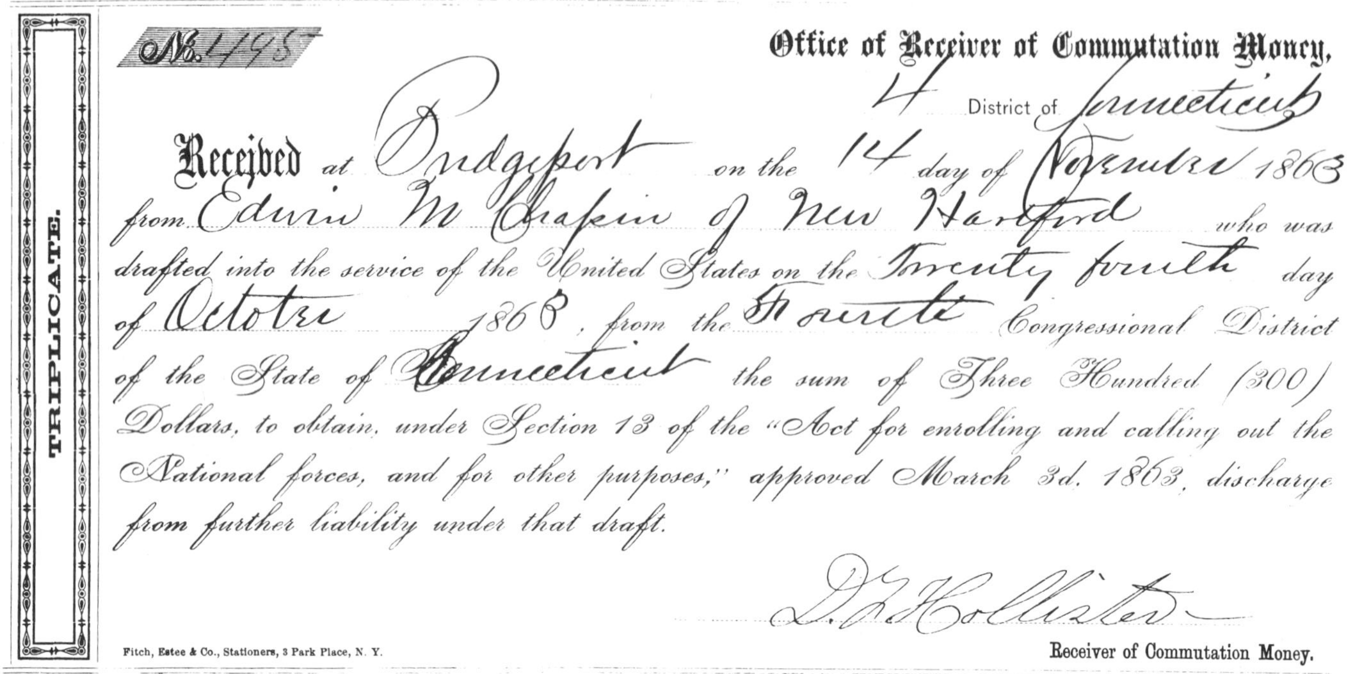

TRIPLICATE.

No. 4145

Office of Receiver of Commutation Money,

4 District of Connecticut

Received at Bridgeport on the 14 day of November 1863 from Edwin M Chapin of New Hartford who was drafted into the service of the United States on the Twenty fourth day of October 1863, from the Fourth Congressional District of the State of Connecticut the sum of Three Hundred (300) Dollars, to obtain, under Section 13 of the "Act for enrolling and calling out the National forces, and for other purposes," approved March 3d, 1863, discharge from further liability under that draft.

D. L. Hollister

Receiver of Commutation Money.

Fitch, Estee & Co., Stationers, 3 Park Place, N. Y.

Agreements among the principal manufacturers of planes regarding mutual interests appear to have started in 1861. This subsequently led to the formation of the Plane Manufacturer's Association, similar to the Rule Manufacturer's Association. Since Hermon Chapin was a founding member of the latter, he may have been the initiator of the Plane Manufacturer's Association. The foreward to the *1869 Greenfield Tool Company Catalogue* (See Vol. I, Plate IV, p. 29) stated:

> "...our New Illustrated Catalogue and Invoice Price List of Mechanics' Tools...has been revised...The Invoice numbers have not been altered from our List of 1861, and the prices are those adopted by *all* the leading manufacturers two years since..."

This statement implies that these leading manufacturers had agreed on uniform prices sometime during 1863. In 1861 the leading plane manufacturers were: H. Chapin & Sons, Greenfield Tool Co.,[8] Auburn Tool Co.,[9] Ohio Tool Co. and D.R. Barton.[10] In all probability they had first met during 1861 and agreed on uniform terminology, but required two additional years to agree on uniform prices. The earliest extant document presently known of the Plane Manufacturer's Association is an announcement made July 1, 1873 by the Greenfield Tool Co. (See Vol. I, Plate XLII, p.220), which stated:

> "Rates adopted by the 'Plane Manufacturer's Association at Kennard House, Cleveland, Ohio, December 18, 1872."

Among the Chapin manuscript material at the Connecticut Historical Society are several papers pertaining to the Plane Manufacturer's Association, the earliest dated being 1880. It is assumed that earlier documents relating to this subject were unfortunately discarded before this collection was given to the CHS. Considerable data will be subsequently presented in a later chapter disclosing that not only prices and discounts were fixed by this Association, but production quotas and sales territories were regulated. It suffices to state here that this practice appears to have started about 1863 and continued through the balance of the 19th century.

The final catalogue of H. Chapin & Son was 16 pages, issued April 1865. (Plate VII) This was an increase of four pages from the previous 1862 edition. New plane products included in this were: German or bull smooth, ship, cooper, iron screw self-regulating sash and some special varieties of plows. During the year a new procedure of altering discounts followed. Price changes made by the Association for rules and planes were effected by issuing revised discount schedules. Four such sheets were printed for the Union Factory during 1865, two of which, dated July 1 and December 13, are shown as Plate VIII. The Rule Manufacturer's Association had agreed to modify discounts on March 1, 1864. (See Table IX)

Prices of plane irons made by the Baldwin Tool Co. were listed in the last page of the 1865 Catalogue. It is evident from an inventory that sometime in 1864 H. Chapin & Sons had purchased the tools and patterns for making planes from the Baldwin Tool Co. (See Table X) After Baldwin Tool Co. discontinued making planes, it was succeeded by the Middletown Tool Co., who made and sold only plane irons. An agreement whereby Middletown Tool Co. would sell H. Chapin & Sons' products was made April 12, 1865. (See Table XI) This was likely in return for H. Chapin & Sons selling their plane irons. An 1865 inventory of plane irons at H. Chapin & Sons (See Table XII) indicated that approximately 70% of the stock was for bench planes.

During January 1865 Hermon Chapin entered a memorandum in his account book as to the value and inventory of his plane and rule shops. (Table XIII) In April he decided to transfer from his holdings $28,000 to each of his three sons. These property transfers were recorded in his ledger and are transcribed as Tables XIV & XV. The firm of H. Chapin & Sons was dissolved on July 1, 1865 (See Table XVI), Hermon Chapin retiring from the business on that date (See Table XVII) He deeded the Plane & Rule Shop to E.M. and George Chapin (Table XVIII) and the Machine Shop and "Old Brick Shop" to Philip Chapin.[11] Edward and George formed the new firm of H. Chapin's Sons. (Table XIX) Edward continued to manage the firm at New Hartford. George resided at Cleveland, Ohio and was engaged in a meat packing business with his cousin. Hermon Chapin died January 31, 1866 at Savannah, Georgia during his 67th year. His last letter to Edward M. Chapin, dated January 23, 1866, stated: "Give my regards to all the old shop hands. Tell them that I occasionally see some of the tools they have made." Apparently he had experienced ill health since 1860, but fortunately had the foresight to divide his business interest among his sons.

The title page of the 1865 Catalogue (Plate VII) indicated "Gauges, Hand Screws and Bench Screws" were among the products. Several varieties of five types of marking, cutting, mortice, panel and slitting gauges had appeared in H. Chapin's list since 1839. The deletion of these items in this copy of the 1865 Catalogue is suggested to have been an error by the printer or complier. The July 1, 1865 Discount Notice (Plate VIII) calls to attention "Discount 33-1/3 plus 5 per cent" on these items. The December 13, 1865 Notice reduced these discounts to 20 per cent and brought to attention "Circular List of August 15, 1865" with a footnote notice: — "We have discontinued the manufacture of Gauges Nos 248 to 260½ inclusive, list April 1865, and Gauges, *see circular list, August 15th, 1865,* (Formerly Steele, Clark & Co.) we shall make a special branch of our business." This August 15, 1865 *Price List of Gauges* is shown as Plate IX. This *Price List* of four pages noted 22 gauges as well as try squares and T bevels, the latter two items then made by S.A. Jones & Co. The proprietors of the Union Factory announced they had purchased "the entire Stock and Machinery of Steele, Clark & Co., successors to R.H. Wheeler, New Hartford, Conn...."[12]

190

UNITED STATES INTERNAL REVENUE.

4th District, State of Connecticut

Div. No. _____

Aug ____, 1865.

Collector's Office, Bridgeport, Ct.

Mr E. M. Chapin } To U. S. Internal Revenue, Dr.
Nr Hartford   } N. F. Hollister, Collector.

								RATE.	ABSTRACT NO.	AMOUNT TAX.
Tax on Income for the year 1864, viz:										
Income not exceeding $5,000: Amount, $417 at 5 per cent										20 85
" exceeding 5 000: " $____ " 10 " "										
							Total			20 85
							Tax withheld			
Tax on the following articles, for the year ending May 1, 1866:										
____	Billiard Tables, kept for private use							$10 each.	261	
____	Carriages, valuation over $50 and not over $100							1 "	262	
____	"	"	"	100	"	"	200	2 "	263	
____	"	"	"	200	"	"	300	3 "	264	
____	"	"	"	300	"	"	500	6 "	265	
____	"	"	"	500				10 "	266	
1	Pianofortes, &c., valuation over $100 and not over $200							2 "	267	2 00
____	"	"	"	200	"	"	400	4 "	268	
____	"	"	"	400				6 "	269	
	Gold Plate, kept for use ____ oz.							50c. per oz.	270	
	Silver Plate, " " " ____ oz.							5c. " "	271	
____ X	Gold Watches, kept for use, valuation not over $100							$1 each.	272	
1	" " " " " " over 100							2 "	273	2 00
____	Yachts,									

Amount of Tax $24 85

Received Payment.

T M Clark Dy
Collector.

Plate V - E.M. Chapin's U.S. Internal Revenue Income Tax for 1864

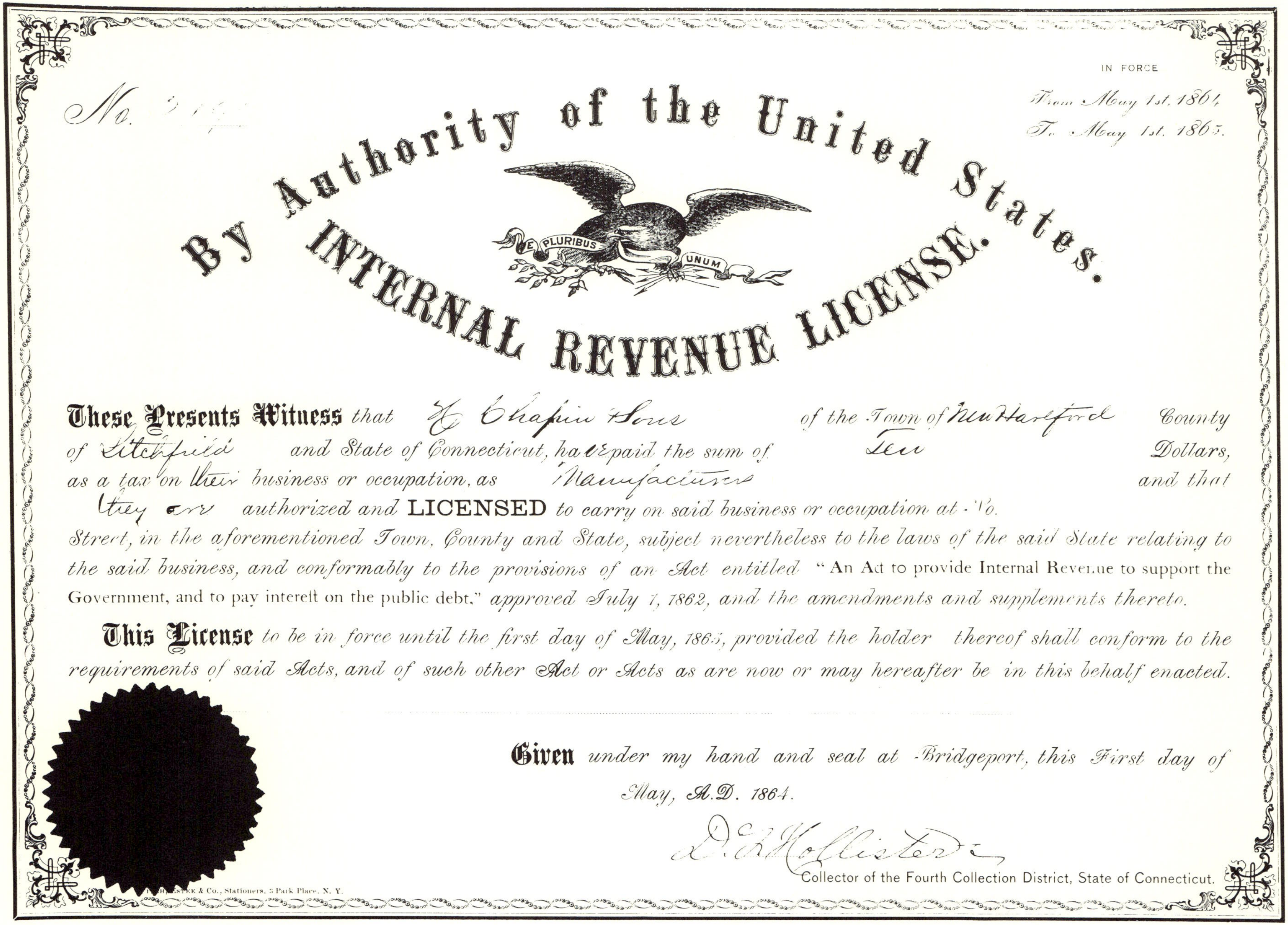

Plate VI - U.S. Internal Revenue License for H. Chapin & Son, May 1, 1864

Plate VII

(Continued pages 193 - 200)

PRICE LIST

OF

RULES, PLANES, GAUGES,

HAND SCREWS, BENCH SCREWS,

LEVELS, &c.,

MANUFACTURED BY

H. CHAPIN & SONS,

UNION FACTORY,

ESTABLISHED, 1826,

PINE MEADOW, CONN.

APRIL, 1865.

HARTFORD.
PRESS OF CASE, LOCKWOOD AND COMPANY.
1865.

Front Cover H. Chapin & Sons 1865 Price List

PRICE LIST

OF

RULES, PLANES, GAUGES,

HAND SCREWS, BENCH SCREWS,

LEVELS, &c.

BOXWOOD RULES.

One Foot, Four Fold, Narrow.

Price per dozen.

No.							
1,	Round Joint,	-	-	8ths and 16ths,	5/8	inch,	$2.66
2,	Square	do	-	"	"	5/8	do	3.66
3,	do	do	Edge Plates,	"	"	5/8	do	5 00
4,	do	do	do	"	"	3/4	do	6.00
5,	do	do	Bound,	"	"	5/8	do	11.00
6,	Arch	do	-	"	"	5/8	do	4.00
7,	do	do	Edge Plates,	"	"	5/8	do	6.00
8,	do	do	do	"	"	3/4	do	6.50
9,	do	do	Bound,	"	"	5/8	do	12.00

Two Feet, Four Fold, Narrow.

No. 10,	Round Joint,	-	8ths and 16ths,	1	inch.	$3.33
11,	Square	do	-	"	"	1	do	4.66
11½,	do	do	Extra,	"	"	3/4	do	5.30
12,	do	do	Edge Plates, 8ths, 16ths, 10ths and scales,	1	do	6 70
13,	do	do	Extra, do	"	"	"	3/4	do	8.00
14,	do	do	Half Bound,	"	"	"	1	do	11 50
15,	do	do	Bound,	"	"	"	1	do	14.00
16,	Arch	do	-	"	"	"	1	do	6.00
17,	do	do	Edge Plates,	"	"	"	1	do	8.00
18,	do	do	Half Bound,	"	"	"	1	do	12.50
19,	do	do	Bound,	"	"	"	1	do	16.00
20,	Double Arch Joint,	-	"	"	"	1	do	9.00
21,	do	do	Bound,	"	"	"	1	do	21.00

BOXWOOD RULES.

Two Feet, Four Fold, Broad.

Price per dozen.

No. 22,	Round Joint,	-	8ths and 16ths,	1 3/8	inch,	$5.00
23,	Square	do	-	"	"	1 3/8	do	7.00
24,	do	do	Edge Plates, 8ths, 16ths, 10ths and scales,	1 3/8	do	9.00
25,	do	do	Half Bound,	"	"	"	1 3/8	do	14 00
26,	do	do	Bound,	"	"	"	1 3/8	do	18.00
27,	Arch	do	-	"	"	"	1 3/8	do	8.66
28,	do	do	Edge Plates,	"	"	"	1 3/8	do	10.66
29,	do	do	Half Bound,	"	"	"	1 3/8	do	15 00
30,	do	do	Bound,	"	"	"	1 3/8	do	20.00
31,	Double Arch Joint,	"	"	"	1 3/8	do	12 00
32,	do	do	Bound,	"	"	"	1 3/8	do	24.00
33,	Arch Joint, Edge Plate, with Slide,	"	1 3/8	do	14.00

Two Feet, Four Fold, Board Measure.

No. 34,	Square Joint, Edge Plates, 8ths, 16ths, 10ths and scales,	1 3/8	inch,	$11 00
35,	do	do	Bound,	"	1 3/8	do	20.00
36,	Arch	do	Edge Plates,	"	"	1 3/8	do	12.50
37,	do	do	Bound,	"	"	1 3/8	do	22.00

Two Feet, Two Fold.

No. 38,	Round Joint,	-	8ths and 16ths,	1 1/2	inch,	$3.66
39,	Square	do	-	"	"	1 1/2	do	5.00
40,	do	do	Board Measure, 8ths, 16ths, 10ths and scales,	1 1/2	do	7.00
41,	Arch	do	-	"	"	1 1/2	do	8.00
42,	do	do	Extra Scales,	-	1 1/2	do	9.00
43,	do	do	do Board Measure, 8ths, 16ths, 10ths and scales,	1 1/2	do	10.00
44,	do	do	do Extra Scales, Thin,	1 1/2	do	10.00
45,	do	do	Bound, Extra Scales,	1 1/2	do	16.00

Two Feet, Two Fold, Slide.

WITH FULL SCALES.

No. 46,	Square Joint,	-	-	Plain Slide,	1 1/2	inch,	$9.00
47,	do	do		Gunter	do	1 1/2	do	12.00
48,	Arch	do	-	do	do	1 1/2	do	14.00
49,	do	do	Bound,	do	do	1 1/2	do	24.00
50,	do	do		Engineers'	do	1 1/2	do	18.00
51,	do	do	Bound,	do		do	1 1/2	do	28.00
Books of Instruction for Engineers,	-	-	1.50

IVORY RULES.
One Foot, Four Fold.
WITH 8THS AND 16THS.

					Price per dozen.
No. 52, Round Joint,		Brass,	½ inch,	$10 50
53, Square do		do	½ do	13.50
54, do do		German Silver,	½ do	14.50
55, do do	Edge Plates,	do	⅝ do	18.50
56, Arch, do	do	do	⅝ do	21.00
57, do do	Bound,	do	⅝ do	36.00
58, Square do	Edge Plates,	do	¾ do	22.00

Two Feet, Four Fold, Narrow.
WITH FULL SCALES.

No. 59, Square Joint, Edge Plates, German Silver,	⅞ inch,	$50.00
60, Arch do do do	1 do	64.00
61, do do Bound, do	1 do	77.00
62, Double Arch Joint, Bound, do	1 do	90.00

Two Feet, Four Fold, Broad.
WITH FULL SCALES.

No. 63, Arch Joint, Edge Plates, German Silver,	1⅜ inch,	$85.00
64, do Bound, do	1⅜ do	100.00
65, do do with Slide, do	1⅜ do	112.00
66, do do with Calliper, do	1⅜ do	120.00
67, Double Arch Joint, Bound, do	1⅜ do	120.00

Two Fold.

No. 68, Round Joint, 6 inch, Brass,	-	½ inch,	$4.70
69, Arch do 12 do German Silver, 8ths, 16ths, 10ths and 12ths,	¾ do	24.00

CALLIPER RULES, Boxwood.
WITH 8THS AND 16THS.

No. 70, Square Joint, Two Fold, 6 inch,	-	⅞ inch,	$7.00
71, do do do 6 do Brass Case,	⅞ do	8.00
72, Arch do Four Fold, 12 do -	⅞ do	12.00
73, do do do 12 do Bound,	⅝ to ⅞ do	20.00

CALLIPER RULES, Ivory.
WITH 8THS, AND 16THS.

		Price per dozen.
No. 74, Square Joint, Two Fold, 6 in., Ger. Silver,	⅞ inch,	$17.00
75, do do do 6 do do Case,	⅞ do	20.00
76, do do Four Fold, 12 do	⅞ do	40 00
77, do do do 12 do Bound,	⅝ do	50.00
78, Arch, do do 12 do do	⅝ do	52.00
79, do do do 12 do do	⅞ do	58 00

MISCELLANEOUS RULES.

No. 80, Bench Rules, 24 inch, - -	1¼ inch,	$3.00
81, do do Board Measure,	1½ do	5 50
82, Yard Sticks, - - - -		1 10
83, do Brass Tipped, - -		3.00
84, Yard Rule, Arch Joint, Four Fold, - -		8 00
85, Ship Carpenters' Bevels, Single or Double Tongue,		6 00
86, Board Sticks, Octagon, 24 inch, 8 Lines,		6.00
87, Board Sticks, Square and Octagon, 24 inch, 16 do		8.00
88, do do do 36 do 16 do		12.00
89, do Walking Canes for Inspectors, 36 inch,		10 50
90, do Flat, with T Head, 36 do		12.00
91, Wood Measures, - - 48 do		8.00
92, Wantage Rods, - - - -		3.50
93, Guaging Rods, - - 36 do		7 00
94, do - - - - 48 do		8.00
94½, do with Wantage Table, 48 do		19.00
95, Three Fold Rules, 12 inch, - -	½ inch,	6.00
96, Six do 24 do Arch Joint, Edge Plates,	¾ do	13 00
97, Yard Sticks, Hickory, - - -		2.00
98, do do Brass Tipped, - -		4.50

Rules with Spanish Measure, made to order.

COMMON BENCH PLANES, Single Irons.

				Price each.
No. 100, Smooth,	Cast Steel Irons,	2 to 2⅛ inch,	$0.50
101, Jack,	do	2 to 2⅛ do	.65
102, Fore 21 inch,	do	2⅜ do	.90
do 22 do	do	2½ do	.95
103, Jointer, 26 do	do	2½ do	1.05
do 28 do	do	2½ do	1.15

EXTRA BENCH PLANES, Single Irons.

No. 104, Smooth,	Best Cast Steel Irons,	2 to 2¼ inch,	$0.60
105, Jack,	do	2 to 2¼ do	.75
106, Fore, 21 inch	do	2⅜ do	.95
do 22 do	do	2½ do	1.00
107, Jointer, 26 do	do	2½ do	1.10
do 28 do	do	2⅝ do	1.20
do 30 do	do	2⅝ do	1.30

COMMON BENCH PLANES, Double Irons.

No. 108, Smooth,	Cast Steel Irons,	2 to 2⅛ inch,	$0.85
109, Jack,	do	2 to 2⅛ do	.95
110, Fore, 21 inch,	do	2⅜ do	1.20
do 22 do	do	2½ do	1.30
111, Jointer, 26 do	do	2½ do	1.40
do 28 do	do	2⅝ do	1.50

EXTRA BENCH PLANES, Double Irons.

No. 112, Smooth,	Best Cast Steel Irons,	2 to 2¼ inch,	$0.90
do Solid Handle,	do	2 to 2¼ do	1.75
113, Jack,	do	2 to 2¼ do	1.00
114, Fore, 21 inch,	do	2⅜ do	1.30
do 22 do	do	2½ do	1.40
115, Jointers, 26 do	do	2½ do	1.50
do 28 do	do	2⅝ do	1.60
do 30 do	do	2¾ do	1.75
116, Single Smooth, Box or Rosewood, do	2 to 2¼ do	1.75
do Solid Handle, do	do	2 to 2¼ do	3.50
117, Double Smooth, do	do	2 to 2¼ do	2.00
do Solid Handle, do	do	2 to 2¼ do	3.75
118, Tooth Plane,	do	2 to 2¼ do	1.00
119, Mitre do Square,	do	1¾ do	.70
do do Smooth Shape,	do	1¾ do	.70
120, Single Compass, Smooth,	do	2 to 2⅛ do	.75
121, Double do do	do	2 to 2⅛ do	1.12

PREMIUM BENCH PLANES, EXTRA C. S. Double Irons.

WITH BOLTED HANDLE AND START. Per set.
Smooth, $1.00 Jack, 1.25, Jointer, 22 inch, 1 75, 28 inch, 2 00, $6.00

WITH BOLTED HANDLE AND START, POLISHED.
Smooth, $1 38, Jack, 1.87, Jointer, 22 inch, 2.25, 28 inch, 2.50, $8.00

WITH DIAMOND BOLTS AND STARTS.
Smooth, $1.25, Jack, 1.50, Jointer, 22 inch, 2.00, 28 inch, 2.25, $7.00

WITH DIAMOND BOLTS AND STARTS, POLISHED.
Smooth, $1.50, Jack, 2.25, Jointer, 22 inch, 2.38, 28 inch, 2.62, $8.75

MISCELLANEOUS PLANES.

				Price each.
Toy, Smooth, Single,	Cast Steel Irons,	1½ inch,	$0 50
do do Double,	do	1½ do	.70
do Jack, Single,	do	1½ do	.60
do do Double,	do	1½ do	.80
Clock Plane, Single, 18 inch,	do	2⅜ do	.95
do Double, do	do	2⅜ do	1.30
Gutter Plane,	do	1½ or 2 do	.90
Pump Plane, for Chain Pump,	do	1 to 1½ do	1.30
Whip Plane, Steel Faced,	do	1¼ to 1¾ do	1.35
Wash Board Plane,	-	-	-	1.20
do do with Handle,	-	-	-	1.75
German Smooth or Bull Plane,	-	-	-	2 00

SHIP PLANES.

Smooth,	Best Double C. S. Iron,	9 inch,	$1.00
Jack,	do do	16 do Razee,	1.20
Fore,	do do	22 do do	1.50
Jointer,	do do	26 do do	1.90
Spar Plane,	do do	- - -	1.50
do Best Single do	- - -	1.00

COOPERS TOOLS.

Leveling Plane,	- - - - -	$1.75
Howel do and Stock, Barrel or Hogshead,	- -	3.75
Croze and Stock,	- - - - -	2.00
Heading Jointers,	to 5½ feet,	Single,	2.25
do do	to 5½ feet,	Double, -	2 75
do do	to 5½ feet,	Single and Double,	5.50
Stave Jointers,	to 5½ feet,	Single, -	2.50
do do	to 5½ feet,	Double, - -	3.00
do do	to 5½ feet,	Single and Double,	6.00

MOULDING PLANES.

Price each.

No. 122, Astragals, - ¼ ⅜ ½ ⅝ ¾ inch, $0.40
do - - - - ⅞ 1 do .50
do - - - 1⅛ 1¼ do .58
123, Beads, Single Boxed, ⅛ $\frac{3}{16}$ ¼ $\frac{5}{16}$ ⅜ $\frac{7}{16}$ ½ do .50
do do - - - ⅝ ¾ do .55
do do - - ⅞ 1 do .70
do do - - 1⅛ 1¼ 1⅜ do .90
do do with Handle, 1½ do 1.90
124, do Double Boxed, ⅛ $\frac{3}{16}$ ¼ $\frac{5}{16}$ ⅜ $\frac{7}{16}$ ½ do .60
do do - - ⅝ ¾ do .65
do do - - - ⅞ 1 do .80
do do - - 1⅛ 1¼ do 1.00
125, do Solid Boxed, Dovetailed, ⅛ $\frac{3}{16}$ ¼ do .70
do do do $\frac{5}{16}$ ⅜ 7 ½ do .80
do do do - ⅝ ¾ do .90
do do do - - ⅞ 1 do 1.00
do do do - 1⅛ 1¼ do 1.10
Beads, Left Hand, same price as above.
126, Base and Band Moulding, - - per inch, .70
do do Handle, - do .85
127, Bed Moulding, Handle, - - do .70
128, Reverse and Back Ogee, - - to ¾ inch, .50
do do - - to 1 do .55
do do - - to 1¼ do .65
129, do do with Bead Bevel or Square, to ¾ do .55
do do do to 1 do .60
do do do to 1¼ do .70
130, Plain Ogee, - - - to ¾ do .50
do - - - - - to 1 do .55
do - - - - - to 1¼ do .60
131, do with Bead Bevel or Square, to ¾ do .55
do do - - to 1 do .60
do do - - to 1¼ do .70
132, Cock Bead, - - - - - - .50
133, Center Beads, - - - to ⅜ do .66
do - - - - - to ¾ do .62
134, do Solid Boxed, Dovetailed, to ⅜ do .64
do do do to ¾ do .78
135, Cornice Plane, - - - per inch, .84
Cabinet Ogee Planes, - - - do .84

2

MOULDING PLANES.

Price each.

No. 136, Dadoes, - - - - - to 1 inch, $ 75
137, do with Stop, - - - to 1 do .85
138, do with Side Stop, - - to 1 do .95
139, do with Screw Stop, - - to 1 do 1.50
140, Door Planes, Ogee, - - ½ to ⅝ do .88
141, do do Bevel, Double Screw Arms, 1.50
142, Antae Caps, - - - - to 1 inch, 1.25
143, do - - - - - to 1¼ do 1.38
144, Antae Base, - - - - to 1½ do 1.63
145, Fluting Planes, - - - to ¾ do .60
do - - - - to 1½ do .75
146, Filletster, - - - - - - - .95
147, do with Stop, - - - - - 1.20
148, do with Stop and Cut, - - - 1.35
149, do with Stop, Cut and Boxed, - - 1.58
150, do with Screw Stop, Cut and Boxed, - 2.50
do with Screw Stop, Cut & Boxed Solid Handle, 3.75
do with Screw Stop, Cut, Solid Box or Rosew'd, 4.00
151, do with Arms, Stop and Cut, - - 2.00
152, do with Arms, Stop, Cut and Boxed, - 2.25
153, do with Screw Arms, Stop, Cut and Boxed, 2.65
154, do with Screw Arms, Screw Stop, Cut & Boxed, 3.70
do with Screw Arms, Screw Stop, Cut, Solid Box or Rosewood, - - 5.75
155, Grecian Ovolo, Plain or Square, - to ¾ inch, .55
do do do - to 1 do .60
do do do - to 1¼ do .65
do do do - to 1½ do .75
156, do do with Handle, per inch, .65
157, do with Fillet, - - to 1 inch, .70
do do - - to 1¼ do .75
do do - - to 1½ do .80
do do - - to 1¾ do .90
do do with Handle, per inch, .75
158, do with Bead, - - to 1 inch, .75
do do - - to 1¼ do .80
do do - - to 1½ do .87
do do - - to 1¾ do 1.00
159, do do Handle, to 2 do 1.50
do do do - to 2½ do 2.00
160, Grecian Ogee, with Bevel or Fillet, to 1 do .65

MOULDING PLANES.

	Price each.
No. 160, Grecian Ogee, with Bevel or Fillet, to 1¼ inch,	$.70
do do to 1½ do	.75
do do to 1¾ do	.85
do do to 2 do	1.00
do do with Handle, per inch,	.65
161, Gothic Bead, with one Iron,	.70
162, do with two Irons, Boxed,	1.05
163, Halving Plane,	.40
164, Halving Planes, Handle and Plated,	.66
165, Half Set, Hollows and Rounds, 9 pairs, 2 to 18,	7.20
166, do do do 12 do 2 to 24,	10.50
167, Hollows and Rounds, No. 1 to 12, per pair,	.75
do do No. 13 to 18, do	.90
do do No. 19 to 24, do	1.10
168, Table Hollows and Rounds, do	.95
169, do do Boxed, do	1.50
170, do do with Fence, do	1.40
171, Match Plane, ½ inch, per pair or Double,	1.25
172, do Plated, to ½ do do do	1.50
173, do to 1 do do do	1.25
174, do Plated, to 1 do do do	1.50
175, do with Handle, to 1¼ inch, per pair,	1.90
176, do Plated, do to 1¼ do do	2.20
177, do for Plank, do	1.85
178, do do Plated, do	2.25
179, do Moving Fence, do	2.20
180, do do Plated, do	2.60
181, do Screw or Slide Arms, do	3.00
182, do do do Plated, do	3.25
183, do Boxwood, Screw Arms, do	3.50
184, do do Plated or Boxed Fence, do	3.75
Extra, for Boxing the Groove, do	.50
185, Nosing or Step Plane, two Irons, to 1¼ inch,	.85
do do Handled, to 1½ do	1.00
186, Hand Rail Plane, Ovolo and Ogee,	1.40
187, Ovolos, to ¾ inch,	.42
do to 1 do	.50
do to 1¼ do	.56
188, do with Bead, to ¾ do	.60
do do to 1 do	.65
do do to 1¼ do	.70
189, Panel Plane, Cast Steel,	1.15

MOULDING PLANES.

	Price each.
No. 190, Panel Plane, Cast Steel,	$1.40
191, do with moving Fence, do	1.50
192, do do and Cut, do	1.70
193, Qk. Ogees, to ¾ inch,	0.55
do to 1 do	.60
do to 1¼ do	.67
194, do with Bead, to ¾ do	.60
do do to 1 do	.65
do do to 1¼ do	.75
195, Reeding Plane, to ⅜ do	.65
do to ¾ do	.80
196, Qk. Ovolo, to ¾ do	.55
do to 1 do	.60
do to 1¼ do	.70
197, do with Bead, to ¾ do	.68
do do to 1 do	.75
do do to 1¼ do	.85
198, Raising Planes, with Stop and Cut, 2½ inch,	2.50
do do do 3 do	3.00
do do do 3½ do	3.50
do do do 4 do	4.00
199, do Double Iron, do 2½ do	3.00
do do do do 3 do	3.75
do do do do 3½ do	4.50
do do do do 4 do	5.25
Extra for Boxing,	.50
200, Rabbet Planes, Square, to 1 inch,	.60
do do to 1¼ do	.65
do do to 1½ do	.70
201, do do Double Boxed, to 1 do	1.00
do do do to 1¼ do	1.08
do do do to 1½ do	1.18
202, do Skew, to 1 do	.60
do do to 1¼ do	.65
do do to 1½ do	.70
do do to 1¾ do	.80
do do to 2 do	.90
do do to 2¼ do	1.00
Extra for Cut,	.20
203, do do Boxed and Cut, to 1 do	.95
do do do to 1¼ do	1.05

MOULDING PLANES.

		Price each.
No. 203, Rabbet Planes, Skew, Boxed and Cut,	to 1½ inch,	$1.10
do do do	to 1¾ do	1.15
do do do	to 2 do	1.20
do do do	to 2¼ do	1.25
No. 204, Rabbet Planes, Skew, Handle and Cut,	to 2 do	1.30
205, do do do two Cuts,	to 2½ do	1.65
206, Sash Planes, one Iron,	- - -	.60
207, do do Boxed,	- - -	.90
208, do two Irons,	- - -	.85
209, do Boxed,	- - -	1.15
210, do Double,	- - -	1.25
do do Iron Screw, Self Regulating,		1.75
211, do do Boxed,	- - -	1.60
do do do Iron Screw, Self Regulating,		1.95
212, do Screw Arms,	- - -	1.50
do do Self Regulating,		2.60
213, do do Boxed,	- -	1.80
do do do Self Regulating		2.90
214, do do Handle, do		2.75
215, do do do Boxed, do		3.15
do do do Solid Box, do		4.50
Templets, Gauges, and Prickers,	- - each,	.15
216, Sash Coping Planes,	- - -	.50
217, do do Boxed,	- - -	.70
218, Sash Filletster, Screw Arms,	- - -	2.00
219, do do Screw Stop,		3.00
220, Scotia,	to ¾ inch,	.44
do	to 1 do	.50
do	to 1¼ do	.56
221, do with Bead,	to ¾ do	.56
do do	to 1 do	.60
do do	to 1¼ do	.70
222, Snipe Bills,	per pair,	1.10
223, do Full Boxed,	do	1.50
224, Side Rabbet Plane,	do	1.08
225, Slip Beads,	to ¾ do	.60
do	to 1 do	.75
226, do Corner Dovetailed Boxed,	to ¾ do	.75
do do do	to 1 do	1.00
227, Torus Beads,	to ¾ do	.50

GROOVING PLOWS.

SLIDE OR SCREW ARMS.

		Price each.
No. 228, Plow, wood Stop,	-	8 Irons, $3.00
229, do Plated, do	-	8 do 3.20
230, do Boxed, do	-	8 do 3.20
231, do wood Stop Plated,	-	8 do 3.40
232, do Plated, do	-	8 do 3.60
233, do Boxed, do	-	8 do 3.60
234, do Screw Stop,	-	8 do 4.50
235, do Plated, do	-	8 do 4.70
236, do Boxed, do	-	8 do 4.70

BOXWOOD SCREW ARMS AND SCREW STOP.

		Price each.
237, Plow, Solid Handle,	-	8 do 5.25
238, do do Boxed Fence,	-	8 do 6.00
239, do do do Best Plate,		8 do 7.00
239½, do do Boxed Fence, Best Plate, Side Stop, Polished,		8 do 7.50
240, do Solid Handle, Boxwood, Best Plate, Side Stop, Polished,		8 do 9.00
240½, do Solid Handle, Rosewood, Boxed Fence, Best Plate, Side Stop, Polished,		8 do 9.00
241, do	- - - -	8 do 4.60
242, do Boxed Fence,	-	8 do 4.80
243, do Best Plate,	- -	8 do 5.10
244, do do Boxed Fence,	-	8 do 5.30
244½, do do do Side Stop, Polished,		8 do 6.00
245, do Boxwood, Best Plate, Side Stop, Polished,		8 do 7.00
245½, do Rosewood, Boxed Fence, Best Plate, Side Stop, Polished,		8 do 7.00

PLUMBS AND LEVELS.

Price per dozen

No.	Description	Size	Price
286,	Levels, Cherry, Side Views, assorted,	12 to 18 inch,	$7.50
287,	do do do do	24 to 28 do	10.00
289,	Plumb and Level, Cherry, Polished, Side Views, assorted,	12 to 18 do	12.00
290,	Plumb and Level, Cherry, Polished, Side Views, assorted,	24 to 30 do	15.00
291,	Plumb and Level, Mahogany, Polished, Side Views, assorted,	24 to 30 do	20.00
292,	Plumb and Level, Mahogany, Polished, Brass Lipped, Side Views, assorted,	24 to 30 do	30.00
293,	Plumb and Level, Cherry, Polished, Brass, Side Views, and Tipped, assorted,	24 to 30 do	30.00
294,	Plumb and Level, Cherry, Triple Stock, Polished, Brass Lipped, Side Views, and Tipped, assorted,	24 to 30 do	38.00
296,	Plumb and Level, Mahogany, Polished, Brass Lipped, Side Views, and Tipped, assorted,	12 to 18 do	32.00
297,	Plumb and Level, Mahogany, Polished, Brass Lipped, Side Views, and Tipped, assorted,	24 to 30 do	42.00
298,	Plumb and Level, Mahogany, Triple Stock, Polished, Brass Lipped, Side Views, and Tipped, assorted,	24 to 30 do	50.00
300,	Plumb and Level, Rosewood, Triple Stock, Polished, Brass Lipped, Side Views, and Tipped,	28 do	75.00
302,	Adjusting, Plumb and Level, Cherry, Polished, Side Views,	18 do	21.00
304,	Adjusting, Plumb and Level, Cherry, Polished, Side Views, assorted,	24 to 30 do	25.00
306,	Adjusting, Plumb and Level, Cherry, Polished, Brass Lipped, Side Views, and Tipped, assorted,	24 to 30 do	48.00
308,	Adjusting, Plumb and Level, Mahogany, Polished, Brass Lipped, Side Views, and Tipped, assorted,	24 to 30 do	60.00
310,	Masons Plumb and Level, Cherry, Varnished, Side Views,	36 do	18.00
311,	Iron Pocket Levels,		2.00
312,	do do with Brass Top,		2.50

LEVEL GLASSES.

Price per dozen.

Level Glasses,	1¾ to 2 inch,	$0.50
do	2½ to 3 do	.75
do	3½ to 4 do	1.00
do	4½ to 5 do	1.50

STOPS.

Plow Screw Stops,	$6.00
Filletster Screw Stops,	8.00
Dadoe do do	3.00
Brass Side Stops and Slides, to order.	

CAST STEEL TOOTH PLANE IRONS, PER DOZEN,

2	2⅛	inches.
$2.75,	3 00.	

CAST STEEL SOFT MOULDING IRONS, PER DOZEN.

¼	⅜	½	⅝	¾	⅞	1	1⅛	1¼	1⅜	1½	1⅝	1¾	1⅞	2	2⅛	2¼	2⅜	2½ inches.
$0.69,	0.69,	0.69,	0.71,	0.71,	0.75,	0.81,	0.88,	0.96,	1.00,	1.06,	1.13,	1 25,	1.38,	1.50,	1.63,	1.75,	1.88,	2.06.

CAST STEEL RABBETT IRONS, SKEW OR SQUARE, PER DOZEN.

½	⅝	¾	⅞	1	1⅛	1¼	1⅜	1½	1⅝	1¾	1⅞	2	2⅛	2¼	2⅜	2½	2⅝ inches.
$0.94,	1.00,	1.04,	1.10,	1.21,	1.25,	1.33,	1.38,	1.44,	1.50,	1.63,	1.69,	1.81,	1.94,	2.06,	2 19,	2.38,	2.75.

CAST STEEL GROOVING IRONS, FOR BOARD MATCH, PER DOZEN.

⅜	½	⅝	¾	⅞	1 inches, Board Match.
$1.04,	1.10,	1.21,	1.25,	1.33,	1.38.

CAST STEEL GROOVING IRONS, FOR PLANK MATCH, PER DOZEN.

1¾	1⅞	2 inches.
$1.75,	1.87½,	2.00

CAST STEEL GROOVING PLOW BITTS, PER SET, $1.00.

CAST STEEL MATCH PLOW BITTS, ⅛ 3/16 ¼ 5/16 ⅜ inches, PER DOZEN, $1.00

CAST STEEL FILLETSTER IRONS, 1½ inches, PER DOZEN, $1 50.

CAST STEEL DADO IRONS.

3-16	¼	5-16	⅜	½	⅝	¾	⅞	1 inches.
$1.00,	1.00,	1.00,	1.00,	1.00,	1.05,	1.10,	1.15,	1.25.

CAST STEEL DADO CUTTERS, PER DOZEN.

3-16	¼	5-16	⅜	½	⅝	¾	⅞	1 inches.
$1.25,	1.25,	1.25,	1.25,	1.25,	1.30,	1.35,	1.40,	1.50.

FILLETSTER CUTTERS, PER DOZEN, $1.00

RABBETT PLANE CUTTERS, PER DOZEN, $0 60.

INVOICE LIST OF PLANE IRONS,

MANUFACTURED FROM

W. & S. BUTCHER'S Superior Refined Cast Steel,

BY THE

BALDWIN TOOL CO.

☞ These Irons are used by us in the manufacture of our Goods, and for which we solicit orders. ☜

SINGLE CAST STEEL PLANE IRONS, OR CUT IRONS, PER DOZEN.

1¼	1⅝	1¾	1⅞	2	2⅛	2¼	2⅜	2½	2⅝	2¾	3 inches.
$1.75,	1.75,	1.75,	1.87½,	2.00,	2.12½,	2.37½,	2.62½,	2.87½,	3.12½,	3.50,	4.50.

DOUBLE CAST STEEL PLANE IRONS, PER DOZEN.

1½	1⅝	1¾	1⅞	2	2⅛	2¼	2⅜	2½	2⅝	2¾	3	3¼	3½	3¾	4 inches.
$3.75,	3.75,	4.00,	4.00,	4.12½,	4.25,	4 50,	4.75,	5.25,	5 50,	6.50,	7.50,	9.00,	10.50,	12.00,	15.00.

SINGLE CAST STEEL PLANE IRONS, assorted from 2 to 2½ PER DOZEN, $2 37½.
DOUBLE do do do do do 4.50.

CAST STEEL RAISING PLANE IRONS, PER DOZEN.

2	2¼	2½	2¾	3	3¼	3½	3¾	4 inches.
$2.25,	2.75,	3.25,	3.75,	4.50,	5.00,	5.50,	6.00,	6.50.

CAST STEEL SOFT IRONS, PER DOZEN.

2	2⅛	2¼	2⅜	2½	2⅝	2¾	3	3¼	3½	3¾	4 inches.
$2.00,	2.12½,	2.37½,	2.62½,	2.87½,	3.12½,	3.50,	4.50,	4.75,	5.50,	6.00,	6.50.

CAST STEEL SINGLE COOPER'S JOINTER IRONS, 11 INCHES LONG, PER DOZEN.

2¾	3	3¼	3½	3¾	4	4¼	4½ inches.
$6.00,	6.25,	6.75,	7.25,	8.00,	8.75,	9.50,	10.50.

CAST STEEL HOWELING IRONS, PER DOZEN,

1¾	2	2⅛	2¼	2½ inches.
$3.00,	3.25,	3.75,	4.00,	4.50.

Table IX - Rule Manufacturers Agreements, 1864 and 1865

March 1, 1864

We the undersigned manufacturers of Rules hereby agree that we shall not, either directly or indirectly, sell Rules at less than the following Discounts from the combination or convention list, viz.

    Discount on Boxwood Rules - Twenty per cent
    Ivory Rules and Miscellaneous good - Ten per cent.

We further agree that the credit shall not exceed Four months in any case; but to the trade, known as the "Jobbing trade" or to wholesale Merchants we may allow for prompt Cash payment a further discount of Ten per cent and to all others only Five per cent discount for Cash.

    Belcher Brothers & Co.   *Stanley Rule & Level Co.*
    J. & G.H. Walker   *H. Chapin & Sons*
                            Stephens & Co.

July 1, 1865

We the undersigned, members of the Convention of Rule Manufacturers, held in the city of New York, June 28/65, having made and adopted a new price list, a copy of which was supplied to each of us, do hereby agree to adopt the said list on the first day of July 1865, and to be governed exclusively by it in all future sales of Rules, or until a change may be made in said list by some future Convention of Rule Manufacturers, and we further agree that we will in no case, either directly or indirectly, sell or permit our agents or representatives to sell for our accounts, at less than the following rates:

    To the Wholesale or Jobbing Trade 30% + 10% for cash
    to the Retail Trade, 30% + 5% for cash from the above
    mentioned list, payable on the delivery of goods, or in
    15 days from the date of Invoice

We hereby bind each other not to authorize nor appoint any person to act as agent in any other place than the cities of New York, Philadelphia, Boston, Baltimore and Columbus, Ohio, nor more than one in either of these cities.

Any two of the undersigned may call a convention, by giving ten days notice when the interest of the trade would be promoted thereby.

Belcher Brothers & Co.	New York
J. & G.H. Walker	New York
Stanley Rule & Level, T.A. Conklin, Agent	New Britain, Conn.
Stephens & Co.	Riverton, Conn.
H. Chapin's Sons	Pine Meadow, Conn.
Willis Thrall & Son	Hartford, Conn.

Table X

H. Chapin & Sons Stock Inventory July 1, 1865

Plane Parts and Unfinished Planes Acquired from Baldwin Tool Co.

761	Smooths Mortised	@ 10¢	$76.10
10	Jacks "	@ 20¢	2.00
5	Fores "	@ 25¢	1.25
285	Plow Fences	@ 3-3/4¢	10.69
161	" " , Apple boxed	@ 25¢	40.25
226	Beads, faced	@ 3-3/4¢	8.48
18	Pairs Hollows & Rounds	@ 7½¢	1.35
49	Rabbits ½ inch, faced	@ 3-3/4¢	1.84
20	Plow Fences, Boxwood	@ 25¢	5.00
432	pairs, sash arms, boxwood	@ 6¼¢	27.00
322	" ,Match " , "	@ 31¢	99.82
710	" " " , maple	@ 22½	159.75
310	" , Plow " , apple		69.75
11,337	Moulding Pieces	@ 3-3/4¢	425.14
488	Plow Fences	@ 3-3/4¢	18.30
424	Plow Bodies	@ 3-3/4¢	15.90
912	Beads, Boxed	@ 3-3/4¢	33.45
480	Toy Smooths	@ 3-3/4¢	18.00
879	Toy Jacks	@ 3-3/4¢	32.95
375	Mitres	@ 3-3/4¢	13.31
133	Sash, boxed	@ 25¢	33.25
28	Handled Mouldings	@ 12½¢	3.50
156	Jointers Mortised	@ 36¢	48.36
27	Fores, "	@ 25¢	6.75
4,738	Moulding Pieces	@ 3-3/4¢	81.84
111	Handled Match Pieces	@ 3-3/4¢	4.16
167	Plow Bodies, apple	@ 3-3/4¢	6.26
180	" " , mouths made	@ 3-3/4¢	6.75
865	Toy Smmoth woods	@ 3-3/4¢	32.43
206	Toy Jacks "	@ 3-3/4¢	7.73
554	Mitres "	@ 3-3/4¢	20.78
101	Tooth "	@ 3-3/4¢	3.78
269	Plow Bodies	@ 3-3/4¢	10.08
209	Plow Fences	@ 3-3/4¢	7.89
110	Jointers, mouths made	@ 50¢	55.00
82	" , mortised	@ 50¢	41.00
25	" ,mouths made,handled	@ 80¢	20.00
18	Smooths, mortised	@ 8¢	1.44
			$1,554.83

Table XI

Agreement between Middletown Tool Co. & Hermon Chapin & Sons, April 12, 1865

Memorandum of an agreement made this twelfth day of April 1865 by and between the Middletown Tool Co. of Middletown, Connecticut and Hermon Chapin & Sons of Pine Meadow, Connecticut. Withnesseth, the said Middletown Tool Co. hereby agrees to solicit orders by themselves and through their employed travelling agent, for such articles that are manufactured by said Hermon Chapin & Sons to wit; Planes, Rules, Guages, Levels, Screw-drivers, Chisel & Plane Handles and Hand and Bench Screws, at such prices as may be agreed upon from time to time between said Middletown Tool Co. and said Hermon Chapin & Sons; and to use every effort to advance the interest of said Hermon Chapin & Sons, by effecting sales in localities where their goods have not been heretofore introduced. And the said Hermon Chapin & Sons hereby agree upon the performance of the foregoing stipulations, to purchase the Plane Irons used in the manufacture of their Planes from Middletown Tool Co., upon such a basis of prices as may be established and agreed upon by the Humphreysville Manufacturing Co. and the said Middletown Tool Co. it being understood between the parties to this instrument, that the Middletown Tool Co. will not bind themselves to sell Plane Irons at a rate, in their judgement below a proper standard of profitable manufacture; and the said Hermon Chapin & Sons agree to finish the planes belonging to the Baldwin Tool Co. now stored at the Connecticut State Prison, upon reasonable terms hereafter to be agreed upon, the said Baldwin Tool Co. delivering said Planes at the factory of said Hermon Chapin & Sons free of all charge and expense excepting the cost of boxes. and the said Hermon Chapin & Sons further agree to sell for the said Baldwin Tool Co. their planes so delivered by them, in preference to manufacturing and selling any of their own stamp. It is mutually agreed bewteen the two parties that a commission of ten per cent shall be allowed the Middletown Tool Co. on sales effected through their agency to parties not previous customers of said Hermon Chapin & Sons, but no such commission shall be charged said Hermon Chapin & Sons upon orders obtained by said agency from the regular customers of said Hermon Chapin & Sons except upon such portion of said orders as may be filled by the planes of Balwin Tool Co.

It is further mutually agreed that the said Hermon Chapin & Sons shall grant to the said Middletown Tool Co. the most liberal terms offered any party, and shall deliver their goods in Boston, New York and Philadelphia.

It is further agreed that statements of account shall be rendered by both parties on the first day of every month, and the balance which ever way it may be, settled in cash at that time.

Either party subscribing to this instrument is at libert to terminate it by giving in writing thirty days notice of their intention.

           Middletown Tool Co.
           A.H. Jackson, President

[Document from the Collection of New Hartford Historical Society]

Table XII

H. CHAPIN & SONS 1865 INVENTORY OF PLANE IRONS
[totaling $1,516.19]

	Number of Irons		Cost in Dollars	Cost per iron	
I.	3000 Single Irons for Bench Planes totaling $604.38				(39.7%)
	763	Baldwin	150.89	.198	
	117	Providence	10.30	.090	
	1281	Hancock	186.05	.140	
	218	Butcher	54.97	.252	
	621	Special	202.17		
II.	1658 Double Irons for Bench Planes totaling $438.14				(28.8%)
	362	Baldwin	116.24	.321	
	414	Providence	81.27	.196	
	515	Hancock	132.21	.257	
	181	Butcher	70.16	.388	
	184	Special	38.23		
III.	5326 Moulding totaling $479.67				(31.5%)
	2657	Moulding	245.81	.093	
	1482	Skew rabbet	153.95	.104	
	445	Square rabbet	36.31	.090	
	712	match	42.10	.059	
	30	plow	1.50	.050	

Table XIII

Memorandum of H. Chapin's January 1865 Appraisal of Plane & Rule Shop

1/4 part Water Power Dam & Canal	$3,000.00
2/3 part Branch Canal & Reservoir	700.00
Plane & Rule Shop, Wheels & Shafting	12,000.00
Allen Shop	150.00
Timber Houses	850.00
Machinery in Saw Room	450.00
Machinery in Front Room	400.00
Machinery in Turning Room	850.00
Machinery in South Room	50.00
Machinery in Finishing Room	1,000.00
Machinery in Joint Room	1,200.00
Machinery of Baldwin Tool Co.	650.00
Tools and Patterns for above	850.00
Stock of H. Chapin & Co. after dividend	20,000.00
Munsonville Property	5,000.00
Store Building & Furniture	2,000.00
	$50,400.00
E. M. Chapin Lot with House	2,800.00
G. W. Chapin Brown House & Lot	2,800.00
Total	$56,000.00

Table XIV

RECORD OF PROPERTY TRANSFERS FROM HERMON CHAPIN TO E.M. CHAPIN
[transcribed from page 153, H.Chapin's Account Journal]

Pine Meadow, Conn. April 1865 - Edward M. Chapin

to half of ¼ Water Power, Dam and Canal as per deed	$1500.00
" " " 2/3 of Branch Canal & Reservoir " "	350.00
" " " Allens Shop	75.
" " " Plane & Rule Shop, Wheels, & Shafting " "	600.
" " " Three Timber Houses	425.
" " " Machinery in Saw Room	225.
" " " " " Front Room	200.
" " " " " Turning "	425.
" " " " " South "	25.
" " " " " Finishing Room	500.
" " " " " Joint Room	600.
" " " " " Rule "	500.
" " " Office Fixtures, Stoves & Pipes	125.
" " " Machinery of Baldwin Tool Co.	325.
" " " Back Tools & Patterns	425.
" " " Stock of H.Chapin & Sons after dividend	10,000.
" " " Munson Mill Property	2500.
" " " Store Buliding & Furniture	1000.
" Lot North of E.M.Chapin's House as per deed	350.
" Balance from old account	2450.
Twenty Eight Thousand Dollars	$28,000

RECORD OF PROPERTY TRANSFERS FROM HERMON CHAPIN to GEORGE W. CHAPIN
[transcribed from page 154, H.Chapin's Account Journal]

Pine Meadow, Conn., April 1865 - George W. Chapin

to half of ¼ Water Power, Dam and Canal as per deed	$1500.00
" " " 2/3 of Branch Canal & Reservoir " "	350.
" " " Allens Shop	75.
" " " Plane & Rule Shop, Wheels, & Shafting "	600.
" " " Three Timber Houses	425.
" " " Machinery in Saw Room	225.
" " " " " Front Room	200.
" " " " " Turning "	425.
" " " " " South "	25.
" " " " " Finishing Room	500.
" " " " " Joint Room	600.
" " " " " Rule "	500.
" " " Office Fixtures, Stoves & Pipes	125.
" " " Machinery of Baldwin Tool Co.	325.
" " " Back Tools & Patterns	425.
" " " Stock of H.Chapin & Sons after dividend	10,000.
" " " Munson Mill Property	2500.
" " " Store Building & Furniture	1000.
" Brown House as per Deed	1200.
" Hedge " " " "	1600.
Twenty Eight Thousand Dollars	$28,000

Table XV

RECORD OF PROPERTY TRANSFERS FROM HERMON CHAPIN TO PHILIP E. CHAPIN
[transcribed from page 155, H.Chapin's Account Journal]

Pine Meadow, Conn., April 1865 - Philip E. Chapin

to 1/8 part Water Power, Dam & Canal as per Deed	1500.00
" 1/5 " Branch Canal & Reservoir per Deed	350.
" Machine Shop, Shafting, Benches &c. per Deed	5000.
" Foundry, Smith Shop, Patterns & Fixtures as per Deed	8500.
" Large Lathe & Tools	500.
" Long " " "	650.
" Bishop " "	225.
" Lincoln " " "	200.
" Winsted " " "	120
" Short " " "	80
" Chuck " " "	100.
" Drill " " "	75.
" 2 " " " "	160.
" Gear Cutter	90.
" Planer with Tools	750.
" Stock on Hand per Inventory	3500.
" Old Brick Shop & Grounds	1600.
" Bragg House as per Deed	1400.
" Cooper " " " "	900.
" Cash on a/c transfer from H.Chapin & Sons	2300.
Twenty Eight Thousand Dollars	$28,000

Table XVI - Agreement to Dissolve Co-partnership H. Chapin & Sons

July 1, 1865 - It is hereby agreed to dissolve the co-partnership of H.Chapin & Sons as herewith annexed in the following manner, to wit, there is to be a correct Inventory made of all the Stock, credits & dues of all kinds and also the debts and liabilities of said Co., and a just and fair dividend of all the gains and profits made and paid to the parties to the said company in proportion to their shares in said company and the said E.M. Chapin. Geo. W. Chapin, and P.E. Chapin are to surrender their rights and interest in property of said Co. to Hermon Chapin which is to be credited in his account in the sum of two thousand dollars each to balance the original charge for the same. And it is further agreed and understood that the said Hermon Chapin is to sell and convey all said Company property (with other property) to the said Edward M. Chapin and Geo. W. Chapin who are to have all credits and dues and are also hereby bound to pay all debts and liabilities of said Company together with the said dividend as heretofor stated all of which when done is to be a full and final settlement and dissolution of said Company of H.Chapin & Sons.

Table XVII - Notice of Hermon Chapin Retiring from the Union Factory Business

Office of the Union Factory - Established 1826, Pine Meadow, Conn.
July, 1, 1865

Gentlemen -
The subscriber is retiring from business and thereby dissolving the firn of H.CHAPIN & SONS and returns meaningful thanks to his many customers of the past Thirty Nine years, hoping that the same liberal patronage with which they have favored him may be continued to his successors this day established under the firm name of H.Chapin's Sons. Very Respectfully,
H.Chapin
E.M. & G.W. Chapin having taken the entire interest of the late firm of H.Chapin & Sons will continue the business under the firm name of
H.Chapin's Sons
and will be found at all times prepared to execute your orders with promptness and at reasonable rates.

Table XVIII

DEED by Hermon Chapin to Edward M. Chapin and George W. Chapin of PLANE and RULE SHOP &c. July 1, 1865 [Recorded New Hartford Land Records B21, p.263]

Know Ye, that I, Hermon Chapin of the town of New Hartford, County of Litchfield, State of Connecticut for the consideration of Twelve Thousand Dollars ($12,000) received to my full satisfaction of Edward M. Chapin of the town, county & state aforesaid and George W. Chapin of Cleveland, County of Cuyahoga, State of Ohio, do give, grant, bargain, sell and confirm unto the said Edward M. & George W. Chapin one cerain piece or parcel of land and mill privilege with the Plane & Rule Shop, Three Timber Houses & Brass Foundry standing thereon, situated in the said town of New Hartford in Pine Meadow so called, bounded and described as follows: Northerly on a line running from the Farmington River from the south corner of the Rye Lot on the fence as it now stands, westerly to the south end of the Bridge across the Canal in front of the said Plane Shop, westerly on the east side of the said canal, southerly on H.B.Kellog's & Co.'s land and land this day deeded to Philip E. Chapin, Easterly on the Farmington River, together with one fourth part of the Dam, Canal and Water Power and also the Branch Canal and Reservoir, they paying their proportionate share of and keeping the same in repair.. . . . Excepting reserving the right of way to the Foundry as this day deeded to Philip E. Chapin, also one third part of the Branch Canal & Reservoir as this day deeded the said Philip E. Chapin & also the right of way for the waste water from the Canal belonging to the Water Power Co. across said Premises. . . Hermon Chapin, July 1, 1865, New Hartford, CT.

Table XIX

Agreement between E.M. Chapin and Geo. W. Chapin to Form Copartnership of Firm H. Chapin's Sons - July 1, 1865

This agreement made the first day of July 1865 by and between Edward M. Chapin of Pine Meadow, Litchfield County, Conn. and George W. Chapin of the City of Cleveland, State of Ohio - Witnesseth

Whereas our father, Hermon Chapin, having conveyed to us (the aforesaid parties) this day the Plane and Rule Shop and Store buildings in the said Pine Meadow and the Mill Property in Barkhamstead with stock and tools for carrying on the manufacturing of Rules, Planes &c heretofore carried on by the firm H.Chapin & Sons. Now therefore for the purpose of continuing and carrying on said business we the subscribers hereunto this day enter into an equal copartnership under the firm name of
H.CHAPIN'S SONS

It is agreed during the continuance of this copartnership the said Edward M. Chapin shall devote his full time and attention in the employ of said Company to the management of said manufacturing business and in charge of the said store property and mill property aforesaid for the joint interest and benefit of said Company to the best of his ability for which the said Edward M. Chapin is to receive from said Company the sum of ten hundred ($1000) per annum, unless otherwise agreed.

It is also further agreed that the said Copartnership bear, pay and discharge equally all expenses that may be required for the support and management of the said Company business, and that all gains, profits and increases that shall grow out of or arise from or by means of said Company business shall be divided equally between the said parties and all losses that shall happen to said Company shall be borne in like manner.

And it is further ageed that the said Edward M. Chapin shall keep at all times during the continuance of the said Company just and true Books of accounts to which the said George W. Chapin shall at all times have free access and the said business shall be mananged as said partners shall from time to time agree and direct.

No Dividend or Capital shall be drawn from said Company by either party except with the consent of the other partner and a true and just Inventory of Timber, Tools and stock shall be taken at least once in five years unless otherwise agreed by both parties to said Company.

The said parties also hereby agree mutually that neither of them will use the Company name to sign any Note or Obligation with the Company's name or so endorse unless it be strickly for the transaction of the Company's business.

Either party to this agreement may dissolve the same by giving the other party in writing six month notice of his intention so to do. This contract to continue during the life time of said parties, unless sooner dissolved by mutual consent or as above.

Plate VIII - Union Factory Discount Sheets Issued in 1865

OFFICE OF THE UNION FACTORY.
ESTABLISHED 1826.

PINE MEADOW, CONN., July 1st, 1865.

GENTLEMEN:

We with pleasure present you our Price List of April, 1865, with reduced prices and rates revised as follows:

Rules—Boxwood, Ivory, and Miscellaneous.	Discount 30 per cent. and 10 per cent.
Bench, Miscellaneous, Ship, Cooper, Moulding Planes, Grooving Plows, and Screw Drivers.	Add 10 per cent. and discount 5 per cent.
Gauges, Hand Screws, Bench Screws, Handles, Levels, & Level Glasses.	Discount 33⅓ per cent. and 5 per cent.
Stops, ...	Discount 10 per cent.
Plane Irons, ...	Add 25 per cent.

Rates subject to changes of the market.

Terms invariably *Cash*, with exchange on New York or Boston.

Boxes charged.

Goods delivered at depot.

Soliciting your orders, we are

Respectfully yours,

H. CHAPIN'S SONS.

OFFICE OF THE UNION FACTORY,
ESTABLISHED 1826.

PINE MEADOW, CONN., Dec. 13, 1865.

GENTLEMEN:

We present you our rates from this date as follows:

Boxwood, Ivory, and Miscellaneous Rules,	Discount 25 per cent. and 10 per cent.
(List price No. 10, $3.50) per doz.	
Bench, Miscellaneous, Ship, Cooper, Moulding Planes, and Grooving Plows,	Add 20 per cent.
Gauges Nos. 246, 247, 261, 262, and 262 1-2, Gauges, (Circular List August 15th, 1865,) Try Squares, " " " " " Sliding T. Bevels, " " " " " Level Glasses, Hand and Bench Screws,	Discount 20 per cent.
Hand Screws, superior, Jaws beaded with extra finish,	Discount 10 per cent.
Handles, Plumbs, and Levels,	Discount 30 per cent. and 10 per cent.
Screw Drivers, - - - - -	Add 10 per cent.
Plane Irons, - - - - -	Add 30 per cent.

Rates subject to changes of the market.

Terms invariably *Cash*, with exchange on New York or Boston.

Boxes charged.

Goods delivered at depot.

We have discontinued the manufacture of Gauges Nos. 248 to 260 1-2 inclusive, list April, 1865, and Gauges, see circular list, August 15th, 1865, (Formerly Steele, Clark & Co.) we shall make a special branch of our business.

Soliciting your orders, we are

Respectfully yours,

H. CHAPIN'S SONS.

Price lists and discount sheets from the Auburn Tool Co. and Ohio Tool Co., issued during 1865 and 1866, received by H. Chapin's Sons, indicate that price fixing of planes was then in effect. (See Plates X & XI) The 1865 Price List of Bench Planes by Auburn Tool Co. noted similar prices to the 1865 H. Chapin & Sons Catalogue. (see Plate VII) The December 18, 1865 notice from Ohio Tool Co. noted "we have the agency of H. Chapin & Sons…Gauges" An announcement from the Auburn Tool Co., presumably dated January 1867 from a penned noted thereon, stated "We have lately moved our Plane Manufacturing Business from the State Prison to our New Factory…" (See Plate XII) A sketch of this factory, built in 1866, appears in their 1869 Catalogue.[9] This Catalogue noted "We also keep on hand superior Rules, manufactured by H. Chapin's Sons. Orders for which are solicited by us." A notice from Augustus Howland & Co., dated November 15, 1867, announced that they were the successors to J.M. Easterly, who had retired from the business. (Plate XIII) Easterly had outbid Auburn Tool Co. in 1866 for the State Prison labor contract, thus forcing Auburn Tool Co. to relocate, but apparently he could not make a financial success of plane manufacturing.[13]

Plate IX - H. Chapin's Sons Price List of Gauges, April 15, 1865
[Continued on Page 211]

PRICE LIST OF GAUGES,

(Formerly Steele, Clark & Co's.)

MANUFACTURED BY

H. CHAPIN'S SONS,

UNION FACTORY,

PINE MEADOW, CONN.

AGENTS ALSO FOR

S. A. JONES & CO'S

TRY SQUARES,

AND

SLIDING T BEVELS.

AUGUST 15, 1865.

OFFICE OF THE UNION FACTORY.

ESTABLISHED 1826.

PINE MEADOW, CONN.,
AUG. 15, 1865.

GENTLEMEN:

Having purchased the entire Stock and Machinery of Steele, Clark & Co., successors to R. H. Wheeler, New Hartford, Conn., we propose to continue under the personal supervision of Mr. GEORGE MAXFIELD, (who has had the management of the business since 1856,) the manufacture of their Gauges so extensively and favorably known to Dealers; and with a full corps of experienced workmen, the distinctive merits of these Gauges will be preserved, and the facilities for supplying them promptly will be greatly increased.

Your special attention is requested to the annexed Price List of these Gauges, as well as to the Price List of S. A. Jones & Co's Try Squares and Sliding T Bevels, for which in connection with other Goods of our manufacture, we would respectfully solicit your orders.

Very truly yours,

H. CHAPIN'S SONS.

Plate IX (Continued from Page 210)

PRICE LIST.

GAUGES.

	per dozen.
No. 1, Marking Gauge, Oval Head and Bar, Steel Points,	$1.15
2, Marking Gauge, Oval Head and Bar, Steel Points with inches,	1.25
3, Cutting Gauge, Oval Bar, Steel Cutters with inches,	2.50
4, Marking Gauge, Appletree, Oval Head and Bar, Steel Points with inches,	2.00
5, Marking Gauge, Box or Rosewood, Oval Head and Bar, Brass Thumb Screw, Steel Points with inches,	3.50
6, Marking Gauge, Box or Rosewood, Plated Oval Head and Bar, Brass Thumb Screw, Steel Points with inches,	6.00
7, Cutting Gauge, Appletree, Oval Bar, Steel Cutters with inches,	3.25
8, Marking Gauge, Mahogany or Appletree, Plated Head and Bar, Brass Thumb Screw, Oval Bar, Steel Points with inches,	5.50
9, Marking Gauge, Mahogany or Appletree, Plated Oval Head and Bar, Steel Points with inches,	4.00
10, Panel Gauge, Oval Bar, Brass Thumb Screw, Steel Points with inches,	4.75
11, Panel Gauge, Appletree, Oval Bar, Brass Thumb Screw, Steel Points with inches,	6.00
12, Panel Gauge, Mahogany, Plated Head and Bar, Oval Bar, Brass Thumb Screw, Steel Points with inches,	12.00
13, Panel Gauge, Rosewood, Plated Head and Bar, Oval Bar, Brass Thumb Screw, Steel Points with inches,	18.00
14, Mortise Gauge, Mahogany or Appletree, Plated Head, Thumb Slide, Brass Thumb Screw, Steel Points,	6.50
15, Mortise Gauge, Mahogany or Appletree, Plated Head and Bar, Thumb Slide, Brass Thumb Screw, Steel Points,	8.00

	per dozen.
No. 16, Mortise Gauge, Mahogany or Appletree, Plated Head, Screw Slide, Brass Thumb Screw, Steel Points,	$9.00
17, Mortise Gauge, Box or Rosewood, Plated Head, Screw Slide, Brass Thumb Screw, Steel Points,	11.00
18, Mortise Gauge, Box or Rosewood, Plated Head and Bar, Screw Slide, Brass Thumb Screw, Steel Points,	14.00
19, Mortise Gauge, Box or Rosewood, Full Plated Head and Plated Bar, Screw Slide, Brass Thumb Screw, Steel Points,	18.00
20, Mortise Gauge, Box or Rosewood, Full Plated Head and Bar, Screw Slide, Brass Thumb Screw, Steel Points,	20.00
21, Slitting Gauge with Handle,	7.50
22, Slitting Gauge with Handle and Rollers,	8.50

PRICE LIST.

S. A. JONES & CO'S
BEST PLATED TRY SQUARES.

	per dozen.
3 inch Rosewood,	$5.50
4½ " "	6.50
6 " "	8.00
7½ " "	9.50
9 " "	11.00
12 " "	16.00
15 " "	20.00
18 " "	24.00

PLATED SLIDING T BEVELS.

	per dozen.
6 inch Rosewood with Thumb Screw,	$5.50
8 " " "	6.00
10 " " "	6.50
12 " " "	7.00
14 " " "	7.50

Plate X – Discount Sheet Auburn Tool Co., Sept. 1865

Price List of Bench Planes,
MANUFACTURED BY THE

AUBURN TOOL CO.
AUBURN, N. Y.

Smooth Planes.
Extra Cast Steel Irons—2 to 2¼ inch.

No.		Price each.
1	Single iron,	$ 55
2	do best,	60
3	Double iron,	85
4	do best,	90
5	do extra, with start pin	1 10
6	do do varnished,	1 25
7	do do solid handle,	1 75
8	do do boxwood,	2 00

Jack Planes.
2⅛ to 2¼ inches.

9	Single iron,	$ 65
10	do best,	95
11	do razee,	1 00
12	Double iron,	95
13	do best,	1 00
14	do extra, with start pin and handle bolt,	1 30
15	do extra varnished,	1 45
16	do do razee,	1 20

Fore Planes.
2⅜ to 2⅝ inches.

17	Single iron,	$ 95
18	do best,	1 00

Fore Planes, [Continued.]

No.		Price each.
19	Single iron, razee,	$1 30
20	Double iron,	1 30
21	do best,	1 40
22	do extra, with start pin and handle bolt,	2 00
23	do extra, varnished,	2 15
24	do razee,	1 60

Jointer Planes.
2½ to 2¾ inches.

25	Single iron, 26 inch	$1 05
26	do 28 do	1 15
27	do best, 26 do	1 10
28	do do 28 do	1 20
29	do razee, 26 do	1 40
30	Double iron, 26 do	1 40
31	do do 28 do	1 50
32	do best, 26 do	1 50
33	do do 28 do	1 60
34	do do 30 do	1 75
35	do extra, with start pin and handle bolt, 26 do	2 31
36	do extra, varnished, 26 do	2 46
37	do razee, 27 do	1 70

Complete Price List of Planes sent on application.

Rates for Planes, Gauges, Handles, &c., - 10 per cent. advance of List.
do   Plane Irons, - - - 25 "   disct. from "
do   Skates, - - - - 30 "   "   "
do   Rules, - - - - - - -

Terms.—Cash—Payable with exchange on New York City.

☞ Orders for Skates received now, to be filled at any time during the Fall or Winter. We have no Agents in New York City. All orders must be addressed to us.

Yours, &c,

AUBURN TOOL CO.

Auburn, N. Y., Sept. 1, 1865.

Plate XI – Ohio Tool Co. Discount Sheet, Dec. 1865

Office of the Ohio Tool Company,
Columbus, Dec. 18, 1865.

Gentlemen:

We have to inform you that our rates on articles manufactured and sold by us are as follows:

Goods to page 16 of Catalogue, inclusive, except Saw Frames, add	-	20 per cent.
Tress Hoops,	-	List.
On articles on pages 17 to 19, inclusive, except Tress Hoops and Plane Irons,	add	33 1-3 "
Plane Irons,	add	40 "
Rules, Boxwood,	discount	30 and 10 per cent.
Rules, Ivory,	discount	10 and 10 "
Patent Auger Handles,	discount	20 "
Superior Wood Saw Frames,		1.75 per doz. net.
Dirt Picks, with Cast Steel Points,		15.00 "
Snell's O. S. Auger Bits,	-	List.
Augers and Gimlets,	-	List.

TERMS.—Cash on receipt of Invoice.

Prices subject to change without notice; and all Bills will be made at ruling rates at date of shipment, payable *here*, in Columbus bankable funds or New York exchange.

Orders executed in turn as received.

We have the Agency of H. Chapin & Son's (formerly Steel, Clark & Co's) Cutting, Panel and Mortising Gauges of all descriptions, which we sell at the manufacturers' prices, saving to our customers a heavy item of freight.

Soliciting a continuance of your favors, we remain

Yours, respectfully,

OHIO TOOL CO.

Office of the Auburn Tool Co.

No. 50 Owasco St., Auburn, N. Y.

We have lately moved our Plane Manufacturing Business from the State Prison to our New Factory, erected the past season, and are now prepared to fill orders with promptness. All our work is done by good Mechanics; we employ no convict labor, consequently are not obliged to receive work that is defective. If any Tools are wanted that are not mentioned in our List, we will make them from Drawings.

Our present rates are as follows:

Planes and Plane-Irons,.................add 20 per cent.
Handles, Gauges, &c.,...................... List.
(DELIVERED.)

Soliciting your orders, we remain,

Respectfully Yours,

AUBURN TOOL CO.

Messrs H. Chapin Son
We represent this Jany 24th/67,
how is it their prices is ast 20%

Plate XII - Auburn Tool Co. Discount Sheet, Jan. 1867

CO-PARTNERSHIP NOTICE.

Mr. J. M. EASTERLY, having this day retired from the firm of EASTERLY & Co, the manufacture of Tools in the Auburn Prison will, on and after December 5th, 1867, be continued by the undersigned under the name and style of *AUGUSTUS HOWLAND & CO.*

Auburn, N. Y., Nov. 15, 1867.

AUGUSTUS HOWLAND,
J. V. BOWEN,
JOHN CURTIS,
GEORGE HUMPHREYS,
CHAS. A. WARDEN.

Office of Augustus Howland & Co.,
Auburn, N. Y. Dec. 5, 1867.

Messrs H. Chapin Son
Wm Maden Our
Gents!

We beg to call your attention to the foregoing notice, and to state that the present firm is composed of the same persons as the late firm of Easterly & Co., with the exception of the retiring partner. Every possible effort will be used to still improve the grade of our Tools, by the addition of new and improved machinery, while the constant attention of skilled mechanics will be given to their manufacture. Hoping for a continuance of your esteemed favors, we are,

Yours truly,

AUGUSTUS HOWLAND & CO.

Plate XIII - Augustus Howland Notice, Nov. 15, 1867

An inventory of wood in the form of splits stored for making planes was taken in 1865 before the dissolution of H. Chapin & Sons. Such wood was being stored and air dried or seasoned for future orders. Such rived pieces required a minimum of three years to dry to proper moisture content. Kiln drying by forced hot air was not introduced until about 1865. A brochure advertising such a process offered by Osgood & Hanna is among the manuscript data from the Union Factory at the Conn. Hist. Society. (Plate XIV) This explains the process of forced hot air drying and its benefits. Whether this equipment was used at the Union Factory is not known, but in all probability within a few years of this date such a drying process was installed there.

```
             1865 INVENTORY OF PLANE STARTS  H. CHAPIN & SONS

    North or Old Timber House
         14615 Jack Plane Wood @ 6¢          $876.90
          5628 Fore    "     "  @ 10¢         562.80
           251 Jointer "     "  @ 13½¢         33.88
          3029 Moulding "    "  @ 2¢           60.58
           378 Handled Smooth   @ 6¢           22.08
           231 Handled Mould.   @ 4¢            9.24
           338 Raising          @ 7¢           23.65

    Garret of Plane Shop
          5823 Jack Plane Wood @ 6¢          349.38
          2954 Fore    "     "  @ 10¢        259.40
           399 Jointer "     "  @ 13½¢        53.86
           310 Smmoth  "     "  @ 3¢           9.30
            10 Handled Smooth   @ 6¢            .60
          1892 Moulding         @ 2¢          37.84
           215 Raising          @ 7¢          15.05
            24 Handled Moulding @ 4¢            .96

    Middle Timber House
          1724 Jack Plane Wood @ 6¢          103.44  Green April 6, 1865
          1917 Fore    "     "  @ 10¢        191.70    "     "    "   "
            40 Jointer "     "  @ 13½¢         5.40    "     "    "   "
           225 Moulding "    "  @ 2¢           4.50    "     "    "   "
          3205 Jack    "     "  @ 6¢         192.30    "   Jan. 6, 1864
          2445 Fore    "     "  @ 10¢        244.50    "     "    "   "
           137 Jointer"     "   @ 13½¢        18.49    "     "    "   "
          1129 Moulding "    "  @ 2¢          22.58    "     "    "   "
            61 Raising  "    "  @ 7¢           4.27    "     "    "   "
           200 Smooth   "    "  @ 3¢           6.00    "     "    "   "
            80 Handled Moulding @ 4¢           3.20

    East Chamber
          1852 Jack Plane Wood @ 6¢          111.70
          1030 Fore    "     "  @ 10¢        103.00
          1259 Smooth  "     "  @ 3¢          37.77
           112 Handled Smooth   @ 6¢           6.72
           670 Jointer "     "  @ 13½¢        90.45
          1403 Moulding "    "  @ 2¢          28.06
           922 Handled Moulding @ 4¢          36.88
```

OSGOOD & HANNA'S

LUMBER DRYER!

Patented Nov. 27, 1866.

The true Method for Drying and Seasoning

LUMBER.

By this process the Tannin and Acids are removed from the wood, and the Albumen is coagulated and rendered insensible to moisture, thus preventing the wood from swelling and warping, and rendering it less liable to decay from *dry rot*.

The lumber is saturated with steam for about four hours, at a temperature of not less than 212° Fahrenheit, and then dried by hot air. This steaming may be done in any room that can be made tight; Exhaust Steam will do. The hot air should be applied immediately after steaming, before the lumber cools, and until it is thoroughly dried, which will be for two-inch Pine in about twenty-four hours; for other wood, more or less time according to the dimension and texture; hard wood requires more time than soft, and plank more than boards; three-inch Pine has been seasoned in forty-eight hours; one and a half inch Black Walnut requires three days to dry thoroughly.

Where large quantities are to be dried, it is better to have separate apartments for the steaming and drying processes, and the lumber stacked on cars so as to be readily transferred from one apartment to the other; the steaming of one load can then be done while the other is drying; but the entire process can be effected in a single room.

The room for steaming should be tight, and that for drying plentifully ventilated, either at the top or bottom, or both. A heat of from 125 to 150 degrees Fah. will be sufficient, if the room is properly ventilated.

This process does not check, warp, or injure the lumber in any way; it will dry and season better and quicker than any other process, and with

No Danger from Fire!

It is now going into general use, and is considered invaluable by all who have adopted it. Special reference is permitted to

Messrs. PICKENS & WASHBURN, Corner Causeway and Merrimac Sts., Boston.
J. F. PAUL, 441 Tremont Street, Boston.
LEVI BRUNER, Wabash, Ind.

The demand for properly seasoned lumber makes this a matter of great importance to Dealers and Manufacturers, and no Builder or Wood-worker can well afford to be without it. Kilns of any kind can be arranged for the use of this process at trifling expense, and the cost of drying is very small. The saving of interest and insurance on investments now required to carry on the lumber trade or manufacture will pay the cost of drying; twenty per cent of freight will be saved by transporting lumber dried instead of green; add to this the saving from checking and other injury incident to drying in the ordinary manner, and it will be seen that a great saving can be made by drying by this process, and selling thoroughly dried lumber at prices now charged for green.

All who have tested or examined this process declare it a great improvement, and that a great and much needed work has been accomplished by this invention.

STATE, COUNTY, TOWN, AND SHOP RIGHTS

for sale, on easy terms.

The erection or alteration of Kilns personally superintended, if desired, upon application at either of the Offices named below.

☞ GREAT INDUCEMENES offered to SMART MEN to sell or license on commission.

We beg attention to the statements, on the opposite page, from leading houses in the trade.

OSGOOD & HANNA,

Office 6, No. 20 Court St., Boston, Mass.
Wabash, Indiana, or
Madison, Wisconsin.

Plate XIV – Brochure Describing Lumber Drying Process Offered by Osgood & Hanna.

The Rule Manufacturers continued to adjust their prices and discounts according to the conditions of the time. An advance to the hardware trade was announced on June 26, 1867. (Plate XV) The firm of Hubbard Hardware & Co. of Middletown, Conn. had joined this cartel of rulemakers.[14] Among the 1865 accounts of rules in the ledger of H. Chapin & Sons were Ohio Tool Co. ($1221) and Bliven & Mead Co. ($920.16)[15]

Plate XV - Notification of Price Advance by Rule Manufacturers.

New York, June 26th, 1867.

To the Hardware Trade.

The undersigned, Rule Manufacturers, owing to the great scarcity of labor, the high prices thereof, and the advanced price of Turkey Boxwood and other materials, are compelled from this date to advance the price of Rules to 20 per cent. Discount from List, subject to the usual Cash discount for par funds.

BELCHER BROS. & CO., of New York.
WILLIS THRALL & SON, of Hartford. Conn.
H. CHAPIN'S SONS, of Pine Meadow, Conn.
STANLEY RULE AND LEVEL CO., of New Britain, Conn.
HUBBARD HARDWARE CO., of Middletown, Conn.
STEPHENS & CO., of Riverton, Conn.
J. & G. H. WALKER, of New York.

While an extant copy of the 1866 H. Chapin & Sons Catalogue is not known, their planes and gauges with the same numbers and prices as listed in their 1865 Catalogue appeared in the *1866 Prices of Hardware Sold by Sargent & Co.,* 70 Beekman St., New York.[16] A discount sheet issued by the office of the Union Factory October 20, 1867 referred to a price list issued during September 1866. This is the first known reference to common bench planes Nos. 100, 101, 102, 103, 108, 109, 110 and 111 being offered with imprint of J. Pearce. Jonathan Pearce made planes at Providence, RI, 1853-1875. He apparently specialized in an inexpensive line of wood bench planes. These were listed in Union Factory trade catalogues for many years thereafter.[17] It is suggested that it was not profitable for E.M. Chapin to make such low priced planes, which he sold unwarranted, but wanted to have a complete line and price range to offer with his more expensive Extra and Premium bench planes.

On January 28, 1868 the co-partnership between E.M. and G.W. Chapin was dissolved. Edward purchased George's interests of the Union Factory.[18] E.M. Chapin continued at Pine Meadow as H. Chapin's Son, while G.W. Chapin continued in business at Cleveland, Ohio. The following printed announcement was circulated among the trade.

Office of the Union Factory.

[ESTABLISHED 1826.]

Pine Meadow, Conn., Jan'y 28, 1868.

The Copartnership heretofore existing between the undersigned, under the firm of H. Chapin's Sons, is this day dissolved by mutual consent, George W. Chapin retiring from the business. The accounts of the firm will be settled by E. M. Chapin.

E. M. CHAPIN,
G. W. CHAPIN.

The undersigned will continue the business under the name and style of

H. CHAPIN'S SON.

Thanking you for past favors, I take pleasure in calling your attention to the annexed circular, and trusting by prompt attention to your wants, to merit a continuance of your patronage, I remain,

Very respectfully,

E. M. CHAPIN.

The first catalogue issued by H. Chapin's Son is believed to have been January 1869. This was probably the first Union Factory catalogue with illustrations. A discount sheet issued June 1, 1869 noted this catalogue contained 39 pages, an increase of 22 over the 1865 issue. Again a copy of this catalogue is not known to exist, but the *1869 Illustrated Catalogue and Price List of Hardware and Mechanics' Tools manufactured and sold by Sargent & Co.* (See Plate XVI) contains illustrations of H. Chapin's Son's products on 12 of 24 pages in their extensive 447 page catalogue. These Chapin products have the same number and prices as listed in the *1865 H. Chapin & Sons' Catalogue.* In all probability the illustrations in the 1869 Sargent catalogue were the same as in the 1869 Chapin catalogue, made from the same cuts. Plates XVII & XVIII respectively show Chapin rules and planes from the 1869 Sargent & Co. catalogue.

Charles Carter of Auburn, New York received a patent on October 6, 1858 for a Mortising Machine: — "for forming the throats of planes after the main part of the mortise has been roughed out by a previous machine wherein an important saving in labor is made."[19] E.M. Chapin in payment on October 11, 1869 received an assignment — "to use one machine of this design in his factory at New Hartford." (See Table XX) In all probability E.M. Chapin had learned of this process then in use at Auburn Tool Co. during a conference of the Plane Manufacturer's Association. In order to compete it was essential to use such an automated process. Such machines had been in use at the Ohio Tool Co. as early as February 14, 1865.[20] On that date three patents were granted at Columbus, Ohio:

F.B. Marble was granted US Patent 46,372 Mortising Machine — "Machine for Planning the Throats of Plane Stocks." (Assignor to Ohio Tool Co.)

John Richards was issued two Patents: No. 46,391 Mortising Machine — "to produce the throats of plane stocks by means of rotary and vibrating cutters in conjunction with contrivances for holding and directing the stocks to said cutters, according to the angle it is desired to give the bed-line, wedge-line, or front-line."

US Patent No. 46,392 Improvement in Machines for Mortising Plane Stocks: "to form the cheeks on each side of the throat of a plane stock by means of an auger which receives a rotary, and also a vibratory motion."

The availability of exotic wood is apparent from an 1867 price list from the London export firm of Joseph Gardner & Sons. (Plate XIX)

From a discount sheet dated January 26, 1870 (See Plate XX) it is evident that an enlarged catalogue of 68 pages was available from H. Chapin's Son of January 1, 1870, while a copy of this is not known to exist, it is believed to have been similar in content to their 1874 issue, with the exception of new products added. The latter 1874 will be reprinted in entirety in Chapter VIII.

The 1870 US Census, Products of Industry Section, revealed the following statistics regarding the Union Factory: 25 males over 16 years of age and 3 females over 15 years of age were employed at an annual salary of $15,000; 2 water wheels totaled 50 HP which ran 3 saws and other machinery; $20,000 cost of materials produced 40,000 planes which sold for $45,000.

Plate XVI - Title Page of 1869 *Sargent & Co. Catalogue*

ILLUSTRATED CATALOGUE

AND

PRICE LIST

OF

HARDWARE

AND

MECHANICS' TOOLS,

MANUFACTURED AND SOLD BY

SARGENT & CO.

No. 70 BEEKMAN STREET,

AND

No. 68 GOLD STREET,

NEW YORK.

FACTORIES AT NEW HAVEN, CONN.,
LEICESTER AND WORCESTER, MASS.

1869.

[Collection of Author]

Plate XVII - Page 311 *1869 Sargent & Co. Catalogue*

RULES. 311

AGENTS FOR H. CHAPIN'S SON'S
RULES, GAUGES, PLANES,
HAND SCREWS, BENCH SCREWS,
PLUMBS, LEVELS, &c.

Boxwood Rules.
One Foot, Four Fold—Narrow.

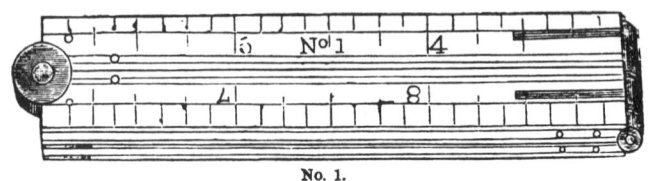

No. 1.

No. 1, Round Joint,   8ths and 16ths, $\frac{5}{8}$ inch wide, per doz., $3 00
No. 2, Square   "   "   " $\frac{5}{8}$ "   "   "   3 50

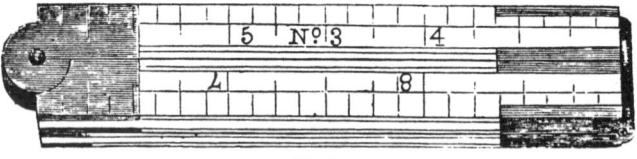

No. 3.

No. 3, Square Joint, Ed. Plates, 8ths & 16ths, $\frac{5}{8}$ in. wide, per doz. $5 00
No. 4,   "   "   Half Bound   "   " $\frac{5}{8}$ "   "   9 00
No. 5,   "   "   Bound,   "   " $\frac{5}{8}$ "   "   11 00
No. 6, Arch   "   -   -   "   " $\frac{5}{8}$ "   "   4 00
No. 7,   "   "   Edge Plates, "   " $\frac{5}{8}$ "   "   6 00
No. 8,   "   "   Half Bound   "   " $\frac{3}{4}$ "   "   10 00

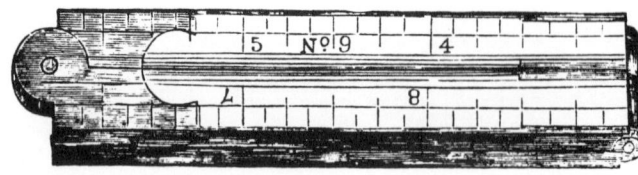

No. 9.

No. 9, Arch Joint, Bound, 8ths & 16ths, $\frac{5}{8}$ in. wide, per doz. $12 00

Plate XVIII - Page 323 *1869 Sargent & Co. Catalogue*

BENCH PLANES. 323

AGENTS
FOR
H. CHAPIN'S SON'S PLANES.

Common Bench Planes.

Single Irons.

No. 100, Smooth,	Cast Steel Irons, - -	each,	$0 50
No. 101, Jack,	" " - -	"	0 65
No. 102, Fore,	" " - -	"	0 95
No. 103, Jointer, 26 inch,	" " - -	"	1 05
No. 103, " 28 "	" " - -	"	1 15

Double Irons.

No. 108, Smooth,	Cast Steel Irons, - -	each,	$0 85
No. 109, Jack,	" " - -	"	0 95
No. 110, Fore,	" " - -	"	1 30
No. 111, Jointer, 26 inch,	" " - -	"	1 40
No. 111, " 28 "	" " - -	"	1 50

Extra Bench Planes.

Single Irons.

No. 104, Smooth, -	Best Cast Steel Irons, 2 to $2\frac{1}{4}$ in.,	each,	$0 60
No. 105, Jack,	" " " 2 to $2\frac{1}{4}$ "	"	0 75
No. 106, Fore, 21 inch,	" " " $2\frac{3}{8}$ "	"	0 95
No. 106, Fore, 22 "	" " " $2\frac{1}{2}$ "	"	1 00
No. 107, Jointer, 26 "	" " " $2\frac{1}{2}$ "	"	1 10
No. 107, " 28 "	" " " $2\frac{5}{8}$ "	"	1 20

Table XX Joseph Gardner & Sons 1867 Price List of Exotic Woods

JOSEPH GARDNER & SON'S MONTHLY CIRCULAR.
[REGISTERED FOR TRANSMISSION ABROAD.]

Regent Road, Bootle, Liverpool, 1st January, 1867.

BOXWOOD.—Our Imports during the past month consisted of 38 tons per "Atlas," and 70 tons per "Danube." Our present stock is 1,419 tons against 1414 last month. We expect several parcels during the present month which we shall offer ex "Quay."

BLACK EBONY.—We have Old Calabar @ £11, and Gaboon at £11 10s. per ton.

COCUSWOOD.—We have in stock 54 tons from Cuba, which we are selling @ £6 per ton.

LANCEWOOD SPARS.—The cargo of 2,900 per "Agnes" is now discharged, and we are selling the prime spars suitable for bending @ £9 per ton, and those suitable for bobbin turners @ £7 per ton; they average over 1 cwt. each.

LIGNUMVITÆ.—Larger sizes continue scarce and are much inquired after. Our stock is 577 tons, against 606 tons last month.

MAHOGANY.—We have an excellent supply of Cuba, very suitable for bobbins, @ 5d. and 5¼d. per foot, Liverpool Brokers' measurement.

ROSEWOOD.—We have Bahia @ £8 to £12 per ton.

VIOLET OR KING WOOD.—We have in stock a few tons of Ceara @ £9, averaging about 66 pieces to the ton, and a small lot of Parnahiba, average 90 pieces, at £10 10s per ton.

STOCK AND PRICES OF BOXWOOD.

ABASSIA SPLIT.

SIZES.	PRIME.	FAIR.	ORDINARY.	COMMON.
Under 4ins	4 tns @ £4/15	68 tons @ £3 10	52 tons @ £2 10	tons @ £2 0
4 & under 5 ins	46 " 5 0	41 " 3 15	" 2 15
5 ins & upwrds	14 " 17	235 " 11 10	146 " 8 0	38 " 5 0

ABASSIA SOUND

Measured one-third from small end.	PRIME.	FAIR.	ORDINARY.	COMMON.
1¼ & under 1½	tons @ £	2 tons @ £7/10	8 tons @ £4	
1½ " 2		28 " 5		
2 " 2¼		27 " 4	9 " 3	
2¼ " 2½	1	9 " 5	18 " 4	
2½ " 2¾	4 " 12	8 " 8	19 " 6	
2¾ " 3	7 " 16	27 " 11	36 " 7	2 tons @ £4/10
3 " 3¼	2 " 21	" 17	33 " 10	3 " 5/10
3¼ " 3½	6 " 21	26 " 17	50 " 10	2 " 5/10
3½ " 3¾	3 " 21		23 " 10	
3¾ " 4	7 " 17	20 " 13	50 " 8	
4 " 4½	5 " 15	19 " 11	33 " 6	
4½ " 5	2 " 11	15 " 8	20 " 5	1 " 4/10
5 " 5½	" 11	21 " 7	14 " 5	1 " 4/10
5½ " 6	6 " 13	11 " 9	10 " 7	
6 " 7	" 17	26 " 11	11 " 8	
7 " 8		3 " 14	3 " 9	

ANATOLIAN SOUND.

Measured one-third from small end.	FIRSTS.	SECONDS.	THIRDS.
2¼ & under 2½	1 tons @ £4	2 tons @ £3	2 tons @ £3
2½ " 2¾	1 " 5	4 " 5	
2¾ " 3	1 " 7	2 " 7	2 " 5
3 " 3¼	2 " 9	2 " 7	2 " 5
3¼ " 3½	"	" .7	1 " 5
3½ " 3¾	"	"	"
3¾ " 4	"	"	"
4 " 4½	"	"	"

The following parcels are in bulk as imported:—

			Per Ton.
31 tons Anatolian	...	1¾ to 4 inches, ex "Laconia"	@ £3 10
42 " Mingrelian	...	Ditto ex "Sahara"	@ £4 10
16 " Abassia	...	1½ to 6 inches, ex "Morocco"	@ £5 5
10 " Ditto	...	4½ in. & up'ds ex "Grecian"	@ £9 0

STOCK AND PRICES OF LIGNUMVITÆ.

CITY ST. DOMINGO, JAMAICA, &c.

SIZES.	PRIME.	FAIR.	OVAL. To make dead eyes of size mentioned.	INFERIOR.
			Sheave way / Plank way	
3 and under 4 in.	16 tons @ £8			tons @ £
4 " 5 "	18 " 8	45 tons @ £6	£4/15 / £3/10	
5 " 6 "		22 " 6		
6 " 7 "		24 " 7/10	5/15 / 4	
7 " 8 "		1 " 8/15	6/10 / 4/10	
8 " 9 "		3 " 11	85 / 5/10	94 tons
9 " 10 "			11 / 8	
10 " 11 "	1 " 22		12 / 10	
11 " 12 "		1 " 14	" 10	
12 " 13 "		1 " 14	" 10	
13 " 14 "	1 " 18	4 " 12	10	
14 in. and upwards		1 " 12		

NEW ST. DOMINGO, BAHAMA, &c.

SIZES.	PRIME.	FAIR.	OVAL. To make dead eyes of size mentioned.	INFERIOR.
			Sheave way / Plank way	
4 and under 5 in.	3 tons @ £5	24 tons @ £3/15	£3	3 tons @ £2
5 " 6 "	16 " 5	37 " 3/15	£2/10 / 2	2
6 " 7 "	32 " 5	51 " 3/15	3 / 2	2/10
7 " 8 "	3 " 7	18 " 5	4 / 3	2/10
8 " 9 "	6 " 10	3 " 7/10	5/15 / 4	5 " 3
9 " 10 "		3 " 10	8 / 6	" 4
10 " 11 "	1 " 18			
11 " 12 "		1		
12 " 13 "				

SAP ROTTEN.

SIZES.	PRIME.	FAIR.	INFERIOR.
3 and under 5 inches.		12 tons @ £	8 tons @ £
5 " 7 "			
7 " 9 "	tons @ £	15 " "	
9 " 10 "			

The following parcels are in Bulk as Imported:

16 Tons selected Jamaica	...	3 to 5 inches, at £6 per Ton.
32 " Jamaica	...	3 " 5 " " £4 0s. "
28 " New St. Domingo		5 " 7 " " £4 "

Quotations for selected parcels are for not less than 2 tons; those for parcels in bulk are for not less than 10 tons. Cartage and delivering 1/ 2/6 per ton.

Plate XX - Assignment of Rights to One Patented Mortising Machine by Charles Carter to E.M. Chapin, Oct. 22, 1869.

Whereas, I, Charles Carter of Auburn in the County of Cayuga and State of New York did obtain Letters Patent of the United States for an improvement in Mortising Machines, which Letters Patent bear the date the Sixth day of October AD 1868 and are numbered 82692. And Whereas, Edward M. Chapin of the town of New Hartford in the State of Connecticut is desirous of acquiring an interest therein: i.e. a shop right only.

Now this Indenture Witnesseth that for and consideration of One Thousand Dollars to me in hand paid, the receipt of which is hereby acknowledged, I has assigned, sold, and set over; and do hereby assign, sell and set over unto the said Edward Chapin, the right to use said invention, as secured to me in said Letters Patent *on one mortising machine in said Chapin's factory in said town of New Hartford and in no other place, but without the right to make or sell said invention, and with the right to use in connection therewith one attachment & improvement for such machine recently invented (but not yet patented) by me for cutting the front of the cheek of a bench plane, also to be used in said factory* and in no other place or places; the same to be held and enjoyed by the said Edward Chapin for his own use and behoof, and for the use and behoof of his legal representatives, to the full end of the term for which said Letters Patent are granted, as fully and entirely as the same would have been held and enjoyed by me had this assignment and sale not been made. In Testimony Whereof I hereunto set my hand and affix my seal this eleventh day of October 1869.

Sealed and Delivered in Presence of   *Charles Carter*
Richard C. Steel

Patent Office Oct. 22, 1869

U.S. Patent Office - Received for record Oct. 22, 1869 and Recorderd in Libra C12 - page 303 of Transfers of Patents, in testimony whereof I have caused the seal of the Patent Office to be herewith affixed.

James J. Fisher, Comr. of Patents

[Transcribed from Document in Collection of the New Hartford Historical Society]

Office of the Union Factory,
ESTABLISHED IN 1820.

PINE MEADOW, CONN., June 1st, 1869.

GENTLEMEN:

The annexed are my cash rates for articles named in List, January, 1869.

RULES—Boxwood, Ivory and Miscellaneous,	Pages 8 to 9,	Discount 40 and 10 per cent.
BENCH PLANKS—stamped J. Pearce,	10,	Net.
PREMIUM PLANES,	11,	Add 20 per cent.
SHIP PLANES,	12,	Add 20 per cent.
COOPER'S PLANES,	13,	Add 20 per cent.
MISCELLANEOUS PLANE,	13,	Add 20 per cent.
MOULDING PLANES,	14 to 20,	Add 10 per cent.
GROOVING PLOWS,	21 to 24,	Add 10 per cent.
GAUGES,	25 to 26,	Discount 30 and 10 per cent.
GAUGES—C. Sholl's Patent,	28,	Discount 25 per cent.
HANDLES,	29,	Discount 25 and 10 per cent.
STOPS,	29,	Net.
PLUMBS AND LEVELS,	31,	Discount 50 and 10 per cent.
POCKET LEVELS,	32,	Discount 50 and 10 per cent.
LEVEL GLASSES,	32,	Discount 50 and 10 per cent.
HAND SCREWS,	33 to 84,	Discount 20 per cent.
BENCH SCREWS,	34,	Discount 20 per cent.
SCREW DRIVERS,	35,	Net.
MINCING KNIVES,	35,	Net.
AWLS,	35,	Net.
TRY SQUARES,	36,	Discount 25 and 10 per cent.
SLIDING T. BEVELS,	37,	Discount 25 and 10 per cent.
PLANE IRONS,	38 to 39,	Add 20 per cent.

Goods Delivered at Depot.

Boxes Charged.

Terms invariably cash, payable in New York Par Funds.

Soliciting a continuance of your patronage,

I remain, respectfully yours,

H. CHAPIN'S SON.

Office of the Union Factory,
ESTABLISHED IN 1826.

Pine Meadow, Conn., Jan. 26th, 1870.

GENTLEMEN:

The annexed are cash rates for articles named in my List, Jan. 1st, 1870.

RULES—Boxwood, Ivory and Miscellaneous,	Pages 3 to 9,	Discount 50 and 10 per cent.
BENCH PLANES—stamped J. Pearce,	10,	Discount 15 per cent.
EXTRA BENCH PLANES,	11 to 12,	Add 10 per cent.
PREMIUM PLANES,	13,	Add 10 per cent.
SHIP PLANES,	14,	Add 10 per cent.
COOPER'S PLANES,	15,	Add 10 per cent.
MISCELLANEOUS PLANES,	16 to 43,	Net.
MOULDING PLANES,	44 to 47,	Net.
GROOVING PLOWS,	48 to 49,	Net.
GAUGES,	50 to 51,	Discount 30 and 10 per cent.
GAUGES—C. Sholl's Patent,	52 to 58,	Discount 30 and 10 per cent.
PLUMBS AND LEVELS,	54,	Discount 50 and 10 per cent.
POCKET LEVELS,	54,	Discount 50 and 10 per cent.
LEVEL GLASSES,	55,	Discount 20 per cent.
HAND SCREWS,	56,	Discount 20 per cent.
HAND SCREWS, BEADED,	56,	Discount 20 per cent.
BENCH SCREWS,	57,	Discount 20 per cent.
TURNING SAW FRAMES,	58,	Discount 30 and 10 per cent.
TURNING SAW FRAMES, AND SAWS,	59,	Discount 30 and 10 per cent.
PLANE AND SAW HANDLES,	60,	Discount 30 and 10 per cent.
CHISEL HANDLES,	61,	Net.
FILE AND AWL HANDLES,	61,	Net.
SCREW DRIVERS,	61,	Net.
MINCING KNIVES,	62,	Discount 25 and 10 per cent.
AWLS,	63,	Discount 25 and 10 per cent.
PREMIUM TRY SQUARES,	63,	Discount 25 and 10 per cent.
PREMIUM TRY SQUARES, PLATED BACK,	64,	Discount 25 and 10 per cent.
TRY SQUARES, Nos. 1 AND 2,	65,	Discount 25 and 10 per cent.
SLIDING T BEVELS, Nos. 1 AND 2,	66 to 67,	Add 15 per cent.
PLANE IRONS,	68,	Net.
TOY TOOL CHEST SUPPLIES,		

Rates subject to fluctuations of market.

Terms invariably CASH, payable in New York par Funds.

Soliciting a continuance of your patronage,

I am respectfully yours,

H. CHAPIN'S SON.

Price List of January, 1870, furnished on application.
Make List Price, No. 449, Carpenter's Badger, Double, $2.50.

Plate XX - Union Factory Discount Sheets: 1869 (left); 1870 (right)

Notes - Chapter VI

1. Additionally D.H. Stephens was granted US Letters Patent #58,871, Jan.26, 1866 Machine for Making Rule Joints. Undoubtedly Stephens invented other machines.
2. Barkhamsted Land Records, B13, p. 80
3. *ibid*, B.16, p. 248, Jan. 8, 1853
4. *ibid*, B.19, p. 22, Oct. 23, 1861
5. Private communication, Douglas Roberts, Riverton, Conn., May 30, 1982
6. Douglas E. Roberts, "The Village of Riverton, Town of Barkhamsted", *Lure of Litchfield Hills*, [Winsted, Conn., 1970], Vol. XX, No.4, p. 41
7. *op. cit., Chapin Genealogy,* p.1740. George was married at New Libson, Ohio in 1868 and entered business with his wife's brother under the name of Hanna, Chapin & Co. They were involved with the production of kerosine and this became affiliated with Standard Oil, which brought a fortune to George.
8. Two trade catalogues of the Greenfield Tool Co., 1854 and 1872, have been reprinted by Ken Roberts Publishing Co. [respectively 1981 & 1978]
9. *1869 Price List of Planes, Plane Irons, Rules, etc.* has been reprinted by Ken Roberts Publishing Co. [1983]
10. *1873 Illustrated Catalogue of Mechanics Tools of D.R. Barton & Co.* has been reprinted by Ken Roberts Publishing Co.]1983]
11. New Hartford Land Records, B.21, p. 252
12. Library Conn. Hist. Soc., Chapin Manuscript material.
13. K.D. and Jane W. Roberts, *op. cit., New York Planemakers, etc.,* p. 95
14. Hubbard Hardware Co. was succeeded by The Hubbard & Curtiss Manufacturing Co. of Middletown, Conn. who advertised in the *1874 Connecticut Business Directory* that they were manufacturers of Boxwood & Ivory Rules and also Framing, Firmer Chisels and Drawing Knives.
15. An 1873 trade catalogue of Hart, Bliven & Mead Manufacturing Co. notes their offices and warehouses at New York with factories at Kensington, Conn., stating on several pages of rules "Agents for H. Chapin's Son's Rules, Gauges, Planes, etc. [CHS Library] Ultimately this firm became part of Peck, Stow and Wilcox, Southington, Conn.
16. Collection of the Connecticut State Library, Hartford. Sargent & Co. was established as a New York hardware sales firm in 1858. They did not manufacture hardware under their own name until 1863 at New Haven, Conn.
17. Common planes were designated "PEARCE" as late as 1922 in the Chapin-Stephens Co. Catalogue No. 122.
18. New Hartford Land Records, B.22, p. 158
19. U.S. Patent No. 82,692
20. Previously US Patent 16,954 had been granted H.S Dewey of Bethel, Vt. "Mortising Machine for Cutting Throats of Carpenter's Plane Stocks", March 31, 1857. It is not know whether this patent was acquired by any large plane manufacturer.

Chapter VII

Solon Rust

Solon Rust was born July 7, 1832 at Barkhamsted, Connecticut.[1] During his youth he moved to the adjacent village of New Hartford and worked at the Greenwood Co. and at D.B. Mills at Pine Meadow.[2] On March 18, 1850 he began work with Hermon Chapin, agreeing to make rules until he became 21. (1853)[3] Apparently soon after starting with Hermon Chapin, he changed trades and followed planemaking. In 1857 he left the firm and became employed as a planemaker with Linson DeForest at Birmingham, (Derby) Connecticut.[4] There he married Ann Tiffany, April 14, 1859, an immigrant from Leeds, England. Two children were born there, first a daughter and then in 1863 a son, Arthur.

The extensive line of 51 varieties of plow plane made by DeForest in 1856 is shown in Plate I from his *"Old New York Price List."* These were made from beech, boxwood, rosewood, zebrawood and ebony. The most expensive was #219, a handled ebony plow, silver mounted, with ivory tips on the arms, ivory nuts and washers at $30. The *1854 Price List of Joiners' Bench Planes of Greenfield Tool Co.* noted 58 varieties of plow planes. (See Plate II)[5] This is the earliest known dated listing offering an ebony plow. Their #570 Handled all ivory plow, silver mounted, was offered at $75. Not to be outdone by Greenfield Tool Co., L&C. H. DeForest noted their #494 Ivory Plow with solid gold nuts and washers (22 carats), gold tips on the arms and gold mounted for $1000 among 44 varieties of plows in their 1860 Price List. (See Plate III) While the more conservative firms of H. Chapin had offered handled plows in beech, rosewood and boxwood as early as 1839, it was not until the 1870's that ebony plows were listed in their catalogue.[6]

In reply to a solicitation for employment, Solon Rust on July 28, 1864 wrote a letter to H. Chapin & Sons. (Table I) It may have been the desire of H. Chapin & Sons to expand their line of plow planes to meet the competition that led to this solicitation to hire Solon Rust. In any event apparently mutual acceptable terms were agreed and Solon Rust returned to Pine Meadow joining H. Chapin & Sons, becoming master plow maker.

Solon Rust and E.M. Chapin were jointly granted US Patent #76,051 on March 31, 1868 for "Improvement in Carpenter's Planes." This concerned an adjusting screw for regulating the fence parallel to the plow skate. Previously US Patents for such regulation had been granted Isreal White in 1834 and E.W. Carpenter in 1838.[7] The patent drawing is shown as Plate IV, and the specifications thereof in Table II. A photograph of this plane in applewood, a later version, as No. 238-3/4, is shown in Fig. 41. This plow plane was first offered in the 1869 catalogue of Sargent & Co. in beech, beech with box fence, boxwood, and rosewood with box fence.[8] Later this plane was also offered in solid rosewood and applewood. Solon Rust's patterns for making this plane are shown in Fig. 42, together with a view from the other side of the plane seen in Fig. 43.

Several years ago these patterns with other jigs and the tool box that had belonged to Solon Rust were acquired for study. A view into this chest is shown as Fig. 44. Undoubtedly this is only a partial collection, but is probably representative of his most important plow and planemaking tools. Figs. 45 and 46 show the floats and chisels, removed from the tray and well of the chest previously illustrated. Many of the moulding planes are stamped "Solon Rust." For the most part these are planes with imprint of "H. Chapin, Union Factory" that have been modified from hollows and rounds, or other configurations, to perform special work making plow fences. The uses of some of these planes in making a plow fence are illustrated in Figs. 50 through 53.

Table I   *Letter from Solon Rust to Chapin & Sons*

Seymour   July 28, 1864

Messrs Chapin & Sons

I received yours on the twenty seventh. you said i could have work on plows if i wished for two months or so. i will come if you will pay me so that i can aford to come. the price you used to pay by the piece for your best plows would be about fifty cents. at the present prices of gold and the necessarys of life a man ought to earn two dollars and half a day and that would be just the same as one dollar a day three years ago. i used to get for

handle box and rose wood plows   1.69
unhandle box and rose wood plows   1.20
handle beach plated box fence plows   1.30
handle beach plated plows   1.20
unhandle beach plated and box fence   97-1/2
"   "   plated plows   87-1/2
that is what deforest gave me

i will come if you will pay me so that i can earn two dollars and a half per day. you can say what you will, pay by the day or the piece by the return mail and i will let you know on monday. if i come i should want my pay every saturday and i will pay the difference between us in weekly instalments.

yours,
Solon Rust

[Copied from Original Letter Courtesy of Mrs. James P. Adams]

Table II - Specification of U.S. Letters Patent No. 76,051, Carpenters' Plane

"Be it known that we E.M. Chapin and Solon Rust of Pine Meadow, in the county of Litchfield, and State of Connecticut, have invented a new and useful improvement in ploughs and other Fence-Tools for Joiners' Use; and we do hereby declare that the following is a full, clear and exact description thereof, which will enable those skilled in the art to make and use the same, reference being had to the accompanying drawing, forming part of this specification.

The object of this invention is to construct a joiner' plow and other similar tools, which are provided with adjustable fences, in such a manner that the fence-guides and screws will not extend through the body or stock of the implement, as is now the case, and which is the source of a great deal of annoyance is using such tools, rendering it necessary for the workman, each time the tool is used, to remove out of the way, or to the side, tools and implements of various kinds on the work bench, which may at chance be at the right-hand side of the tool and near the same.

The invention has further for its object the connecting of the adjusting screw to the stock of the implement in such a manner that the said screw, in case of being broken, or injured in any way, may be detached with the greatest of facility, and a new screw inserted.

. . . . We claim as new, and desire to secure by Letters Patent - The joiners' plough, constructed as described, and consisting of stock A, [See Plate IV] having slotted, flanged guides C, projecting from one side, the fence B, screw D, formed with tenon, d, and fitted with a head, e, and the thumb screws, b,b, provided with collars, c, all arranged and operating in the manner and for the purpose set forth."

OLD
NEW YORK PRICE LIST
OF
PLANES,

MANUFACTURED BY

LINSON DEFOREST,

Birmingham, Conn.

Warehouse No. 22 Cliff Street, New York;
D. H. WAY, Agent.

WATERBURY, CONN.
RICHARDS & COMPANY, PRINTERS, BALDWIN'S BLOCK.

1856.

PLOWS.

215	Handled	Ebony Plow, 8 irons,	17 50
216	do	Ebony Plow, silver mt'ed, do	20 00
217	do	Ebony Plow, with ivory tips on on arms, 8 irons,	20 50
218	do	Ebony Plow, silver mounted, with iv'ry tips on arms, 8 do	23 00

14

258	Beech	do without brass on plate, 1 iron,	6 75
259	do	do without brass on plate, wood stop, 1 iron,	6 00
260	Beech	do slide arms, silver ferrules, 8 irons,	7 50
261	do	do slide arms, 8 irons,	6 50
262	do	do do do without brass on plate, 1 iron,	4 62
263	do	do slide arms, without brass on plate, wood stop, 1 iron,	3 50
264	For a silver plated side stop,		1 00
265	For a brass side stop,		50

Plate I
Plow Planes by Linson Deforest
OLD NEW YORK PRICE LIST, 1856
[Collection of Connecticut Historical Society]

12

219	Handled	Ebony Plow, silver mt'ed, with ivory tips on arms, ivory nuts and washers, 8 irons,	30 00
220	do	Rosewood Plow, 8 irons,	16 50
221	do	Rosewood do silver mounted, 8 irons,	19 00
222	do	Rosewood do with iv'ry tips on arms, 8 irons,	19 50
223	do	Rosewood do silver mounted, with ivory tips on arms, 8 irons,	22 00
224	do	Rosewood Plow, sil'r mt'ed with ivory tips on arms, and ivory nuts and washers, 8 irons,	29 00
225	do	Zebrawood Plow, 8 irons,	16 50
226	do	Zebrawood do silver mt'ed, 8 irons,	19 00
227	do	Zebrawood do with ivory tips on arms, 8 irons,	19 50
228	do	Zebrawood Plow, silver mt'ed with iv'ry tips on arms, 8 irons,	22 00
229	do	Zebrawood Plow, silver mt'ed with ivory tips on arms, and ivory nuts and washers,	29 00
230	do	Boxwood Plow, 8 irons,	16 00
231	do	do do silver mounted, 8 irons,	18 50
232	do	Boxwood Plow, with ivory tips on arms, 8 irons,	19 00
233	do	Boxwood do silver mounted, with ivory tips on arms, 8 irons,	21 50
234	do	Boxwood Plow, sil'r mt'ed, with ivory tips on arms, and ivory nuts and washers, 8 irons,	28 50
235	do	Plows, with solid boxwood fence, 8 irons,	14 00

13

236	Handled Beech Plow, 8 irons,		12 00
237	Ebony Plow, 8 irons,		12 00
238	do	do silver mounted, 8 irons,	14 00
239	do	do silver mounted, with ivory tips on arms, 8 irons,	15 00
240	do	do silver mounted, with ivory tips on arms, 8 irons,	17 00
241	do	do silver mounted, with ivory tips on arms, and ivory nuts and washers, 8 irons,	24 00
242	Rosewood Plow, 8 irons,		11 50
243	do	do silver mounted, 8 irons,	13 50
244	do	do with ivory tips on arms, 8 irons,	14 50
245	do	do silver mounted, with ivory tips on arms, 8 irons,	16 50
246	do	do silver mounted, with ivory tips on arms, and ivory nuts and washers, 8 irons,	23 50
247	Zebra Wood Plow, 8 irons,		11 50
248	do	do silver mounted, 8 irons,	13 50
249	do	do with ivory tips on arms, 8 irons,	14 50
250	do	do silver mounted, with iv'ry tips on arms, and ivory nuts and washers, 8 irons,	23 50
251	Boxwood Plow, 8 irons,		11 00
252	do	do silver mounted, 8 irons,	13 00
253	do	do silver mounted, with iv'ry tips on arms, 8 irons,	16 00
254	Beech	do with solid boxwood fence, 8 irons,	10 00
255	do	do fence boxed, 8 irons,	9 50
256	do	do 8 irons,	9 00
257	do	do without brass on plate, 8 irons,	8 50

PRICE LIST
OF
JOINERS' BENCH PLANES & MOULDING TOOLS,
Manufactured by the
GREENFIELD TOOL COMPANY,
GREENFIELD, MASS.

GREENFIELD:
CHARLES A. MIRICK, PRINTER.
1854.

---

18   PRICE LIST.

Moulding Planes.—*Continued.*

Invoice Nos.						Price.
513	Plows, 1st rate, slide arm,	. . .	8 Irons. .	4 25
514	do. do. do. do. boxed,	. .	8 do. .	4 55
515	do. do. do. do. plated,	. .	8 do. .	4 55
516	do. 2d rate, do. do.	. .	8 do. .	3 90
517	do. do. do. do. boxed,	. .	8 do. .	4 20
518	do. do. do. do. plated,	. .	8 do. .	4 20
519	do. 3d rate, do. do.	. .	8 do. .	3 00
520	do. do. do. do. boxed,	. .	8 do. .	3 30
521	do. do. do. do. plated,	. .	8 do. .	3 30

Plate II

Plow Planes by Greenfield Tool Co.
1854 Price List of Planes, etc.
[Collection of Robert H. Cameron]

PRICE LIST.   19

Moulding Planes.—*Continued.*

Invoice Nos.					Price.
522	Plows, 4th rate, slide arm, . . .	8 Irons..	2 85
523	do. do. do. do. boxed, . .	8 do. .	3 10
524	do. do. do. do. plated, . .	8 do. .	3 10
525	do. 1st rate, screw arms, . .	8 do. .	4 50
526	do. do. do. do. boxed, . .	8 do. .	4 80
527	do. do. do. do. plated, . .	8 do. .	4 80
528	do. 2d rate, do. do. . .	8 do. .	4 20
529	do. do. do. do. boxed, . .	8 do. .	4 50
530	do. do. do. do. plated, . .	8 do. .	4 50
531	do. 3d rate, do. do. . .	8 do. .	3 50
532	do. do. do. do. boxed, . .	8 do. .	3 80
533	do. do. do. do. plated, . .	8 do. .	3 80
534	do. solid Boxwood, . . .	8 do. .	6 50
535	do. do. Rosewood, . . .	8 do. .	6 50
536	do. do. do. boxed fence, .	8 do. .	6 80
537	do. do. Ebony, ...	8 do. .	6 75
538	do. do. Rosewood, ivory bands on nuts,	8 do. .	8 75
539	do. do. Rosewood, ivory bands on nuts, ivory tipped arms,	8 do. .	9 75
540	do. do. Ebony, ivory bands on nuts,	8 do. .	9 00
541	do. do. Ebony, ivory bands on nuts, ivory tipped arms,	8 do. .	10 00
542	Handled Beech Plow, 1st rate, . .	8 do. .	5 75
543	do. do. do. do. boxed, .	8 do. .	6 05
544	do. do. do. do. plated, .	8 do. .	6 05
545	do. do. do. 2d rate, . .	8 do. .	5 25
546	do. do. do. do. boxed, .	8 do. .	5 55
547	do. do. do. do. plated, .	8 do. .	5 55
548	do. Boxwood do. . . .	8 do. .	8 20
549	do. Rosewood do. . . .	8 do. .	8 20
550	do. do. do. boxed, . .	8 do. .	8 50
551	do. do. do. ivory bands on nuts,	8 do. .	10 45
552	do. do. do. do. do. do. boxed,	8 do. .	10 75
553	do. do. do. do. do. do. and ivory tips on arms,	8 do. .	11 45
554	do. do. do. ivory bands on nuts, and ivory tips on arms, bxd,	8 do. .	11 75

---

20   PRICE LIST.

Moulding Planes.—*Continued.*

Invoice Nos.					Price.
555	Handl'd Rsew'd Plow, ivory trimmed, .	8 Irons..	14 50
556	do. do. do. do. do. boxed,	8 do. .	14 80
557	do. do. do. do. do. arms ivory tipped,	8 do. .	15 50
558	do. do. do. ivory trimmed, arms ivory tipped, boxed,	8 do. .	15 80
559	do. do. do. ivory trimmed, silver mounted,	8 do. .	17 00
560	do. do. do. ivory trimmed, silver mounted, boxed,	8 do. .	17 30
561	do. Ebony do.	8 do. .	9 50
562	do. do. do. boxed, . .	8 do. .	9 80
563	do. do. do. ivory bands on nuts,	8 do. .	12 05
564	do. do. do. do. do. ivory tips on arms,	8 do. .	13 05
565	do. do. do. iv'ry bands on n'ts, iv'y tips on arms, boxed,	8 do. .	13 35
566	do. do. do. ivory trimmed,	8 do. .	15 50
567	do. do. do. do. boxed,	8 do. .	15 80
568	do. do. do. do. silver m'ted,	8 do. .	18 00
569	do. do. do. do. do. do. boxed,	8 do. .	18 30
570	do. all ivory do. silver mounted, .	8 do. .	75 00

PRICE LIST

OF

Joiners' Bench Planes,

MOULDING PLANES,

MANUFACTURED BY

L. & C. H. DeFOREST,

BIRMINGHAM, CONN.

NEW HAVEN:
J. H. BENHAM, PRINTER, COR. CHURCH AND CHAPEL STREETS.
1860.

PRICE LIST. 17

MOULDING PLANES.—Cont'd.

P.

Invoice Nos.		Price.
454	Pannel, or Raising Jack Plane,	1.15
455	do. do. do. with cut,	1.40
456	do. do. do. moving fence,	1.40
457	do. do. do. do. and cut,	1.65

All Plows from No. 471 to No. 504 inclusive, are French polished, and superior to all others in market.

458	Plows, 1st rate, slide arms, 8 irons,	4.25
459	do. do. do. boxed fence, do.	4.55
460	do. 2d rate, do. do.	3.90
461	do. do. do. do. do.	4.20
462	do. 3d rate, do. do.	3.00
463	do. do. do. do. do.	3.30

PRICE LIST. 18

MOULDING PLANES.—Cont'd.

Invoice Nos.		Price.
464	Plows, 1st rate, screw arms, 8 irons,	4.50
465	do. do. do. boxed fence, do.	4.80
466	do. do. do. solid Boxw'd fence, do.	5.00
467	do. 2d rate, do. do.	4.20
468	do. do. do. boxed fence, do.	4.50
469	do. do. do. solid Boxw'd fence, do.	4.75
470	do. solid Boxwood, do.	6.50
471	do. do. Rosewood, do.	6.50
472	do. do. do. boxed fence, do.	6.80
473	do. do. Ebony, do.	8.00
474	Handled Beech Plow, do.	5.75
475	do. do. do. boxed fence, do.	6.05
476	do. do. do. solid Boxwood fence, do.	6.35
477	do. do. do. 2d rate, do.	5.25
478	do. Boxwood Plow, do.	8.20
479	do. do. do. silver mounted, do.	9.20
480	do. do. do. do. do. Ivory tips on arms, do.	10.20
481	do. do. do. do. do. Ivory tips on arms, solid Ivory nuts and wash. do.	17.00
482	do. Rosewood Plow, do.	8.20
483	do. do. do. boxed, do.	8.50
484	do. do. do. do. silver mounted, do.	9.50
485	do. do. do. do. silver mounted, Ivory tips on arms, do.	10.50
486	do. do. do. do. silver mounted, Ivory tips on arms, and solid Ivory nuts and washers, do.	17.30
487	do. Ebony, Plow, do.	12.00
488	do. do. do. boxed, do.	12.35
489	do. do. do. silver mounted, do.	13.00
490	do. do. do. do. do. boxed, do.	13.35
491	do. do. do. do. do. Ivory tips on arms. do.	14.00

PRICE LIST. 19

MOULDING PLANES.—Cont'd.

Invoice Nos.		Price.
492	Handled Ebony Plow, silver mounted, boxed, Ivory tips on arms, solid Ivory nuts and washers, 8 irons.	22.80
493	do. do. do. do. do. Ivory tips on arms, and solid Ivory nuts and washers, boxed, do.	18.35
494	do. Ivory Plow, with solid gold nuts and washers, 22 carats fine, golden tips on arms, and golden mounted, do.	1000.00

PATENTED MOSAIC PLOWS.

495	Plows, screw arms, with fence boxed, do.	8.00
496	do. do. do. do. silver plated, do.	9.00
497	do. do. do. do. silver plated, Ivory tipped, do.	10.00
498	Handled Plows, screw arms, with fence boxed, do.	13.00
499	do. do. do. do. silver plated, do.	14.00
500	do. do. do. do. silver plated, Ivory tipped, do.	15.00
501	do. do. do. do. silver plated, Ivory tipped, Ivory nuts and washers, do.	24.00

Plate III

Plow Planes by L. & C.H. DeForest
1860 Price List of Joiner Planes, etc.
[Collection of Conn. Hist. Society]

Plate IV - Patent Drawing of E.M. Chapin's and Solon Rust's Joiner's Plow.

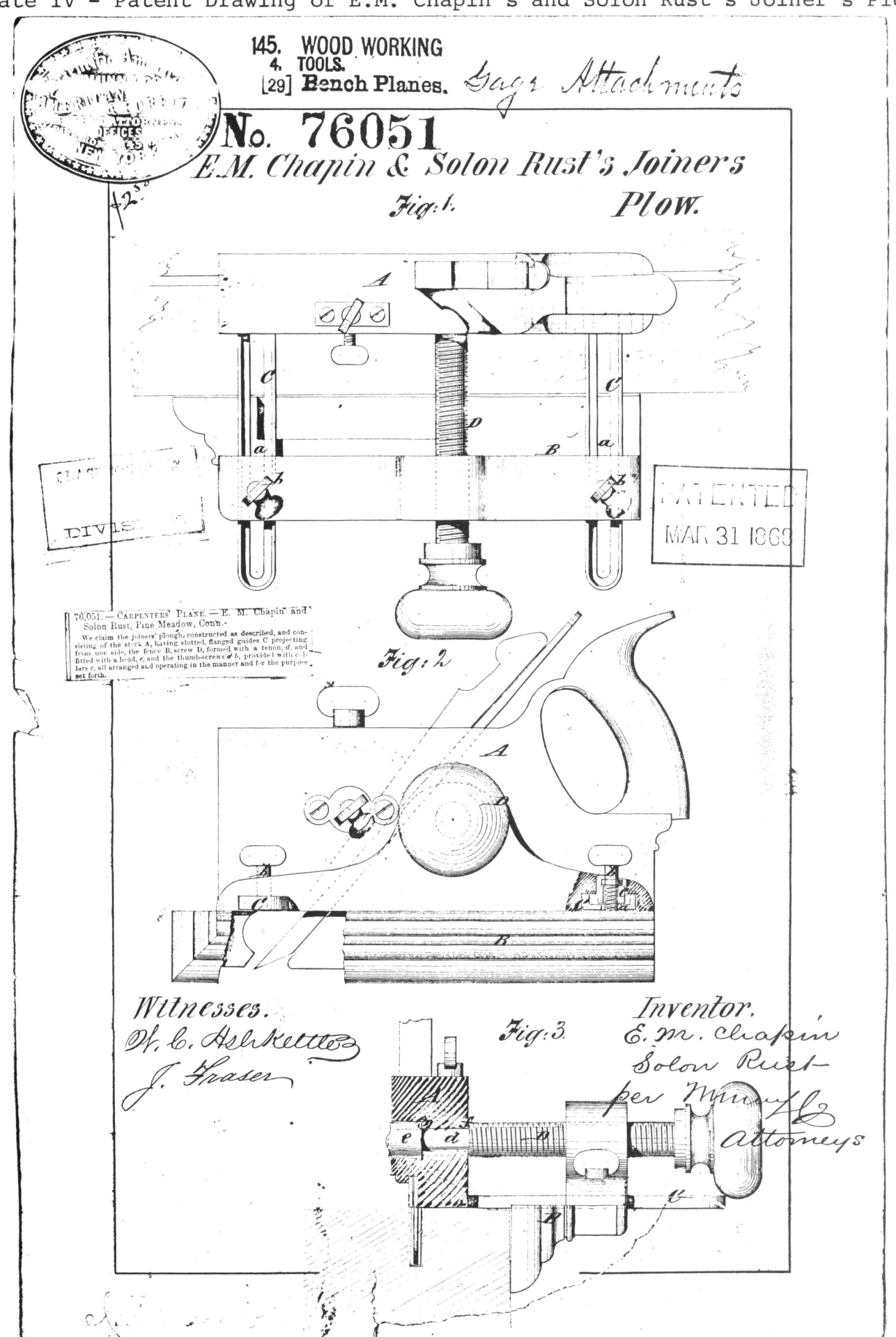

Fig. 41 - Chapin-Rust Patent Plow in Applewood

Fig. 43 –No. 239-3/4 Chapin-Rust Patent Plow in Applewood with Boxed Fence, PATENT March 31, 1868

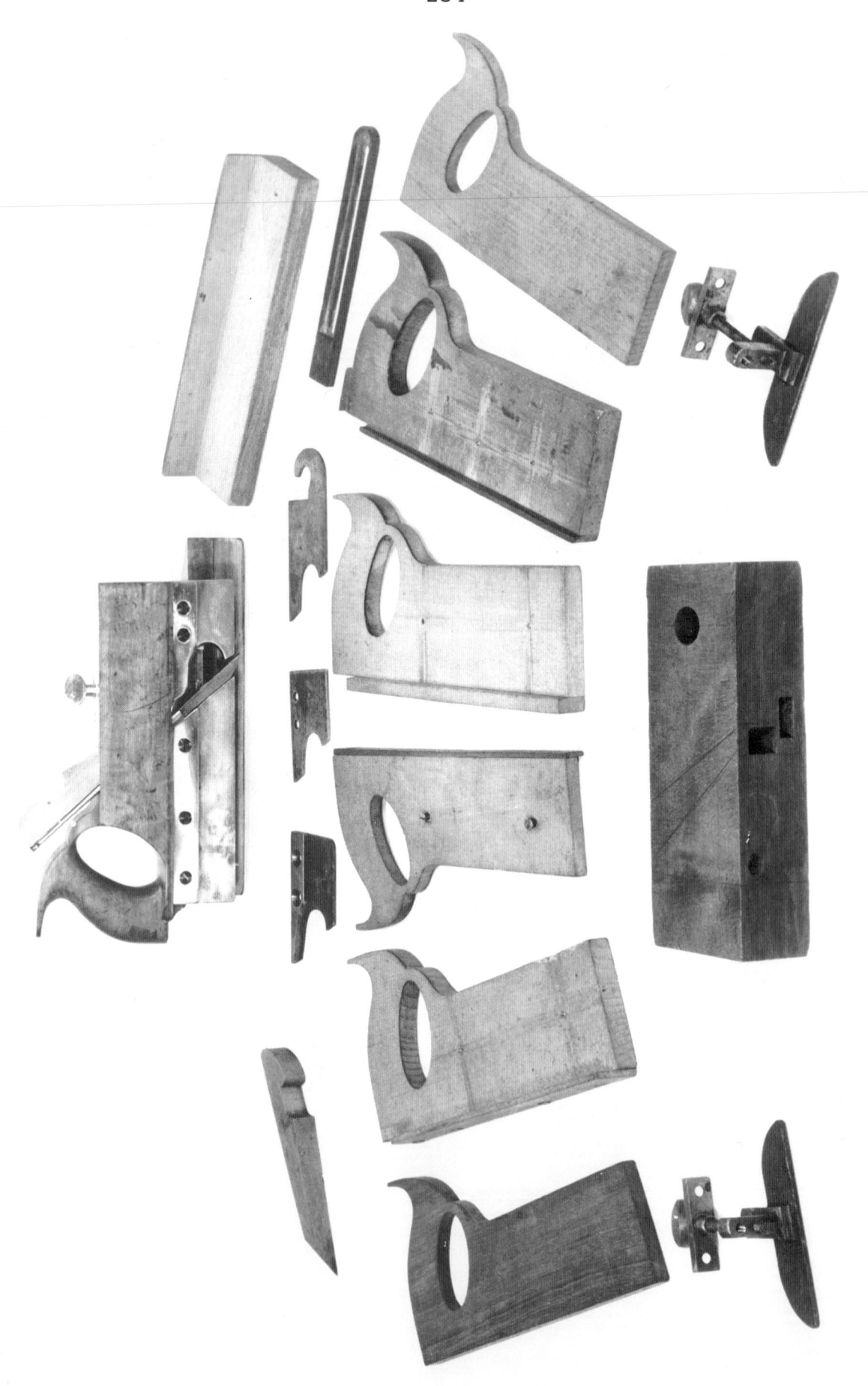

Fig. 42 - Solon Rust's Patterns for Making the Patent Plow Plane.

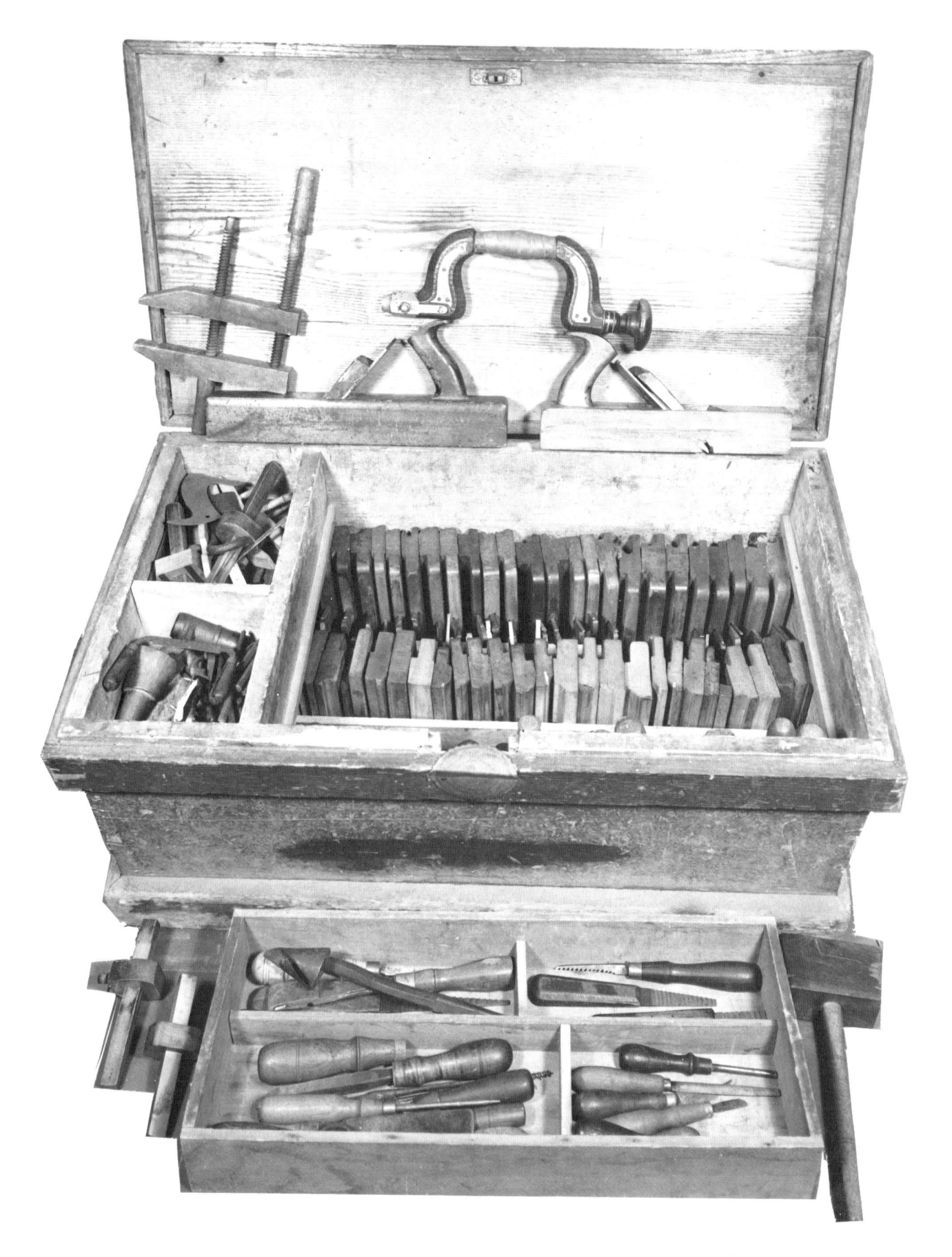

Fig. 44 - Solon Rust's Tool Chest and His Plane-making Tools.

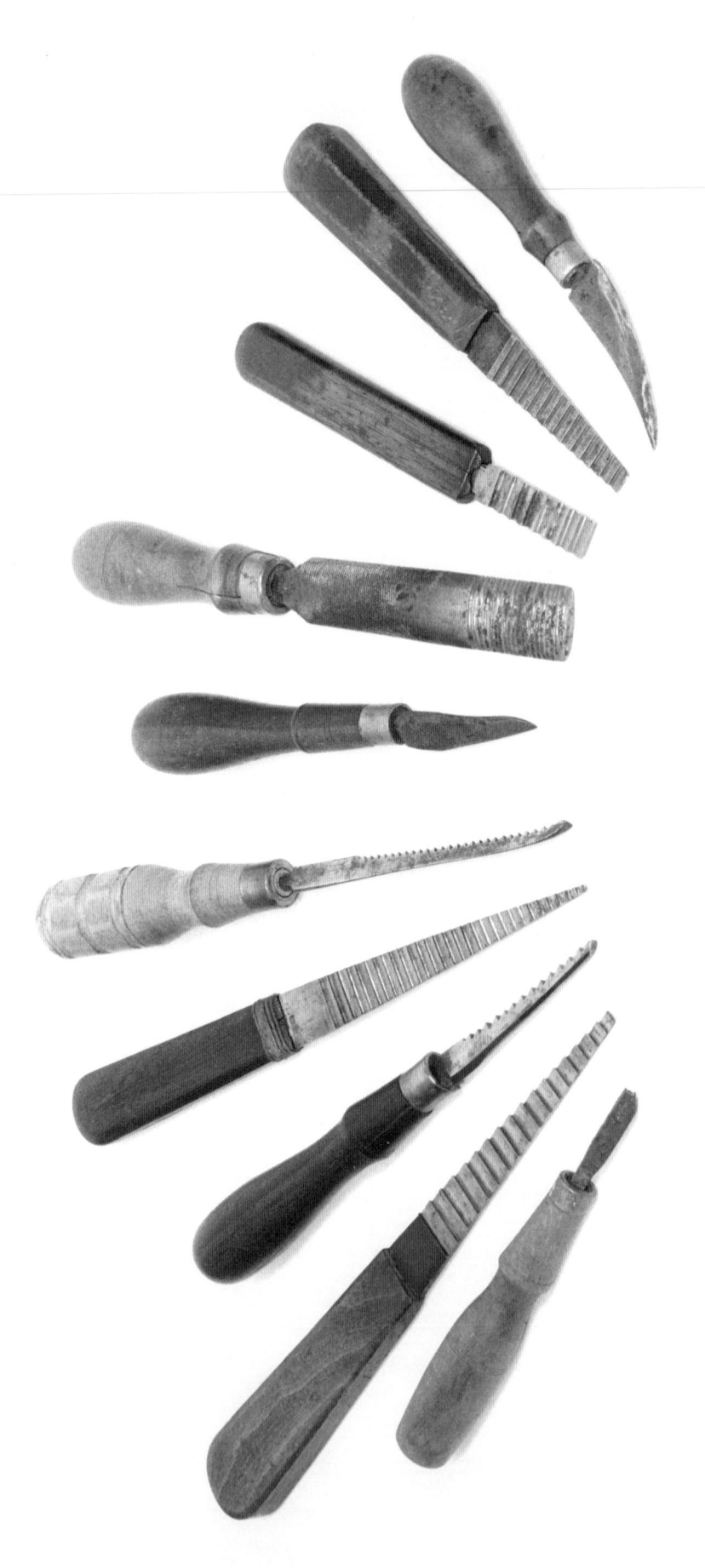

Fig. 45 - Solon Rust's Plane-making Floats and Knives

Fig. 46 - Solon Rust's Plane-making Chisels and Knives.

238

Fig. 47 - Parts of a Plow Plane

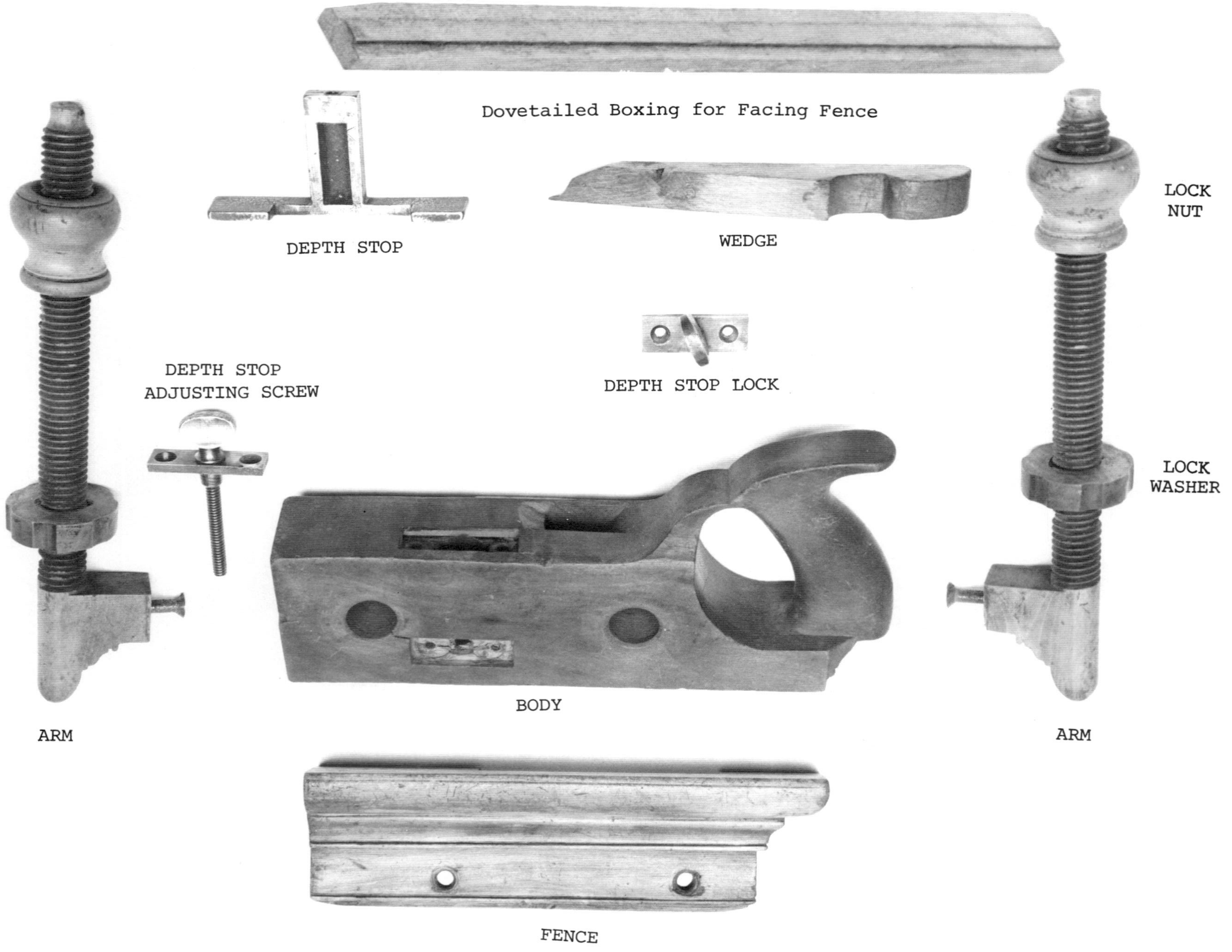

LOCK NUT

LOCK WASHER

ARM

Dovetailed Boxing for Facing Fence

WEDGE

DEPTH STOP LOCK

BODY

FENCE

PARTS OF A PLOW PLANE

DEPTH STOP

DEPTH STOP ADJUSTING SCREW

ARM

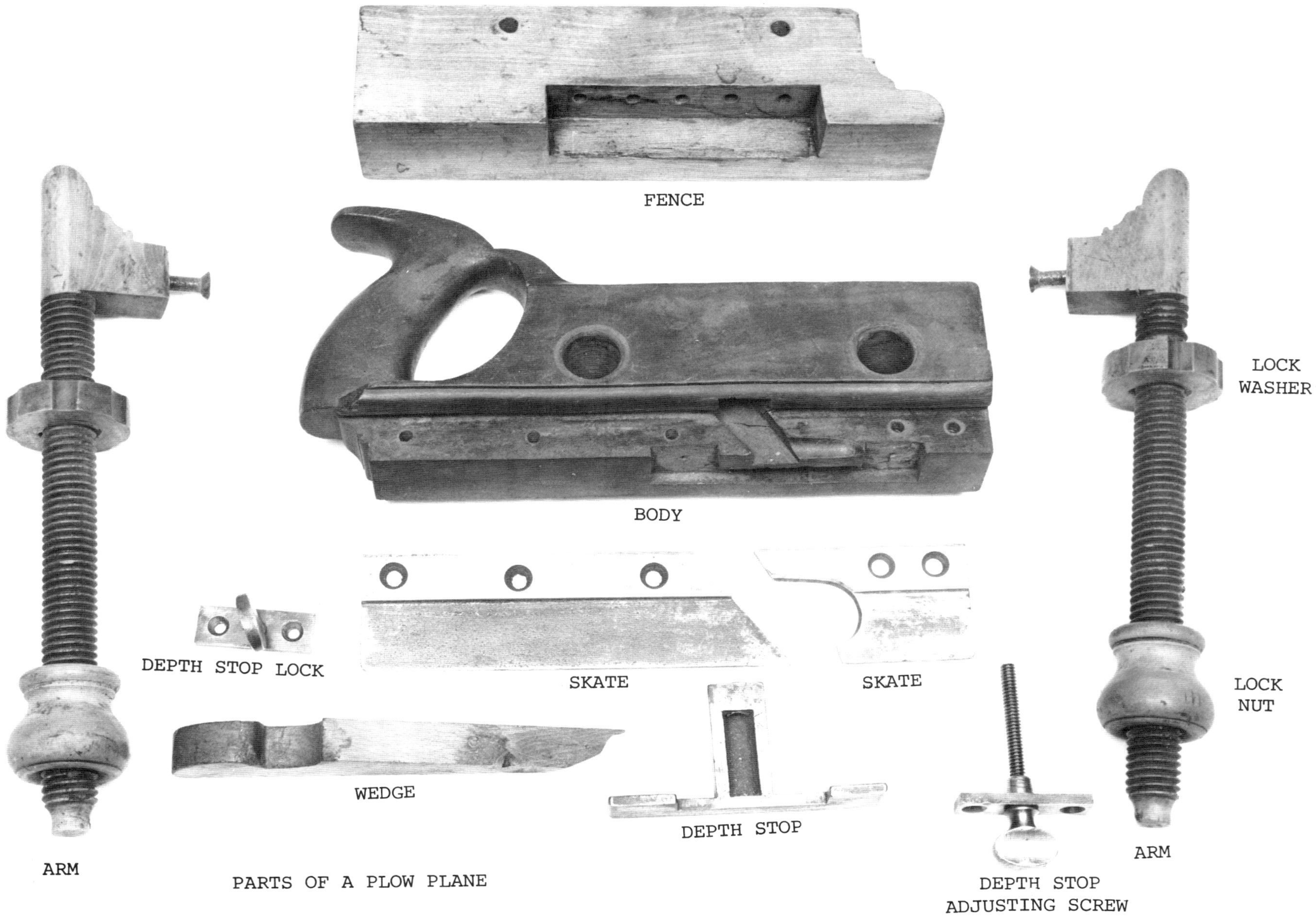

Fig. 48 - Parts of a Plow Plane

In order to understand how a plow plane is made it is essential to define the various parts. This is accomplished by taking apart a plow and labeling the various pieces. (Figs. 47 & 48) Section III of the article in the Appendix to Chapter II has some information on making plows. Incidentally the English terminology differs slightly from the American; the arms being called stems and the body being called stock. It is almost self evident as to the making of the stock. Plows were made in groups of three to six. After cutting out solid blocks for the fence, these were put in a vise and the end grain shaped according to a pattern scribed on the lead piece. (Fig. 49 illustrates the template, but in the position of longitudinal grain) After shaping the ends, each individual piece was planed with matching contours along the length. The top moulding was formed with a plane having an attached fence, similar to that used for shaping hollow and round sections. The slot in the fence for accomodating the depth stop was hand chiseled after drilling a series of holes. Blanks for a dozen or more arms were placed in a vise and planed against the grain, forming the contour, traced from a template. A portion was removed by sawing from each arm, leaving a square section. This was turned round in a lathe and threaded by a hand die. (Fig. 54) The nuts and washers were cut from turned hollow stock and threaded by a matching tap. The handle of the body was shaped using spokeshaves and draw knives. The final sizing was developed by a special shaping tool. (See Fig. 55)

A tool, having the appearance of a bung auger, is seen in the upper compartment of the central tray, shown in front of the chest in Fig. 44. What use would Solon Rust have for this tool? Several months after acquiring this tool chest the answer became apparent, while examining a skew rabbet plane. This blacksmith-made conical reamer was used for cutting out the mouth on the side of such rabbet planes. Examination of Figs. 56, 57 & 58 will prove this observation.

Another puzzle that came with this collection was a set of three jigs shown in Fig. 59. These are bench clamps for holding a smoothing plane through the mouth slot in the sole while working from the top and shaping the cheeks and plane iron slot. A central bar, longer than the clamp base and recessed flush with its top surface, has a tapered middle section. Sliding this bar forward by tapping from the rear actuates protruding sections, perpendicular to the bar at the middle, bringing the ends together. A plane can then be slipped over the fixture with the clamp fitting loosely through the mouth on the sole. Then tapping the central rod from the front expands the sections and locks the plane in the fixture. After completing the work, the central rod is tapped from the rear and the plane can be removed.

In addition to the special moulding planes for making plows, there were three sets of backing planes for making hollow and round planes in Solon Rust's tool chest. These are illustrated in Fig. 60.

A modification of the Rust-Chapin plow, known as *Improved Patent V Slide Arm Plow,* first appeared in H. Chapin's Son July 1879 list. (See Plate V) This improvement consisted of V grooves in the bottom of each slide arm which were guided through a central casting attached to the fence and actuated by a central screw turned in the casting. An illustration of this model appears on page 55 of the 1882 Catalogue. (See Chapter VIII) Both styles, the *Patent Adjusting Plow,* as originally offered in 1869, and the later *Improved Patent V Slide Arm Plow* were continued in Chapin catalogues through 1902.

Plate V - July 1, 1879 Announcement by H. Chapin's Son

Pine Meadow, Conn., July 1th, 1879.

Gentlemen:

In presenting you my Price List and Illustrated Catalogue for July, 1879, your attention is requested to changes in a few numbers and List prices. New Tools have been added, especially Moulding Planes, Improved Patent Slide-Arm Plow, Davis Levels, Etc.

I shall maintain the high standard that the Chapin Planes have had for fifty three years, and with the improved facilities, all my goods will bear the closest comparison. Your orders are respectfully solicited, and will have prompt attention.

Yours,

H. CHAPIN'S SON.

IMPROVED PATENT V SLIDE ARM PLOW.

With Adjusting Screw.

From page 59, *H. Chapin's Son & Co. Catalogue*

Fig. 49 - Template for Marking Fence Moulding (top right)

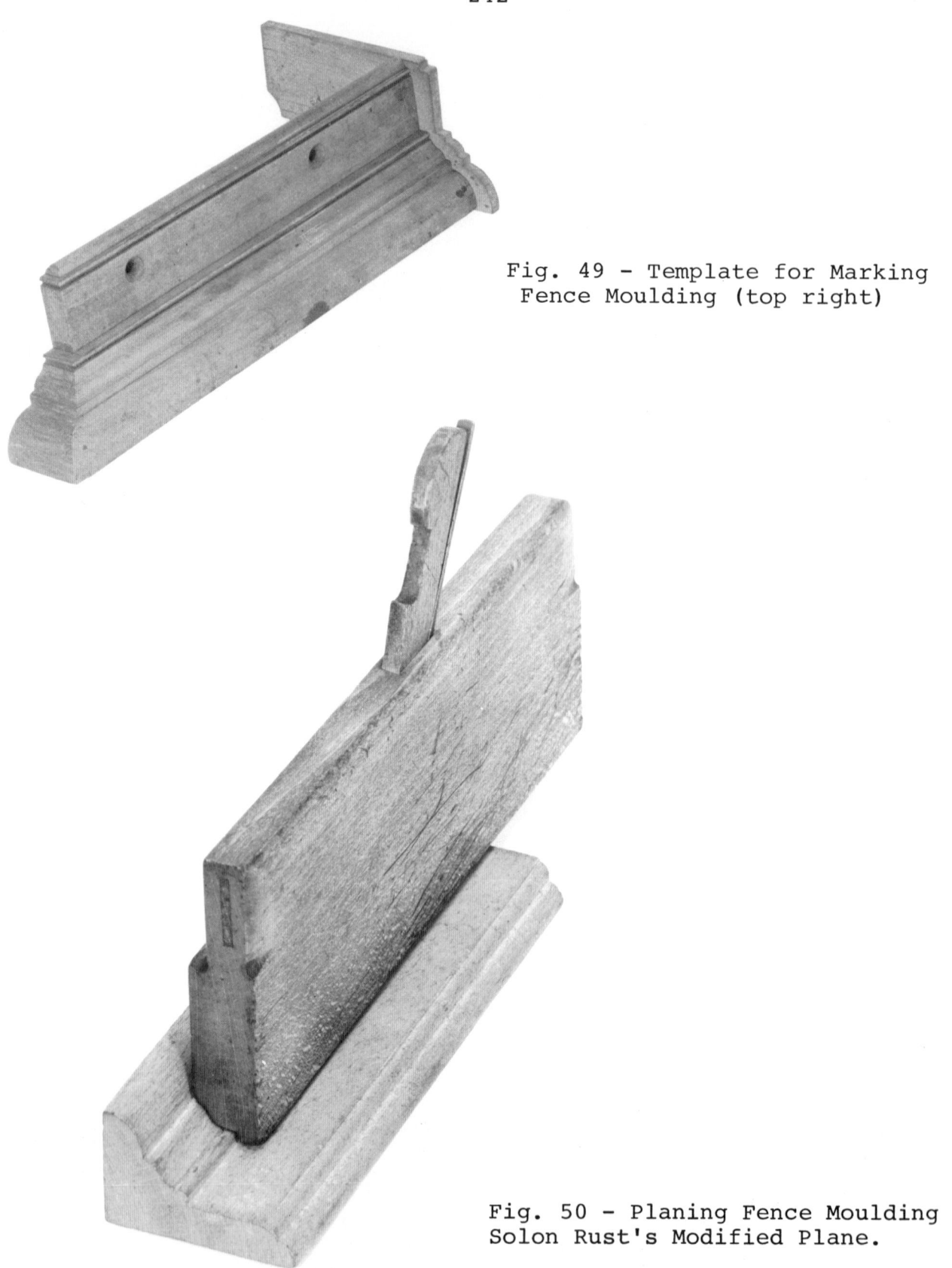

Fig. 50 - Planing Fence Moulding Solon Rust's Modified Plane.

243

Fig. 51 - Planing Edge Step in Fence with Solon Rust's Modified Plane.

Fig. 52 - Planing Edge of Fence with Solon Rust's Modified Plane.

Fig. 53 - Planing Fence Moulding with Solon Rust's Modified Plane.

Fig. 54 -
Threading Plow Arms,
Lock Nut and Washer.
[Note V-knife, removed from Die at right of Die.]

Fig. 55 - Finish Shaping Contour of Plow Handle with Solon Rust's Special Draw Shave.

Fig. 56 - Skew Dado Plane and Solon Rust's Tapered Auger for Shaping Side Mouth.

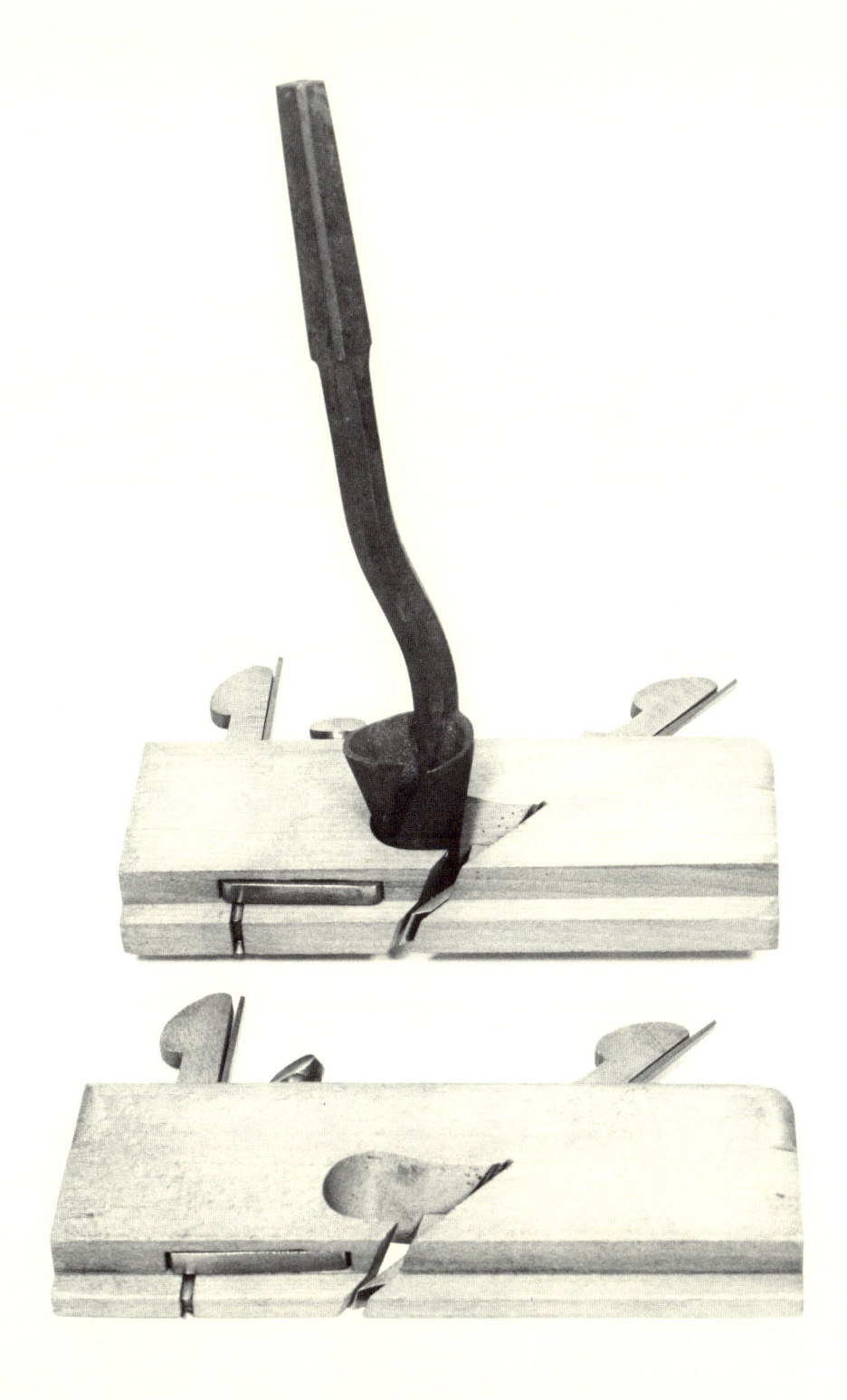

Fig. 57 - Finished Skew Dado Plane (bottom) and Position of Tapered Auger for Shaping Side Mouth. (top)

Fig. 58 - Handled Side Rabbet Planes Showing Templates for Marking Mouth and Solon Rust's Tapered Auger for Shaping Mouth.

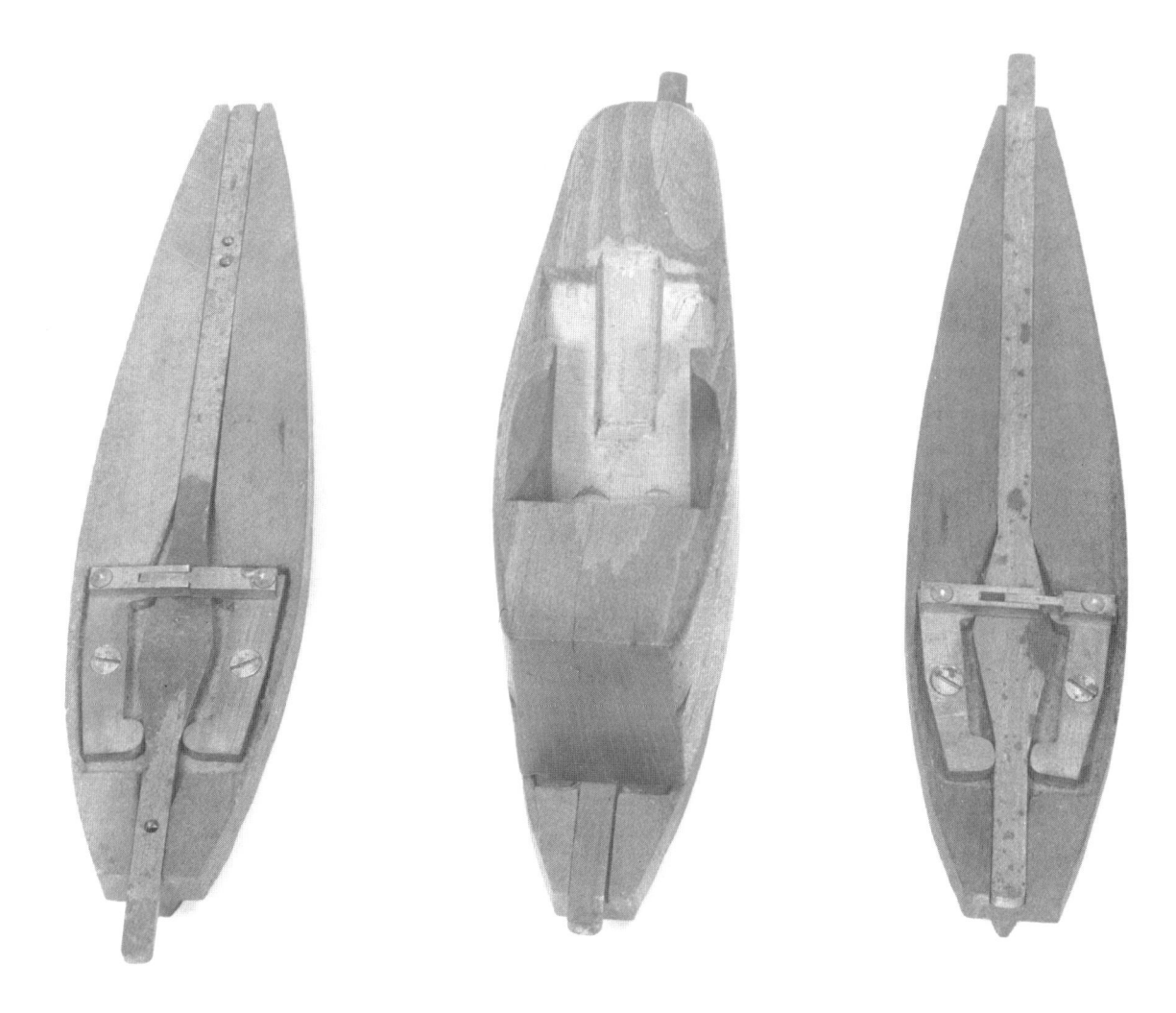

Fig. 59 - Solon Rust's Bench Plane Jigs for Holding Plane.
         Jig Open (left); Smooth Plane in Jig (closed)[Middle]
         Jig in Closed Position without Plane (right)

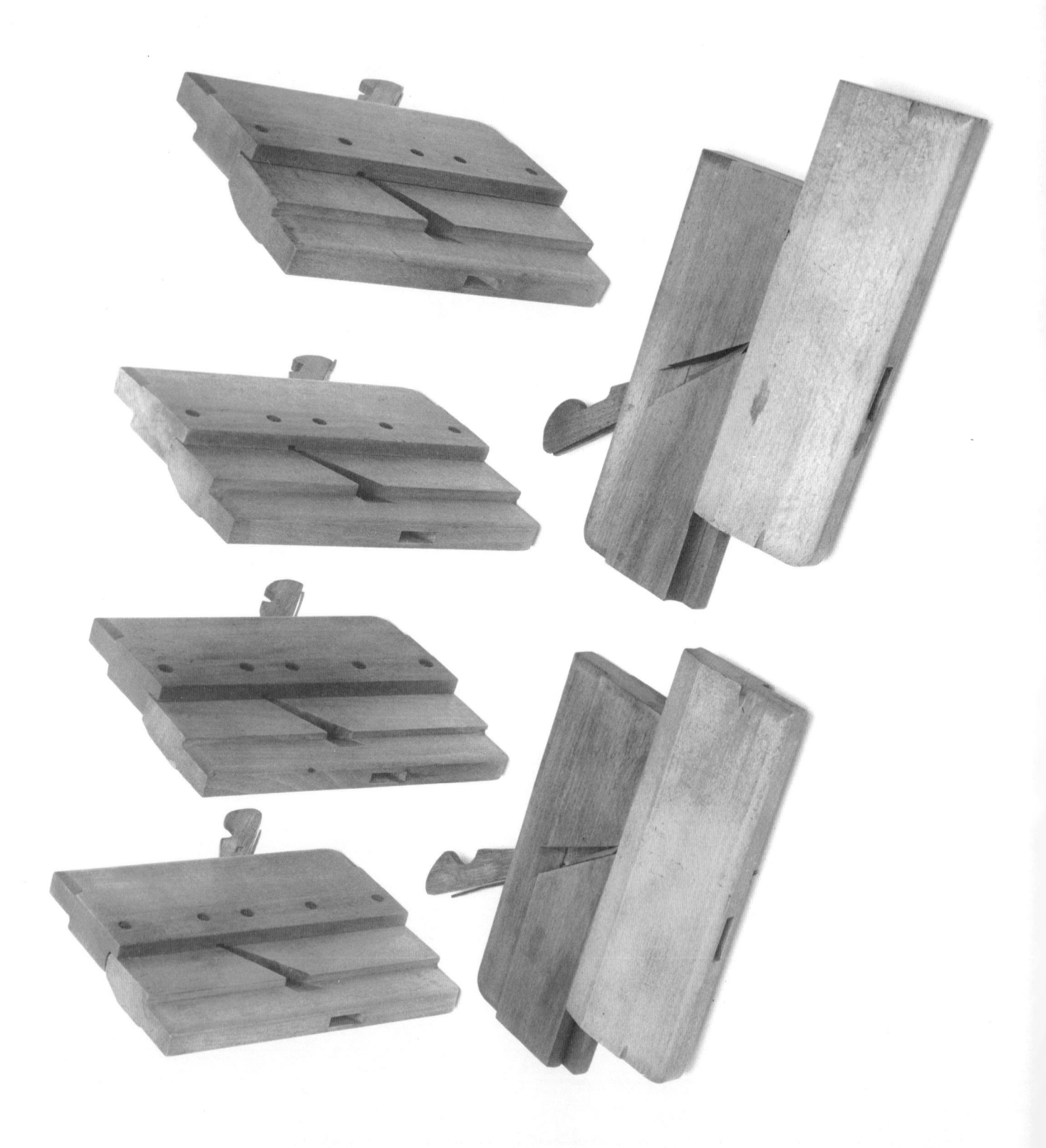

Fig. 60 - Solon Rust's Backing Planes for Shaping Hollow and Round Planes.

During the period 1882-1901 Solon Rust was granted eight patents concerning planes.[9] He was co-patentee of five of these with his son, Arthur. While the majority of these concerned iron planes, some features were also applicable to transitional planes. U.S. Patent No. 287, 584, issued September 30, 1883 was assigned to Standard Rule Co. of Unionville. (See Vol. I, pg. 212) Among surviving papers that belonged to Solon Rust was an invoice dated August 19, 1882 on which was written "in act. with S.R. Co.," which is assumed to have been Solon Rust Co. It is therefore suggested that at that date he may have been working for himself and also at that time may have been a contractor for the Standard Rule Co. His obituary stated that he had worked at Unionville for a period, at which time he probably introduced planemaking at that concern. Later he returned to Chapin-Stephens Co.[10]

List of Plane Patents Granted to Solon Rust

Title	Date	U.S. Pat. No.
Carpenter's Plane *	March 31, 1868	76,051
Iron Bench Plane	May 16, 1882	257,981
Iron Bench Plane **	June 19, 1883	279,885
Metal Toy Plane	July 31, 1883	282,468
Improvement in Plane **	Oct. 30, 1883	287,584
Joiner's Plane **	Nov. 20, 1883	288,866
Circular Plane **	June 17, 1884	300,399
Block Plane	Oct. 22, 1889	413,329
Iron Bench Plane **	Dec. 17, 1901	688,969

* Granted Jointly with E.M. Chapin   ** Granted Jointly with A.E. Rust

Additionally A.E. Rust was granted U.S. Pat. No. 435,951, Sept., 9, 1890 which he assigned one-half to his father, Solon Rust.

Also see: R.K. Smith, *Patented Transitional & Metallic Planes in America, 1827 - 1927*, [Lancaster, MA, 1981], p. 74

It seems strange that E.M. Chapin did not acquire rights to Solon Rust's patents for these planes that were made by Standard Rule Co. With proper marketing this line would have been competitive with those manufactured at Stanley Rule & Level Co. It is possible that after loss of considerable money from the financial failure of the Chapin Machine Co. E.M. Chapin did not desire to risk any further investments in either metal or transitional planes.

A photograph of Solon Rust, probably taken about the turn of the 20th century is shown as Fig. 61.[11] He died April 27, 1908 at his home at Pine Meadow. His obituary stated: "He had been in poor health since the loss of his home by fire about two years ago. He kept at his work at Chapin-Stephens Co. until last winter, when he was compelled to give up active work."[12] Further details concerning a modification of the Rust-Chapin Patent Plow will be presented in a subsequent chapter.

Fig. 61 - Solon Rust

Solon Rust

[*The Messenger Family in the Colony of Connecticut*,
(West Hartford, CT., 1963), p.66]

Notes - Chapter VII

1. *Genealogy of Descendants of Henry Rust,* p. 329

2. obit, *New Hartford Tribune,* May 1, 1908, p. 3

3. H. Chapin's Work Agreement Book

4. Personal communication with Nettie Wright Adams, great-granddaughter of Solon Rust.

5. Reprinted by Ken Roberts Publishing Co., 1981

6. Library of the Connecticut Historical Society

7. K.D. Roberts, "Self-Adjusting Plow Planes", CHRONICLE OF EAIA, [Vol.34, No.2, June 1981], p. 28

8. It was probably also illustrated and offered in the 1869 *H. Chapin's Son Catalogue*

9. An earlier photograph of Solon Rust appears in R. Smith's *Patented Transitional & Metallic Planes in America, 1827-1927,* Fig. 81, p. 75

10. Private Communication with Allen M. Raymond, Plainville, Conn. Jan. 28, 1977, who as a boy brought Solon Rust his lunch at his shop at Pine Meadow.

11. See Note 9 above, Fig. 81, p. 75

12. *New Hartford Tribune,* Vol. XXVIII, May 1, 1908

A. No. 240½ Handled, Solid Rosewood Plow with Boxwood Arms and Locking Nuts with Best Brass Face Plate.

B. O.G. Cornice Handled Moulder [4 in. wide × 14 in. long] with Attached Fence.

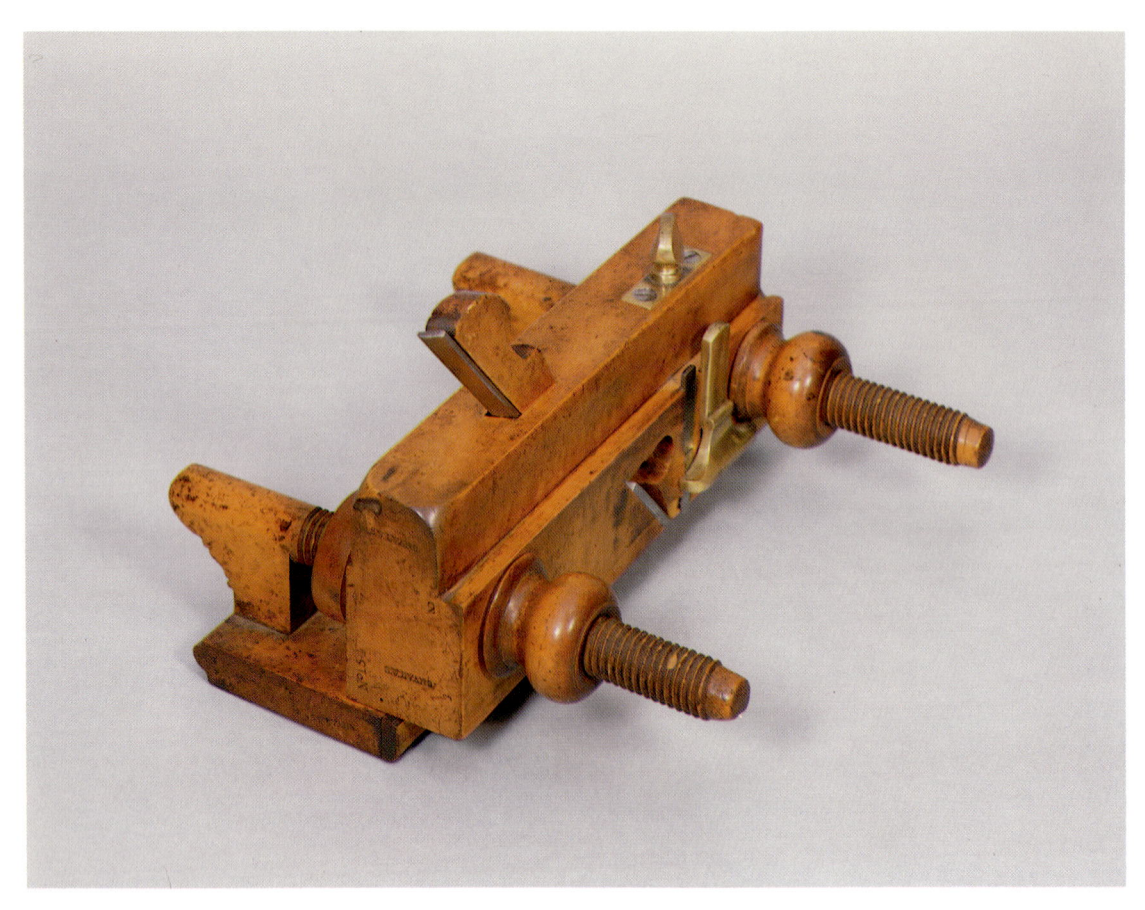

C. No. 154 Screw Arm Sash Filletster in Curly (Striped) Boxwood.

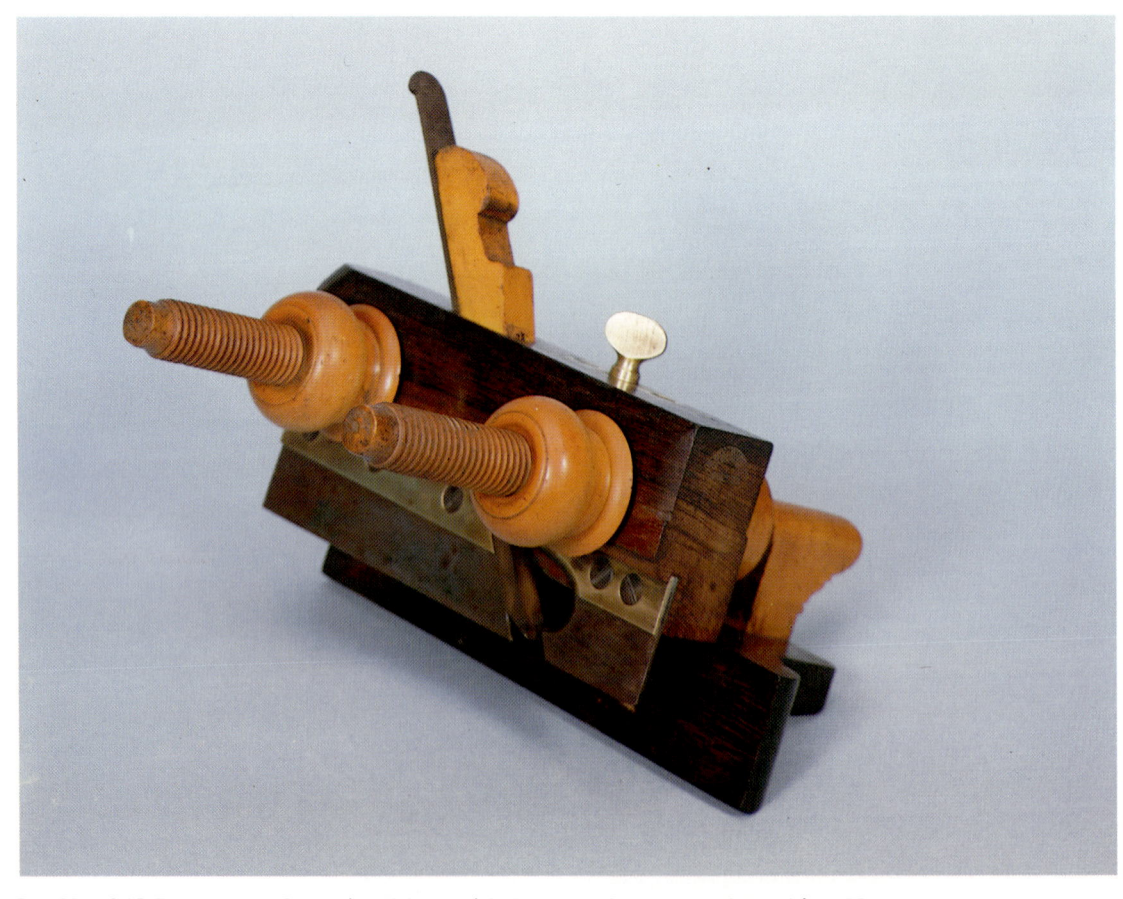

D. No. 245 Rosewood Grooving Plow with Boxwood Arms and Locking Nuts.

E. No. 241½ Handled, Solid Ebony Plow with Boxwood Arms and Locking Nuts. Boxwood Insert on Fence.

F. Pair of Recessed Handled Crown Moulding Planes [2½ & 1½ in. wide by 14 in. long] with Attached Fences.

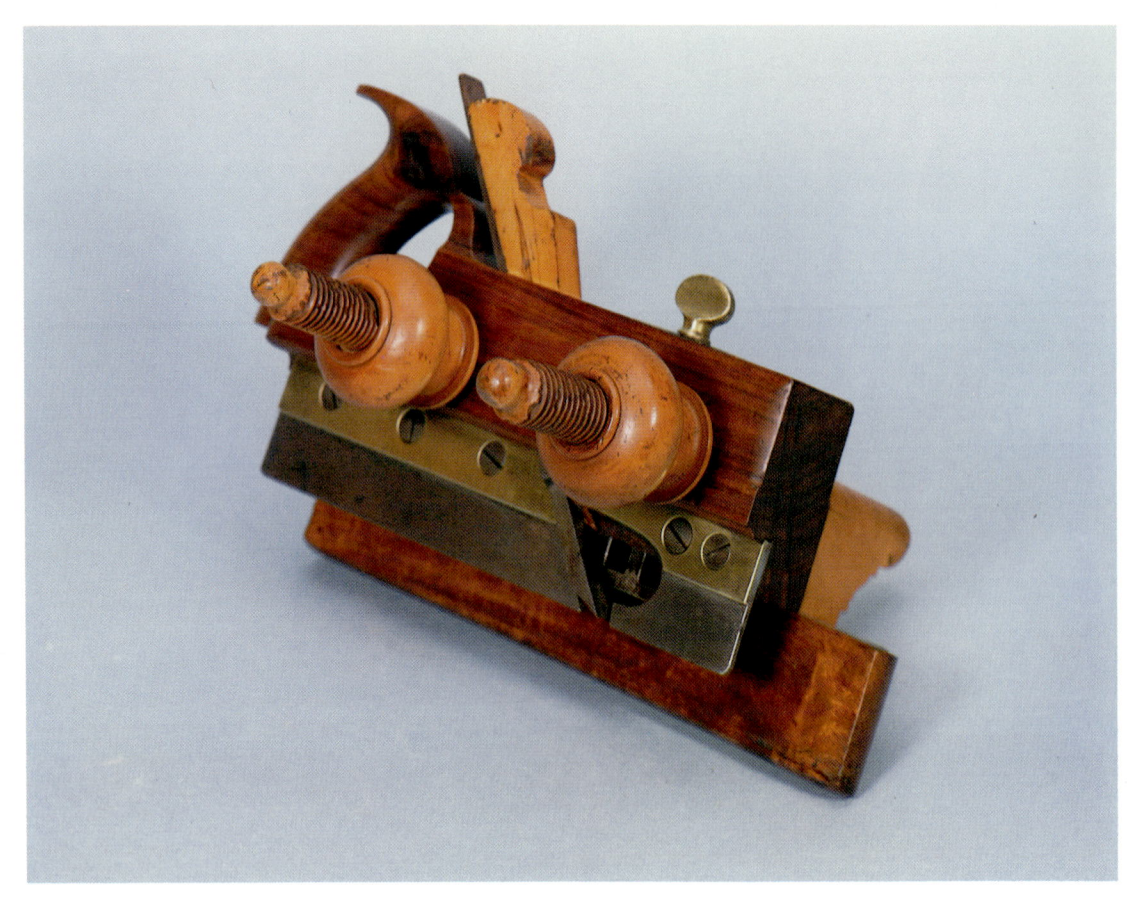

G. Unusual Cocobola Handled Screw Arm Grooving Plow with Boxwood Wedge, Arms and Locking Nuts. Made by *SHELTON & OSBORN,* Birmingham, CT. Note: With this exception all photographs herein are of Union Factory Planes.

H. No. 151 Slide Arm Filletster with Wood Locking Screws.

I. No. 240 Handled, Solid Boxwood Plow.

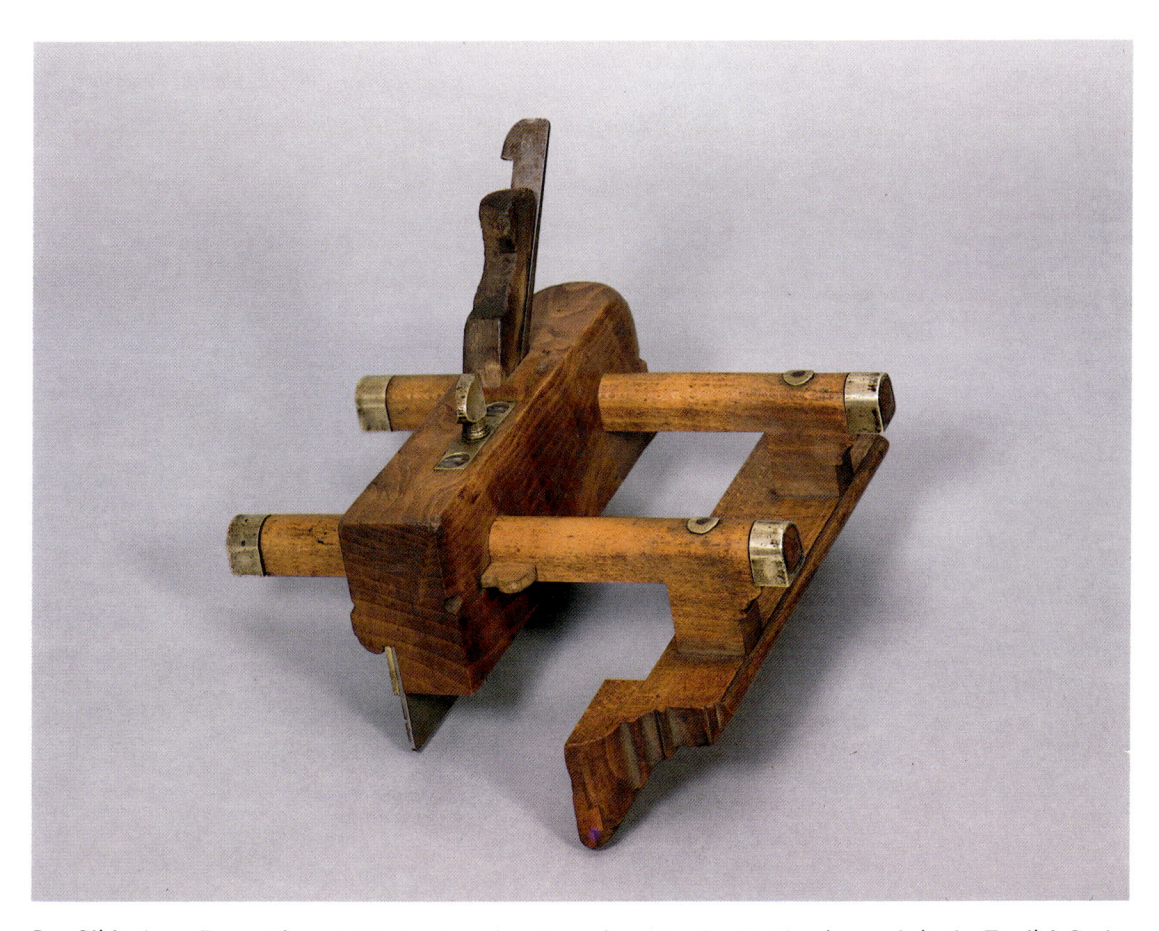

J. Slide Arm, Brass Tipped, Wedge Locking Grooving Plow by H. Chapin, made in the English Style.

K. No. 196 Screw Arm, Self-Regulating Sash Plane.

L. No. 199 Handled, Screw Arm, Self-Regulating Sash Plane.

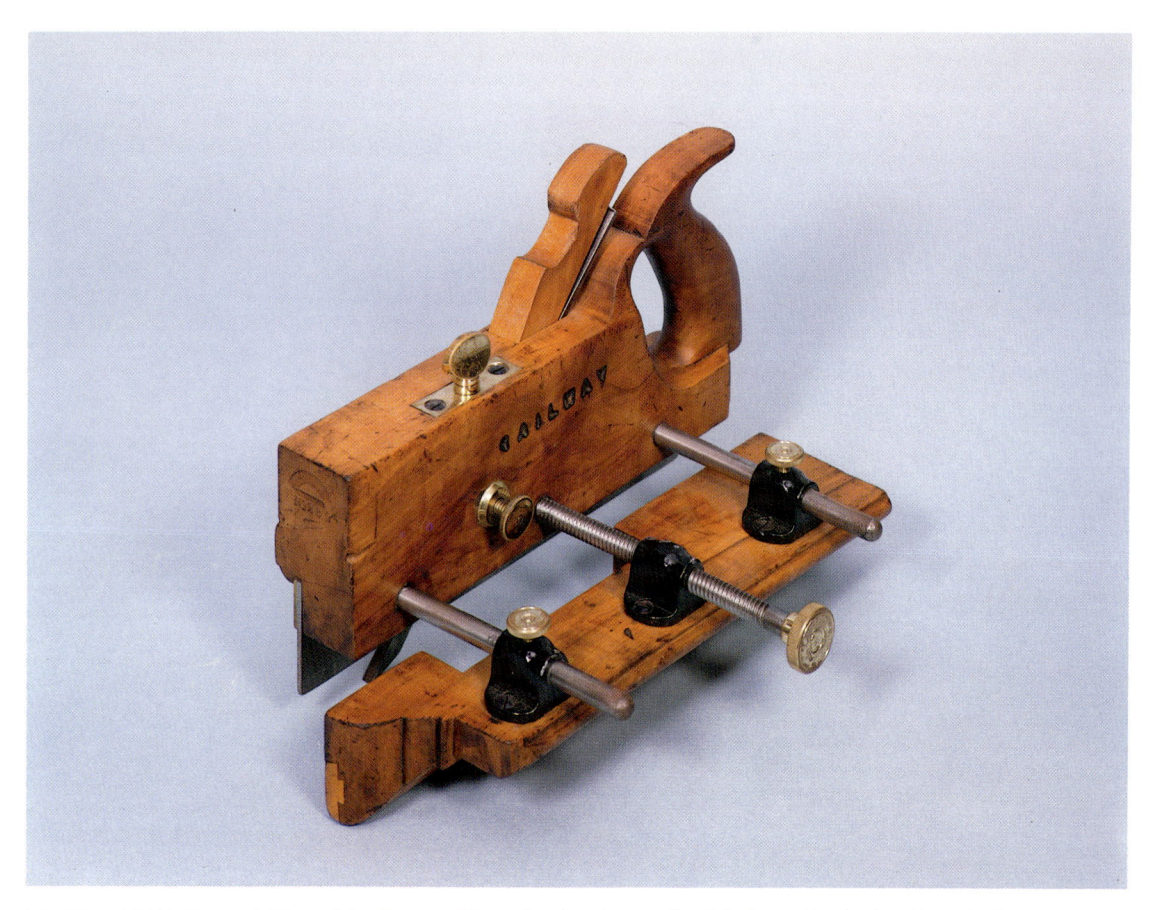

M. No. 239¼ Rare Adjustable Patent Plow in Applewood with Iron Rods for Regulating Fence.

N. No. 240½ Rosewood Adjustable Plow Patent Plane. Rust-Chapin Patent, March 31, 1868.

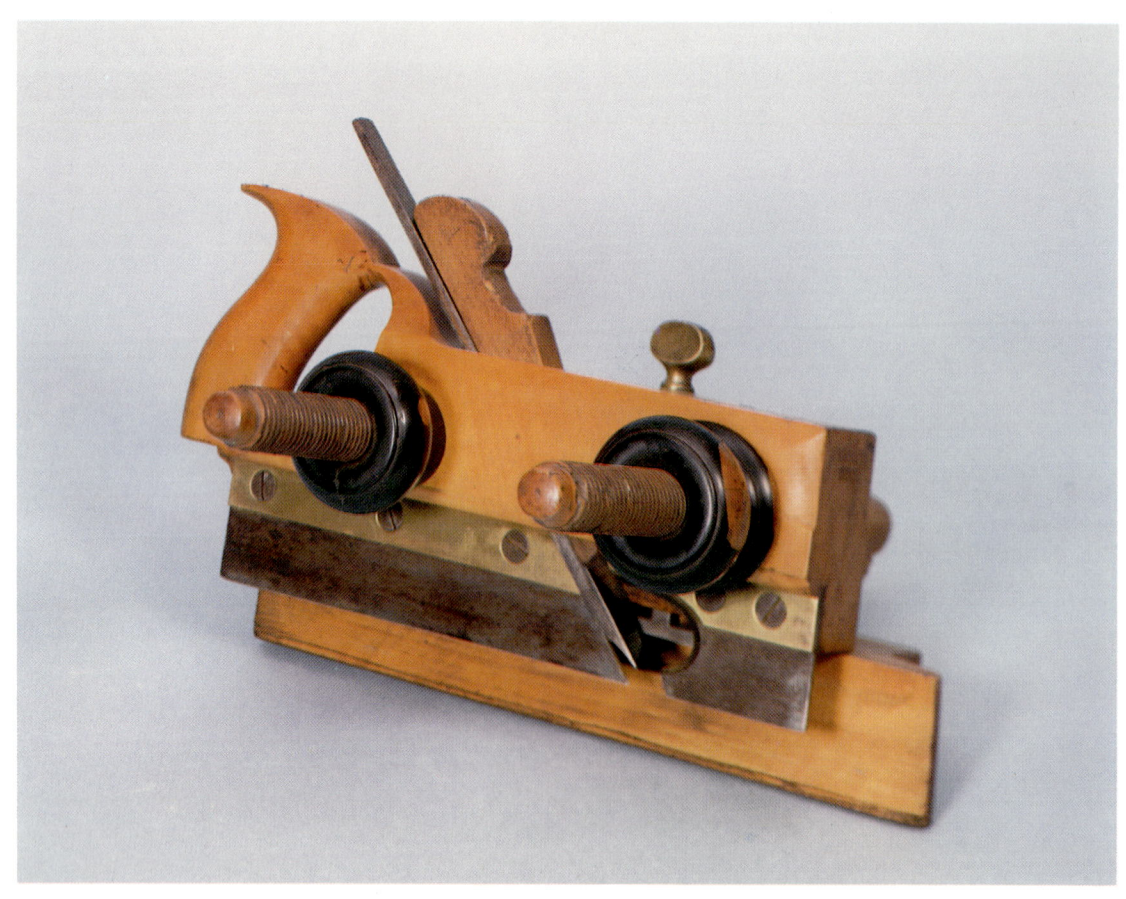

O. No. 240 Handled, Curly (Striped) Boxwood Screw Arm Plow with Rosewood (Sap Wood) Locking Nuts. H. Chapin Union Factory Stamp Over-struck by *WAY & SHERMAN*, New York.

P. No. 203 Screw Arm, Filletster with Wood Stop and Boxwood Arms and Locking Nuts.

Chapter VIII

Union Factory Trade Catalogues, 1874-1882

Studies of trade catalogues provide excellent insights into the introduction, deletion and price changes of products. Plate XX, Chapter VI, noted the January 1, 1870 Union Factory Price List had 68 pages. The *1874 Price List and Illustrated Catalogue of Rules, Planes, Gauges, etc. Manufactured by H. Chapin's Son,* dated January 1, had 79 pages [6½ in. x 10 in.] This is reprinted in entirety in this chapter, but reduced about 10% in size. This was probably the largest tool catalogue of products, exclusively produced by one manufacturer, published in the United States up to that date.[1] The *1874 Catalogue of Tools and Hardware Manufactured by the Stanley Rule & Level Co.* had 64 pages (9 additional with the 1876 Supplement).[2]

The Cash Discount Sheet issued January 26, 1870 (See Plate XX, Chapter VI) noted that the *1870 H. Chapin's Son Catalogue* had 68 pages. Among the new products introduced in this catalogue since 1865 were premium bench planes with diamond style knock-outs; No. 449 Carpenter's Badger Plane; Sholl's [incorrectly spelled Scholl in both the 1874 & 1882 Chapin catalogues] Patent Marking Gauges; Turning Saw Frames; Brass Plane Stops; Try Squares and Sliding T Bevels.

A discount sheet from the Office of the Union Factory issued on July 1, 1871 listed the same items as in January 26, 1870, but at about 10% lower costs. Another discount sheet dated March 13, 1872 listed the same items, but with less discount on rules and an additonal 10% for planes. A list, dated October 3, 1872, (Plate I) referred to an appendix of thirteen pages added to the 1870 catalogue. New items in this Appendix were iron planes (see pages 20-21, 1874 catalogue); Razee planes (see page 17, 1874 catalogue) and the 1870 list of grooving plows was voided. Reference was made to a new listing of plows, suggesting that the applewood and ebony plows were added at that date. (See pages 52 & 53, 1874 catalogue.)

New products that appeared in the 1874 catalogue, not listed on the October 3, 1872 discount sheet, were boring machines, Butler's patent gauge and screw drivers. It is evident from studying this 1874 catalogue that the following types of planes were renumbered: reeding; torus bead; rabbet; raising; sash; sash filletster; ogee; reverse ogee; Grecian; quirk ogee; Grecian ovolo; scotia; snipe bills and base, band and bed moulding. This renumbering system may have been initiated in 1869 or 1870. The details of iron planes offered by E.M. Chapin, patent marking gauges and levels will be presented in subsequent chapters. The discount list accompanying the 1874 Catalogue is shown as Plate II. On November 1, 1874 H. Chapin's son announced a "Big Discount" on his product for cash. (Plate III)

The next catalogue issued by H. Chapin's Son is believed to have been in 1882. The title page of this is shown as Plate IV. The frontispiece, a sketch of the Union Factory, appears as Plate V. The index and pages from this 1880 catalogue, illustrating products not appearing in the 1874 edition, follow. These are also reduced 10% in size. An explanation of gauging rod tables is of interest. Bench planes, made from boxwood and rosewood, are noted on page 20. The improved patent V slide arm plow, a modification of the Rust-Chapin Patent previously described in Chapter VII, is shown on page 55. Carriage-makers's tools are shown on page 56. Marden's Patent Gauge appears on page 61. New levels are shown on pages 63-70. Mosher's Patent Iron Spokeshaves are noted on page 79. The discount sheet accompanying the 1882 Catalogue is shown as Plate VI. Levels and marking gauges will be discussed in Chapter X.

Plate I - October 3, 1872 Union Factory Discount Sheet

☞ Destroy former Rate Sheets.

OFFICE OF THE
Union Factory.
ESTABLISHED IN 1826.

Pine Meadow, Ct., Oct. 3d, 1872.

GENTLEMEN:

The annexed are NET CASH rates for articles named in my List, Jan. 1st, 1870, and Appendix, Oct. 1st, 1872.

RULES—Boxwood, Ivory, and Miscellaneous, pages 3 to 9,   Discount 30 and 10 per cent.

Change List prices, Catalogue of 1870, page 5, No. 10 to $4.00, No. 11 to $5.00, and on page 8, No. 83, to $3.50 per dozen.

	Appendix, page 4,	Disc't 5 per cent.
BENCH PLANES—Stamped J. Pearce, change List page 10, see		
" " Extra, stamped H. Chapin,	page 11 and 12,	Net.
" " Premium, " "	" 13,	"
" " Razee, see Appendix,	" 4,	"
" " Sets in cases. " "	" 5,	"
SHIP PLANES, List 1870,	" 14,	"
COOPERS' PLANES, " "	" 14,	"
MISCELLANEOUS PLANES, " "	" 15,	"
MOULDING PLANES, see Appendix and List 1870,	" 16 to 43,	"
GROOVING PLOWS, make void List of Jan. 1870, see		
Appendix for new List.	" 10 to 13,	Disc't 10
IRON PLANES, see Appendix,	" 6 to 8,	" 25 & 10
GAUGES, List 1870,	" 48 to 49,	" 40 & 10
GAUGES—C. Sholl's patent, " "	" 50 to 51,	" 40 & 10
PLUMBS AND LEVELS, " "	" 52 to 53,	" 50 & 10
POCKET LEVELS, " "	" 54,	" 50 & 10
LEVEL GLASSES.	" 54,	" 50 & 10
HAND SCREW	" 55,	" 20 & 10
HAND SCREWS, Beaded, " "	" 56,	" 20 & 10
BENCH SCREWS,	" 56,	" 20 & 10
TURNING SAW FRAMES,	" 57,	" 20 & 10
TURNING SAW FRAMES AND SAWS,	" 57,	" 20 & 10
PLANE AND SAW HANDLES,	" 58,	" 40 & 10
STOPS,	" 58,	" 10
CHISEL HANDLES,	" 59,	" 40 & 10
FILE AND AWL HANDLES,	" 60,	" 40 & 10
SCREW DRIVERS,	" 61,	" 10
MINCING KNIVES,	" 61,	" 10
AWLS,	" 61,	" 10
PREMIUM TRY SQUARES,	" 62,	" 25 & 10
PREMIUM TRY SQUARES, Plated Back,	" 63,	" 25 & 10
TRY SQUARES, No, 1,	" 64,	" 25 & 10
TRY SQUARES, No, 2,	" 64,	" 30 & 10
SLIDING T BEVELS, No. 1,	" 65,	" 25 & 10
SLIDING T BEVELS, No. 2,	" 65,	" 30 & 10
PLANE IRONS.	" 66 to 67,	" 10
TOY TOOL CHEST SUPPLIES,	" 68,	" 10

Terms CASH within 30 days from date of invoice.

Soliciting a continuance of your patronage,

I am respectfully yours,

H. CHAPIN'S SON.

Make List Price, No. 449, Carpenter's Badger, Double, $2.00.

Plate II - Net Cash Discounts from 1874 Union Factory Catalogue

H. CHAPIN'S SON'S
NET CASH DISCOUNTS
FROM
Illustrated Catalogue of January, 1874.

Pine Meadow, Conn., Nov. 1st, 1874.

	Catalogue Page.	Discount Per Ct.
AWL HANDLES,	69,	40
BOXWOOD RULES,	3–10,	66⅔
BENCH PLANES, Common, Pearce,	14,	45
" " Extra,	15–16,	20 & 10
" " Premium,	17–18,	20 & 10
" " Sets in Cases,	19,	20 & 10
" " Razee,	17,	20 & 10
BENCH PLANES,	15–23, inclusive.	
with English irons instead of American,		Add 20
BORING MACHINES,	74,	Discount, 20
BENCH SCREWS,	65,	20
COOPERS' PLANES,	22,	20 & 10
CLAMP HEAD SCREWS,	65,	20
CHISEL HANDLES,	68,	40
DOOR STOPS,	72,	30
FILE HANDLES,	69,	40
GAUGES,	55–56,	45
" Scholl's Patent,	57–58,	45
" Butler's Patent,	59–60,	45
HAND SCREWS,	64,	25
" " Beaded,	65,	25
IVORY RULES,	11–12,	50
IRON PLANES,	20–21,	25
LEVELS,	61,	66⅔
LEVEL GLASSES,	63,	60
MISCELLANEOUS RULES,	13,	50
" PLANES,	23,	20 & 10
MOULDING PLANES,	24–50,	20 & 10
PLOWS, Grooving,	51–54,	20 & 10
" " Pat. Adjusting,	54,	20 & 10
PLUMBS AND LEVELS,	62,	66⅔
POCKET LEVELS,	63,	50
PLANE HANDLES,	69,	40
PLANE IRONS,	78–79,	10
SHIP PLANES,	22,	20 & 10
SAW HANDLES,	69,	60
STOPS,	70–71,	10
SCREW DRIVERS,	72,	10
SLIDING T BEVELS, No. 1,	76,	30
" " No. 2,	75,	30
TRY SQUARES, Premium,	76–77,	30
" " No. 1,	76,	30
" " No. 2,	75,	30
TURNING SAW FRAMES,	66,	20
" " " AND SAWS,	67,	20
TOY TOOL CHEST SUPPLIES,	73,	10

Discount 10 per ct. for Cash, if received within 30 days from date of invoice.

Accounts unpaid the first of month succeeding the expiration of the thirty days, subject to Draft payable at sight, for the full amount of invoices.

Former Catalogues and Rate Sheets are hereby made void.

Catalogues of 1874, furnished on application.

See inside for additions to List of January, 1874.

Title Page to January 1874 Union Factory Catalogue

PRICE LIST

AND

Illustrated Catalogue

OF

RULES, PLANES, GAUGES,

IRON PLANES, MOULDING TOOLS,
GROOVING PLOWS, PLUMBS AND LEVELS,
DOOR STOPS, HAND SCREWS, BENCH SCREWS,
HANDLES, TRY-SQUARES, SLIDING T-BEVELS, TURNING
SAW FRAMES AND SAWS, C. SCHOLL'S PATENT
GAUGE, BUTLER'S PATENT GAUGE, BORING
MACHINES, PLANE IRONS, &c., &c.

MANUFACTURED BY

H. CHAPIN'S SON,
(E. M. CHAPIN,)

UNION FACTORY,

ESTABLISHED IN 1826,

PINE MEADOW, CONN.

JANUARY, 1874.

HARTFORD:
PRESS OF CASE, LOCKWOOD AND BRAINARD,
1874.

Index to January 1874 Union Factory Catalogue

INDEX.

	PAGE.		PAGE.
Astragals,	25	Miscellaneous Rules,	13
Awl Handles,	69	" Planes,	23
Boxwood Rules,	3 to 10	Moulding Planes,	24 to 50
Board Measure,	7	Match Planes,	37
Bench Rules,	13	Nosing Planes,	27
Board Sticks,	13	Ogee Planes,	41–42
Bench Planes,	14 to 19	" Grecian Planes,	43–44
Bead Planes,	24 to 26	Ovolo Planes,	46–47
Bench Screws,	65	" Grecian Planes,	46
Boring Machines,	74	Planes, Common Bench,	14
Calliper Rules, Boxwood,	9	" Extra Bench,	15–16
" " Ivory,	12	" Premium Bench,	17–18
Coopers' Planes,	22	" Panel,	28
Cornice Planes,	50	Plows, Grooving,	51 to 54
Clamp Heads,	65	" " Pat. adjusting,	54
Chisel Handles,	68	Plumbs and Levels,	62
Dado Planes,	27	Pocket Levels,	63
Door Stops,	72	Plane Handles,	69
Filletster Planes,	28	Plane Irons,	78–79
File Handles,	69	Rules,	3 to 13
Gauges,	55 to 60	Rabbet Planes,	29
" Marking,	55	Ship Carpenter's Bevels,	10
" Cutting,	56	Slide Rules,	9
" Panel,	56	Ship Planes,	22
" Mortise,	56	Sash Planes,	38 to 40
" Slitting,	56	Saw Handles,	69
" Scholls' Patent,	57–58	Stops, Plane,	70–71
" Butler's Patent Marking,	59	" Door,	72
" " " Mortise,	60	Sliding T Bevels,	75–76
Gauging Rods,	13	Screw Drivers,	72
Hollows and Rounds,	30 to 35	Table Planes,	36
Hand Screws,	64	Turning Saw Frames,	66
" " Beaded,	65	" " " and Saws,	67
Ivory Rules,	11–12	Try Squares,	75 to 77
Iron Planes,	20–21	Toy Tool Chest Supplies,	73
Level Glass,	63	Wantage Rods,	13
Log Sticks,	13	Yard Sticks,	13
Levels,	61		

BOXWOOD RULES.

Boxwood Rules.

One Foot, Four Fold, Narrow.

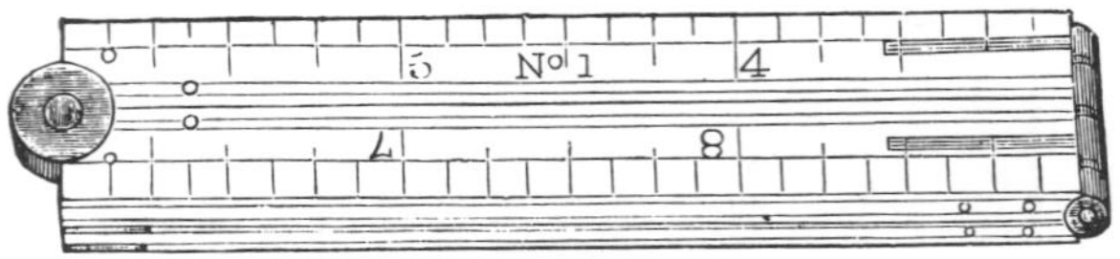

No. 1.

		Per dozen.
No. 1, Round Joint, Middle Plates, 8ths and 16ths, $\frac{5}{8}$ inch wide,	-	$3.00
2, Square " " " " " " $\frac{5}{8}$ " "	-	3.50

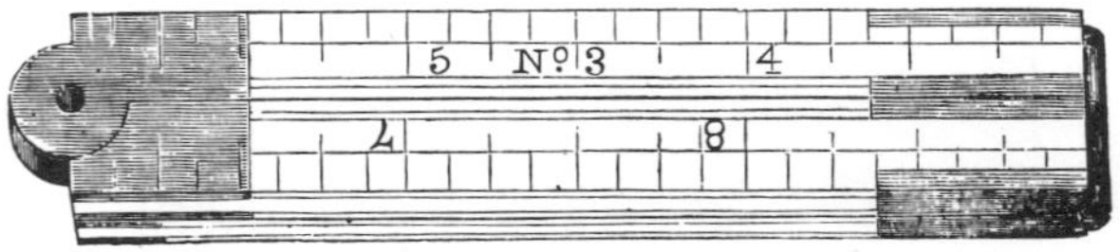

No. 3.

No. 3, Square Joint, Edge Plates, 8ths and 16ths, $\frac{5}{8}$ inch wide,	-	5.00
4, " " " Half Bound, " " " $\frac{5}{8}$ " "	-	9.00
5, " " " Bound, - " " " $\frac{5}{8}$ " "	-	11.00
6, Arch " Middle Plates, " " " $\frac{5}{8}$ " "	-	4.00
7, " " Edge Plates, " " " $\frac{5}{8}$ " "	-	6.00
8, " " Half Bound, " " " $\frac{5}{8}$ " "	-	10.00

No. 9.

9, Arch Joint, Bound, - 8ths and 16ths, $\frac{5}{8}$ inch wide,	-	12.00

OFFICE OF

H. CHAPIN'S SON,

Pine Meadow, Ct.,

November 1st, 1874.

Gentlemen:

Herewith enclosed I hand you my present "CASH DISCOUNT SHEET," on goods enumerated in my Catalogue of JANUARY, 1874, and would invite your attention to the low price or "BIG DISCOUNT," on Rules, Planes, Plumbs and Levels, &c., &c., which has greatly increased the demand, and to meet this demand, I am now increasing machinery, and hope to be able in a short time to fill all orders promptly; at present shall execute all orders to the extent of my stock, and ship balance when made unless instructed otherwise.

Catalogue of January, 1874, and Comparative Rule Lists furnished on application.

Respectfully,

H. CHAPIN'S SON.

Boxwood Rules.

Two Feet, Four Fold, Narrow.

No.		Per dozen.
10, Round Joint, Middle Plates, - 8ths and 16ths, 1 inch wide,		$4.00
11, Square " " " " 1 "		5.00
11½, " " Extra quality, 8ths and 16ths, - " " ¾ "		5.50
12, Square Joint, Edge Plates, 8ths, 16ths, 10ths, and scales, - " " 1 "		7.00
13, Square Joint, Edge Plates, Extra quality, 8ths, 16ths, 10ths, and scales, - " " ¾ "		8.00
14, Square Joint, Half Bound, 8ths, 16ths, 10ths, and scales, - " " 1 "		12.00
15, Square Joint, Bound, 8ths, 16ths, 10ths, and scales, - " " 1 "		15.00
16, Arch Joint, Middle Plates, 8ths, 16ths, 10ths, and scales, - " " 1 "		6.00
17, Arch Joint, Edge Plates, 8ths, 16ths, 10ths, and scales, - " " 1 "		8.00
18, Arch Joint, Half Bound, 8ths, 16ths, 10ths, and scales, - " " 1 "		13.00
19, Arch Joint, Bound, 8ths, 16ths, 10ths, and scales, - " " 1 "		16.00
20, Double Arch Joint, 8ths, 16ths, 10ths, and scales, 1 "		9.00
21, " " Bound, 8ths, 16ths, 10ths, and scales, - " " 1 "		21.00

Boxwood Rules.

Two Feet, Four Fold, Narrow.

No. 21, Double Arch Joint, Bound.

No. 14, Square Joint, Half Bound.

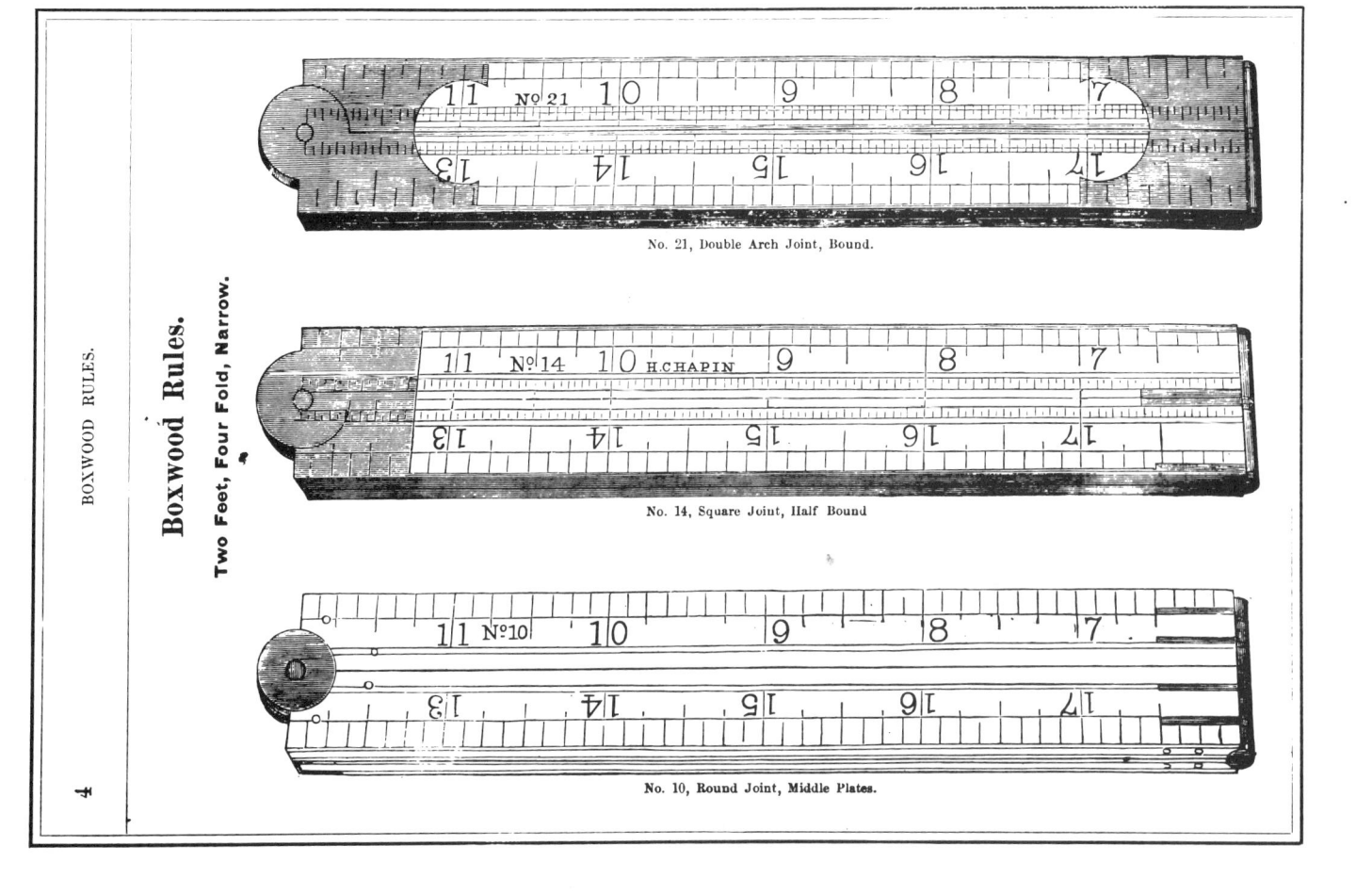

No. 10, Round Joint, Middle Plates.

Boxwood Rules.

Two Feet, Four Fold, Broad.

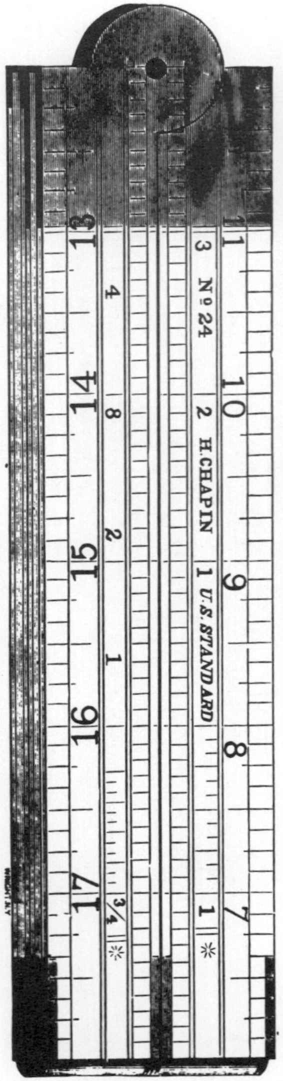

No. 24, Square Joint, Edge Plates.

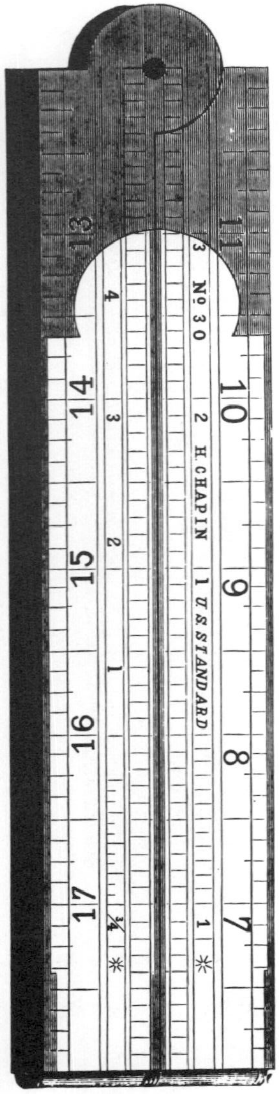

No. 30, Arch Joint, Bound.

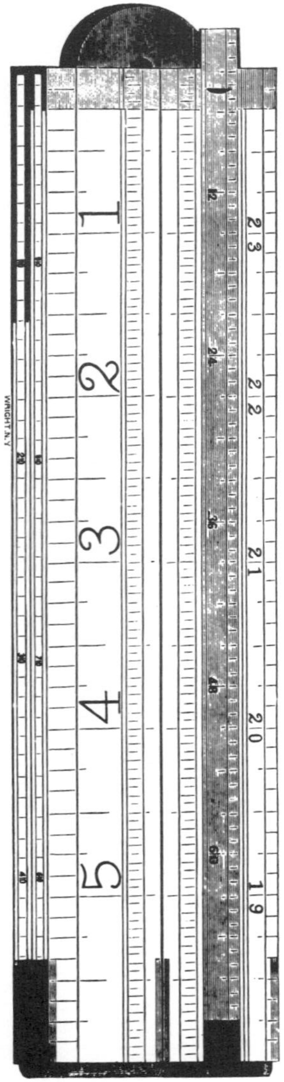

No. 33, Arch Joint, Edge Plates, with Slide.

Boxwood Rules.

Two Feet, Four Fold, Broad.

No.			Per dozen.
22,	Round Joint, Middle Plates, 8ths and 16ths,	$1\frac{3}{8}$ inch wide,	$5.00
23,	Square " " " " "	$1\frac{3}{8}$ " "	7.00
24,	" " Edge Plates, 8ths, 16ths, 10ths and scales, - - - - - - -	$1\frac{3}{8}$ " "	9.00
25,	Square Joint, Half bound, 8ths, 16ths, 10ths and scales, - - - - - - -	$1\frac{3}{8}$ " "	14.00
26,	Square Joint, Bound, 8ths, 16ths, 10ths and scales, - - - - - - - -	$1\frac{3}{8}$ " "	18.00
27,	Arch Joint, Middle Plates, 8ths, 16ths, 10ths and scales, - - - - - - -	$1\frac{3}{8}$ " "	9.00
28,	Arch Joint, Edge Plates, 8ths, 16ths, 10ths and scales, - - - - - - - -	$1\frac{3}{8}$ " "	11.00
29,	Arch Joint, Half Bound, 8ths, 16ths, 10ths and scales, - - - - - - - -	$1\frac{3}{8}$ " "	16.00
30,	Arch Joint, Bound, 8ths, 16ths, 10ths and scales, - - - - - - - -	$1\frac{3}{8}$ " "	20.00
31,	Double Arch Joint, 8ths, 16ths, 10ths and scales, - - - - - - - -	$1\frac{3}{8}$ " "	12.00
32,	Double Arch Joint, Bound, 8ths, 16ths, 10ths and scales, - - - - - - -	$1\frac{3}{8}$ " "	24.00
33,	Arch Joint, Edge Plate, with Slide, 8ths, 16ths, 10ths and scales, - - - - - -	$1\frac{3}{8}$ " "	14.00

Two Feet, Four Fold, Board Measure.

34,	Square Joint, Edge Plates, 8ths, 16ths, 10ths and scales, - - - - - - -	$1\frac{3}{8}$ inch wide,	$11.00
35,	Square Joint, Bound, 8ths, 16ths, 10ths, and scales, - - - - - - - -	$1\frac{3}{8}$ " "	20.00
36,	Arch Joint, Edge Plates, 8ths, 16ths, 10ths and scales, - - - - - - - -	$1\frac{3}{8}$ " "	13.00
37,	Arch Joint, Bound, 8ths, 16ths, 10ths and scales,	$1\frac{3}{8}$ " "	22.00
$34\frac{1}{2}$,	Square Joint, Edge Plates, with Board Stick Table, 9 lines, 10 to 18 ft., - - - - - - - - -		11.00

Two Feet, Two Fold, Board Measure.

40,	Square Joint, 8ths, 16ths, 10ths and scales, -	$1\frac{1}{2}$ inch wide,	$7.00
43,	Arch Joint, Extra Scales, 8ths, 16ths, 10ths and scales, - - - - - - - -	$1\frac{1}{2}$ " "	10.00

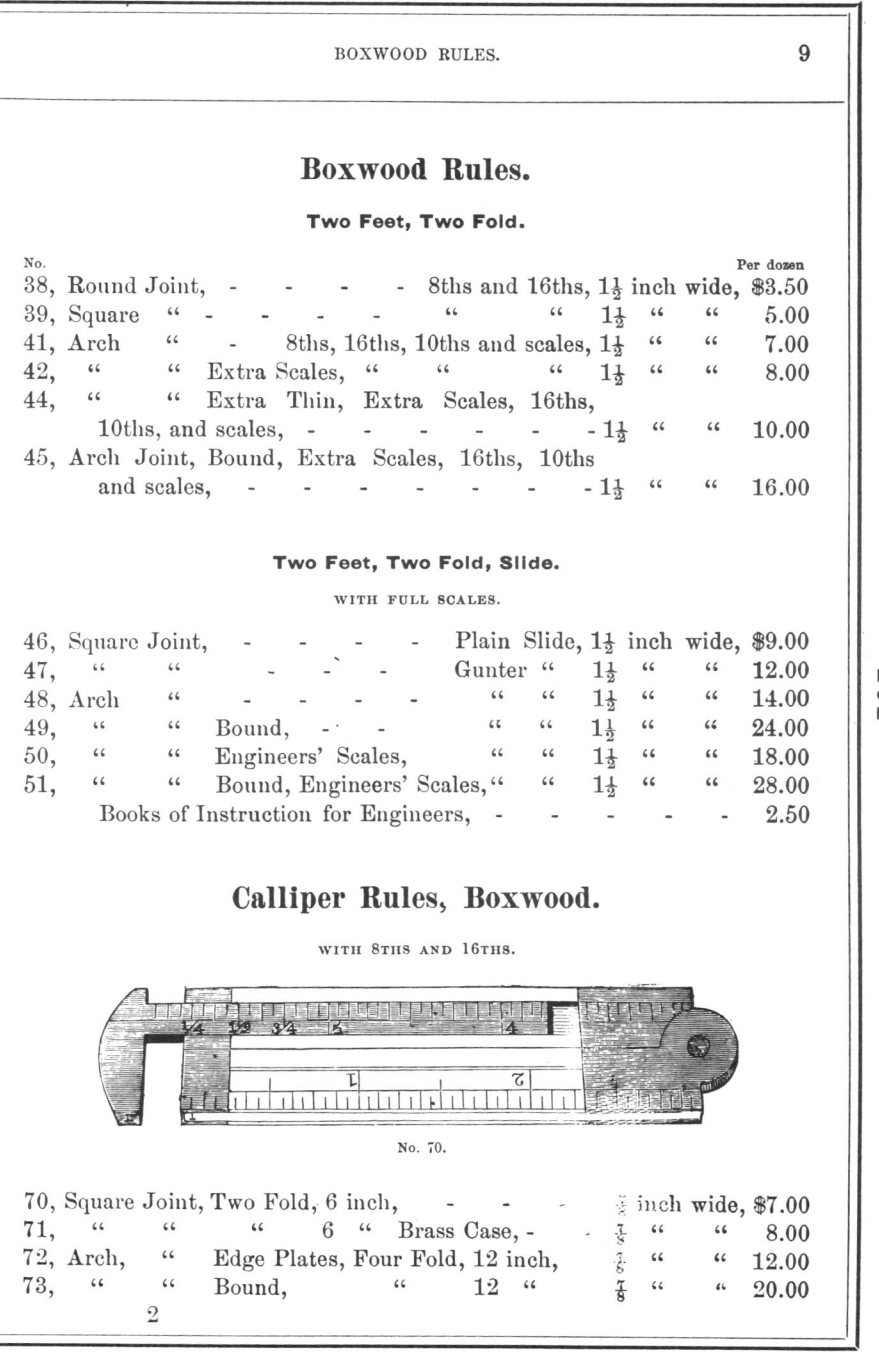

Boxwood Rules.

Two Feet, Two Fold.

			Per dozen
No. 38, Round Joint,	8ths and 16ths, 1½ inch wide,		$3.50
39, Square "	" 1½ " "		5.00
41, Arch "	8ths, 16ths, 10ths and scales, 1½ " "		7.00
42, " "	Extra Scales, 1½ " "		8.00
44, " "	Extra Thin, Extra Scales, 16ths,		
	10ths, and scales, 1½ " "		10.00
45, Arch Joint, Bound, Extra Scales, 16ths, 10ths			
	and scales, 1½ " "		16.00

Two Feet, Two Fold, Slide.

WITH FULL SCALES.

No. 46, Square Joint,	Plain Slide, 1½ inch wide,	$9.00
47, " "	Gunter " 1½ " "	12.00
48, Arch "	" 1½ " "	14.00
49, " "	Bound, " 1½ " "	24.00
50, " "	Engineers' Scales, " 1½ " "	18.00
51, " "	Bound, Engineers' Scales, " 1½ " "	28.00
	Books of Instruction for Engineers,	2.50

Calliper Rules, Boxwood.

WITH 8THS AND 16THS.

No. 70.

No. 70, Square Joint, Two Fold, 6 inch, ⅞ inch wide,	$7.00
71, " " " 6 " Brass Case, - ⅞ " "	8.00
72, Arch " " Edge Plates, Four Fold, 12 inch, ⅞ " "	12.00
73, " " " Bound, " 12 " ⅞ " "	20.00

Boxwood Rules.

No. 46, Square Joint, Plain Slide.

No. 48, Arch Joint, Gunter Slide.

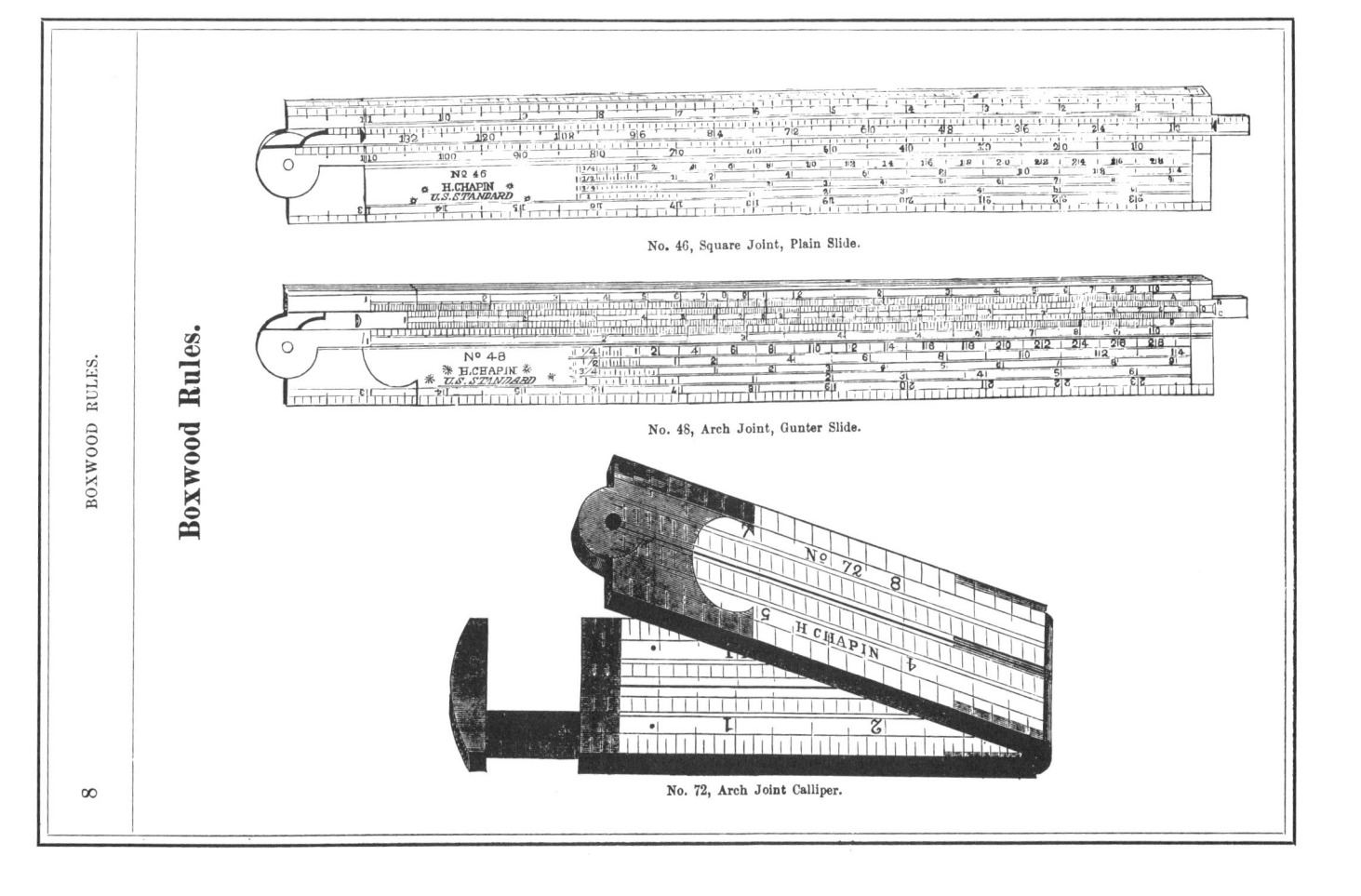

No. 72, Arch Joint Calliper.

Ivory Rules.

One Foot, Four Fold.
WITH 8THS AND 16THS.

No. 53, Square Joint, Middle Plates.

No. 57, Arch Joint, Bound.

No.					Per dozen.
52,	Round Joint, Middle Plates, Brass,	-	$\frac{1}{2}$ inch wide,	$10.00
53,	Square " " "	"	$\frac{1}{2}$ " "	12.00
54,	" " " German Silver,	-	$\frac{5}{8}$ " "	14.00
55,	Arch " Edge Plates, "	-	$\frac{5}{8}$ " "	17.00
56,	" " " Bound,	-	$\frac{5}{8}$ to $\frac{3}{4}$ " "	21.00
57,	" " " "	-	$\frac{5}{8}$ to $\frac{3}{4}$ " "	32.00
58,	Square " " "	-	$\frac{5}{8}$ " "	28.00

Two Feet, Four Fold, Narrow.
WITH FULL SCALES.

59,	Square Joint, Edge Plates, German Silver,	-	$\frac{5}{8}$ inch wide,	$54.00
60,	Arch " " "	1 " "	64.00
61,	" " Bound,	1 " "	80.00
62,	Double Arch Joint, Bound,	1 " "	92.00

Two Feet, Four Fold, Broad.
WITH FULL SCALES.

63,	Arch Joint, Edge Plates, German Silver, -	$1\frac{3}{8}$ inch wide,	$84.00
64,	" " Bound, " "	$1\frac{3}{8}$ " "	102.00
65,	" " " with slide, "	$1\frac{3}{8}$ " "	112.00
66,	" " " with Calliper, "	$1\frac{3}{8}$ " "	120.00
67,	Double Arch Joint, Bound,	$1\frac{3}{8}$ " "	116.00

Boxwood Rules.

No. 96, Three Fold.

No. 96, Six Fold.

Two, Three, Four, and Six Fold Rules.

No.				Per dozen.
1½,	Round Joint, Two Fold, - 6 inch, 8ths and 16ths, $\frac{5}{8}$ inch wide,	$2.00
84,	Arch Joint, Middle Plates, Four Fold, 36 inch, 8ths	"	8.00
	and yard divisions, - - - - - 1 " "		
84½,	Arch Joint, Bound, Four Fold, 36 inch, 8ths and		22.00
	yard divisions, - - - - - 1 " "		
95,	Edge Plates, Three Fold, 12 inch, 8ths and 16ths, - ½ " "	6.00
96,	Arch Joint, Edge Plates, Six Fold, 24 inch, 8ths		13.00
	and 16ths, - - - - - - ¾ " "		

Ship Carpenters' Bevels.

| 85, | Boxwood, Double Tongue, 8ths and 16ths, - - - | 6.00 |
| 85½, | " Single " " " - - - | 6.00 |

Ivory Rules.

Two Fold.

No.		Per dozen.
68,	Round Joint, 6 inch, Brass, - - - - - $\frac{1}{2}$ inch wide,	\$4.50
69,	Arch " 12 " German Silver, 8ths, 16ths, 10ths and 12ths, - - - - - - - $\frac{3}{4}$ " "	24.00

Calliper Rules, Ivory.

WITH 8THS AND 16THS.

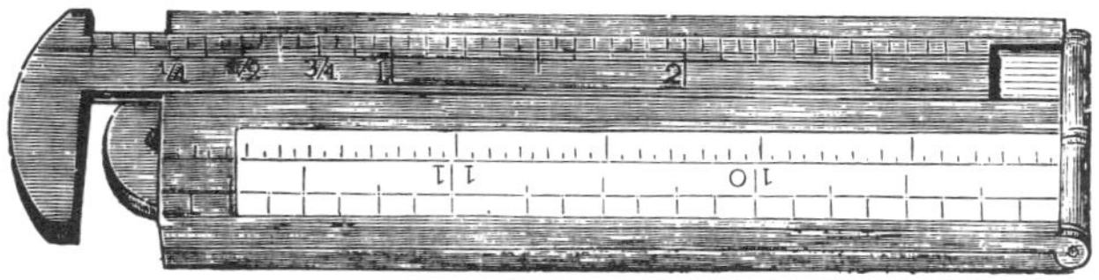

No. 77.

74,	Square Joint, Two Fold, 6 inch, German Silver, - $\frac{7}{8}$ inch wide,	\$15.00
74½,	" " " 6 " " Bound, $\frac{7}{8}$ " "	18.00
75,	" " " 6 " " Case, $\frac{7}{8}$ " "	18.00
76,	" " Edge Plates, Four Fold, 12 inch, German Silver, - - - - - - - - $\frac{7}{8}$ " "	38.00
77,	Square Joint, Bound, Four Fold, 12 inch, German Silver, - - - - - - - - - $\frac{5}{8}$ " "	44.00
78,	Arch Joint, Bound, Four Fold, 12 inch, German Silver, - - - - - - - - - $\frac{5}{8}$ " "	48.00
79,	Arch Joint, Bound, Four Fold, 12 inch, German Silver, - - - - - - - - - $\frac{7}{8}$ " "	60.00

Rules with Spanish Measure, made to order.

Miscellaneous Rules.

Bench Rules.

No.		Per dozen.
80,	Bench Rule, 24 inch, - - - - - - 1¼ inch wide,	\$3.00
81,	" 24 " Board Measure Table, - 1½ " "	6.00

Yard Sticks.

82,	Yard Stick, - - - - - - - - - -	\$1.50
83,	" Brass Tipped, Polished, - - - - -	3.50
97,	" Hickory, - - - - - - - - -	2.00
98,	" " Brass Tipped, Polished, - - -	4.50

Board Measures.

Explanation of Board Sticks:—Know the length of boards you wish to measure,—the figures on the end, eight and upwards, is the length in feet; place the Stick on the flat surface to the outer edge of the board, follow the length column to the opposite edge, and the figure on the edge will be the contents in feet of 1 inch boards.

No.		Per dozen.
86,	Board Stick, Octagon, 8 Lines, 9 to 16 feet, - - - 24 inch,	\$6.00
87,	" Square and Octagon, 16 Lines, 8 to 23 feet, 24 "	8.00
88,	" " " 16 " 8 " 23 " 36 "	12.00
89,	" Walking Cane, Brass Head and Tip, 8 lines, 9 to 16 feet, - - - - - - - 36 "	12.00
90,	Board Stick, Flat, with T Head, 10 Lines, 9 to 19 feet, 36 "	9.00
90½	" Hickory, Flat, with T Head, 8 Lines, 9 to 16 feet, - - - - - - - - - - 36 "	12.00

Log Measures.

Explanation of Log Sticks:—These Sticks give the number of feet of one inch square edge boards sawed from a log from 12 to 36 inches in diameter. The figures 12 to 20, near the head, are for the length of logs in feet; follow the column under the length of the log to the diameter of the log, which will give the number of feet the log will make. Logs not over 15 feet long, the diameter should be taken at the small end; over 15 feet in length, at the middle.

No.		Per dozen.
91,	Log Stick, Flat, with T Head, - - - - - 36 inch,	\$9.00
91½	" Hickory, Flat, with T Head, - - 36 "	12.00
89½	" Walking Cane, Brass Head and Tip, - - 36 "	12.00

Wantage and Gauging Rods.

92,	Wantage Rod, - - - - - - - - - - -	\$5.00
93,	Gauging Rod, - - - - - - - - 36 inch,	7.00
94,	" - - - - - - - - - 48 "	8.00
94½,	" with Wantage Table, - - - 48 "	18.00

Desk Rules.

99	Boxwood, Extra Thin, 12 inch, - - - - $\frac{3}{4}$ inch wide,	\$1.50

BENCH PLANES.

Common Bench Planes.

STAMPED J. PEARCE.

Not Warranted.

Common Bench Planes, Single Irons.

Not Warranted.

		Price each.
No.		
100, Smooth,	Cast Steel Irons,	$0.60
101, Jack,	"	.75
102, Fore,	"	1.00
103, Jointer, 26 inch,	"	1.10
" 28 "	"	1.20

Common Bench Planes, Double Irons.

Not Warranted.

108, Smooth,	Cast Steel Irons,	$0.90
109, Jack,	"	1.00
110, Fore,	"	1.40
111, Jointer, 26 inch,	"	1.50
" 28 "	"	1.60
Common Planes, Double Irons, per set,		4.80

Iron Starts furnished in above, if desired.

BENCH PLANES.

Extra Bench Planes.

No. 112.

No. 113.

No. 114. 22 inch.

Extra Bench Planes, Single Irons.

			Price each.
No.			
104, Smooth,	Best Cast Steel Iron,	1¾ to 2¼ inch,	$0.60
105, Jack,	"	2¼ "	.75
106, Fore,	18 to 21 inch,	2⅜ "	1.00
"	22 "	2½ "	1.00
107, Jointer, 24 to 26 "		2⅝ "	1.10
"	28 "	2¾ "	1.20
Planes with extra sized Irons,		per ¼	.10
" English Irons, Single, Extra,			.10

Iron or wood Starts furnished in above, if desired.

BENCH PLANES.

Extra Bench Planes.

No. 115. 26 in.

No. 116.

Extra Bench Planes, Double Irons.

No.			Price each.
112, Smooth, Best Cast Steel Iron,		$1\frac{7}{8}$ to $2\frac{1}{4}$ inch	$0.90
113, Jack, " " "		2 to $2\frac{1}{4}$ "	1.00
114, Fore, 18 to 21 inch, Best Cast Steel Iron,		$2\frac{3}{8}$ "	1.40
" 22 " " " "		$2\frac{3}{8}$ "	1.40
115, Jointers, 24 to 26 " " " "		$2\frac{1}{2}$ "	1.50
" 28 " " " "		$2\frac{5}{8}$ "	1.60
" 30 " " " "		$2\frac{3}{4}$ "	1.75
116, Smooth, Beech, Solid Handle, Best Cast Steel Iron,		2 to $2\frac{1}{4}$ "	1.75
116½, Smooth, Beech, Solid Handle, Polished, Best Cast Steel Iron,		2 to $2\frac{1}{4}$ "	2.00
117, Smooth, Boxwood, Best Cast Steel Iron,		2 to $2\frac{1}{4}$ "	2.50
118, " Rosewood, " " " "		2 to $2\frac{1}{4}$ "	2.00
119, " " Solid Handle, Best Cast Steel Iron,		2 to $2\frac{1}{4}$ "	4.00
120, Smooth, Boxwood, Solid Handle, Best Cast Steel Iron,		2 to $2\frac{1}{4}$ "	4.50
121, Smooth, Applewood, Solid Handle, Polished, Best Cast Steel Iron,		2 to $2\frac{1}{4}$ "	2.25
Planes with extra sized Irons,		per $\frac{1}{8}$ inch,	.15
" English Irons, Double Extra,		-	.25

Iron or Wood Starts furnished with above, if desired.

Carpenter's Razee or Recess Handle Planes.

No.		Price each.
105½, Jack, Best C. S. Single Iron,		$1.00
113½, " " " Double "		1.20
114½, Fore, to 22 inch " Double "		1.60
115½, Jointer, to 28 " " Double "		1.85

Iron or wood Starts furnished with above if desired.

Premium Bench Planes.

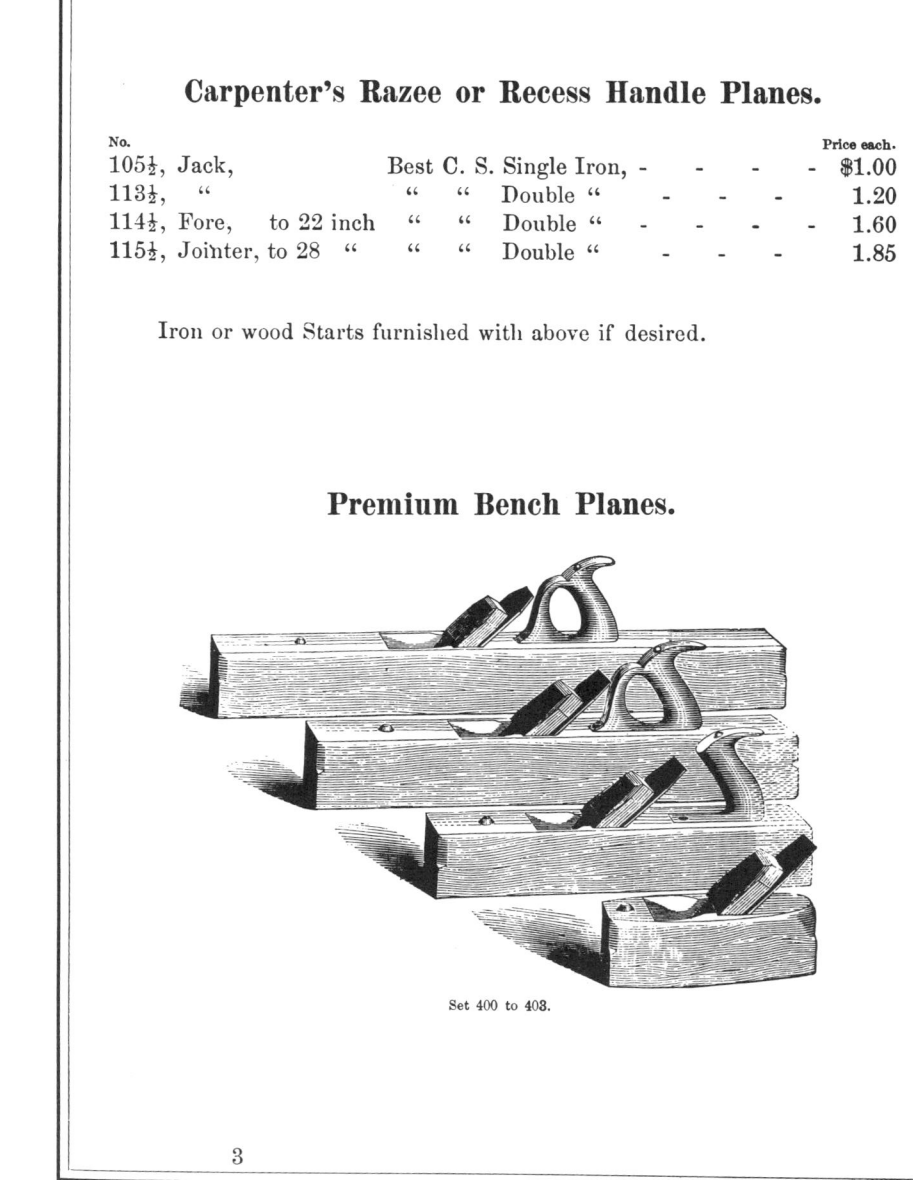

Set 400 to 408.

BENCH PLANES.

Premium Bench Planes, Extra C. S.

DOUBLE IRONS.

With Bolted Handle and Start.

No.		Price each.
400, Smooth,	- - - - - - -	$1.10
401, Jack,	- - - - - - -	1.35
402, Fore, 22 inch,	- - - - -	1.85
403, Jointer, 28 "	- - - - -	2.20
	Per set,	6.50

With Bolted Handle and Start. Polished.

404, Smooth,	- - - - - - -	$1.35
405, Jack,	- - - - - - -	1.75
406, Fore, 22 inch,	- - - - -	2.35
407, Jointer, 28 "	- - - - -	2.80
	Per set,	8.25

With Diamond Bolts and Starts.

408, Smooth,	- - - - - - -	$1.25
409, Jack,	- - - - - - -	1.50
410, Fore, 22 inch,	- - - - -	2.00
411, Jointer, 28 "	- - - - -	2.50
	Per set,	7.25

With Diamond Bolts and Starts. Polished.

412, Smooth,	- - - - - - -	$1.50
413, Jack,	- - - - - - -	1.90
414, Fore, 22 inch,	- - - - -	2.50
415, Jointer, 28 "	- - - - -	3.10
	Per set,	9.00

Premium Planes with English Irons, Extra, - .25

BENCH PLANES.

Set of Planes, No. 502.

Sets of Planes in Cases.

Irons ground and tested, ready for working, neatly packed in wood cases. Sets of four consist of Double Iron Smooth, Jack, Fore 22 in., Jointer 28 inch.

No.		
500,	Set of Four Planes, with Iron Starts, extra quality, -	$6.00
501,	" " " " " " Razee,	6.75
502,	" " " Premium Planes, Bolted Handle and Starts,	8.00
503,	" " " Premium Planes, Bolted Handle and Starts, Razee,	8.75
504,	" " " Premium Planes, Bolted Handle and Starts, Polished,	10.00
505,	" " " Premium Planes, Bolted Handle and Starts, Razee, Polished,	10.75

Solid Handle Smooth, in place of Double Smooth, - extra, .90
"   "   "   with set, "   "   1.75
Mitre Plane, Single, "   "   .75

Ebony or Boxwood Starts, in place of Iron, will be furnished if desired.

Perfected Iron Planes.

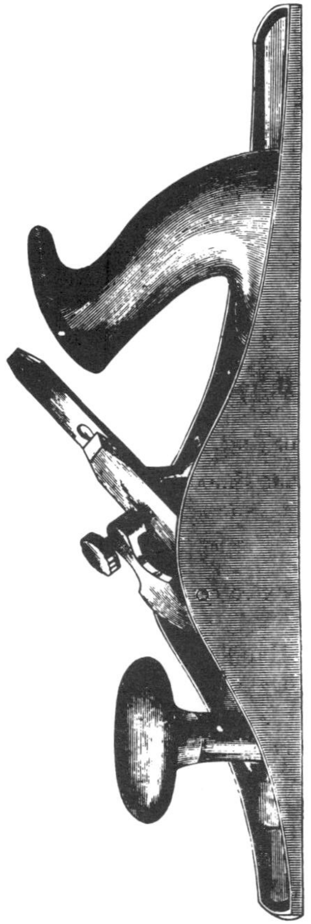

More than Fifty Thousand of these Iron Planes are already in use by our very best wood-workers, and their sale is constantly and largely increasing. The adjustable throat, the perfection of their work, the simple and convenient method of fastening the iron, the fact that they are the only iron Planes made in which ordinary bits can be used, and the price,

Twenty-five per cent. less

than others, make these the favorite iron Planes among all classes of wood-workers.

The Cutting Irons

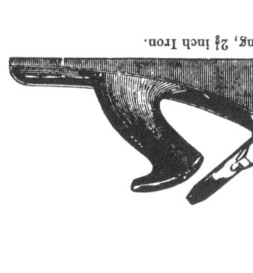

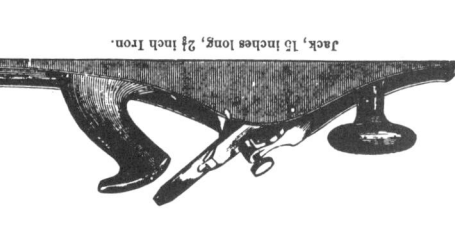

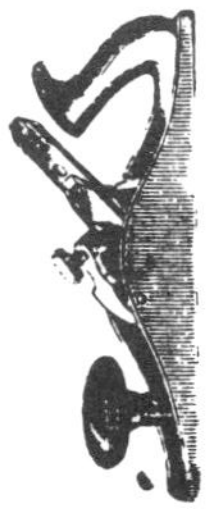

are made of the finest English plane iron steel, and are unequaled for fineness of the cutting edge. They are finished and fitted in the neatest manner before leaving the factory, and warranted.

Iron Planes.

NEATLY PACKED IN PAPER BOXES.

				Price each.
No. 506, Smooth Plane,	8 in. long,	2⅜ in. Cutter,	-	$4.00
507, Jack Plane,	15 "	2⅜ "	-	5.00
508, Jointer Plane,	21 "	2⅜ "	-	6.00
Set complete,	-	-	-	$15.00
Set complete with Rosewood Knobs and Handles				16.00
With Rosewood Knobs and Handles, extra per Plane,				.50

Iron Block Plane.

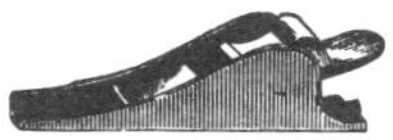

No. 509. 5¼ x 1¼.   No. 510. 7 x 2.

No Tool was ever made that has sold more rapidly than this, or given more complete satisfaction. It works so neatly on end wood, casings, mouldings, and all mitre-work.

		Price each.
No. 509, Block Plane, 5¼ in. long, 1¼ in. Cutter,	-	$1.50
510, Block Plane, 7 " 2 " "	with Knobs and Handle,	2.50

Ship Planes.

No. 417.

No. 418.

No. 420.

No.				Price each.
416,	Smooth,	Best Double C. S. Iron, - -	9 inch,	$1.00
417,	Jack,	" " - -	16 " Razee,	1.20
418,	Fore,	" " - -	22 " "	1.60
419,	Jointer,	" " - -	26 " "	1.80
420,	Spar Plane,	" " - - - - - - -		1.50
	"	Best Single, " - - - - - -		1.00

Coopers' Planes.

No. 421.

421,	Leveling Plane, - - - - - - - - - -		$1.75
422,	Howel " and Stock, Barrel or Hogshead, - -		3.75
423,	Croze and Stock, - - - - - - - - - -		2.00
424,	Heading Jointer, to 5½ feet,	Single Iron, - -	2.25
425,	" " to 5½ feet,	Double " - - -	2.75
426,	" " to 5½ feet, solid	Single and Double Iron,	5.50
427,	Stave Jointer, to 5½ feet,	Single, " -	2.50
428,	" " to 5½ feet,	Double, "	3.00
429,	" " to 5½ feet, solid,	Single and Double "	6.00

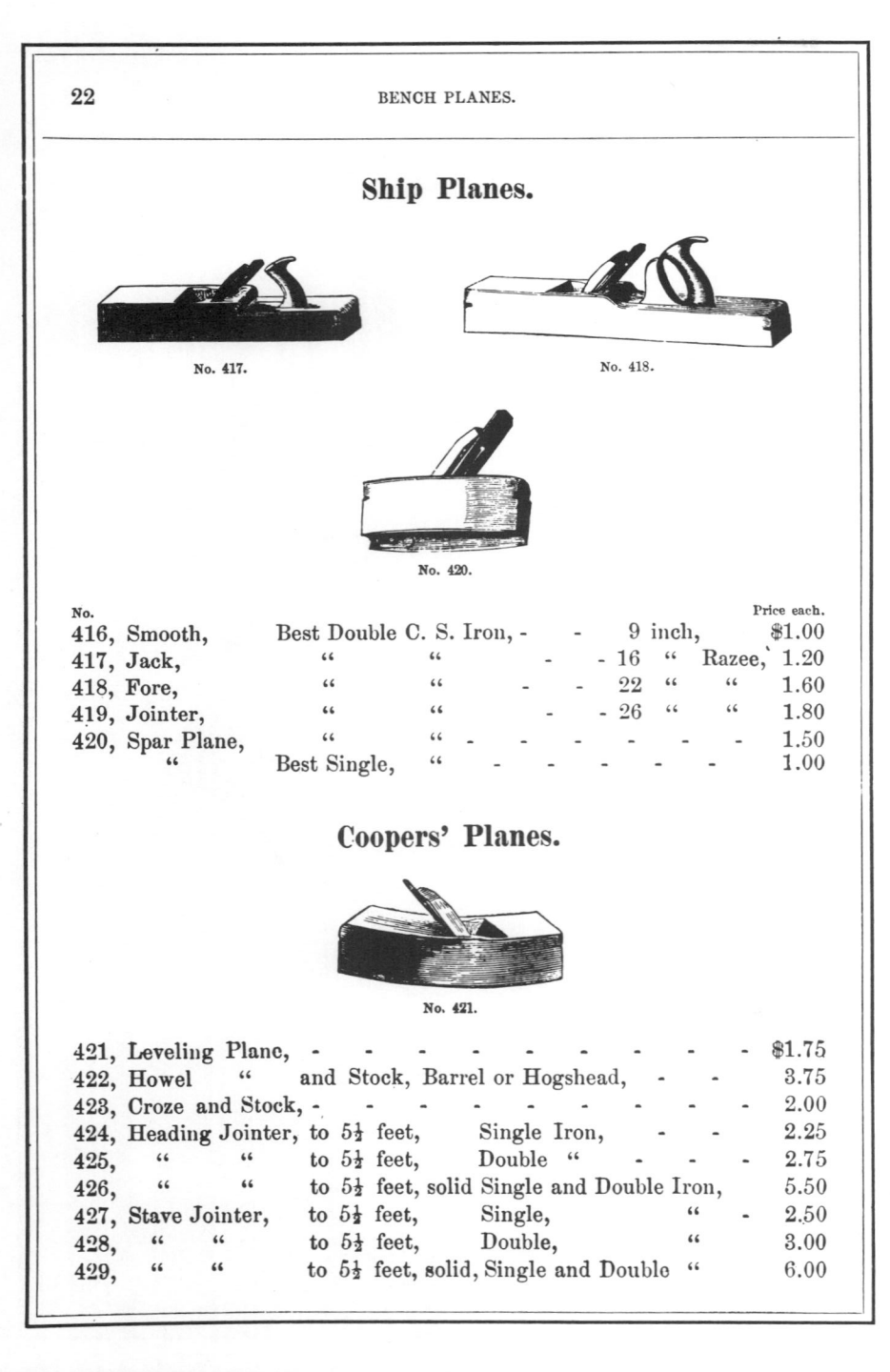

Miscellaneous Planes.

No. 431.

No. 432.

No.			Price each.
430,	Tooth Plane,	Iron, 2 to 2¼ inch,	$1.00
431,	Mitre " Square,	" 1½ to 1¾ "	.75
432,	" " Smooth Shape,	" 1½ to 1¾ "	.75
433,	" " Square,	Double Iron, 1¾ "	1.00
434,	" " Smooth Shape,	" 1¾ "	1.00
435,	Block Mitre,	Single Iron, 2½ "	1.00
436,	Compass Smooth,	" 2 to 2⅛ "	1.00
437,	" "	Double Iron, 2 to 2⅛ "	1.25
	Mitres, Polished,	Extra, - - -	.30
	Rosewood or Boxwood Mitres,	" - - -	1.00

No. 438.

No. 440.

438,	Toy, Smooth,	Single Iron, 1½ inch,	$0.50
439,	" "	Double " 1½ "	.70
440,	" Jack,	Single " 1½ "	.60
441,	" "	Double " 1½ "	.80

No. 443.

No. 442.

No. 447.

442,	Gutter Plane,	1½ to 2 inch,	$1.25
443,	Pump Plane, for Chain Pump,	1 to 1½ "	1.65
444,	Whip Plane, Steel Faced,	1¼ to 1¾ "	1.25
445,	Wash Board Plane, - - - - - - - - -		1.20
446,	" " with Handle, - - - - - -		1.75
447,	German Smooth or Bull Plane, Single, - - - - - -		1.40
448,	" " Double, - - - - -		1.60
449,	Carpenter's Badger, Double, - - - - - - - -		2.00

Moulding Planes.

Beads.

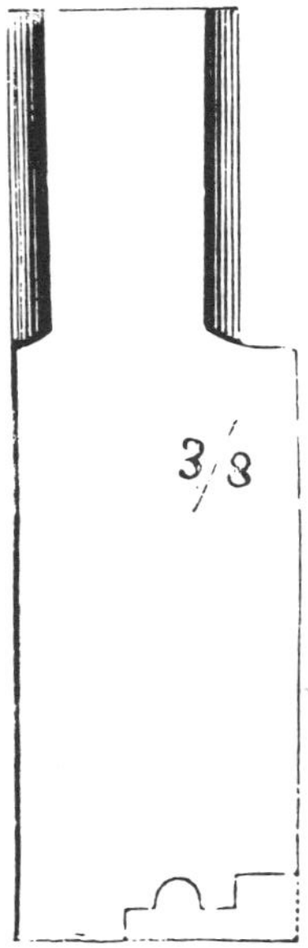

No. 122.

No. 123.

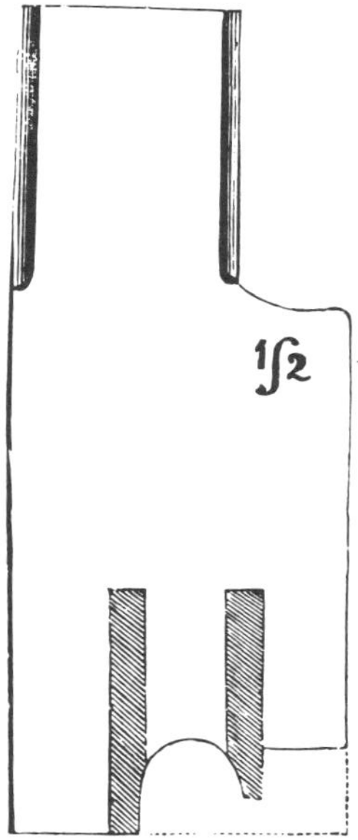

No. 124.

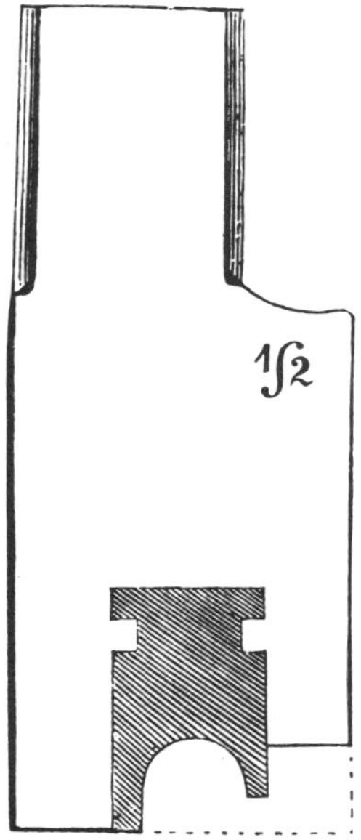

No. 125.

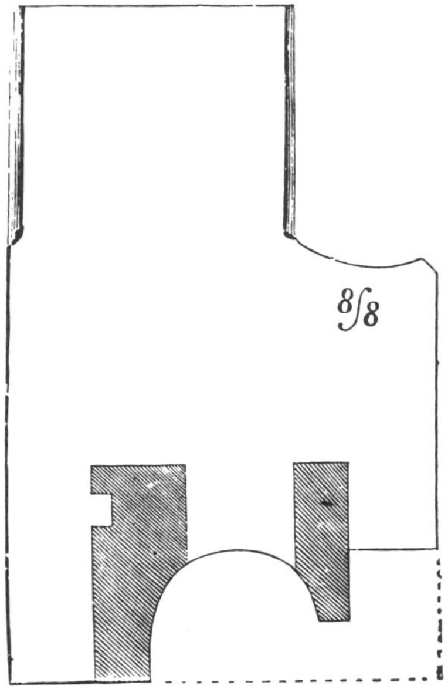

No. 125.

Moulding Planes.

Beads.

No.		Sizes	Price each.
122,	Astragals,	$\frac{1}{4}$ $\frac{3}{8}$ $\frac{1}{2}$ $\frac{5}{8}$ $\frac{3}{4}$ inch,	$0.50
	"	$\frac{7}{8}$ 1 "	.55
	"	$1\frac{1}{8}$ $1\frac{1}{4}$ "	.60
123,	Beads, Single Boxed,	$\frac{1}{8}$ $\frac{3}{16}$ $\frac{1}{4}$ $\frac{5}{16}$ $\frac{3}{8}$ $\frac{7}{16}$ $\frac{1}{2}$ "	.50
	" "	$\frac{5}{8}$ $\frac{3}{4}$ "	.55
	" "	$\frac{7}{8}$ 1 "	.70
	" "	$1\frac{1}{8}$ $1\frac{1}{4}$ "	.90
	" "	$1\frac{3}{8}$ $1\frac{1}{2}$ "	1.00
	" " with Handle,	$1\frac{1}{2}$ "	1.90
124,	" Double Boxed,	$\frac{1}{8}$ $\frac{3}{16}$ $\frac{1}{4}$ $\frac{5}{16}$ $\frac{3}{8}$ $\frac{7}{16}$ $\frac{1}{2}$ "	.60
	" "	$\frac{5}{8}$ $\frac{3}{4}$ "	.65
	" "	$\frac{7}{8}$ 1 "	.80
	" "	$1\frac{1}{8}$ $1\frac{1}{4}$ "	1.00
125,	" Solid Boxed, Dovetailed,	$\frac{1}{8}$ $\frac{3}{16}$ $\frac{1}{4}$ "	.70
	" " "	$\frac{5}{16}$ $\frac{3}{8}$ $\frac{7}{16}$ $\frac{1}{2}$ "	.80
	" " "	$\frac{5}{8}$ $\frac{3}{4}$ "	.90
	" " "	$\frac{7}{8}$ 1 "	1.00
	" " "	$1\frac{1}{8}$ $1\frac{1}{4}$ "	1.20

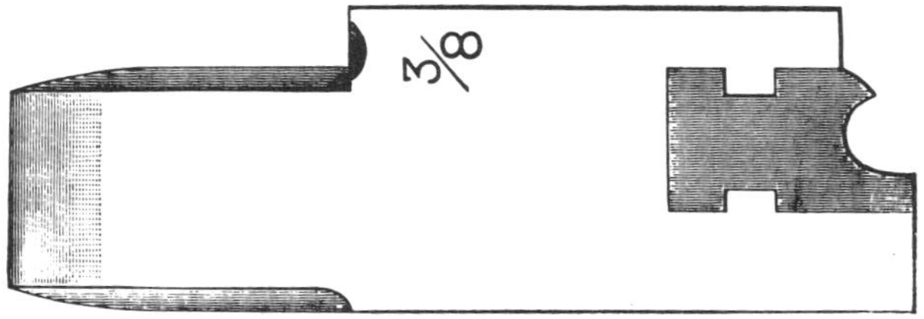

No. 125. Bead, with Bevel Quirk.

123,	Beads, extra for Bevel Quirk,	$0.10
124,	" " "	.10
125,	" " "	.10

Beads, Double, Right and Left Hand, in one Block, double price.

Beads with Solid Handle, extra, - - - - - - **$1.00**

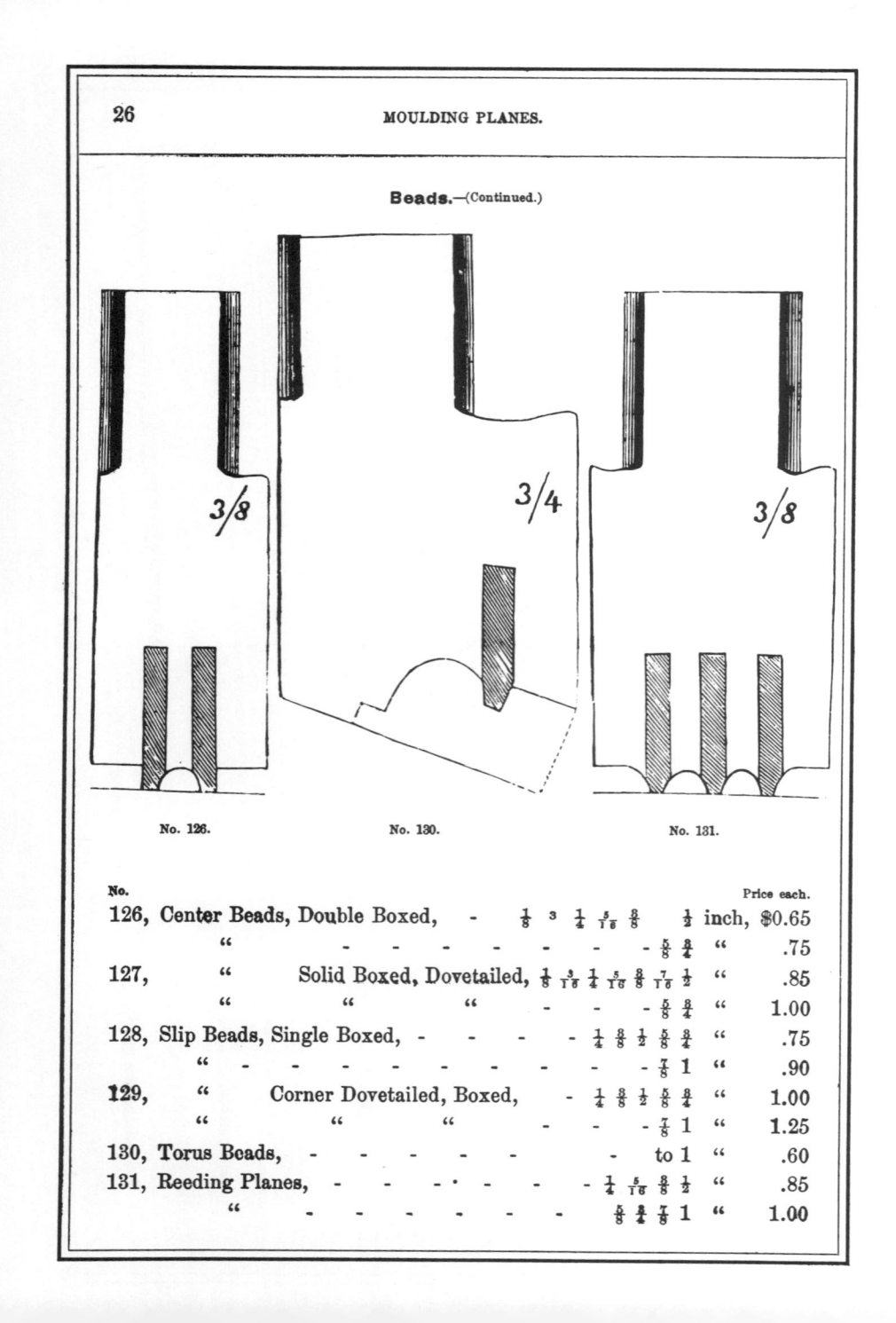

Beads.—(Continued.)

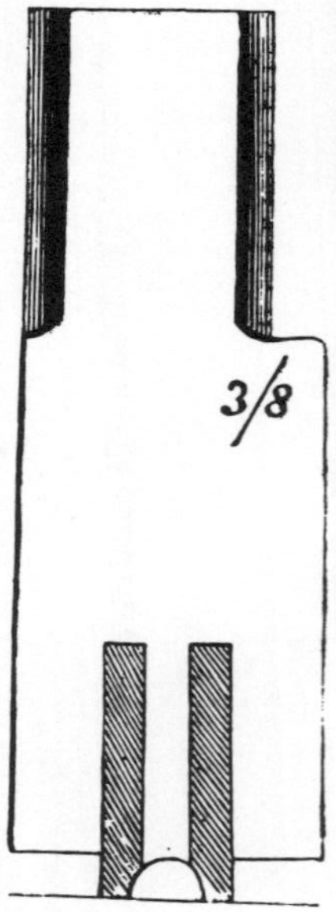

No. 126.

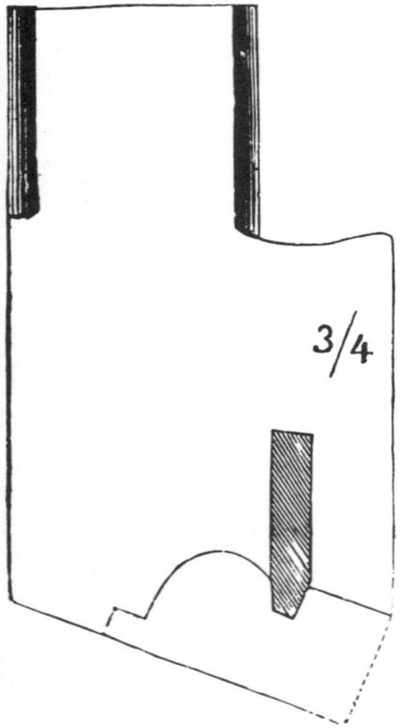

No. 130.

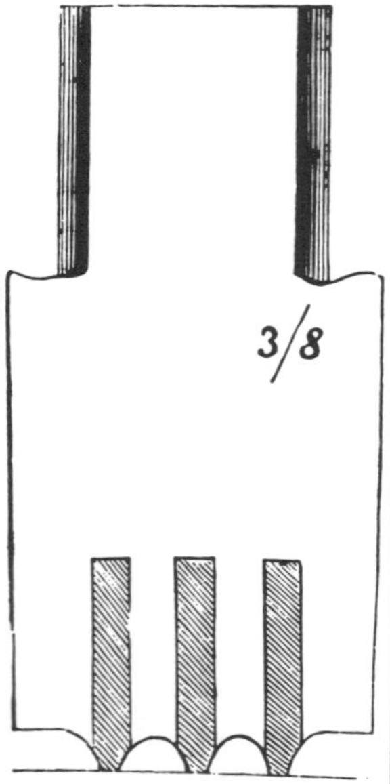

No. 131.

No.		Sizes		Price each.
126,	**Center Beads**, Double Boxed, -	1/8 3 1/4 5/16 3/8 1/2	inch,	$0.65
	" - - - - - - - -	5/8 3/4	"	.75
127,	" Solid Boxed, Dovetailed,	1/8 3/16 1/4 5/16 3/8 7/16 1/2	"	.85
	" " " - - -	5/8 3/4	"	1.00
128,	**Slip Beads**, Single Boxed, - - - -	1/4 3/8 1/2 5/8 3/4	"	.75
	" - - - - - - - - - -	7/8 1	"	.90
129,	" Corner Dovetailed, Boxed, -	1/4 3/8 1/2 5/8 3/4	"	1.00
	" " " - - -	7/8 1	"	1.25
130,	**Torus Beads**, - - - - - - -	to 1	"	.60
131,	**Reeding Planes**, - - - - - - -	1/4 5/16 3/8 1/2	"	.85
	" - - - - - - -	5/8 3/4 7/8 1	"	1.00

Step or Stair Planes.

No 133.

No.		Sizes		Price each.
132,	Nosing or Step Plane, one Iron, - - -	3/4 7/8 1	inch,	$0.80
	" " " - -	1 1/8 1 1/4 1 3/8 1 1/2	"	1.00
133,	" " two Irons, - - -	3/4 7/8 1	"	1.10
	" " "	1 1/8 1 1/4 1 3/8 1 1/2	"	1.20
133½,	" " " Handled, -	3/4 7/8 1	"	1.50
	" " " " -	1 1/8 1 1/4 1 3/8 1 1/2	"	1.75
134,	" " Single Iron, Handled,	1 1/8 1 1/4 1 3/8 1 1/2	"	1.25
135,	Hand Rail Plane, Ovolo or Ogee, - - - - - -			1.40

Dadoes.

No. 139.

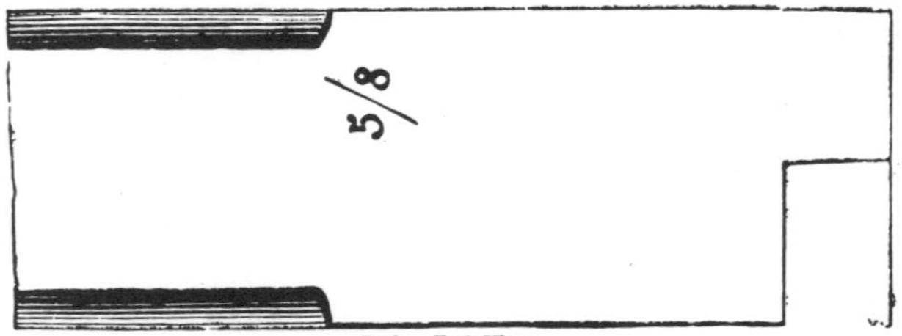

Dado—End View.

No.		Sizes		Price each.
136,	Dado, - - - - -	1/8 3/16 1/4 5/16 3/8 1/2 5/8 3/4 7/8 1	inch,	$0.75
137,	" with Wood Stop, -	1/8 3/16 1/4 5/16 3/8 1/2 5/8 3/4 7/8 1	"	1.00
138,	" with Brass Side Stop, -	1/8 3/16 1/4 5/16 3/8 1/2 5/8 3/4 7/8 1	"	1.10
139,	" with Screw Stop, -	1/8 3/16 1/4 5/16 3/8 1/2 5/8 3/4 7/8 1	"	1.50
	Dado, with Solid Handle, - - - - -		Extra,	1.00

Panel Planes.

No.		Price each.
140,	Panel Plane, - - - - - - - - - - - - -	$1.15
141,	" - - - - - - and Cut, - -	1.40
142,	" with moving Fence, - - - - - -	1.50
143,	" " - and Cut, - -	1.70

Door Planes.

144,	Door Planes, Ogee, - - - - - - - ½ to ⅝ inch,	$0.88
145,	" " Bevel, Double Screw Arms,	1.50

Filletsters.

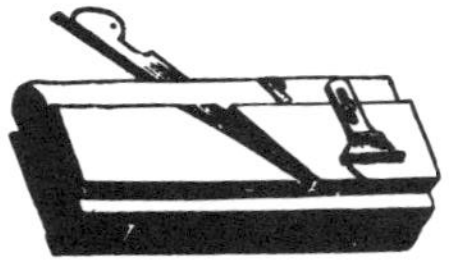

No. 148.

No. 150.

146,	Filletster, - - - - - - - - - - - - -	$1.10
147,	" with Stop, - - - - - - - - -	1.25
148,	" with Stop and Cut, - - - - - - -	1.40
149,	" with Stop, Cut and Dovetailed, Boxed, - -	1.85
150,	" with Screw Stop, Cut and Dovetailed Boxed, -	2.50
150½,	" " " " " " " and Boxwood Fence, - - - - - - - - - - -	3.00
150¾,	Filletster, with Screw Stop, Cut, Solid Box or Rosewood, -	5.00
151,	" " " Cut and Dovetailed Boxed, Solid Handle, - - - - - - - - - -	3.75
	Extra for Rabbet Mouth,	.25
152,	Filletster, with Arms, Stop, Cut and Dovetailed Boxed, -	2.75
153,	" with Screw Arms, Stop, Cut and Dovetailed Boxed,	3.00
154,	" with Screw Arms, Screw Stop, Cut, " "	4.00
154½,	" with Screw Arms, Screw Stop, Cut, Solid Box or Rosewood, - - - - - - - - - - - -	6.25

Rabbet Planes.

No. 155.

No. 157.

No. 159.

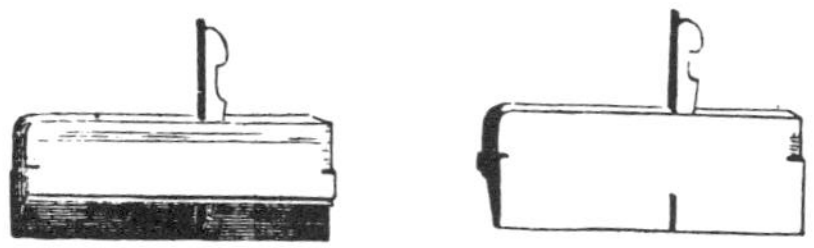

One pair. No. 161.

No.			Price each.
155,	Rabbet Planes, Square, - - - - -	½ ⅝ ¾ ⅞ 1 inch,	$0.60
	" " - - - - -	1⅛ 1¼ "	.65
	" " - - - - - - -	1⅜ 1½ "	.70
156,	" " Double Boxed,	½ ⅝ ¾ ⅞ 1 "	1.10
	" " " - -	1⅛ 1¼ "	1.20
	" " " - -	1⅜ 1½ "	1.30
157,	" Skew, - - - -	½ ⅝ ¾ ⅞ 1 "	.60
	" " - - - - - -	1⅛ 1¼ "	.65
	" " - - - - - -	1⅜ 1½ "	.70
	" " - - - - - -	1⅝ 1¾ "	.80
	" " - - - - - -	1⅞ 2 "	.90
	" " - - - - - - -	2¼ "	1.00
		Extra for Cut,	.20
158,	" " Boxed and Cut, -	½ ⅝ ¾ ⅞ 1 "	1.25
	" " " - -	1⅛ 1¼ "	1.30
	" " " - -	1⅜ 1½ "	1.35
	" " " - -	1⅝ 1¾ "	1.40
	" " " - -	1⅞ 2 "	1.45
	" " " - -	2¼ "	1.50
159,	" " Handle and Cut,	to 2½ "	1.50
160,	" " " two Cuts,	to 2½ "	1.70
161,	Side Rabbet Planes, - - - - -	Per pair	1.25

Raising Planes.

No. 162.

162,	Raising Plane, with Stop and Cut,	2½ 3 3½ 4 inch, per inch,	$1.00
	" Double Iron, "	2½ 3 3½ 4 " "	1.25
	Shoulder Boxed,	Extra,	.50

272

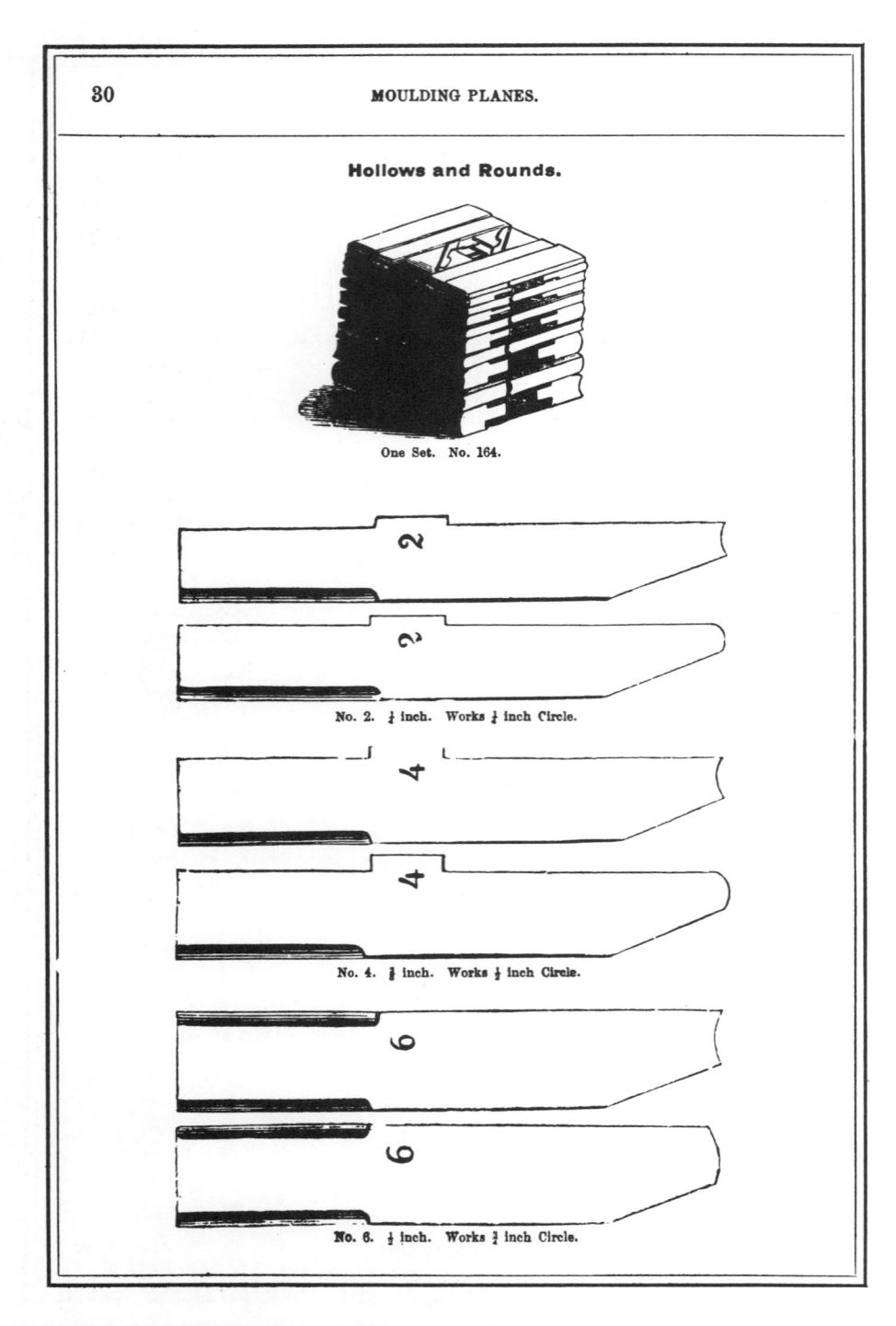

MOULDING PLANES.

Hollows and Rounds. *Continued.*

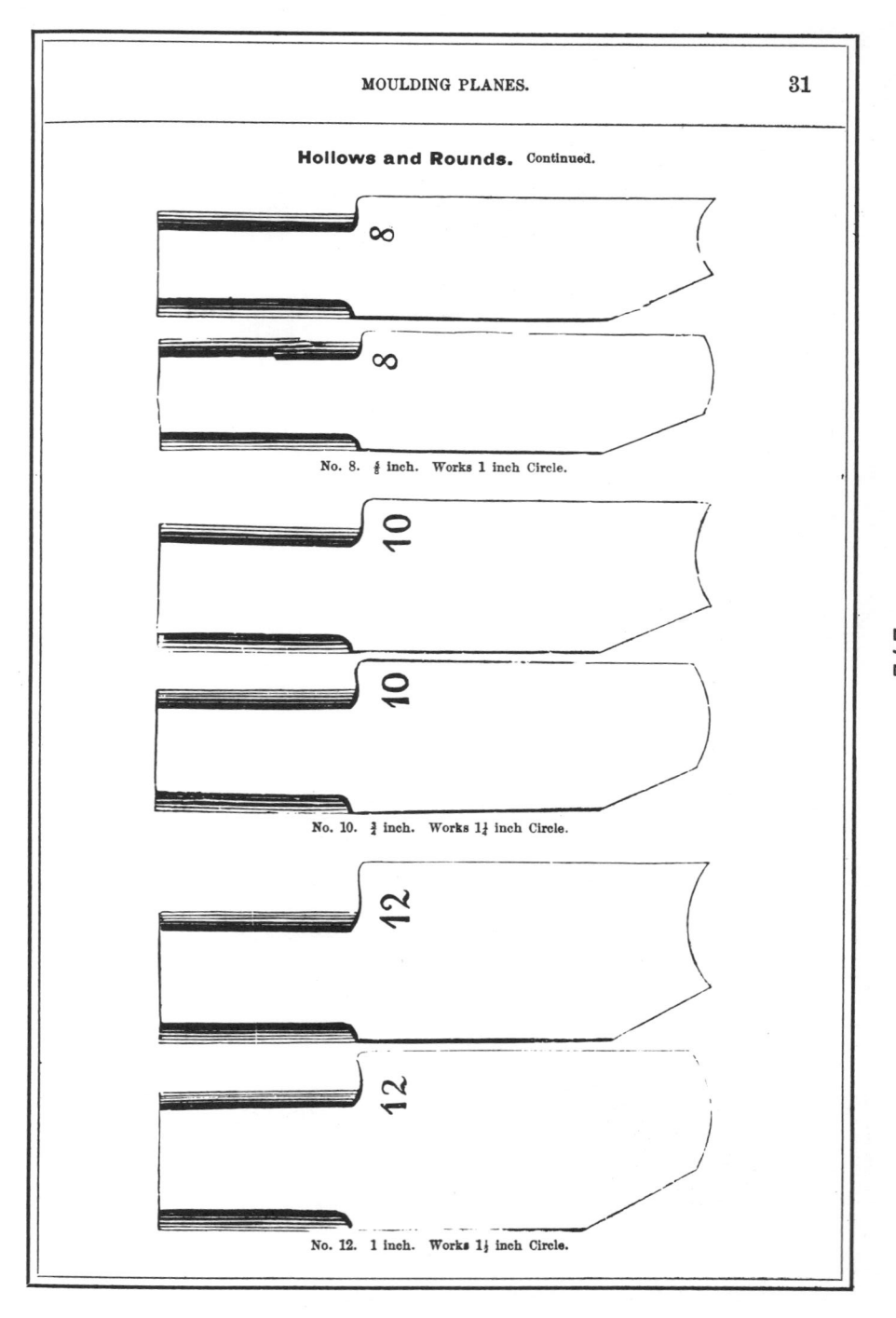

No. 8. ⅜ inch. Works 1 inch Circle.
No. 10. ¾ inch. Works 1¼ inch Circle.
No. 12. 1 inch. Works 1½ inch Circle.

31

MOULDING PLANES.

Hollows and Rounds.

One Set. No. 164.

No. 2. ¼ inch. Works ¼ inch Circle.
No. 4. ⅜ inch. Works ½ inch Circle.
No. 6. ½ inch. Works ¾ inch Circle.

30

MOULDING PLANES.

Hollows and Rounds. Continued.

No. 14. 1¼ inch. Works 1¼ inch Circle.

No. 16. 1¾ inch. Works 2 inch Circle.

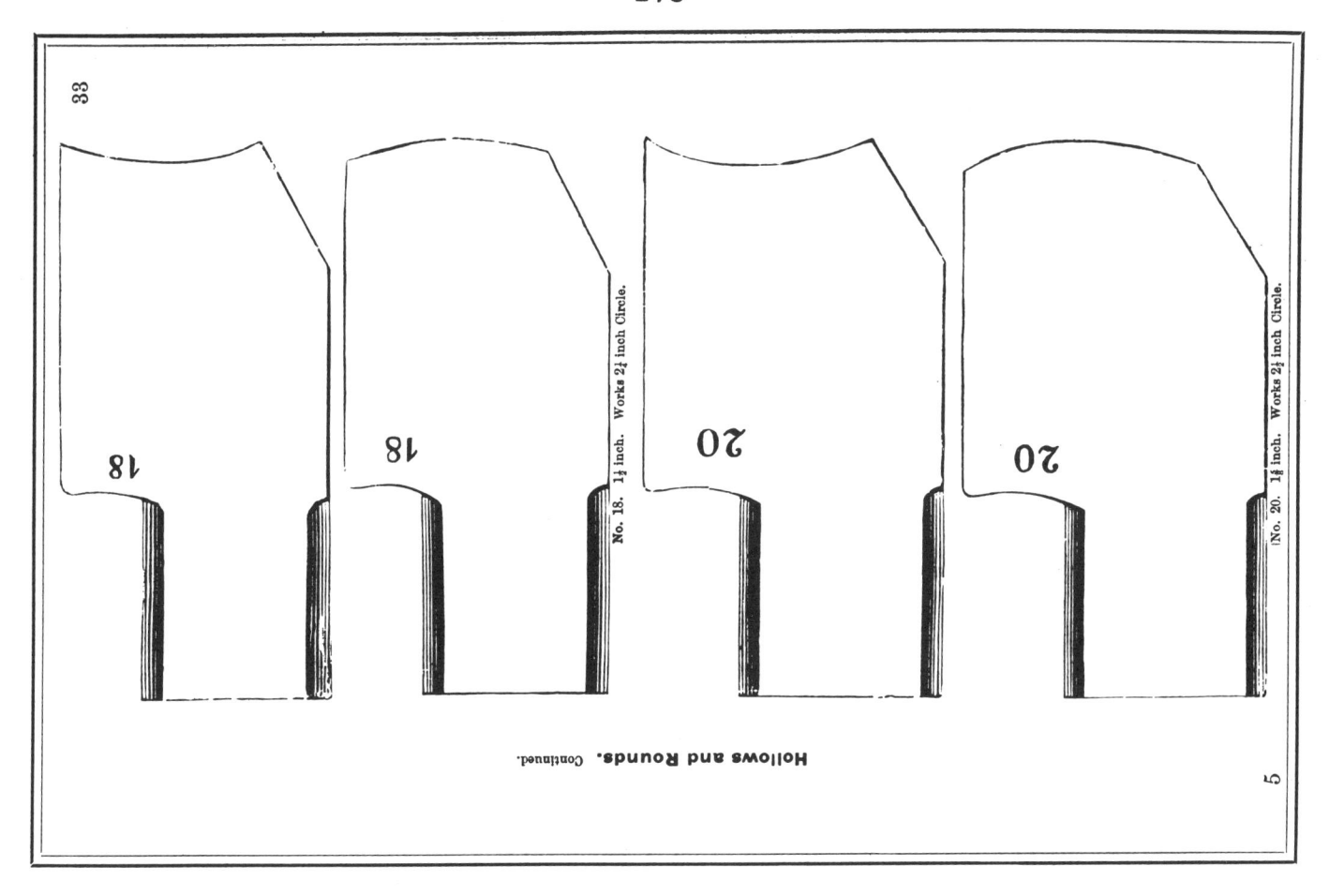

Hollows and Rounds. Continued.

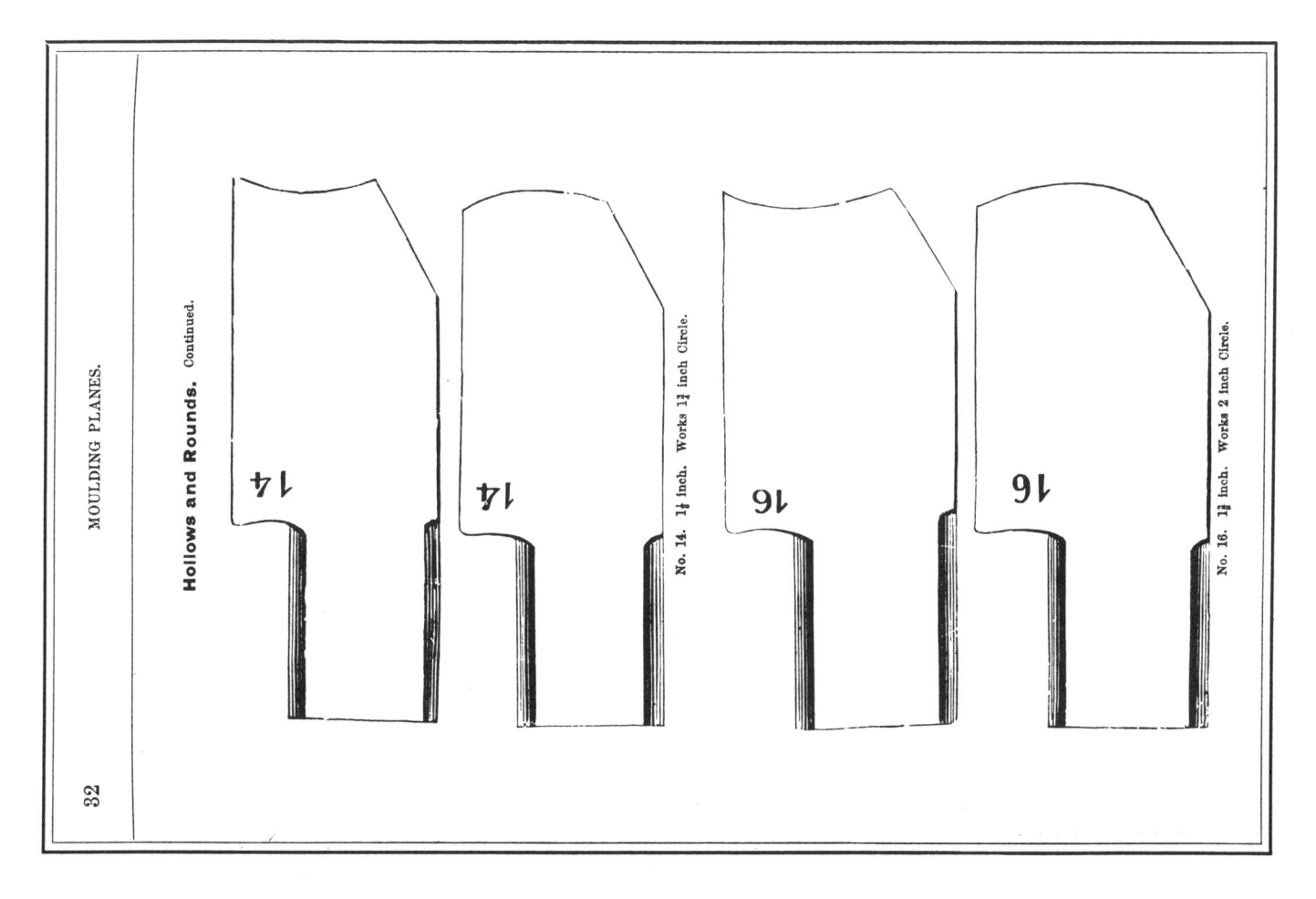

No. 18. 1½ inch. Works 2¼ inch Circle.

No. 20. 1¾ inch. Works 2½ inch Circle.

MOULDING PLANES.

Hollows and Rounds. Continued.

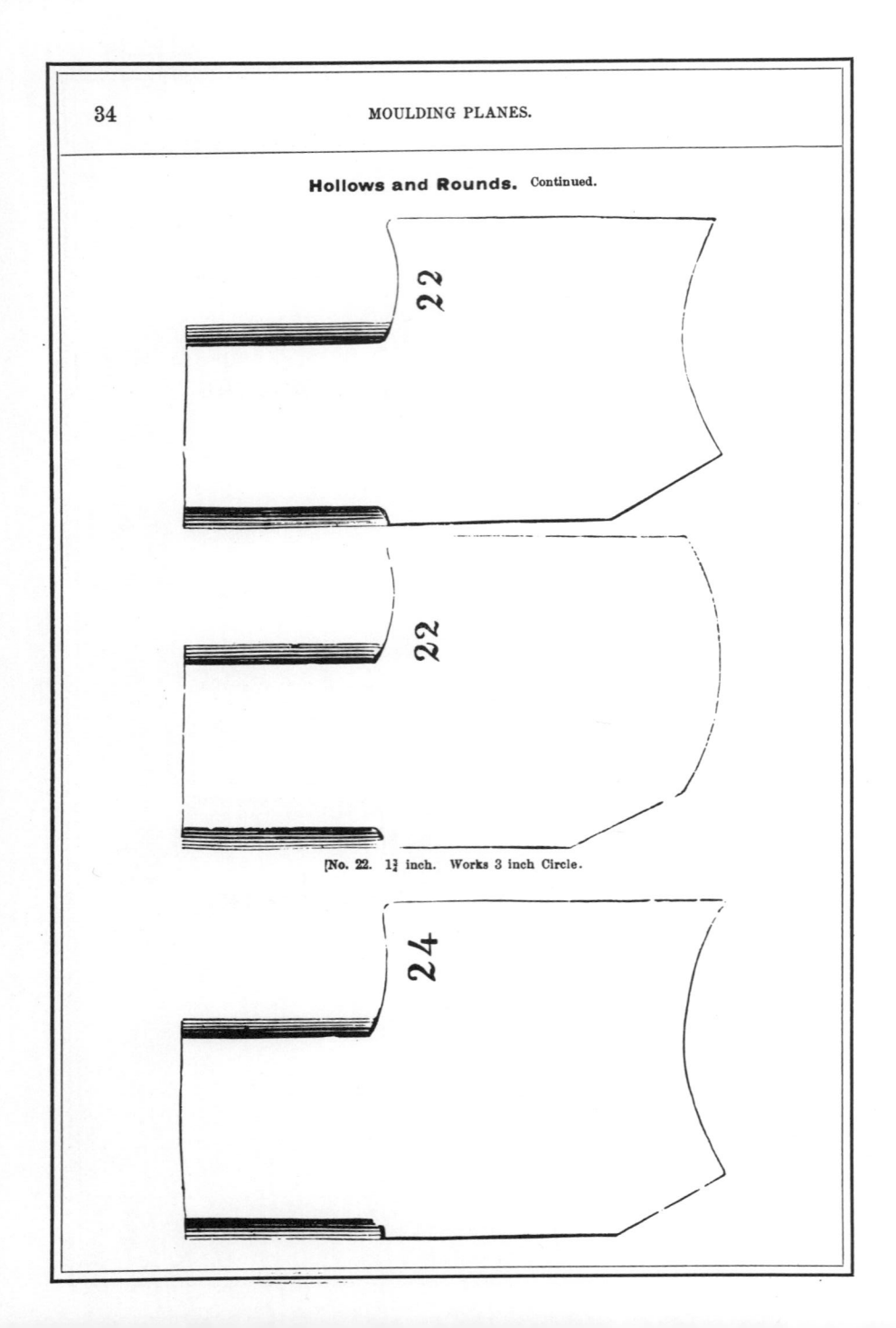

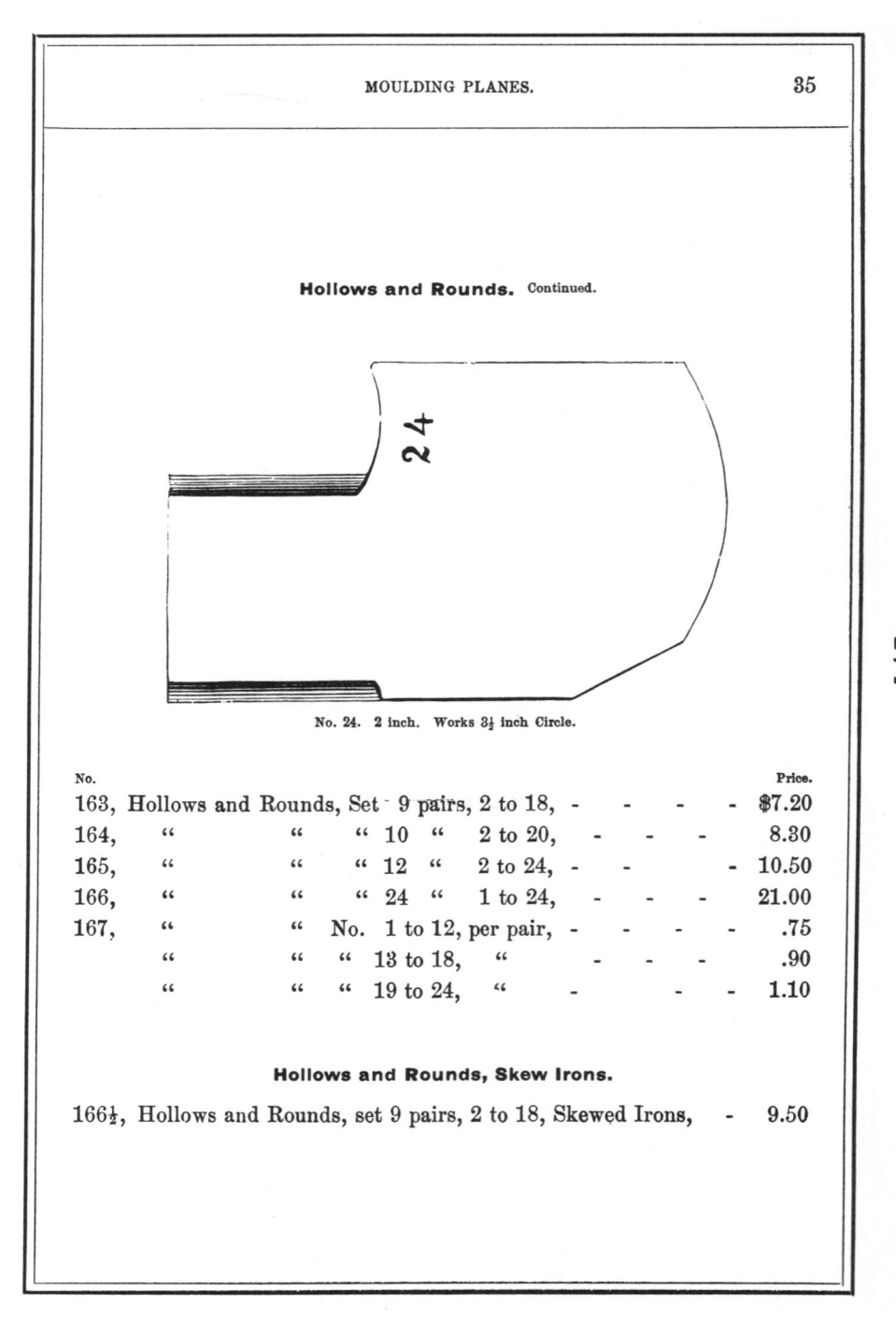

No. 24. 2 inch. Works 3½ inch Circle.

No.		Price.
163, Hollows and Rounds, Set 9 pairs, 2 to 18,	- - -	$7.20
164, " " " " 2 to 20,	- - -	8.30
165, " " " " 2 to 24,	- - -	10.50
166, " " " " 1 to 24,	- - -	21.00
167, " " " No. 1 to 12, per pair,	- - -	.75
" " " " 13 to 18, "	- - -	.90
" " " " 19 to 24, "	- - -	1.10

Hollows and Rounds, Skew Irons.

166½, Hollows and Rounds, set 9 pairs, 2 to 18, Skewed Irons, - 9.50

MOULDING PLANES.

Hollows and Rounds. Continued.

[No. 22. 1¼ inch. Works 3 inch Circle.]

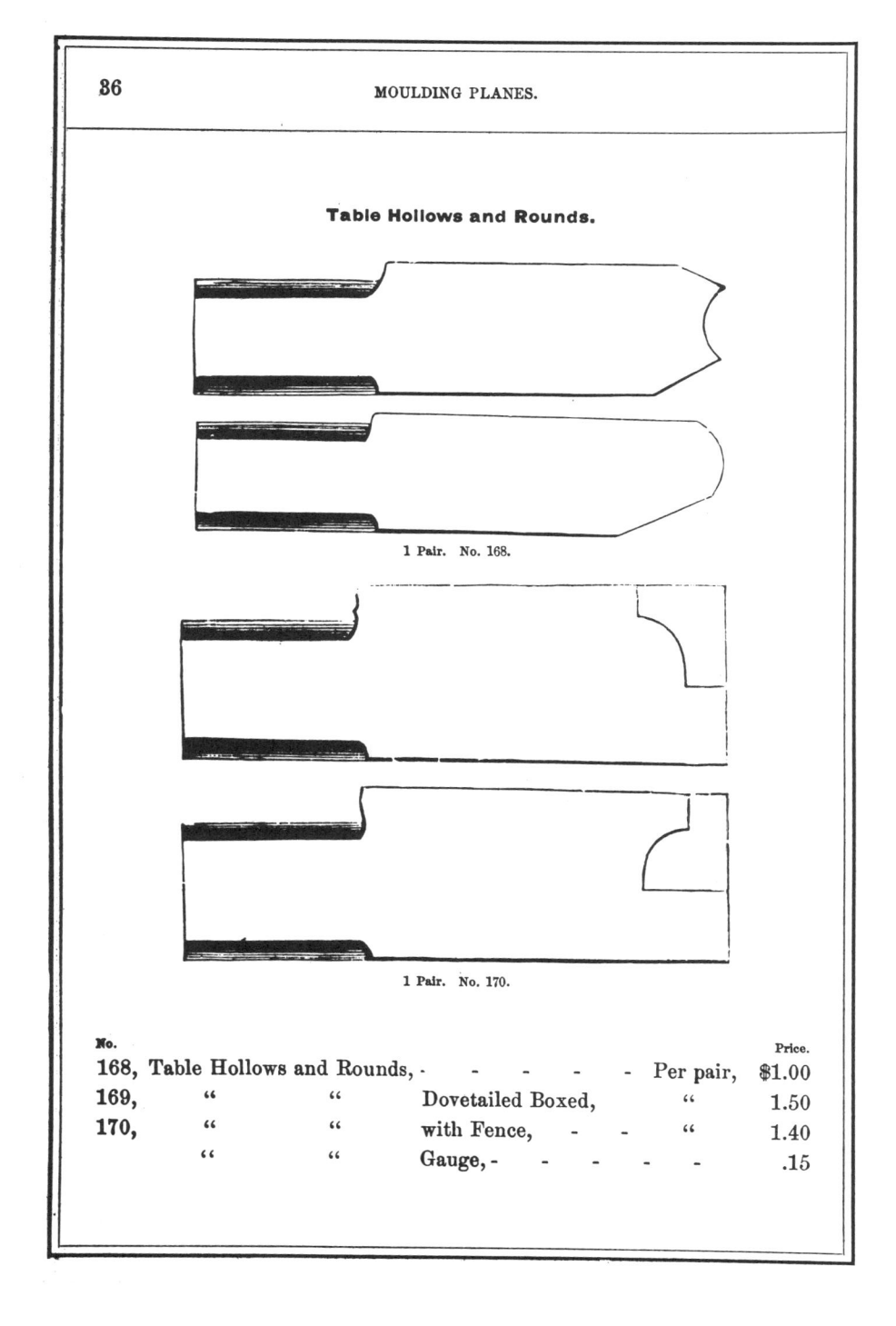

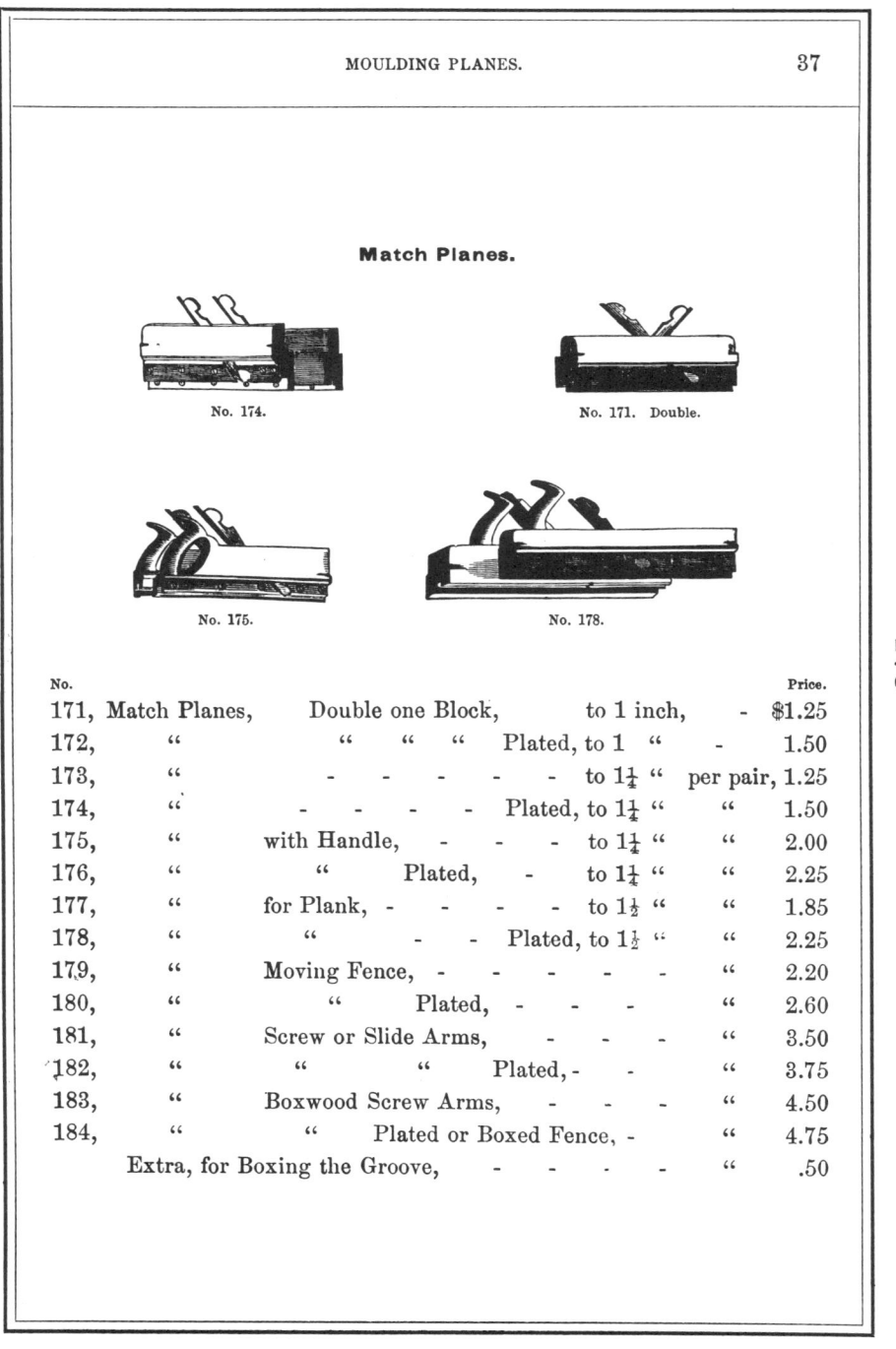

MOULDING PLANES. 37

Match Planes.

No. 174. No. 171. Double.
No. 175. No. 178.

No.			Price.
171,	Match Planes,	Double one Block, to 1 inch, -	$1.25
172,	"	" " " Plated, to 1 "	1.50
173,	"	" " " - to 1¼ " per pair,	1.25
174,	"	" " " Plated, to 1¼ " "	1.50
175,	"	with Handle, - to 1¼ " "	2.00
176,	"	" Plated, - to 1¼ " "	2.25
177,	"	for Plank, - - to 1½ " "	1.85
178,	"	" Plated, to 1½ " "	2.25
179,	"	Moving Fence, - -	2.20
180,	"	" Plated, - -	2.60
181,	"	Screw or Slide Arms, - -	3.50
182,	"	" " Plated, -	3.75
183,	"	Boxwood Screw Arms, - -	4.50
184,	"	" " Plated or Boxed Fence, -	4.75
	Extra, for Boxing the Groove, - -		.50

MOULDING PLANES.

Table Hollows and Rounds.

1 Pair. No. 168.
1 Pair. No. 170.

No.			Price.
168,	Table Hollows and Rounds, - - -	Per pair,	$1.00
169,	" " " Dovetailed Boxed, -	"	1.50
170,	" " " with Fence, - -	"	1.40
	" " " Gauge, - - - -		.15

86

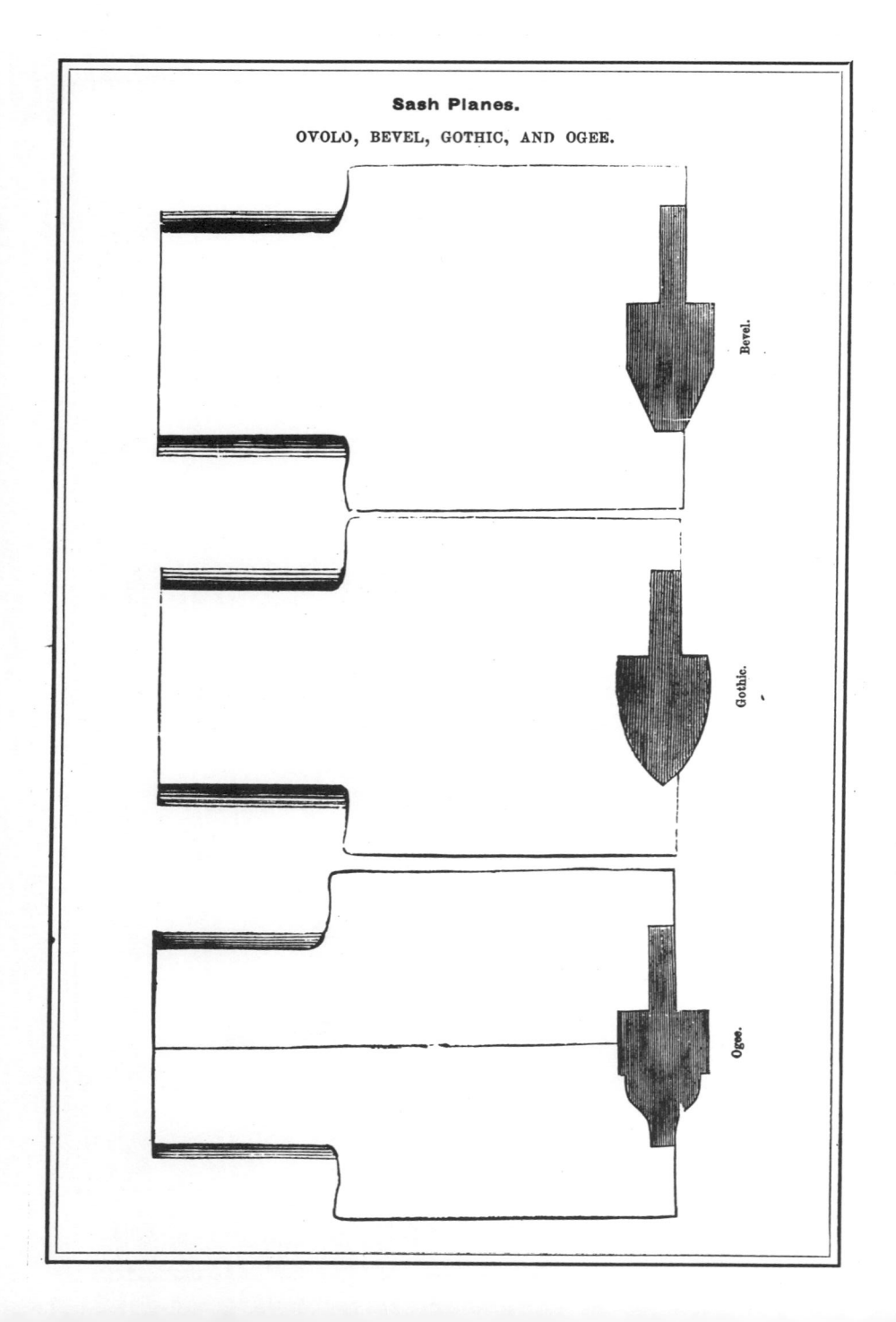

MOULDING PLANES. 39

Sash Planes. (Continued.)
OVOLO, BEVEL, GOTHIC, AND OGEE.

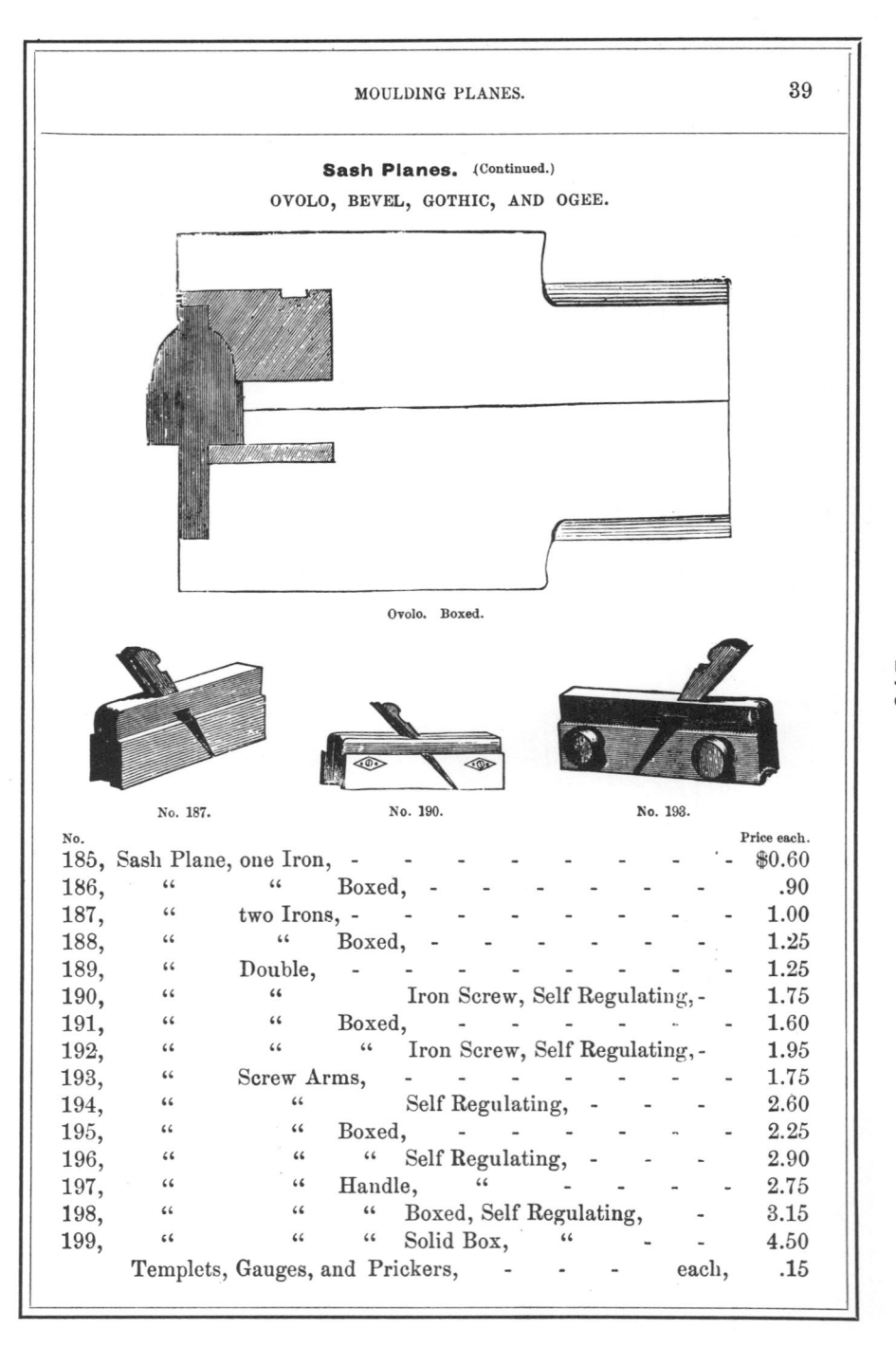

Ovolo. Boxed.

No. 187. No. 190. No. 198.

No.		Price each.
185,	Sash Plane, one Iron, - - - -	$0.60
186,	" " Boxed, - - -	.90
187,	" two Irons, - - -	1.00
188,	" " Boxed, - - -	1.25
189,	" Double, - - -	1.25
190,	" " Iron Screw, Self Regulating, -	1.75
191,	" " Boxed, - - -	1.60
192,	" " Iron Screw, Self Regulating, -	1.95
193,	" Screw Arms, - - -	1.75
194,	" " Self Regulating, - -	2.60
195,	" " Boxed, - - -	2.25
196,	" " " Self Regulating, -	2.90
197,	" " Handle, - - -	2.75
198,	" " " Boxed, Self Regulating, -	3.15
199,	" " " Solid Box, - -	4.50
	Templets, Gauges, and Prickers, - - each,	.15

Sash Planes.
OVOLO, BEVEL, GOTHIC, AND OGEE.

Ogee.   Gothic.   Bevel.

277

MOULDING PLANES. 41

Moulding Planes.

SIZE GIVEN IS THE WIDTH THE TOOL WORKS. DEPTH USUALLY ONE-HALF THE WIDTH.

Plain Ogees.

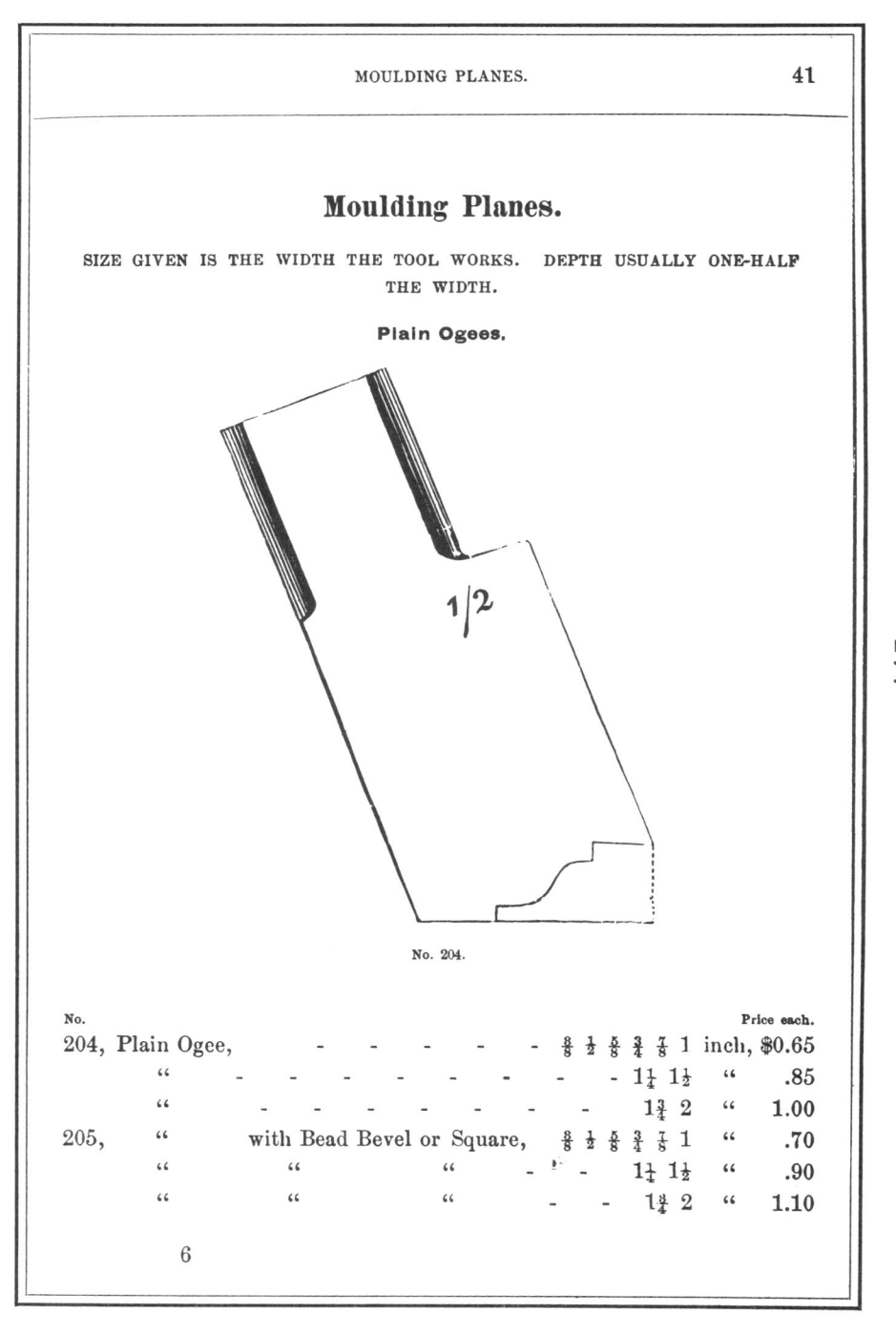

No. 204.

							Price each.
No. 204, Plain Ogee,	-	-	-	$\tfrac{3}{8}$ $\tfrac{1}{2}$ $\tfrac{5}{8}$ $\tfrac{3}{4}$ $\tfrac{7}{8}$ 1 inch,			$0.65
" "	"			1¼ 1½	"		.85
" "	"			1¾ 2	"		1.00
205, "	with Bead Bevel or Square,			$\tfrac{3}{8}$ $\tfrac{1}{2}$ $\tfrac{5}{8}$ $\tfrac{3}{4}$ $\tfrac{7}{8}$ 1	"		.70
" "	"	"		1¼ 1½	"		.90
" 6	"	"		1¾ 2	"		1.10

Sash Coping Planes.

OVOLO, BEVEL, GOTHIC, AND OGEE.

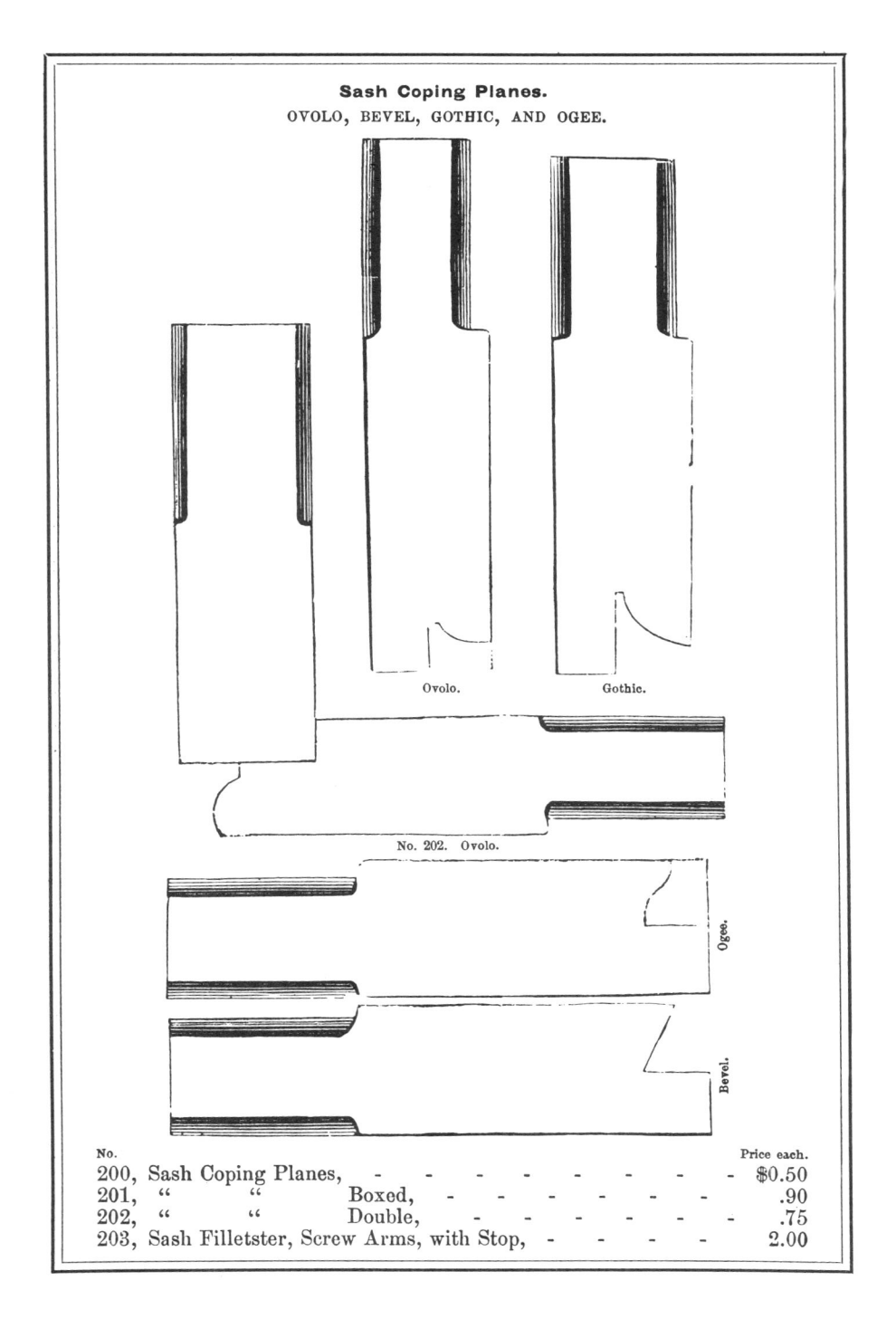

Ovolo. Gothic. No. 202. Ovolo. Ogee. Bevel.

		Price each.
No. 200, Sash Coping Planes,	-	$0.50
201, " " Boxed,	-	.90
202, " " Double,	-	.75
203, Sash Filletster, Screw Arms, with Stop,	-	2.00

278

MOULDING PLANES.

Reverse Ogees.

No. 206.

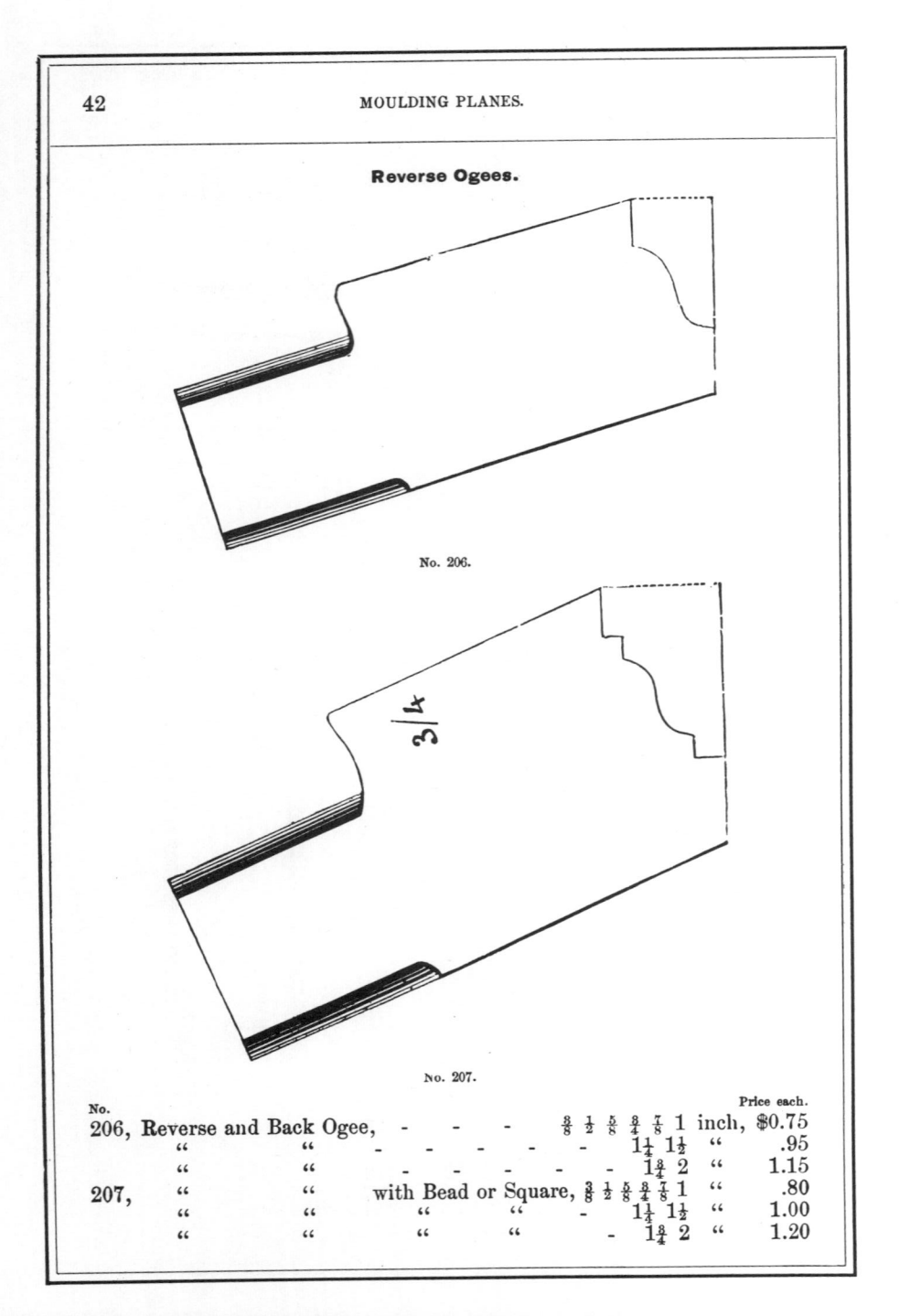

No. 207.

							Price each.
No. 206, Reverse and Back Ogee,	-	-	-	$\tfrac{3}{8}$	$\tfrac{1}{2}$ $\tfrac{5}{8}$ $\tfrac{3}{4}$ $\tfrac{7}{8}$ 1 inch,	$0.75
" " " "	-	-	-		$1\tfrac{1}{4}$ $1\tfrac{1}{2}$	"	.95
" " " "	-	-	-		$1\tfrac{3}{4}$ 2	"	1.15
207, " " " with Bead or Square,	$\tfrac{3}{8}$	$\tfrac{1}{2}$ $\tfrac{5}{8}$ $\tfrac{3}{4}$ $\tfrac{7}{8}$ 1	"	.80
" " " " " "	-	-	$1\tfrac{1}{4}$ $1\tfrac{1}{2}$	"	1.00
" " " " " "	-	-	$1\tfrac{3}{4}$ 2	"	1.20

MOULDING PLANES.

Grecian Ogees.

No. 208.

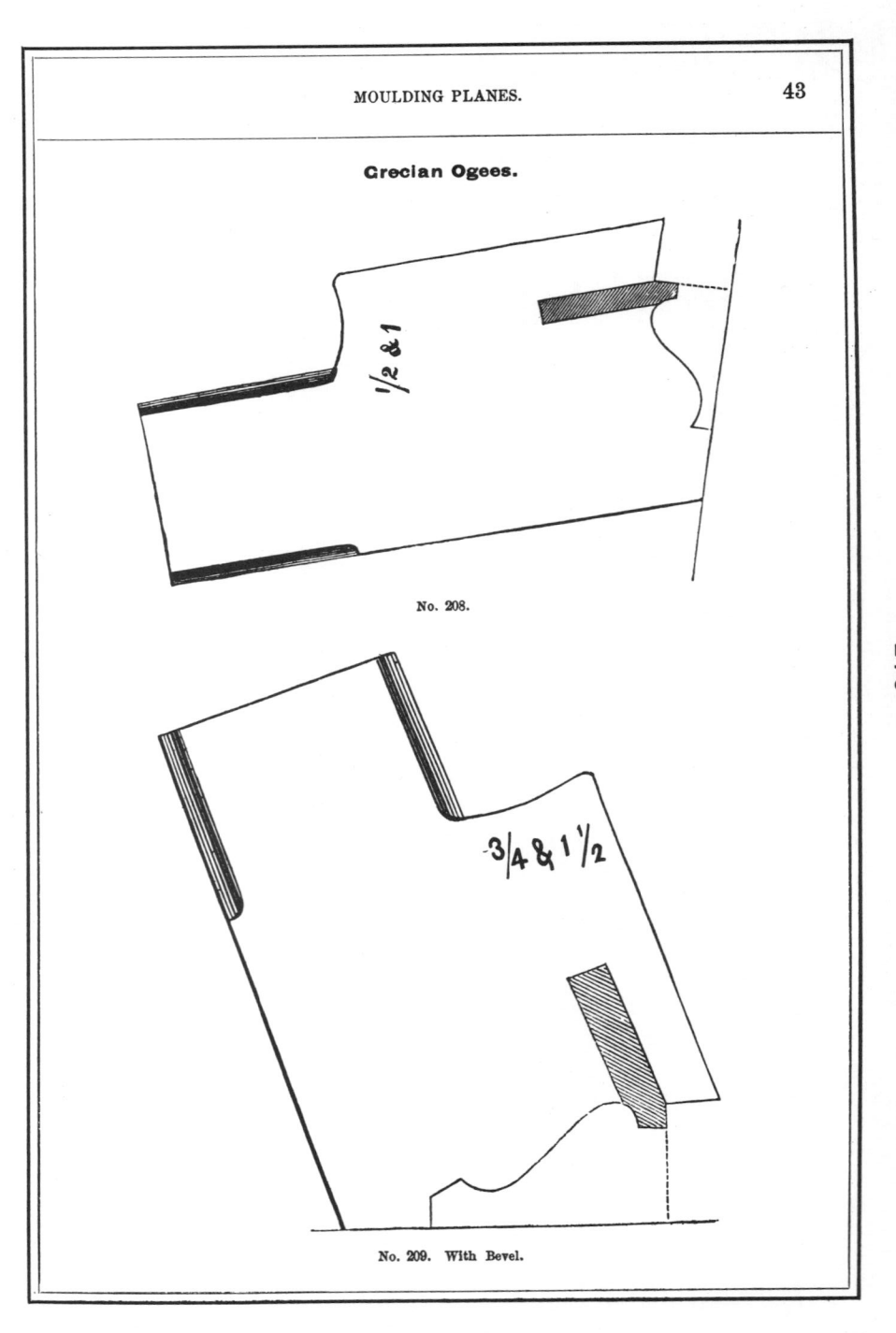

No. 209. With Bevel.

MOULDING PLANES.

Grecian Ogees.

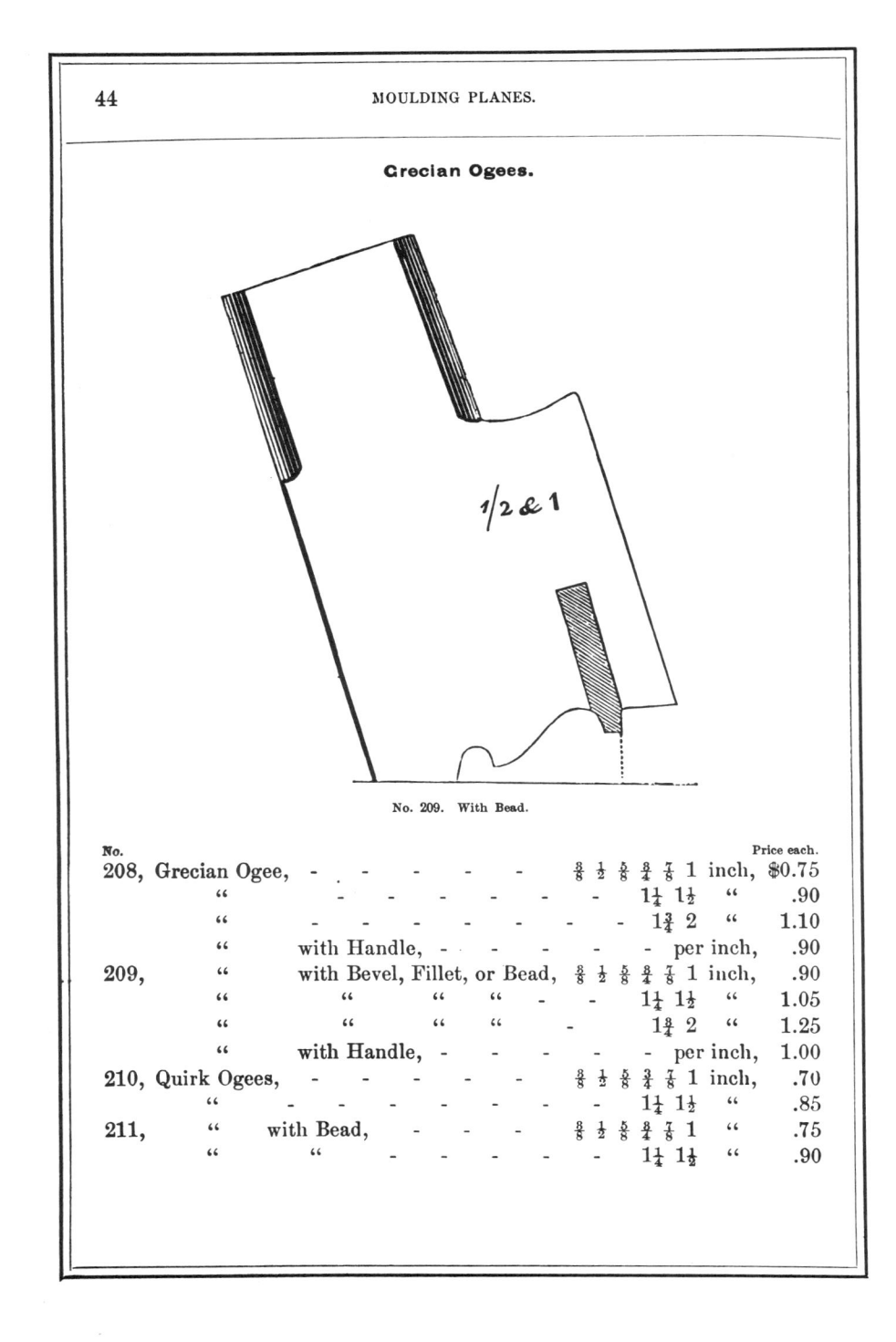

No. 209. With Bead.

		Price each.
No. 208, Grecian Ogee,	$\frac{3}{8}$ $\frac{1}{2}$ $\frac{5}{8}$ $\frac{3}{4}$ $\frac{7}{8}$ 1 inch,	$0.75
" "	1¼ 1½ " "	.90
" "	1¾ 2 " "	1.10
" with Handle,	- - per inch,	.90
209, " with Bevel, Fillet, or Bead,	$\frac{3}{8}$ $\frac{1}{2}$ $\frac{5}{8}$ $\frac{3}{4}$ $\frac{7}{8}$ 1 inch,	.90
" "	1¼ 1½ " "	1.05
" "	1¾ 2 " "	1.25
" with Handle,	- - per inch,	1.00
210, Quirk Ogees,	$\frac{3}{8}$ $\frac{1}{2}$ $\frac{5}{8}$ $\frac{3}{4}$ $\frac{7}{8}$ 1 inch,	.70
" "	1¼ 1½ " "	.85
211, " with Bead,	$\frac{3}{8}$ $\frac{1}{2}$ $\frac{5}{8}$ $\frac{3}{4}$ $\frac{7}{8}$ 1 "	.75
" "	1¼ 1½ " "	.90

MOULDING PLANES.

Grecian Ovolos.

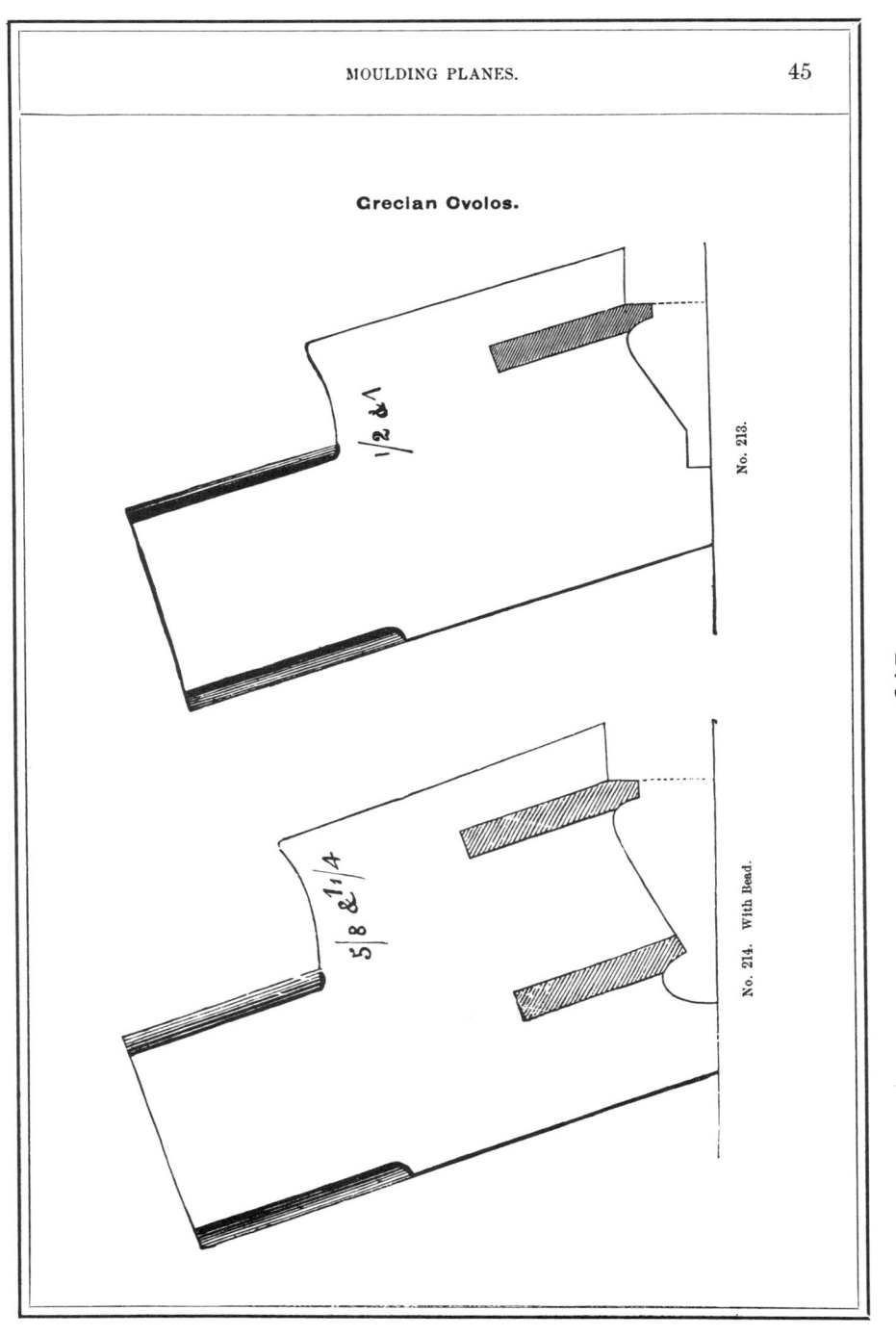

No. 213.

No. 214. With Bead.

Grecian Ovolos.

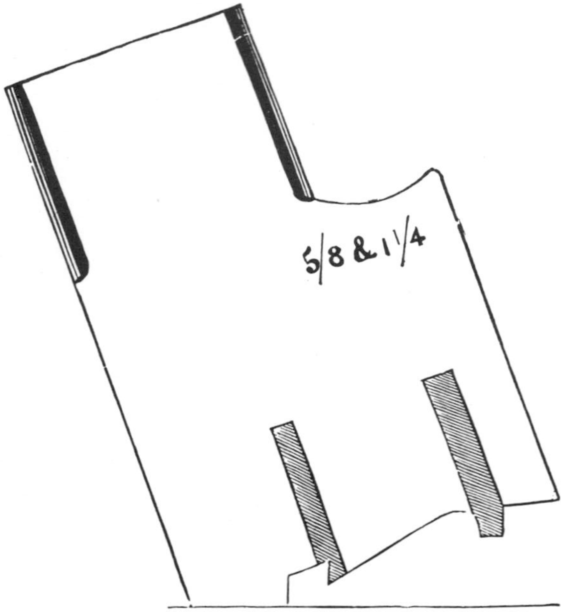

No. 214. With Fillet.

No.		Sizes	Price each.
212,	Grecian Ovolo,	½ ⅝ ¾ ⅞ 1 inch,	$0.70
	"	1¼ 1½ "	.80
	"	1¾ 2 "	.90
	" with Handle,	per inch,	.75
213,	Grecian Ovolo, with Square,	½ ⅝ ¾ ⅞ 1 inch,	.75
	" "	1¼ 1½ "	.90
	" "	1¾ 2 "	1.10
	" with Handle,	per inch,	.90
214,	Grecian Ovolo, with Bead, or Fillet,	½ ⅝ ¾ ⅞ 1 inch,	1.00
	" " "	1¼ 1½ "	1.10
	" " "	1¾ 2 "	1.25
	" " "	with Handle, per inch,	1.25
215,	Quirk Ovolo,	½ ⅝ ¾ ⅞ 1 inch,	.70
	"	1¼ 1½ "	.80
216,	" with Bead,	½ ⅝ ¾ ⅞ 1 "	.85
	" "	1¼ 1½ "	1.00

Ovolos and Scotias.

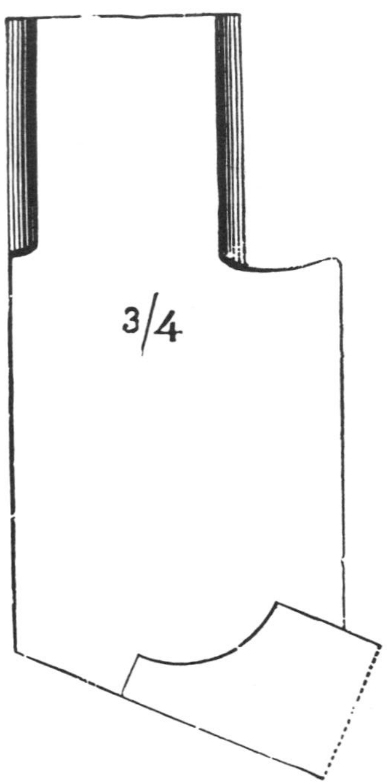

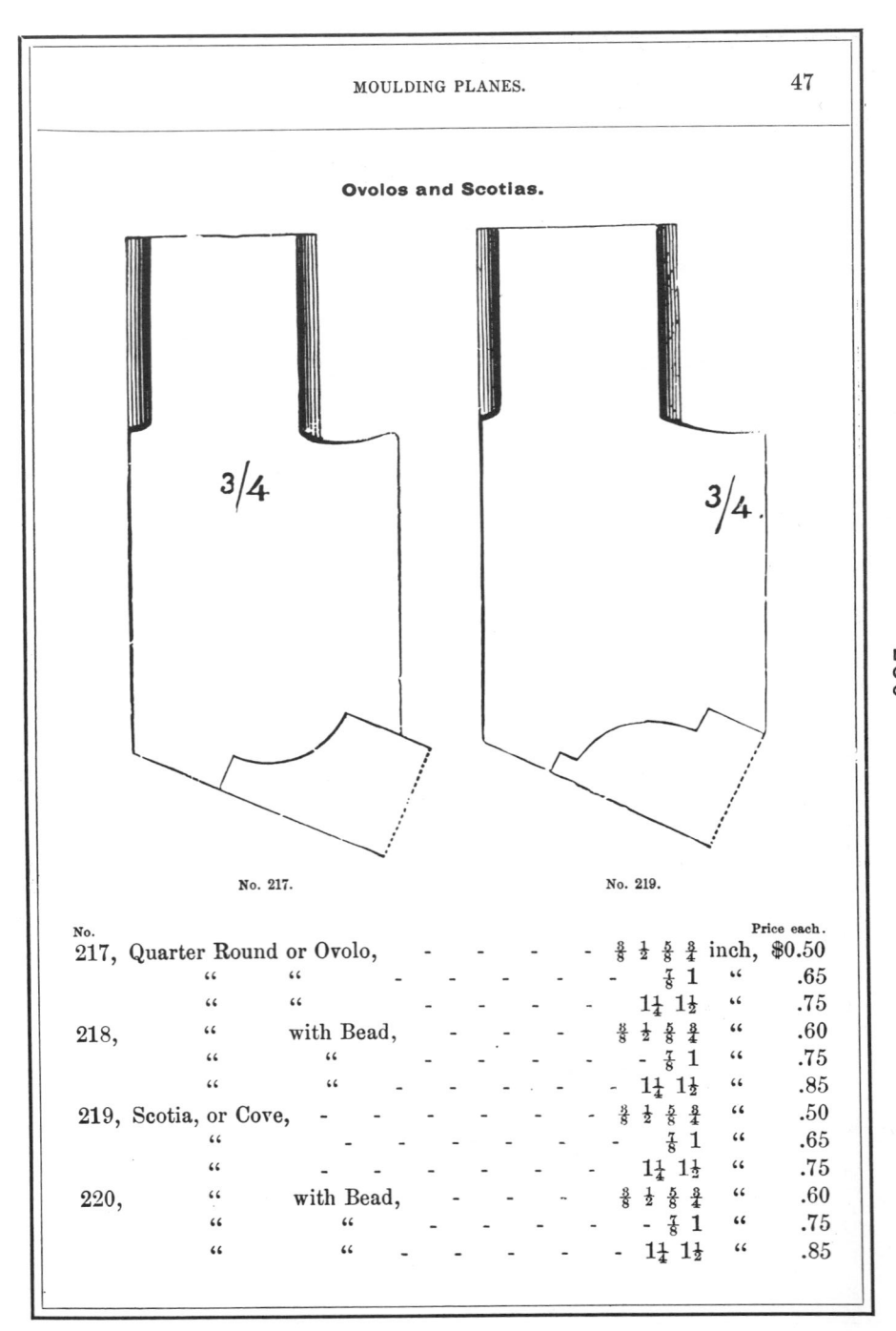

No. 217.

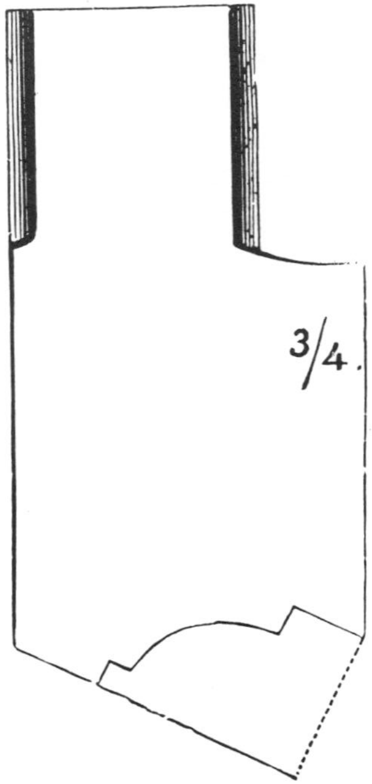

No. 219.

No.		Sizes	Price each.
217,	Quarter Round or Ovolo,	⅜ ½ ⅝ ¾ inch,	$0.50
	" "	⅞ 1 "	.65
	" "	1¼ 1½ "	.75
218,	" with Bead,	⅜ ½ ⅝ ¾ "	.60
	" "	⅞ 1 "	.75
	" "	1¼ 1½ "	.85
219,	Scotia, or Cove,	⅜ ½ ⅝ ¾ "	.50
	"	⅞ 1 "	.65
	"	1¼ 1½ "	.75
220,	" with Bead,	⅜ ½ ⅝ ¾ "	.60
	" "	⅞ 1 "	.75
	" "	1¼ 1½ "	.85

MOULDING PLANES.

Snipe Bills and Base Mouldings.

No. 221. Single Boxed.
No. 221. Full Boxed.

	Price.
No. 221, Snipe Bills, - - - - - per pair,	$1.25
" " Full Boxed, - - - - - "	1.75
222, Base and Band Moulding, - - - per inch,	$0.70
" " with Handle, - - "	1.00
223, Bed Moulding, - - - - - "	1.00

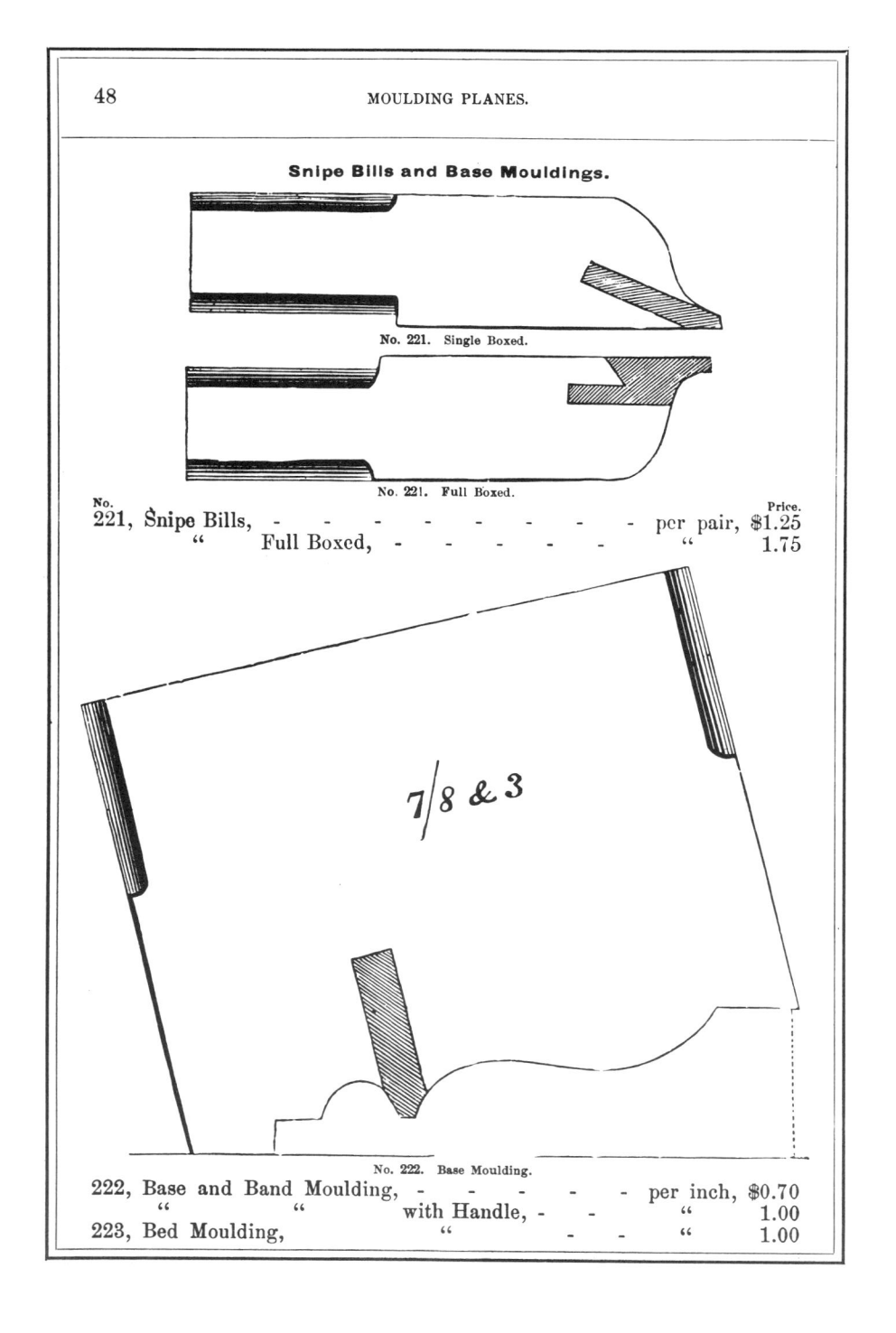

48

MOULDING PLANES.

Cornice Planes.

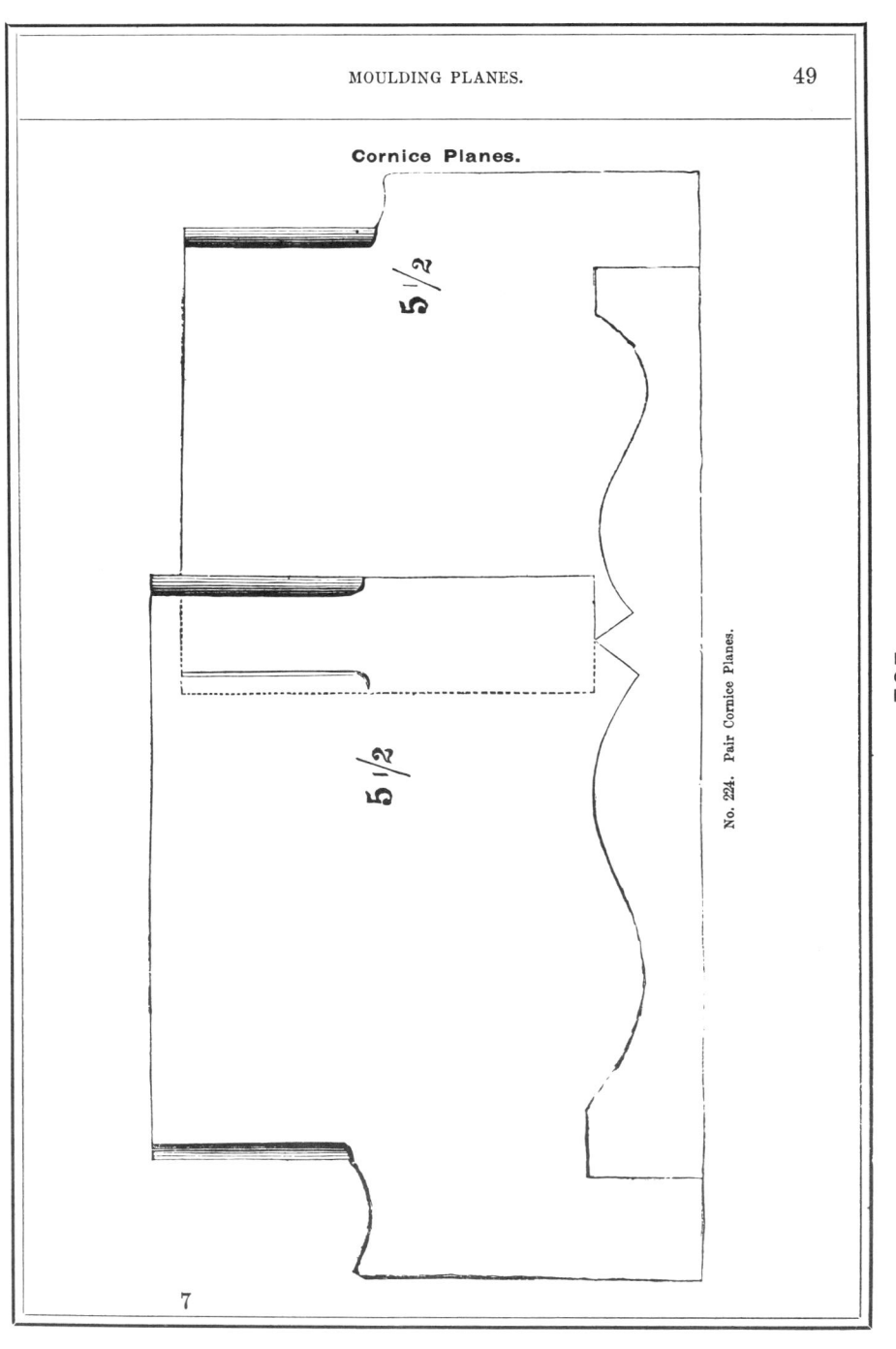

No. 224. Pair Cornice Planes.

49

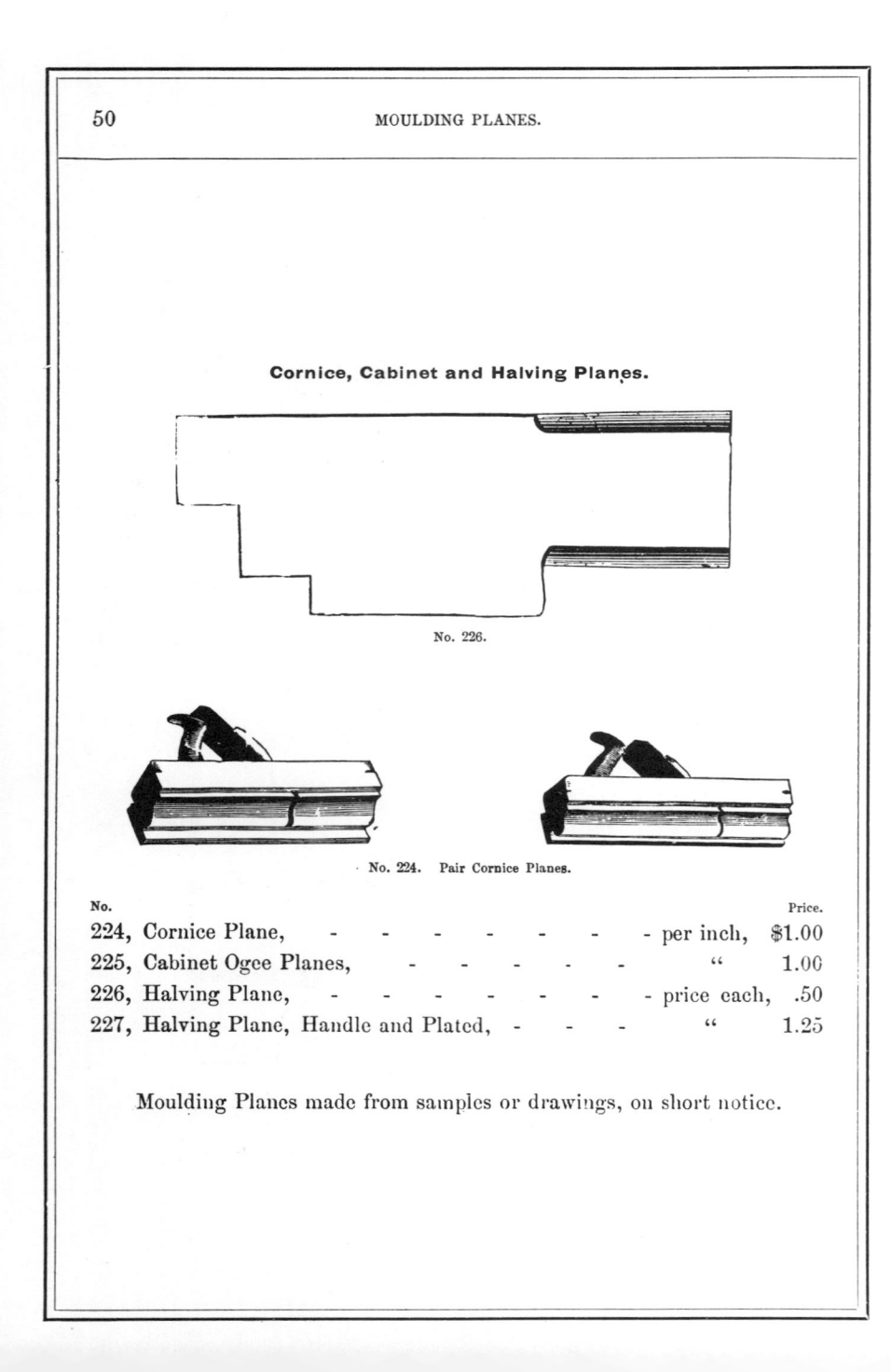

MOULDING PLANES.

Cornice, Cabinet and Halving Planes.

No. 226.

No. 224. Pair Cornice Planes.

No.		Price.
224, Cornice Plane,	- - - - - - per inch,	$1.00
225, Cabinet Ogee Planes,	- - - - - "	1.00
226, Halving Plane,	- - - - - price each,	.50
227, Halving Plane, Handle and Plated,	- - - "	1.25

Moulding Planes made from samples or drawings, on short notice.

GROOVING PLOWS.

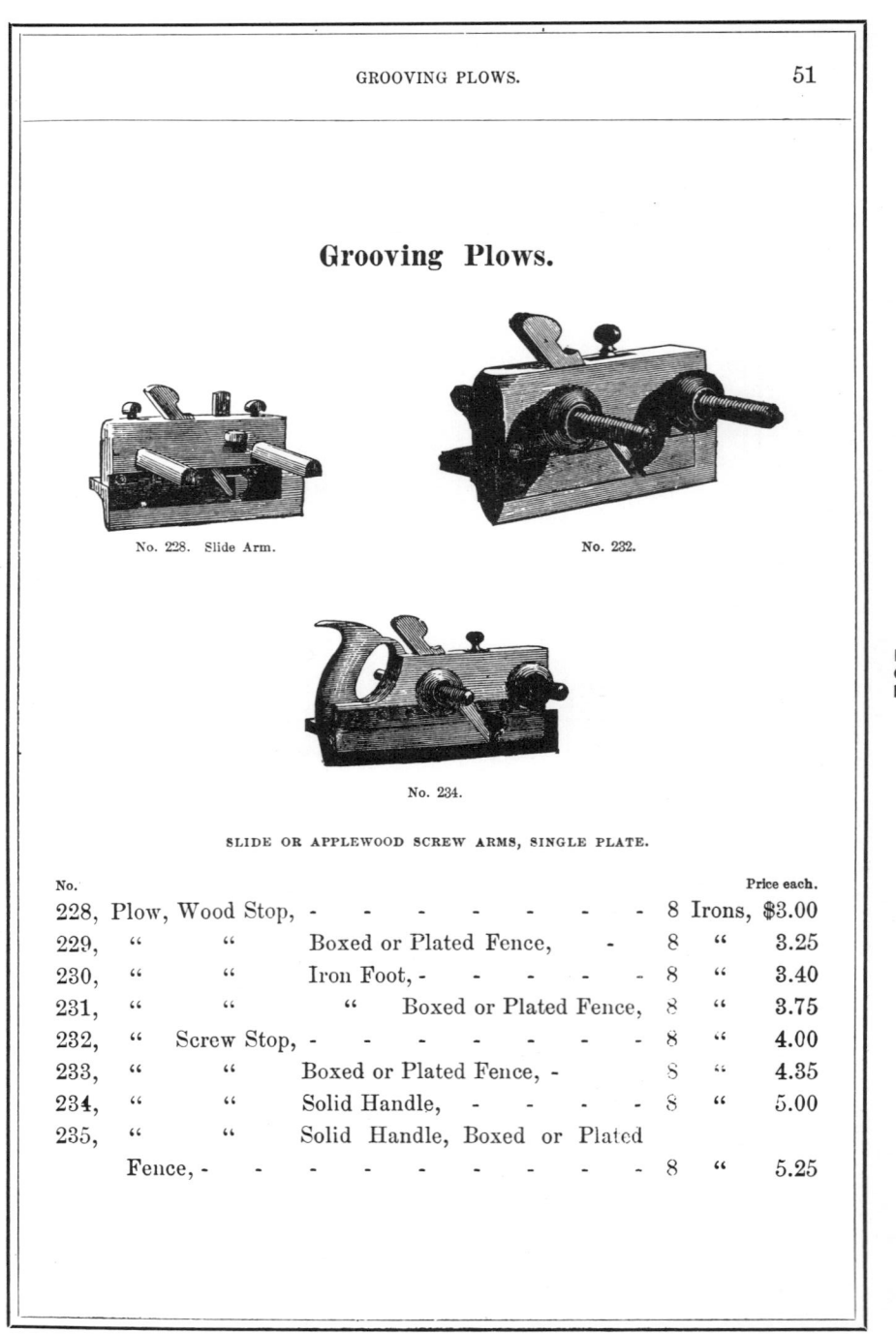

Grooving Plows.

No. 228. Slide Arm.

No. 232.

No. 234.

SLIDE OR APPLEWOOD SCREW ARMS, SINGLE PLATE.

No.			Price each.
228, Plow, Wood Stop,	- - - -	8 Irons,	$3.00
229, " " Boxed or Plated Fence,	-	8 "	3.25
230, " " Iron Foot,	-	8 "	3.40
231, " " Boxed or Plated Fence,		8 "	3.75
232, " Screw Stop,	- - -	8 "	4.00
233, " " Boxed or Plated Fence,	-	8 "	4.35
234, " " Solid Handle,	-	8 "	5.00
235, " " Solid Handle, Boxed or Plated Fence,	- - -	8 "	5.25

GROOVING PLANES.

Grooving Plows. (Continued.)

No. 228.

SOLID HANDLE, BOXWOOD, SCREW ARMS AND SCREW STOP, WITH SIDE STOP.

No.		Price each.
236,	Handled Plow, Beech, Single Plate, - - - 8 Irons,	$5.50
237,	" " Boxed Fence, Single Plate, - " 8 "	6.00
238,	" " " " Best Plate, - " 8 "	6.50
239,	" " " " Best Plate, " 8 "	7.00
239½,	" " " " Polished, - - - - " 8 "	7.50
240,	Handled Plow, Applewood, Boxed Fence, Best Plate, Polished, - - - - " 8 "	9.00
240½,	Handled Plow, Solid Boxwood, Best Plate, Polished, " 8 "	9.00
241,	" Solid Rosewood, Boxed Fence, Best Plate, Polished, - - - - " 8 "	12.00
241½,	Handled Plow, Solid Ebony, Best Plate, Polished, " 8 "	12.35
	" " Boxed Fence, Best Plate, Polished,	

GROOVING PLANES.

Grooving Plows. (Continued.)

No. 244.

BOXWOOD SCREW ARMS AND SCREW STOP, WITH SIDE STOP.

No.		Price each.
242,	Plow, Single Plate, - - - - - 8 Irons,	$4.60
243,	" Boxed Fence, Single Plate, - - " 8 "	4.80
244,	" " " Best Plate, - - " 8 "	5.30
244½,	" " Applewood, " Polished, " 8 "	6.00
245,	" " Solid Boxwood, " " " 8 "	7.00
245½,	" " Solid Rosewood, Boxed Fence, Best Plate, Polished, - " 8 "	7.00
245¼,	" " Solid Ebony, Boxed Fence, " 8 "	8.50
245¾,	" " " " Best Plate, Polished, - " 8 "	8.85
	Plows with Skate Iron pattern Plates, extra, -	1.00
	Plows with Steel Facing on Fence, " - per pair,	.50
	Boxwood Plow Arms, complete, - - -	1.25

GAUGES.   55

Marking Gauges.

1 DOZEN IN A BOX.

No. 247½.

		Per dozen.
No. 246, Common Marking Gauge,	with inches,	$0.75
246½, " " "	" "	.90
247, " " "	Oval Bar,	.85
247½, " " "	" " with inches,	1.00

Premium Gauges.

1 DOZEN IN A BOX.

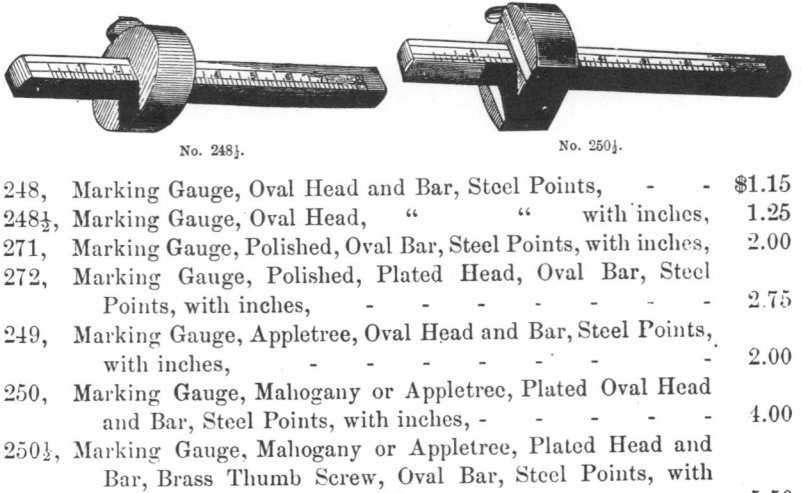

No. 250½.

No. 248½.

No. 248, Marking Gauge, Oval Head and Bar, Steel Points,	$1.15
248½, Marking Gauge, Oval Head, " " with inches,	1.25
271, Marking Gauge, Polished, Oval Bar, Steel Points, with inches,	2.00
272, Marking Gauge, Polished, Plated Head, Oval Bar, Steel Points, with inches,	2.75
249, Marking Gauge, Appletree, Oval Head and Bar, Steel Points, with inches,	2.00
250, Marking Gauge, Mahogany or Appletree, Plated Oval Head and Bar, Steel Points, with inches,	4.00
250½, Marking Gauge, Mahogany or Appletree, Plated Head and Bar, Brass Thumb Screw, Oval Bar, Steel Points, with inches,	5.50
251, Marking Gauge, Box or Rosewood, Oval Head and Bar, Brass Thumb Screw, Steel Points, with inches,	3.50
252, Marking Gauge, Box or Rosewood, Plated Oval Head and Bar, Brass Thumb Screw, Steel Points, with inches,	6.00

GROOVING PLANES.   54

Grooving Plows. (Continued.)

Patent Adjusting Plow.

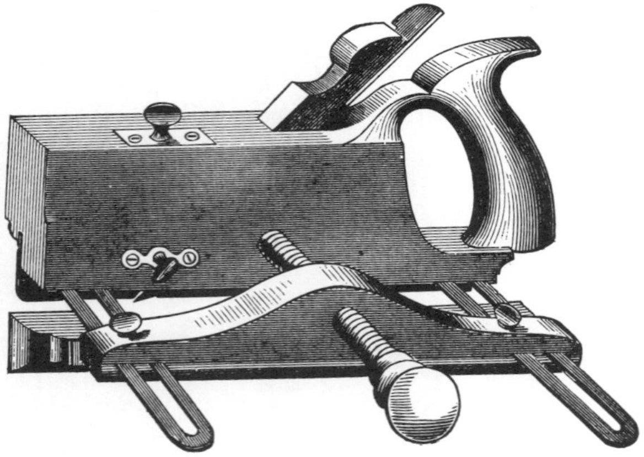

SOLID HANDLE, SCREW STOP, WITH SIDE STOP.

THE adjusting of the Fence to this Plow will be found a great improvement over the old style of Plow. It is simple in its construction, easily and accurately adjusted; as all projections are on the left hand side, the mechanic is not obliged to remove his tools from the work-bench in order to use it.

This attachment is applicable to all Screw Arm Tools.

		Price each.
No. 236¼, Handled, Beech, Single Plate,	8 Irons,	$5.50
238½, " " Boxed Fence, Best Plate,	8 "	6.50
239¾, " Applewood, Boxed Fence, Best Plate, Polished,	8 "	7.50
240¼, " Solid Boxwood, Best Plate, Polished,	8 "	9.00
240⅜, " Solid Rosewood, Boxed Fence, Best Plate, Polished,	8 "	9.00

C. Scholl's Patent Combination Gauge.

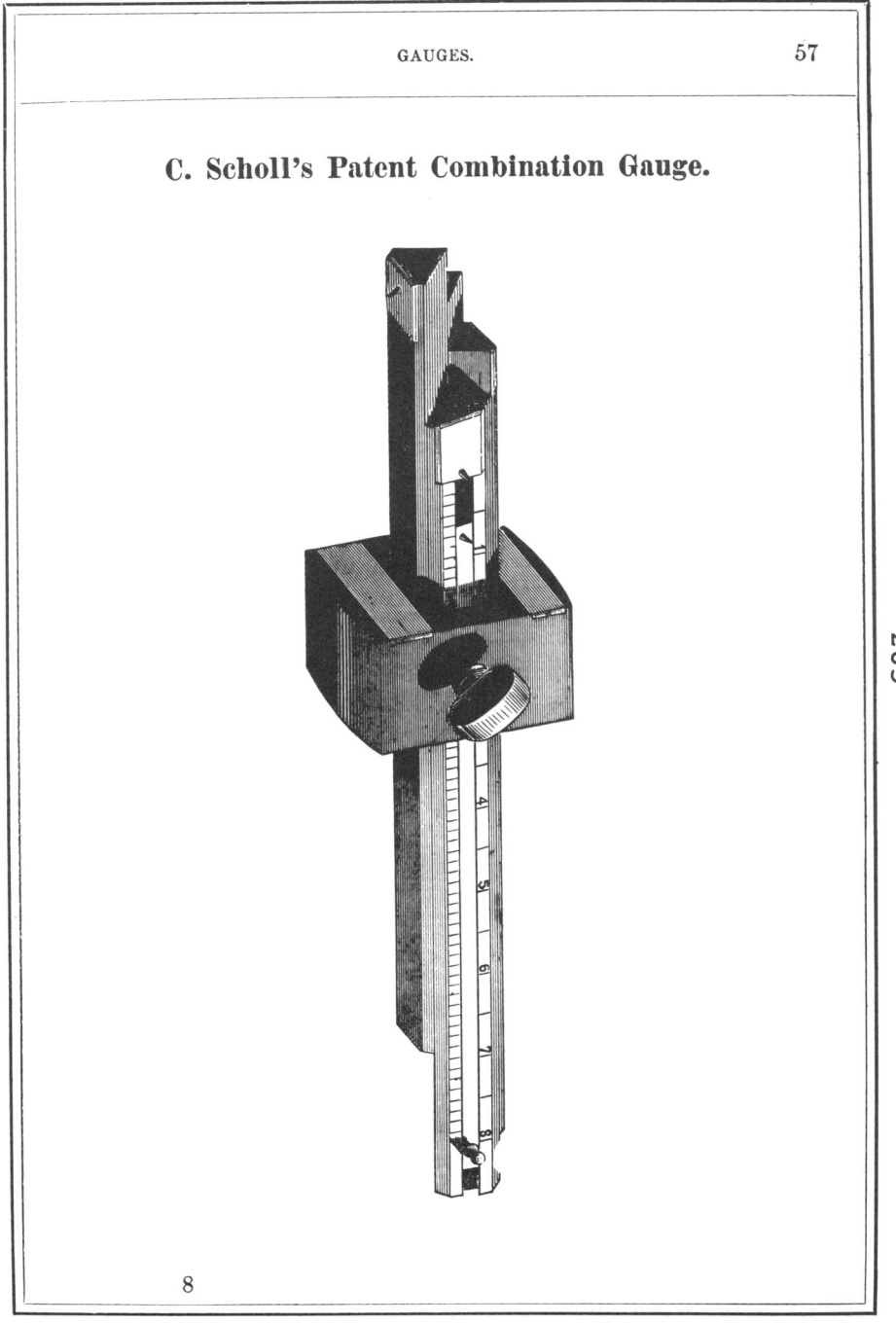

Cutting, Panel, Mortise and Slitting Gauges.

Cutting Gauges.
1 DOZEN IN A BOX.

No.		Per dozen.
253,	Cutting Gauge, Oval Bar, Steel Cutters, with inches,	$2.50
254,	Cutting Gauge, Appletree, Oval Bar, Steel Cutters, with inches,	3.25

Panel Gauges.
½ DOZEN IN A BOX.

255,	Panel Gauge, Oval Bar, Brass Thumb Screw, Steel Points, with inches,	$4.75
256,	Panel Gauge, Appletree, Oval Bar, Brass Thumb Screw, Steel Points, with inches,	6.00
257,	Panel Gauge, Mahogany, Plated Head and Bar, Oval Bar, Brass Thumb Screw, Steel Points, with inches,	12.00
258,	Panel Gauge, Rosewood, Plated Head and Bar, Oval Bar, Brass Thumb Screw, Steel Points, with inches,	18.00

Mortise Gauges.
⅓ DOZEN IN A BOX.

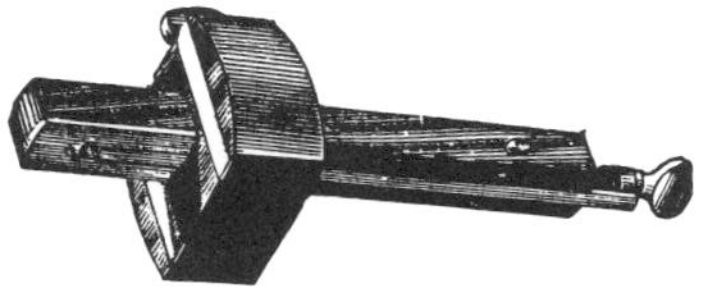

No. 252.

259,	Mortise Gauge, Mahogany or Appletree, Plated Head, Thumb Slide, Brass Thumb Screw, Steel Points,	$6.50
259½,	Mortise Gauge, Mahogany or Appletree, Plated Head and Bar, Thumb Slide, Brass Thumb Screw, Steel Points,	8.00
260,	Mortise Gauge, Mahogany or Appletree, Plated Head, Screw Slide, Brass Thumb Screw, Steel Points,	9.00
261,	Mortise Gauge, Box or Rosewood, Plated Head, Screw Slide, Brass Thumb Screw, Steel Points,	11.00
262,	Mortise Gauge, Box or Rosewood, Plated Head and Bar, Screw Slide, Brass Thumb Screw, Steel Points,	14.00
263,	Mortise Gauge, Box or Rosewood, Full Plated Head and Plated Bar, Screw Slide, Brass Thumb Screw, Steel Points,	18.00
264,	Mortise Gauge, Box or Rosewood, Full Plated Head and Bar, Screw Slide, Brass Thumb Screw, Steel Points,	20.00

Slitting Gauges.

| 265, | Slitting Gauge, with Handle, | $9.00 |
| 266, | Slitting Gauge, with Handle and Rollers, | 10.00 |

C. Scholl's Patent Gauge.

½ DOZEN IN A BOX.

		Per dozen.
No.		
267,	Rosewood, Four Bars—three Bars Marking and one Mortise, Plated Head and Bar, Brass Thumb Screw, Steel Points, with inches,	$24.00
268,	Rosewood, Three Bars—two Bars Marking and one Mortise, Plated Head and Bar, Brass Thumb Screw, Steel Points, with inches,	22.00
269,	Mahogany, Four Bars—three Bars Marking and one Mortise, Plated Head and Bar, Wood Thumb Screw, Steel Points, with inches,	21.00
270,	Mahogany, Three Bars—two Bars Marking and one Mortise, Plated Head and Bar, Wood Thumb Screw, Steel Points, with inches,	19.00

Butler's Patent.

Marking Gauges.

No. 274.

		Per dozen.
No.		
273,	Marking Gauge, Beech, steel points, ½ doz. in a box,	$1.50
274,	Marking Gauge, Beech, steel points, with inches, ½ doz. in a box,	1.75
275,	Marking Gauge, Beech, steel points, with inches, polished, ½ doz. in a box,	2.25
276,	Marking Gauge, Applewood, steel points, with inches, ½ doz. in a box,	3.00
277,	Marking Gauge, Rosewood, steel points, with inches, ½ doz. in a box,	4.00

No. 278.

| 278, | Marking Gauge, Rosewood, Plated Head and bar steel points, with inches, ½ doz. in a box, | 6.00 |

287

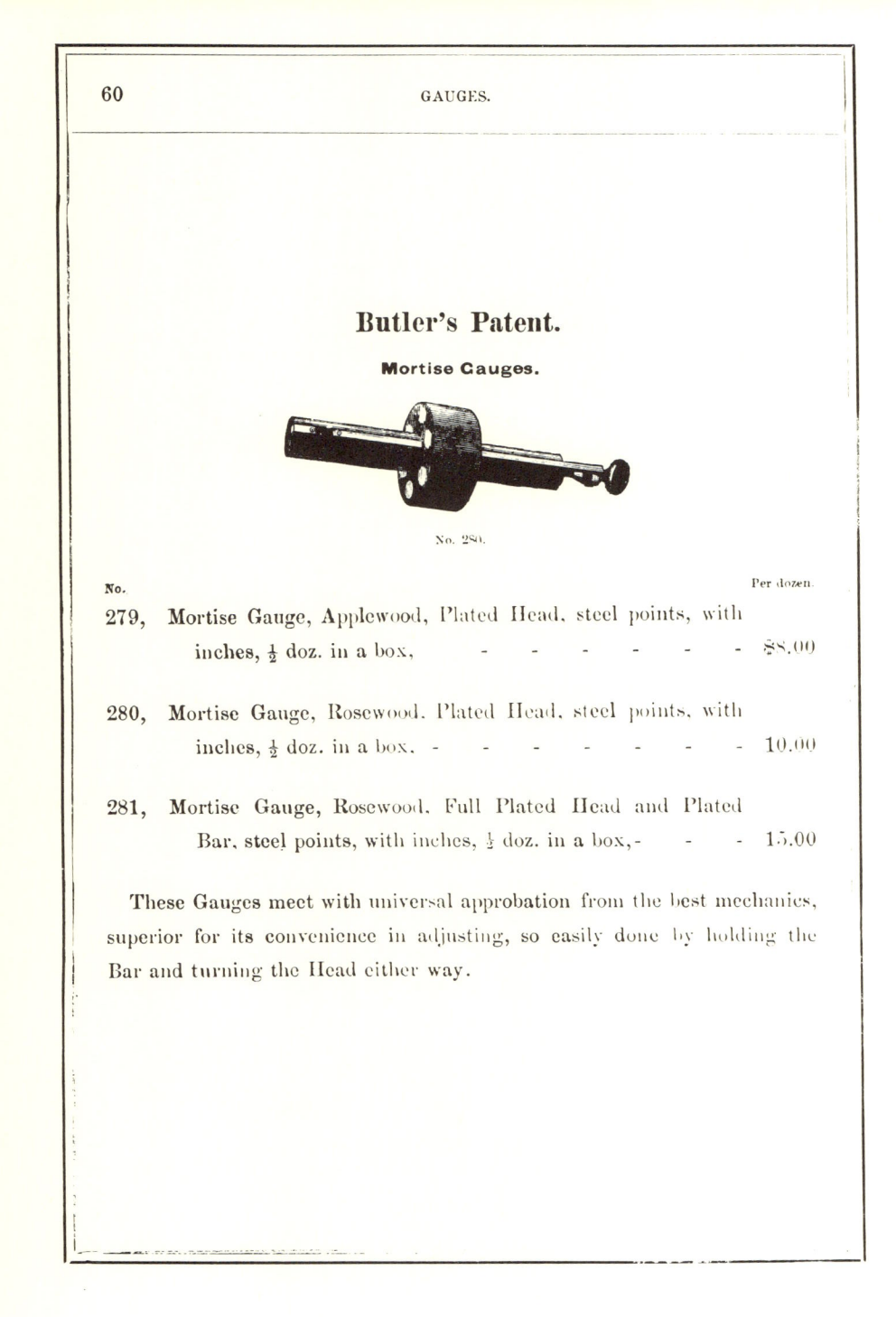

GAUGES.

Butler's Patent.

Mortise Gauges.

No. 286.

No.		Per dozen.
279,	Mortise Gauge, Applewood, Plated Head, steel points, with inches, ½ doz. in a box,	$8.00
280,	Mortise Gauge, Rosewood, Plated Head, steel points, with inches, ½ doz. in a box,	10.00
281,	Mortise Gauge, Rosewood, Full Plated Head and Plated Bar, steel points, with inches, ½ doz. in a box,	15.00

These Gauges meet with universal approbation from the best mechanics, superior for its convenience in adjusting, so easily done by holding the Bar and turning the Head either way.

60

PLUMBS AND LEVELS.

No. 291.

No. 250.

Levels.

No.			Per dozen.
286,	Level, Cherry, Side Views, assorted,	12 to 18 inches,	$10.00
287,	" " "	24 to 28 "	13.50

61

Plumbs and Levels.

No.			Per dozen.
289,	Plumb and Level, Cherry, Polished, Side Views, assorted,	12 to 18 inches,	$14.00
290,	Plumb and Level, Cherry, Polished, Side Views, assorted,	24 to 30 "	18.00
290¼,	Plumb and Level, Cherry, Polished, Brass Lipped, Side Views, assorted,	24 to 30 "	27.00
291,	Plumb and Level, Mahogany, Polished, Side Views, assorted,	24 to 30 "	22.50
292,	Plumb and Level, Mahogany, Polished, Brass Lipped, Side Views, assorted,	24 to 30 "	33.00
293,	Plumb and Level, Cherry, Polished, Brass Lipped, Side Views, & Tipped, assorted,	24 to 30 "	39.00
293½,	Plumb and Level, Cherry, Polished, Side Views, and Tipped, assorted,	24 to 30 "	30.00
294,	Plumb and Level, Cherry, Triple Stock, Polished, Brass Lipped, Side Views, and Tipped, assorted,	24 to 30 "	48.00
296,	Plumb and Level, Mahogany, Polished, Brass Lipped, Side Views, and Tipped, assorted,	12 to 18 "	38.00
297,	Plumb and Level, Mahogany, Polished, Brass Lipped, Side Views, and Tipped, assorted,	24 to 30 "	48.00
298,	Plumb and Level, Mahogany, Triple Stock, Polished, Brass Lipped, Side Views, and Tipped, assorted,	24 to 30 "	65.00
300,	Plumb and Level, Rosewood, Triple Stock, Polished, Brass Lipped, Side Views, and Tipped,	28 "	102.00

Plumbs and Levels, with Graduating Adjustment.

302,	Graduated Adjusting Plumb and Level, Cherry, Polished, Side Views,	18 inches,	$25.00
304,	Graduated Adjusting Plumb and Level, Cherry, Polished, Side Views, assorted,	24 to 30 "	30.00
306,	Graduated Adjusting Plumb and Level, Cherry, Polished, Brass Lipped, Side Views, and Tipped, assorted,	24 to 30 "	57.00
308,	Graduated Adjusting Plumb and Level, Mahogany, Polished, Brass Lipped, Side Views, and Tipped, assorted,	24 to 30 "	66.00

Mason's Plumbs and Levels.

310,	Mason's Plumb and Level, Cherry, Polished, Side Views,	36 inch,	$21.00
310¼,	Mason's Plumb and Level, Two Plumbs, Cherry, Polished, Side Views,	36 "	25.00
310½,	Mason's Plumb and Level, Two Plumbs, Mahogany, Polished, Side Views,	36 "	40.00

Pocket Levels.

No. 311.

No.			Per dozen.
311,	Iron Pocket Level,	-	$2.50
312,	" " "	with Brass Top,	3.00

Level Glasses.

				Per gross.
Level Glasses,	-	-	1¾ inch,	$12.00
"	-	-	2 "	12.00
"	-	-	2½ "	12.75
"	-	-	3 "	13.50
"	-	-	3½ "	15.00
"	-	-	4 "	16.50
"	-	-	4½ "	18.00
"	-	-	5 "	20.00
"	assorted,			14.50

Hand Screws (Hickory).

No.	Diameter of Screw.	Length of Screw.	Length of Jaw.	Size of Jaw.	Per doz.
313,	$\frac{1}{2}$ inch,	10 inch,	6 inch,	1 ×1$\frac{1}{4}$ inch,	$2.25
314,	$\frac{5}{8}$ "	12 "	8 "	1$\frac{3}{8}$×1$\frac{3}{8}$ "	2.75
315,	$\frac{3}{4}$ "	16 "	10 "	1$\frac{5}{8}$×1$\frac{5}{8}$ "	3.25
316,	$\frac{7}{8}$ "	18 "	13 "	1$\frac{7}{8}$×1$\frac{7}{8}$ "	4.50
317,	1 "	20 "	14 "	2$\frac{1}{4}$×2$\frac{1}{4}$ "	6.00
318,	1 "	20 "	16 "	2$\frac{1}{4}$×2$\frac{1}{4}$ "	6.50
319,	1$\frac{1}{4}$ "	24 "	18 "	2$\frac{5}{8}$×2$\frac{5}{8}$ "	8.50
320,	1$\frac{1}{4}$ "	24 "	20 "	2$\frac{5}{8}$×2$\frac{5}{8}$ "	10.50
321,	1$\frac{1}{4}$ "	30 "	22 "	3 × 3 "	14.00
322,	Jewelers Thumb Screws, $\frac{3}{8}$ inch,	-	-	-	2.00
	Toy Hand Screws, $\frac{3}{8}$ inch,	-	-	-	1.50

Hand Screws, packed one dozen in a case, no charge for case. Orders for assorted sizes, less than a full case packed together, cases charged.

Hand Screws, Extra Quality, Jaws Beaded.

No.	Diameter of Screw.	Length of Screw.	Length of Jaw.	Size of Jaw.	Per doz.
323,	$\frac{1}{2}$ inch,	10 inch,	6 inch,	1 ×1$\frac{1}{4}$ inch,	$2.50
324,	$\frac{5}{8}$ "	12 "	8 "	1$\frac{3}{8}$×1$\frac{3}{8}$ "	3.00
325,	$\frac{3}{4}$ "	16 "	10 "	1$\frac{5}{8}$×1$\frac{5}{8}$ "	3.75
326,	$\frac{7}{8}$ "	18 "	13 "	1$\frac{7}{8}$×1$\frac{7}{8}$ "	5.00
327,	1 "	20 "	14 "	2$\frac{1}{4}$×2$\frac{1}{4}$ "	6.75
328,	1 "	20 "	16 "	2$\frac{1}{4}$×2$\frac{1}{4}$ "	7.25
329,	1$\frac{1}{4}$ "	24 "	18 "	2$\frac{5}{8}$×2$\frac{5}{8}$ "	9.50
330,	1$\frac{1}{4}$ "	24 "	20 "	2$\frac{5}{8}$×2$\frac{5}{8}$ "	11.50
331,	1$\frac{1}{4}$ "	30 "	22 "	3 × 3 "	15.25

Bench Screws.

332,	Hickory,	-	-	-	-	-	-	-	2 inch,	$6.00
333,	"	-	-	-	-	-	-	-	2$\frac{1}{8}$ "	9.00
334,	"	33 inch Jaw,	-	-	-	-	-	-	2$\frac{1}{4}$ "	12.00
335,	"	33 "	-	-	-	-	-	-	2 "	10.00
336,	Birch,	-	-	-	-	-	-	-	2$\frac{1}{4}$ "	6.00
337,	Clamp Head or Tail Screws,	-	-	-	-	-	-		5.00
338,	"	Brass Ferrule,	-	-	-	-		6.00

Moulders' Flask Screws and Press Screws made to order.

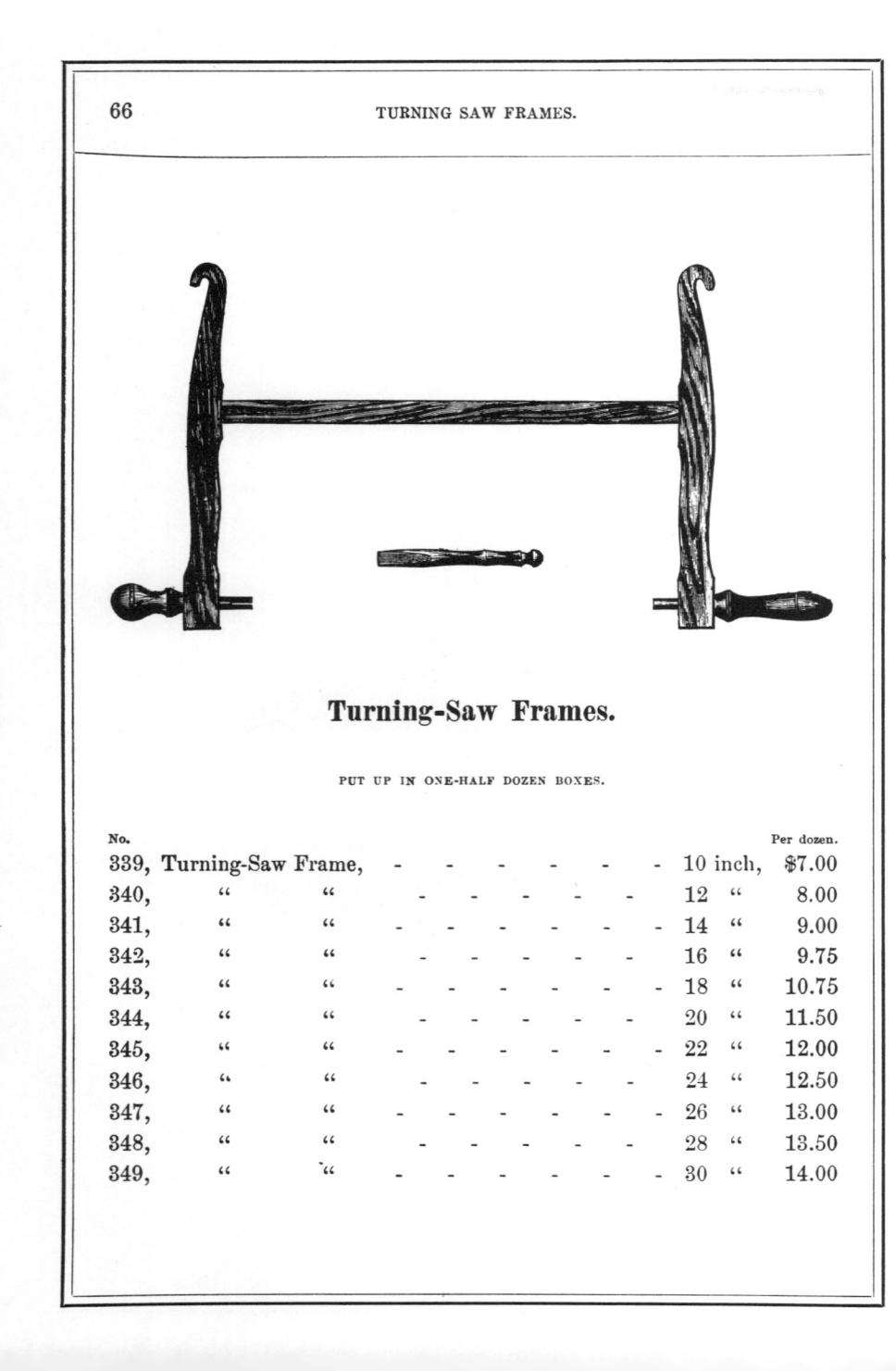

TURNING-SAW FRAMES.

66

Turning-Saw Frames.

PUT UP IN ONE-HALF DOZEN BOXES.

No.			Per dozen.
339,	Turning-Saw Frame,	10 inch,	$7.00
340,	"	12 "	8.00
341,	"	14 "	9.00
342,	"	16 "	9.75
343,	"	18 "	10.75
344,	"	20 "	11.50
345,	"	22 "	12.00
346,	"	24 "	12.50
347,	"	26 "	13.00
348,	"	28 "	13.50
349,	"	30 "	14.00

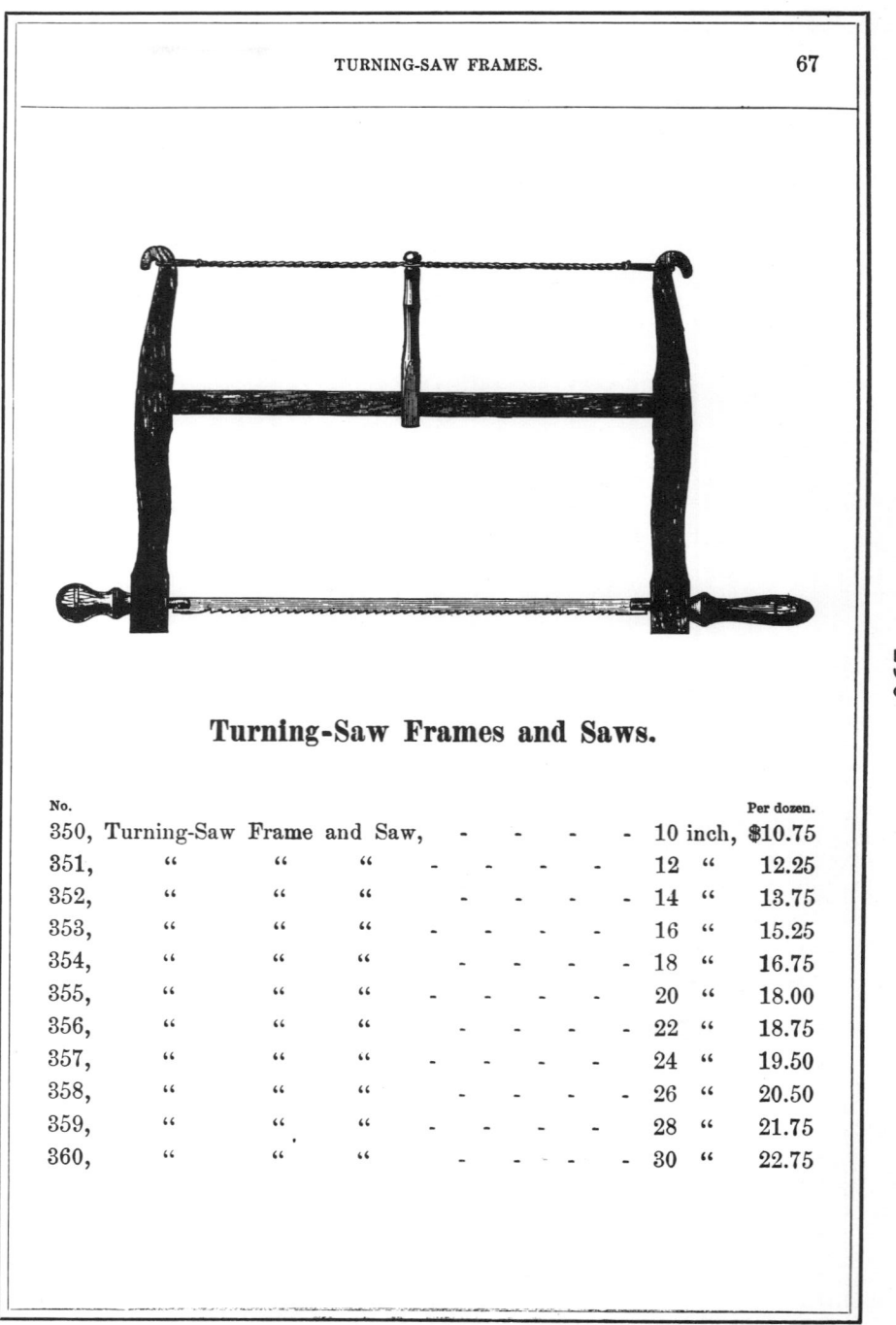

TURNING-SAW FRAMES.

67

Turning-Saw Frames and Saws.

No.			Per dozen.
350,	Turning-Saw Frame and Saw,	10 inch,	$10.75
351,	"	12 "	12.25
352,	"	14 "	13.75
353,	"	16 "	15.25
354,	"	18 "	16.75
355,	"	20 "	18.00
356,	"	22 "	18.75
357,	"	24 "	19.50
358,	"	26 "	20.50
359,	"	28 "	21.75
360,	"	30 "	22.75

Chisel Handles.

IN PAPER BOXES.

POLISHED AND BRASS TUBING FERRULES.

No.			Per gross.
361,	Hickory, assorted,	1 to 3 inch,	$11.50
362,	" "	¼ to 2 "	9.25
363,	" "	⅛ to 1½ "	7.75
364,	Appletree, "	1 to 3 "	12.00
365,	" "	¼ to 2 "	9.75
366,	" "	⅛ to 1½ "	8.25
367,	Rosewood, Extra Finish, assorted,	⅛ to 2 "	20.00

WITH PRESSED BRASS FERRULES.

No.			Per gross.
368,	Hickory, assorted,	1 to 3 inch,	$10.75
369,	" "	¼ to 2 "	8.50
370,	" "	⅛ to 1½ "	6.50
371,	Appletree, "	1 to 3 "	11.25
372,	" "	¼ to 2 "	9.00
373,	" "	⅛ to 1½ "	7.00

Socket Chisel Handles.

POLISHED.

No.		Per gross.
374,	Socket Firmer, Hickory, assorted,	$6.00
375,	" " Appletree, "	6.50
376,	" Framing, Hickory, "	6.00
377,	" " " Iron Ferrule, assorted,	9.00

File and Awl Handles.

BRASS FERRULED.

No.		Per gross.
378,	File Handles, assorted, large,	$6.00
379,	" " " medium,	5.50
380,	" " " small,	4.50
381,	Brad-Awl Handles,	4.50
382,	Scratch-Awl " Appletree,	6.50
383,	" " Rosewood,	9.25
384,	Screw-Driver " Appletree, assorted,	9.75

Plane and Saw Handles.

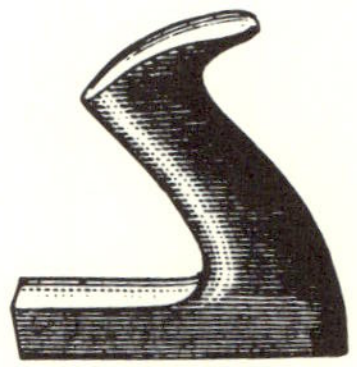

No. 385.
No. 387. 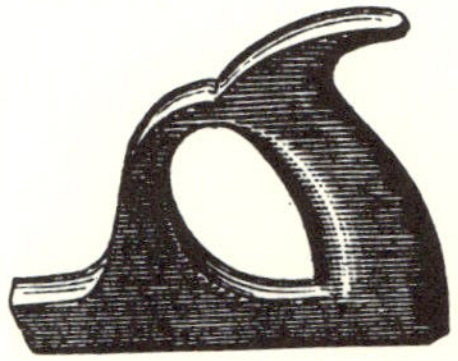
No. 389. 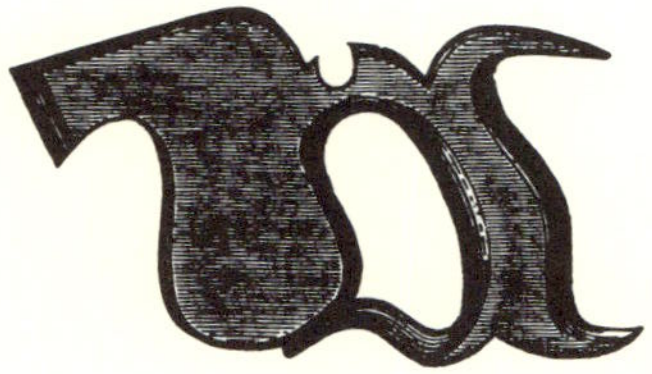

No.		Per dozen.
385,	Jack Plane Handles,	$0.85
386,	" " " with Bolts,	2.00
387,	" Fore " "	1.45
388,	" " " with Bolts,	2.60
389,	Saw Handles,	3.00
390,	" extra, Varnished Edge,	3.50
391,	" with Brass or Iron Screws,	5.00

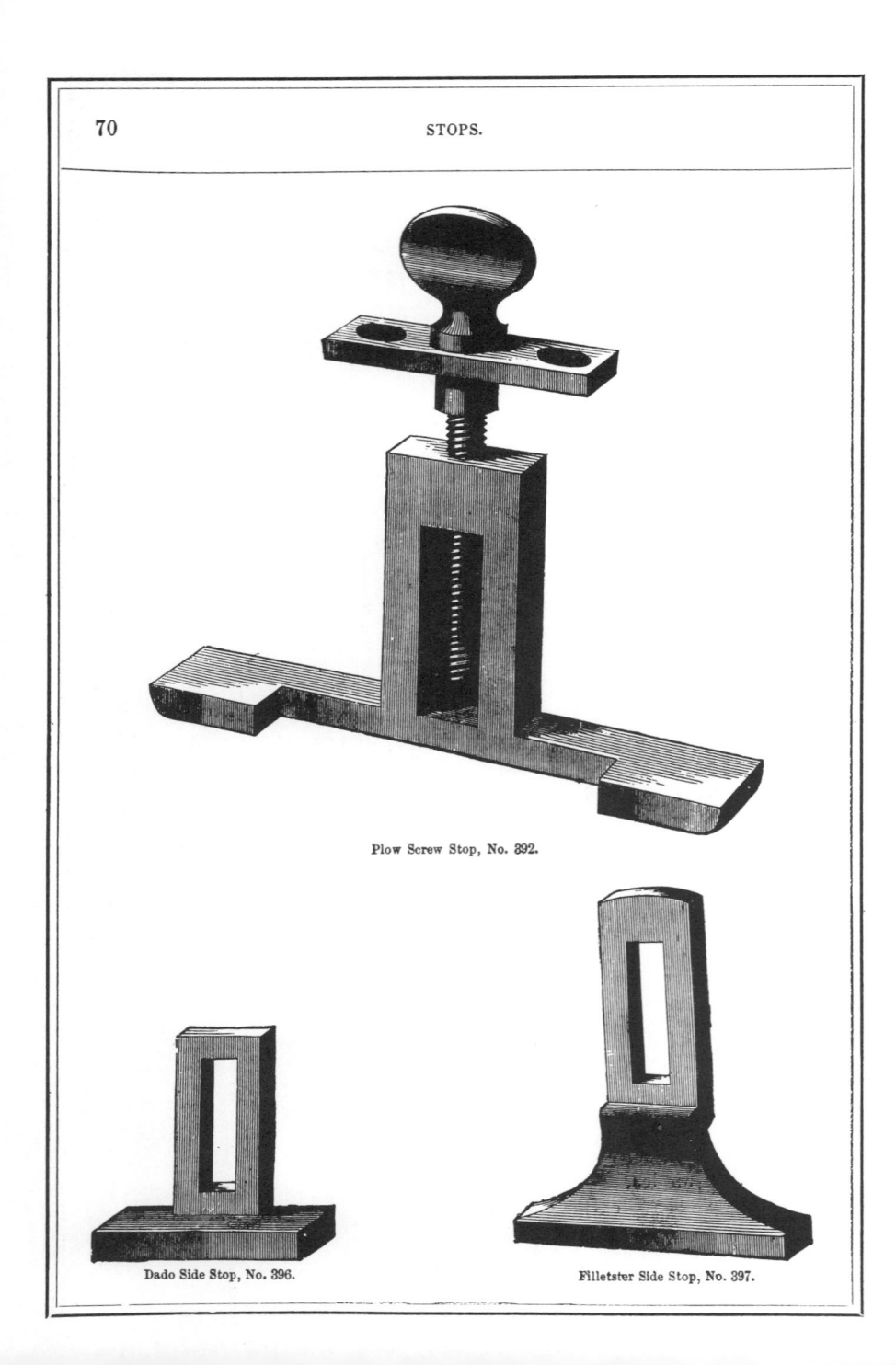

292

71

STOPS.

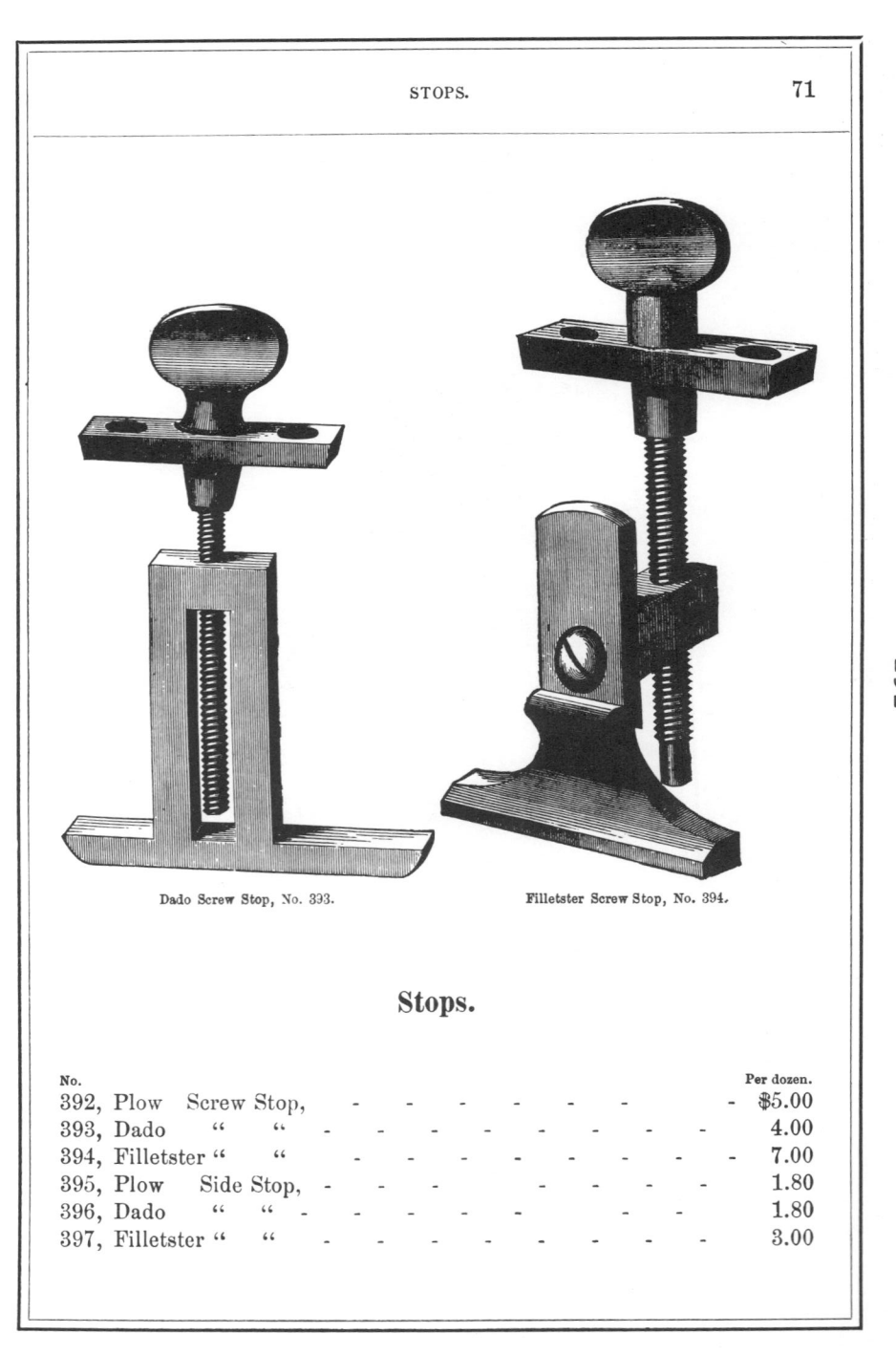

Filletster Screw Stop, No. 394.

Dado Screw Stop, No. 393.

Stops.

			Per dozen.
No. 392,	Plow	Screw Stop,	$5.00
393,	Dado	" "	4.00
394,	Filletster	" "	7.00
395,	Plow	Side Stop,	1.80
396,	Dado	" "	1.80
397,	Filletster	" "	3.00

STOPS.

Plow Screw Stop, No. 392.

Filletster Side Stop, No. 397.

Dado Side Stop, No. 396.

70

Screw Drivers, Mincing Knives, and Awls.

	Per dozen.
Screw Drivers, Best Flat, 1½ to 2 inch,	$1.00
" " " 3 "	1.50
" " " 4 "	2.00
" " " 5 "	2.50
" " " 6 "	3.00
" " " 7 "	3.50
" " " 8 "	4.00
" " " 10 "	5.00
" " " 12 "	6.00
Mincing Knives,	4.00
Scratch Awls,	1.00
" " Rosewood Handle,	1.50
" " " " Extra fine, 3 inch Point,	1.25
Belt	1.25
Brad	.60

Door Stops.

	Per gross.
2½ inch Birch, Plain,	$4.50
3 " " "	5.00
2½ " Black Walnut, "	5.25
3 " " " "	6.00
2½ " Birch, Rubber Tipped,	9.00
3 " " "	10.00
2½ " Black Walnut, "	10.00
3 " " "	11.00

Packed in ¼ Gross Paper Boxes.

Toy Tool-Chest Supplies.

	Price per dozen.
Gauge Round Bar,	$0.30
" Square "	.35
Wood Try Square,	.45
Plane, Sheet Steel Iron,	2.00
Rule, 8 inch,	.30
Brad and Scratch-Awl Handles,	.25
Chisel and File Handles,	.35
Hand Screws, ⅜ inch,	1.20
Smooth Plane, Single Iron,	4.00
Jack " " "	5.00
Mallets, 2 ×4½ inch Head,	.65
" 2½×5¼ "	.70
" 3 ×6 "	.75

10

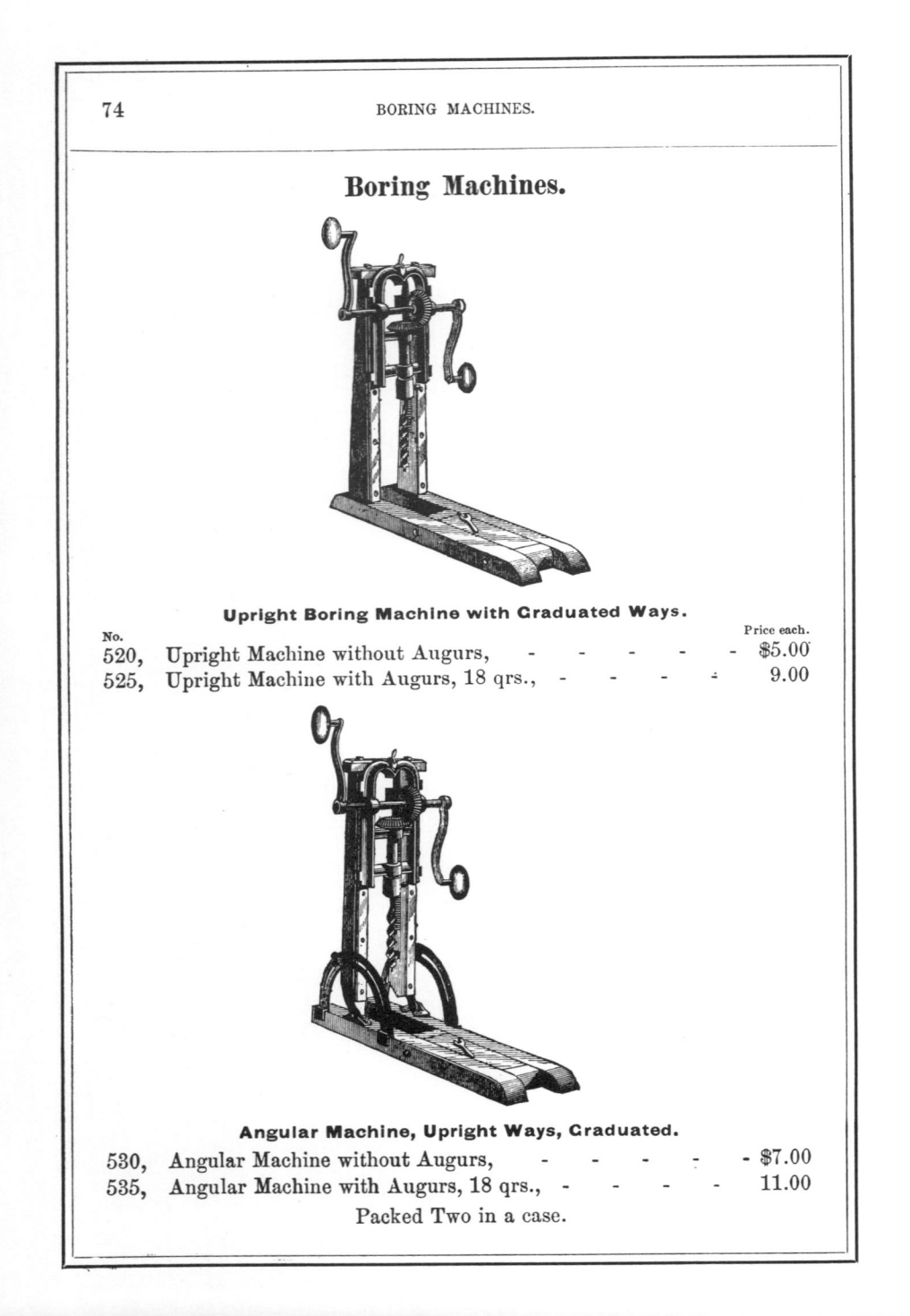

TRY SQUARES AND BEVELS.

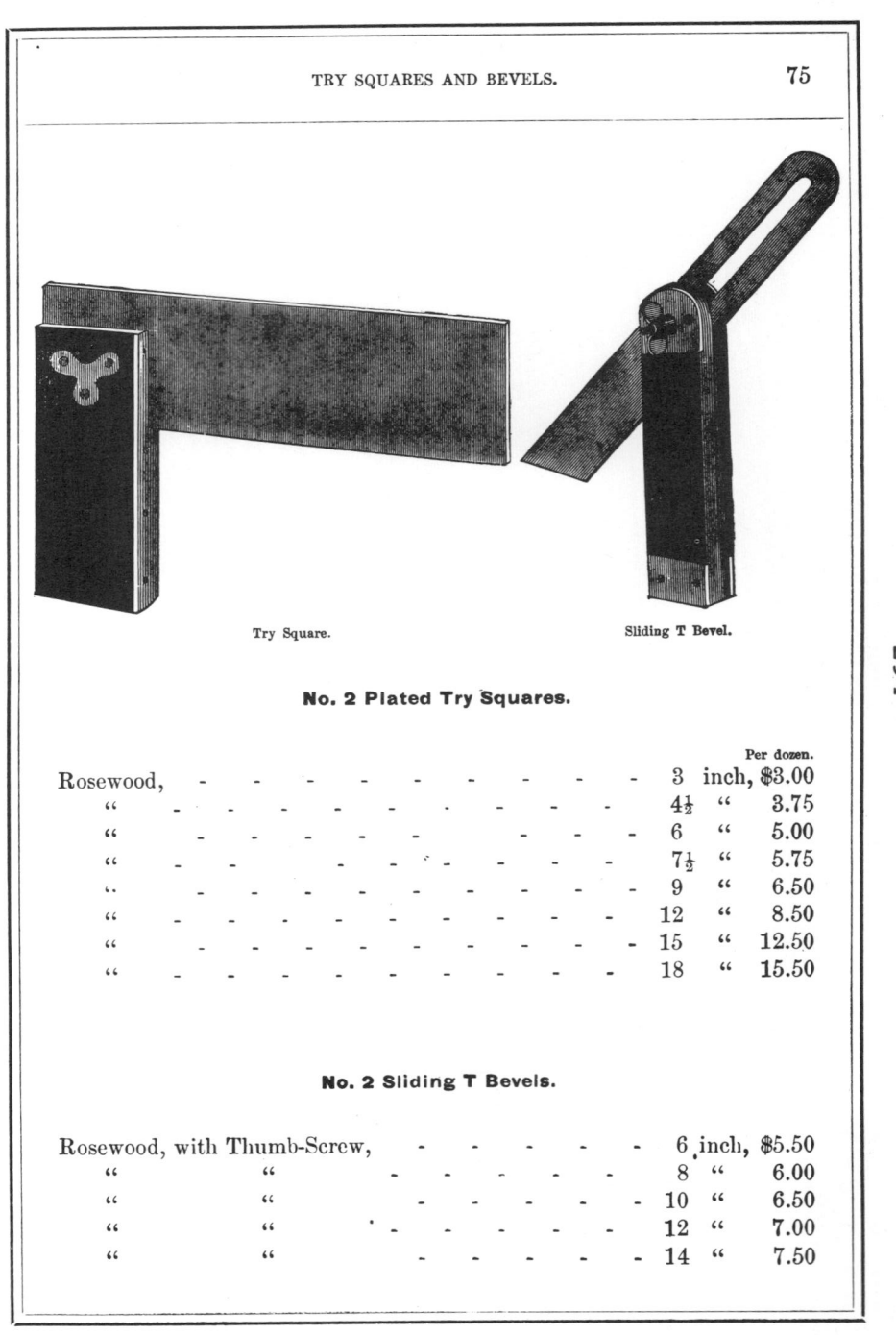

Try Square.

Sliding T Bevel.

No. 2 Plated Try Squares.

		Per dozen.
Rosewood,	3 inch,	$3.00
"	4½ "	3.75
"	6 "	5.00
"	7½ "	5.75
"	9 "	6.50
"	12 "	8.50
"	15 "	12.50
"	18 "	15.50

No. 2 Sliding T Bevels.

Rosewood, with Thumb-Screw,	6 inch,	$5.50
"	8 "	6.00
"	10 "	6.50
"	12 "	7.00
"	14 "	7.50

BORING MACHINES.

Boring Machines.

Upright Boring Machine with Graduated Ways.

No.		Price each.
520,	Upright Machine without Augurs,	$5.00
525,	Upright Machine with Augurs, 18 qrs.,	9.00

Angular Machine, Upright Ways, Graduated.

530,	Angular Machine without Augurs,	$7.00
535,	Angular Machine with Augurs, 18 qrs.,	11.00

Packed Two in a case.

TRY SQUARES AND BEVELS.

No. 1 Best Plated Try Squares.

		Per dozen.
Rosewood,	3 inch,	$5.50
"	4½ "	6.50
"	6 "	8.00
"	7½ "	9.50
"	9 "	11.00
"	12 "	16.00
"	15 "	20.00
"	18 "	24.00

No. 1 Best Sliding T Bevels.

		Per dozen.
Rosewood, with Thumb-Screw,	6 inch,	$8.00
"	8 "	8.50
"	10 "	9.00
"	12 "	9.50
"	14 "	10.00

Premium Try Squares.

		Per dozen.
Rosewood, marked in Inches,	3 inch,	$8.50
"	4 "	9.75
"	5 "	11.00
"	6 "	12.50
"	7 "	14.00
"	8 "	15.50
"	9 "	17.00
"	10 "	20.25
"	12 "	25.00
"	15 "	31.50
"	18 "	37.50

TRY SQUARES.

Premium Plated Back Try Squares.

Premium Plated Back Try Squares.

THIS SQUARE IS A PERFECT SQUARE, OUTSIDE AND INSIDE EDGES.

		Per dozen.
Rosewood, Plated Back, marked in Inches,	3 inch,	$16.00
"	4 "	18.50
"	5 "	20.50
"	6 "	23.50
"	7 "	26.50
"	8 "	29.50
"	9 "	32.50

Plane Irons.

MADE FROM SUPERIOR REFINED CAST STEEL.

Single or Cut Plane Iron.

Single Cast Steel Plane Irons, or Cut Irons, per Dozen.

1½	1⅝	1¾	1⅞	2	2⅛	2¼	2⅜	2½	2⅝	2¾	3 In.
$1.75,	1.75,	1.75,	1.87½,	2.00,	2.12½,	2.37¼,	2.62½,	2.87½,	3.12½,	3.50,	4.50.

Assorted from 2 to 2½, - - - - - - - per dozen, $2.37½.

Cast Steel Tooth Plane Irons, per Dozen.

2	2⅛ In.
$2.75,	3.00.

Plane Irons (continued).

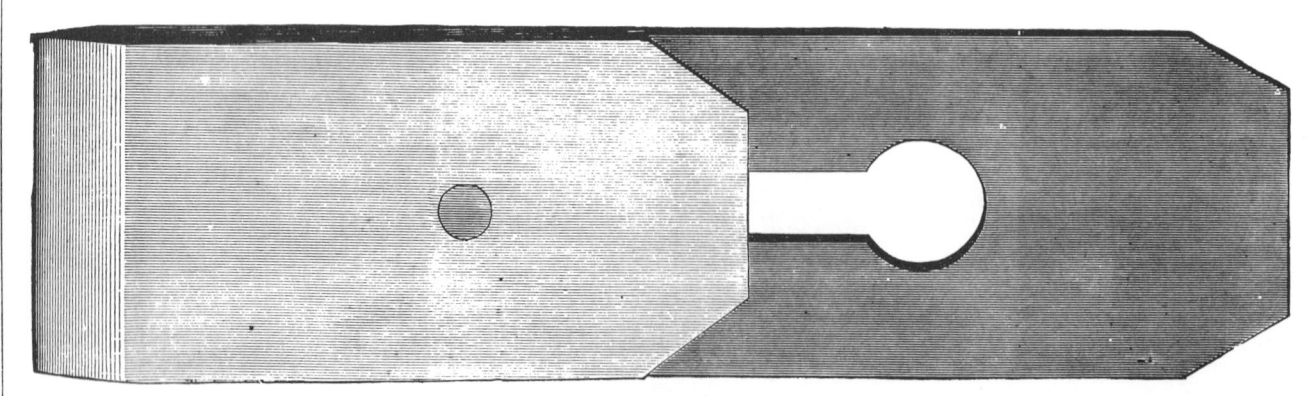

Double Plane Iron.

Double Cast Steel Plane Irons, per Dozen.

1½	1⅝	1¾	1⅞	2	2⅛	2¼	2⅜	2½	2⅝	2¾	3	3¼	3½	3¾	4 In.
$3.75,	3.75,	4.00,	4.00,	4.12½,	4.25,	4.50,	4.75,	5.25,	5.50,	6.50,	7.50,	9.00,	10.50,	12.00,	15.00.

Assorted from 2 to 2½, - - - - - - - - - per dozen, $4.50

Cast Steel Grooving Plow Bitts.

Per Set, - - - - - - - - - - - ⅛ to ⅝ Inch, $1.25.

Filletster Cutters.

Per Dozen, - - - - - - - - - - - - - - $1.00

Rabbet Plane Cutters.

Per Dozen, - - - - - - - - - - - - - - $1.00

PRICE LIST

AND

Illustrated Catalogue

OF

RULES, PLANES, GAUGES,

Moulding Planes, Grooving Plows, Plumbs and Levels,

DOOR STOPS, HAND SCREWS, HANDLES,

Turning Saw Frames and Saws,

C. SCHOLL'S PATENT GAUGE, MARDEN'S PATENT GAUGE,

PLANE IRONS, SPOKE SHAVES, Etc., Etc.

MANUFACTURED BY

H. CHAPIN'S SON,

(E. M. CHAPIN),

UNION FACTORY,

ESTABLISHED 1826,

PINE MEADOW, CONN., U.S.A.

JULY, 1882.

NEW HAVEN
TUTTLE, MOREHOUSE & TAYLOR, PRINTERS, 371 STATE STREET.
1882.

Plate IV - Title Page to 1882 Union Factory Catalogue

298

Plate V - Frontispiece to 1882 Union Factory Catalogue. Sketch of the Factory by Asher & Adams

INDEX.

	PAGE.
Astragals,	24
Awl Hafts,	77
Awl Handles,	77
Applewood Planes,	20
Boxwood Rules,	3 to 10
Board Measure,	7, 13
Bench Rules,	13
Board Sticks,	13
Bench Planes,	15 to 20
Boxwood Planes,	20
Bead Planes,	23 to 25
Caliper Rules, Boxwood,	9
" Ivory,	12
Carriage Makers' Tools,	56
Coopers' Planes,	21
Cornice Planes,	50
Chisel Handles,	76
Dado Planes,	26
Door Stops,	78
Filletster Planes,	27
File Handles,	77
Gauges,	57 to 61
" Marking,	57
" Cutting,	58
" Panel,	58
" Mortise,	58
" Slitting,	58
" Scholl's Patent.	59 to 60
" Marden's Patent,	61
Gauging Rods,	14
Hollows and Rounds,	29 to 34
Hand Screws,	72
" Beaded,	73
Ivory Rules,	11, 12
Level Glass,	71
Log Sticks,	13
Levels,	62

	PAGE.
Miscellaneous Rules,	13, 14
" Planes,	22
Moulding Planes,	23 to 50
Match "	36
Nosing "	26
Ogee "	40 to 44
" Grecian Planes,	43, 44
Ovolo "	45 to 48
" Grecian "	43 to 46
Planes, Common Bench,	15
" Extra "	16, 17
" Premium "	18, 19
" Panel,	27
Plows. Grooving,	51 to 55
" Pat. Adjusting,	54, 55
Plumbs and Levels,	62 to 70
" " Pat. Adjustable,	64 to 66
" " L. L. Davis' "	67 to 70
Pocket Levels,	71
Plane Handles,	78
" Irons,	80
" Stops,	80
Rules,	3 to 14
Rabbet Planes,	28
Rosewood Planes,	20
Ship Carpenters' Bevels,	10
" Planes,	21
" Scrapers,	79
Slide Rules,	9
Sash Planes,	37 to 39
Saw Handles,	78
Spoke Shaves.	79
Table Planes.	35
Turning-Saw Frames,	74
" " " and Saws,	75
Wantage Rods,	14
Yard Sticks,	13

Index to 1882 Union Factory Catalogue

MISCELLANEOUS RULES.

Wantage and Gauging Rods.

No.			Per Dozen.
92,	Wantage Rod,		$5.00
93,	Gauging Rod,	36 inch,	7.00
94,	"	48 "	8.00
94½,	" with Wantage Table,	48 "	18.00

Explanation of Gauging Rod Tables.

In ascertaining the amount of liquid in a Hogshead of 108 gallons, use No. 94½ Rod. Drop the pointed end of the Rod into the bung of the Hogshead, while lying on its side, and observe on the scale of inches how far up the Rod is wet. Then look at the Table marked "Hhd.," and against the figures in the columns marked "inches" and "parts in.," agreeing with the point at which the wet line appears on the scale of inches, will be found the number of gallons contained in the Hogshead. Should the Hogshead be more than half full, the contents will be ascertained by deducting the "inches" and "parts in." of dry space above the liquid—or the gallons indicated in the Table against the same—from the full capacity of the Hogshead (108 gals.) The other Tables (for Tierce, Bbl. and Half Bbl.) may be used in the same manner for Casks of their respective contents. The graduations on the opposite side from the Tables, will indicate the total capacity of any regularly shaped cask, by carrying the brass tip on the Rod down to the inner end of the cask at the chime, the bung being at the middle of the upper side; and observing the graduation which comes at the center of the bung hole, while the Rod is in this position, you will have the total capacity in gallons.

School Rules.

99,	Beech, 12 inch,	¾ inch wide,	$0.60
99½,	Boxwood, 12 inch, graduated two Lines,	¾ "	1.50

APPLEWOOD, BOXWOOD and ROSEWOOD PLANES.

POLISHED.

Extra C. S. Double Irons.

No.				Price Each.
411,	Smooth, Applewood,		2 to 2¼ inch,	$1.50
411½,	" "	Solid Handle,	2 to 2¼ "	2.50
412,	Jack, "	Bolted Handle,	2 to 2¼ "	1.75
413,	Fore, "	" to 22 inch,	2½ "	2.50
414,	Jointer, "	" to 26 inch,	2½ "	3.25
415,	Smooth, Boxwood,		2 to 2¼ "	2.50
415½,	" "	Small Extra,	1¾ "	1.75
416,	" "	Solid Handle,	2 to 2¼ "	5.00
417,	" Rosewood,		2 to 2¼ "	2.00
417½,	" "	Small Extra,	1¾ "	1.50
418,	" "	Solid Handle,		4.00
419,	Mitre, Boxwood,	Single Iron,	1½ to 1¾ "	1.75
420,	" "	Double "	1½ to 1¾ "	2.00
421,	" Rosewood,	Single "	1½ to 1¾ "	1.50
422,	" "	Double "	1½ to 1¾ "	1.75
	Planes with English Irons, Single,		add	.10
	Planes with English Irons, Double,		add	.25

CARRIAGE MAKERS' TOOLS.

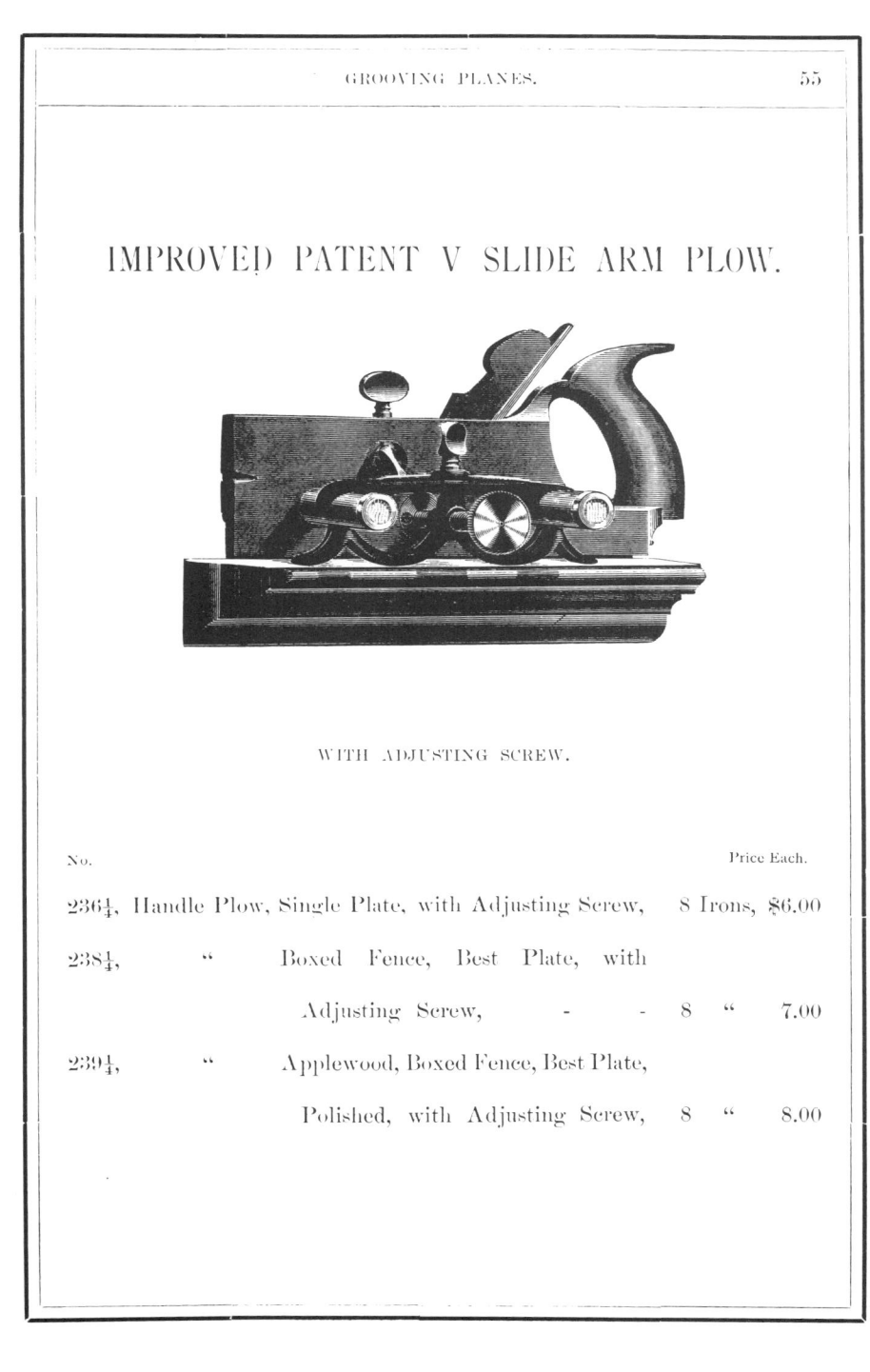

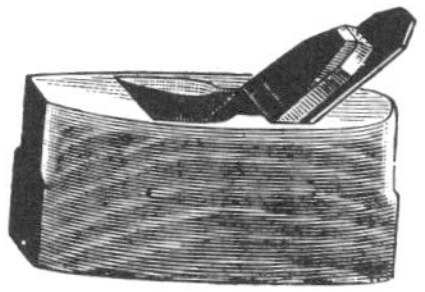

No. 1, Carriage Makers' Smooth, Double Iron, to 1⅝ inch, $1.10
No. 2,   "   "   Circle Face, Dbl. Iron, to 1⅝ "   1.25

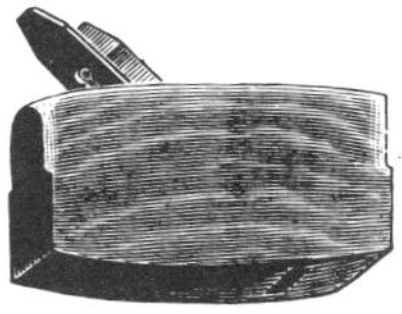

No. 3, Carriage Makers' Rabbet Plane, Circle Face, 1 inch, $1.00
No. 4,   "   "   "   "   "   1 "   1.10
No. 5,   "   "   "   "   T   1.20
No. 6,   "   "   "   Circle Face, T   1.35

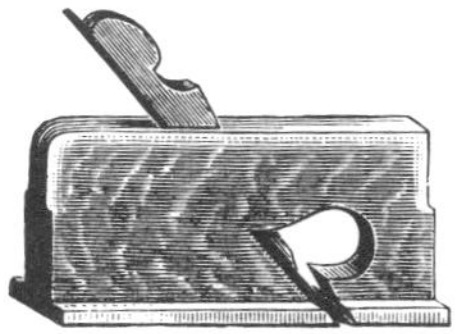

No. 7, Carriage Makers' Beading Tool, - - - - $1.75

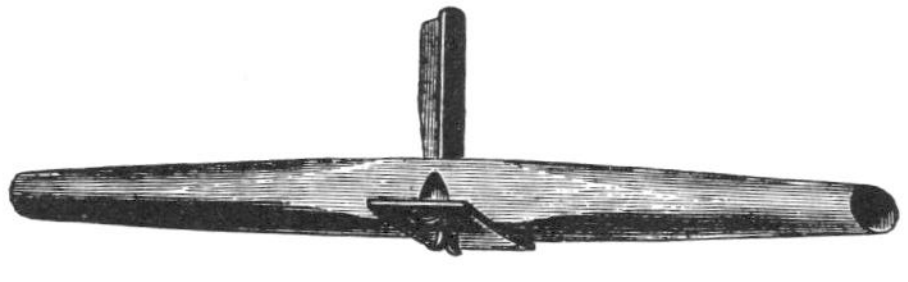

No. 8, Carriage Makers' Router, Single Cutter, - $1.00
No. 9,   "   "   "   Double   "   1.20

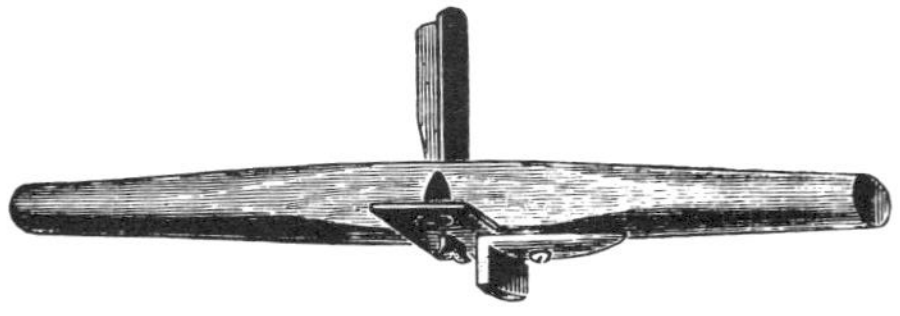

No. 10, Carriage Makers' Router, Double Cutter, with Guard, $1.40
No. 11,   "   Panel Router,   5.00
No. 12,   "   Boxing Tool,   1.60

IMPROVED PATENT V SLIDE ARM PLOW.

WITH ADJUSTING SCREW.

Price Each.

No. 234, Handle Plow, Single Plate, with Adjusting Screw, 8 Irons, $6.00
    234,   "   "   Boxed Fence, Best Plate, with
                      Adjusting Screw, - 8 "   7.00
    234,   "   "   Applewood, Boxed Fence, Best Plate,
                      Polished, with Adjusting Screw, 8 " 8.00

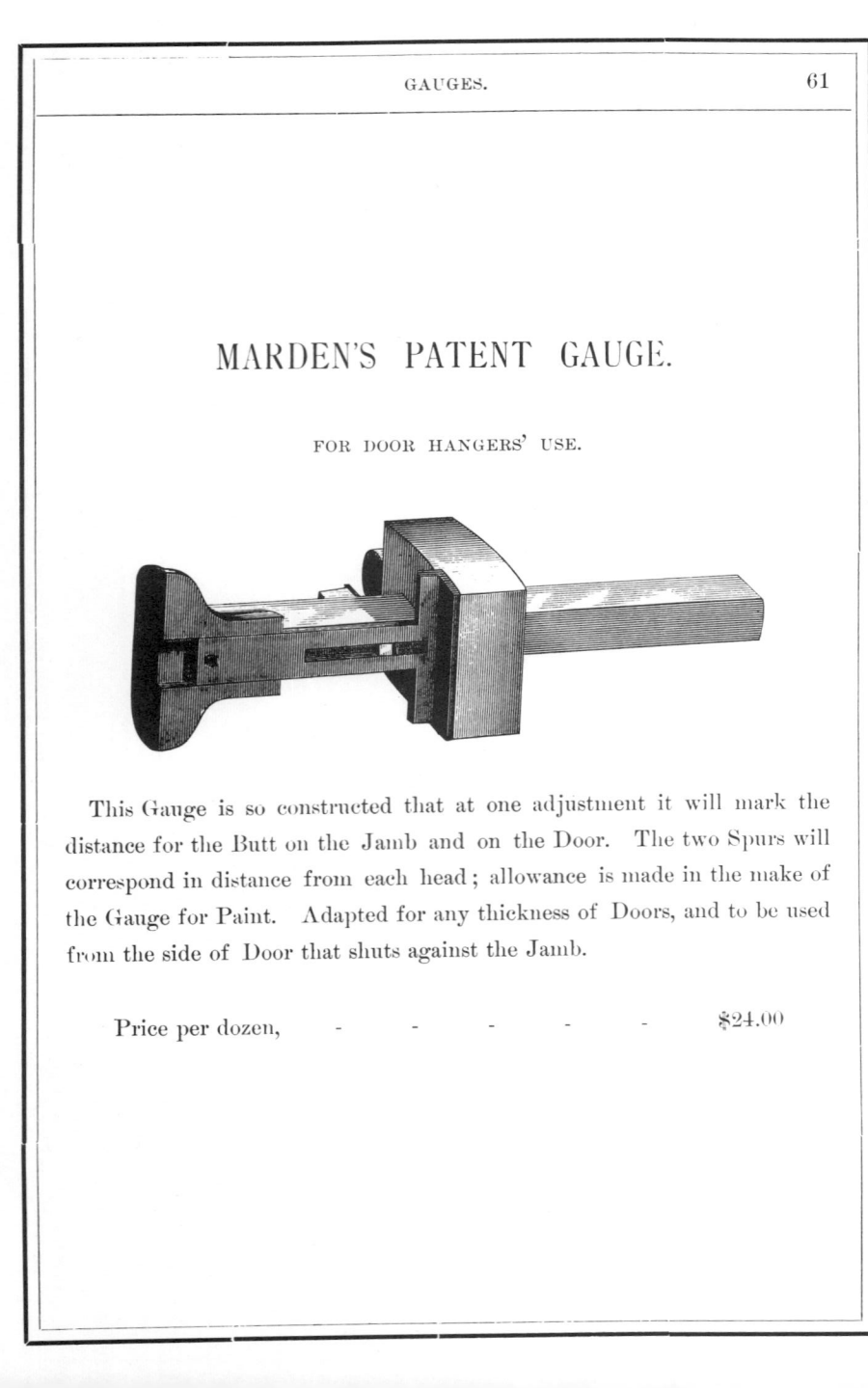

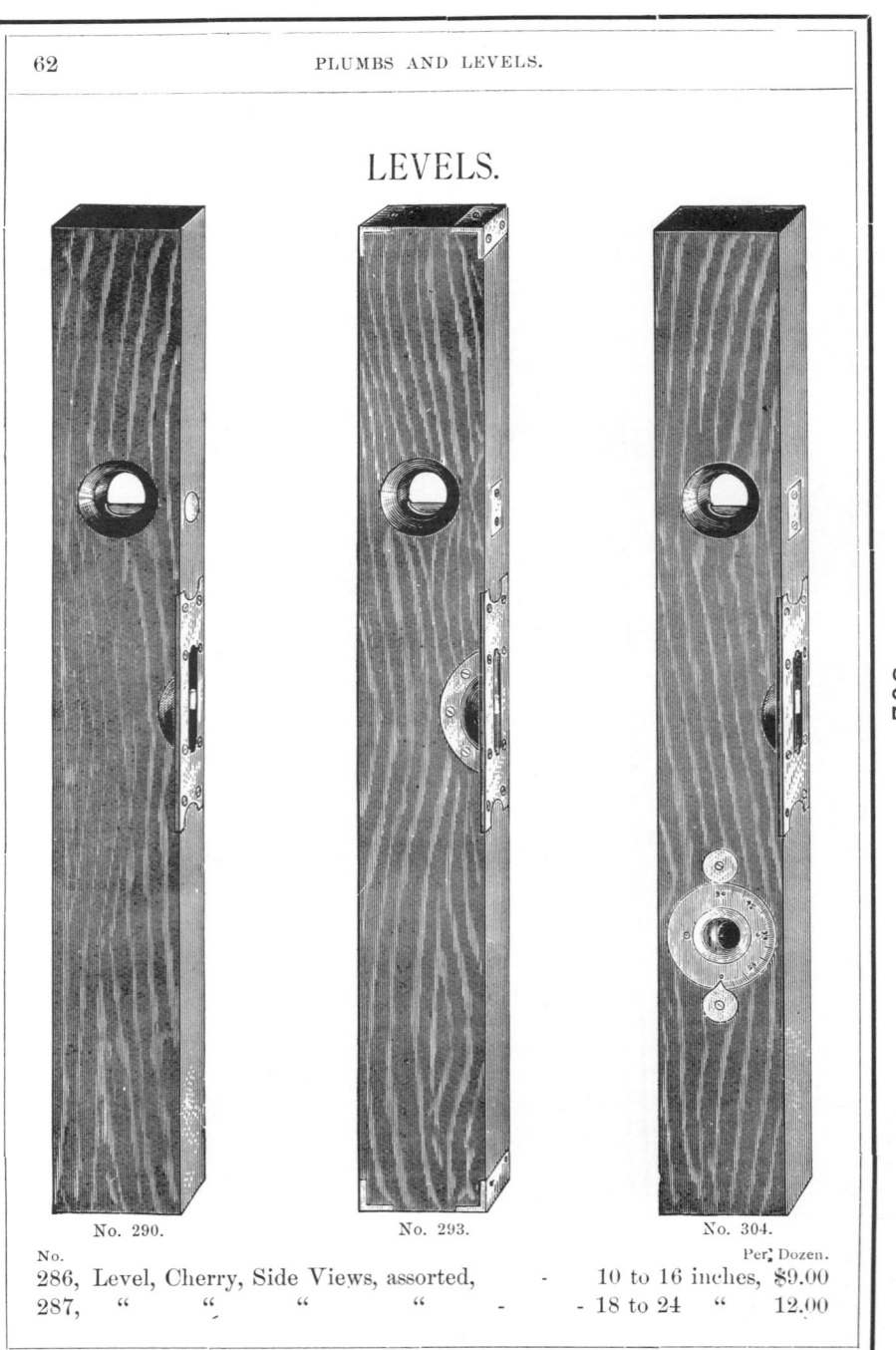

PLUMBS AND LEVELS.

LEVELS.

No. 290.

No. 293.

No. 304.

		Per Dozen.
No. 286, Level, Cherry, Side Views, assorted,	10 to 16 inches,	$9.00
287, " " " "	- 18 to 24 "	12.00

GAUGES.

MARDEN'S PATENT GAUGE.

FOR DOOR HANGERS' USE.

This Gauge is so constructed that at one adjustment it will mark the distance for the Butt on the Jamb and on the Door. The two Spurs will correspond in distance from each head; allowance is made in the make of the Gauge for Paint. Adapted for any thickness of Doors, and to be used from the side of Door that shuts against the Jamb.

Price per dozen, - - - - $24.00

ADJUSTABLE PLUMBS AND LEVELS.

PATENT ADJUSTABLE
PLUMBS AND LEVELS.

The drawing represents an Adjustable Plumb and Level with the plates removed. The metallic case or glass holder is constructed at its two ends with an ear or lug, inclined upon the under side. Beneath these two ears the adjustable seats are arranged. These are inclined upon their upper surfaces corresponding to the incline of the ears, and are slotted so that the screw which is introduced through the ear, and into the wood through the slots, the seats resting solidly upon the wood.

To adjust the glass, either of the seats is forced beneath its respective ear, or drawn therefrom until the bubble indicates the perfect level. The screws are then set, thus securing the case and seats in place. The transverse or plumb glass, is adjusted in the same manner, save that the ears are at one end of the glass-holder, and at right angles thereto.

This improvement in adjusting the spirit glass, is highly commended by the mechanic for its simplicity, and being reliable in all its parts, beneath the plates, and not exposed to meddlesome persons, no springs to become inefficient by constant use or careless handling.

SECTIONAL VIEW.

PLUMBS AND LEVELS.

PLUMBS AND LEVELS.

No.			Per Dozen.
289,	Plumb and Level, Cherry, Polished, Side Views, assorted,	12 to 18 in.	$14.00
289½,	Plumb and Level, Cherry, Polished, Side Views, assorted,	18 to 24 in.	16.00
290,	Plumb and Level, Cherry, Polished, Side Views, assorted,	24 to 30 in.	18.00
290½,	Plumb and Level, Cherry, Polished, Brass-Lipped Side Views, assorted,	24 to 30 in.	24.00
291,	Plumb and Level, Mahogany, Polished, Side Views, assorted,	24 to 30 in.	22.50
292,	Plumb and Level, Mahogany, Polished, Brass-Lipped Side Views, assorted,	24 to 30 in.	30.00
293,	Plumb and Level, Cherry, Polished, Brass-Lipped Side Views and Tipped, assorted,	24 to 30 in.	35.00
293½,	Plumb and Level, Cherry, Polished, Side Views and Tipped, assorted,	24 to 30 in.	28.00
294,	Plumb and Level, Cherry, Triple Stock, Polished, Brass-Lipped Side Views and Tipped, assorted,	24 to 30 in.	45.00
296,	Plumb and Level, Mahogany, Polished, Brass-Lipped Side Views and Tipped, assorted,	12 to 18 in.	27.00
297,	Plumb and Level, Mahogany, Polished, Brass-Lipped Side Views and Tipped, assorted,	24 to 30 in.	48.00
298,	Plumb and Level, Mahog., Triple Stock, Polished, Brass-Lipped Side Views and Tipped, assorted,	24 to 30 in.	58.00
300,	Plumb and Level, Rosewood, Triple Stock, Polished, Brass-Lipped Side Views and Tipped,	28 in.	102.00

PLUMBS AND LEVELS, WITH GRADUATING ADJUSTMENTS.
To work at any Angle or Elevation required.

304,	Graduated Adjusting Plumb and Level, Cherry, Polished, Side Views, assorted,	24 to 30 in.	30.00
306,	Graduated Adjusting Plumb and Level, Cherry, Polished, Brass-Lipped Side Views and Tipped,	24 to 30 in.	57.00
308,	Graduated Adjust. Plumb and Level, Mahogany, Polished, Brass-Lipped Side Views and Tipped,	24 to 30 in.	66.00

MASONS' PLUMBS AND LEVELS.

310,	Masons' Plumb and Level, Cherry, Polished, Side Views,	36 in.	21.00
310¼,	Masons' Plumb and Level, Two Plumbs, Cherry, Polished, Side Views,	36 in.	25.00
310½,	Masons' Plumb and Level, Two Plumbs, Mahogany, Polished, Side Views,	36 in.	40.00

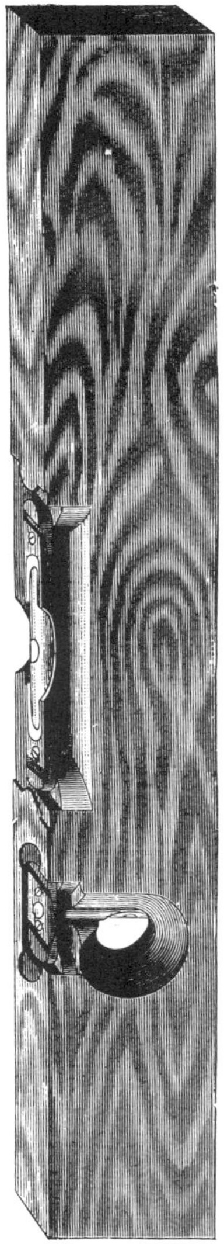

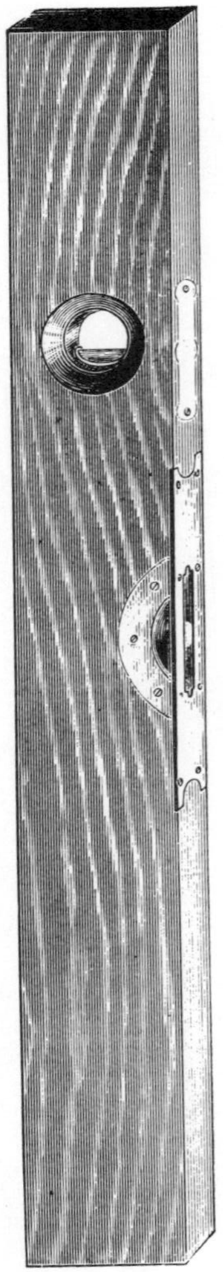

PATENT ADJUSTABLE PLUMBS AND LEVELS.

No.			Per Dozen.
490½,	Patent Adjustable Plumb and Level, Brass-Lipped, Side Views, Polished, assorted,	24 to 30 inches,	$27.00
493,	Patent Adjustable Plumb and Level, Brass-Lipped, Side Views, and Tipped, Polished, assorted,	24 to 30 inches,	39.00
493½,	Patent Adjustable Plumb and Level, Side views, and Tipped, Polished, assorted,	24 to 30 inches,	30.00
494,	Patent Adjustable Plumb and Level, Triple Stock, Brass-Lipped, Side Views, and Tipped, Polished, assorted,	24 to 30 inches,	48.00
491,	Patent Adjustable Mahogany Plumb and Level, Side Views, Polished, assorted,	24 to 30 inches,	27.00
492,	Patent Adjustable Mahogany Plumb and Level, Brass-Lipped, Side Views, Polished, assorted,	24 to 30 inches,	33.00
497,	Patent Adjustable Mahogany Plumb and Level, Brass Lipped, Side Views, and Tipped, Polished, assorted,	24 to 30 inches,	48.00
498,	Patent Adjustable Mahogany Plumb and Level, Triple Stock, Brass-Lipped, Side Views, and Tipped, Polished, assorted,	24 to 30 inches,	60.00

PATENT ADJUSTABLE PLUMBS AND LEVELS
WITH GRADUATING ADJUSTMENTS.
To work at any Angle or Elevation required.

504,	Patent Adjustable Plumb and Level, with Graduating Adjustment, Brass-Lipped, Side Views, Polished, assorted,	24 to 30 inches,	36.00
506,	Patent Adjustable Plumb and Level, with Graduating Adjustment, Brass-Lipped, Side Views, and Tipped, Pol., assorted,	24 to 30 inches,	58.00
508,	Patent Adjustable Mahogany Plumb and Level, with Graduating Adjustment, Brass-Lipped, Side Views, and Tipped, Polished, assorted,	24 to 30 inches,	66.00

PATENT ADJUSTABLE MASONS' PLUMBS AND LEVELS.

No.			Price.
410½,	Masons' Patent Adjustable Plumb and Level, Cherry, Two Plumbs, Side Views, Polished.	36 inch,	$30.00
490¾,	Masons' Patent Adjustable Plumb and Level, Cherry, Brass-Lipped, Side Views, Polished.	42 inch,	33.00

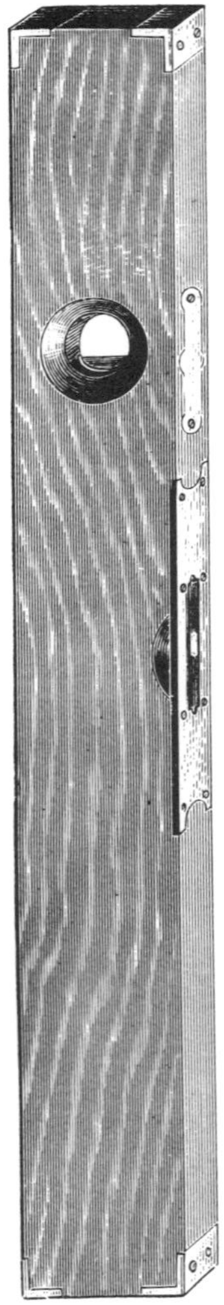

No. 490½.

No. 493¾.

ADJUSTABLE PLUMBS AND LEVELS.

L. L. DAVIS' PATENT

ADJUSTABLE PLUMBS AND LEVELS,

MANUFACTURED BY

H. CHAPIN'S SON.

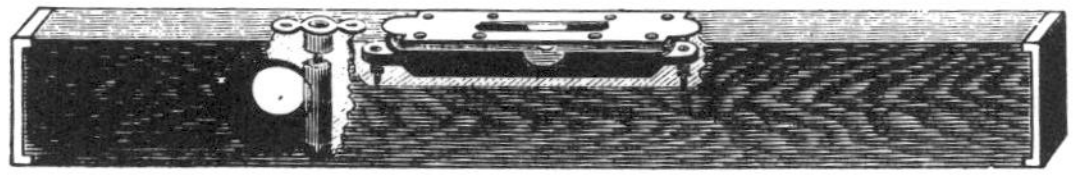

SECTIONAL VIEW.

The adjustments of this Level and Plumb are perfectly reliable in all their parts. Should the level glass become out of true with the base of the Level from any accident, it can be readily adjusted again to its proper place simply by removing the top plate and turning the adjusting screws at each end of the bubble-case, turning one screw back and the other forward will cause the bubble to move at any point desired. This adjustment has no springs, or any elastic substance whatever, and when once adjusted there is no liability of its getting out of order. The Plumb is adjusted by an eccentric step; removing the Plumb plate and turning the eccentric step either way will adjust the Plumb.

ADJUSTABLE PLUMBS AND LEVELS.

No. 10.

No. 12.

Per Dozen.

No. 6, Patent Adjustable Mahogany Plumb and Level, Brass-Lipped Side Views, Polished and Tipped, assorted, - 15 to 20 inches, $39.00

10, Patent Adjustable Mahogany Plumb and Level, Brass-Lipped Side Views, Polished and Tipped, assorted, - 26 to 30 inches, 60.00

11, Patent Adjustable Rosewood Plumb and Level, Brass-Lipped Side Views, Polished and Tipped, assorted, - 26 to 30 inches, 114.00

12, Patent Adjustable Mahogany Plumb and Level, *Double* Plumb, Brass-Lipped Side Views Polished and Tipped, assorted, - 26 to 30 inches, 69.00

13, Patent Adjustable Rosewood Plumb and Level, *Double* Plumb, Brass-Lipped Side Views, Polished and Tipped, assorted, - 26 to 30 inches, 130.00

ADJUSTABLE PLUMBS AND LEVELS.

L. L. DAVIS' PATENT
MASONS' ADJUSTABLE PLUMBS AND LEVELS.

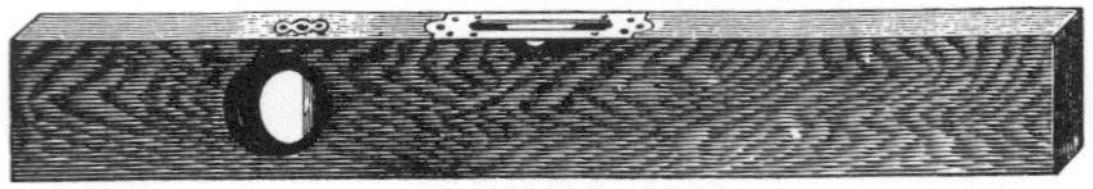

		Per Dozen.
No. 32,	Masons' Patent Adjustable Mahogany Plumb and Level, Side Views, Polished, 36 inch,	$39.00
33,	Masons' Patent Adjustable Mahogany Plumb and Level, *Double* Plumb, Brass-Lipped Side Views, Polished, 36 inch,	45.00
34,	Masons' Patent Adjustable Mahogany Plumb and Level, *Double* Plumb, Brass-Lipped Side Views, Polished and Tipped, 36 inch,	72.00
35,	Masons' Patent Adjustable Mahogany Plumb and Level, *Double* Plumb, Side Views, Polished, 42 inch,	63.00

ADJUSTABLE PLUMBS AND LEVELS.

		Per Dozen.
No. 20,	Patent Adjustable Mahogany Plumb and Level, Side Views, Polished, assorted, 15 to 20 inches,	$21.00
22,	Patent Adjustable Mahogany Plumb and Level, Side Views, Polished, assorted, 26 to 30 inches,	30.00
25,	Patent Adjustable Mahogany Plumb and Level, Brass-Lipped Side Views, Polished, assorted, 26 to 30 inches,	48.00
28,	Patent Adjustable Mahogany Plumb and Level, Side Views, Polished and Tipped, assorted, 26 to 30 inches,	54.00

MOSHER'S PATENT IRON SPOKE SHAVES.

Mosher's Patent Spoke Shaves and Box Scrapers, superior to any for the reason of the readiness of adjustment, and the Cutters made of the best English Cast Steel, tempered and ground, equal to the best Plane Irons.

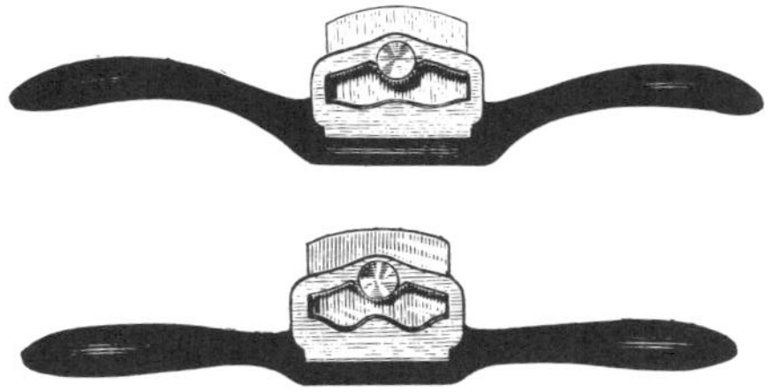

No.			Per Dozen.
50,	Patent Double Iron, Raised Handle,	10 inch, 2 inch Cutter,	$4.00
51,	Patent Double Iron, Straight Handle,	10 " 2 " "	4.00
52,	Patent Double Iron, Raised Handle, Rounding Face,	10 " 2 " "	4.00
53,	Patent Double Iron, Straight Handle,	10 " 2 " "	4.00
54,	Patent Double Iron, Hollow Face,	10 inch, 2¼ inch Cutter,	$4.00
55,	Patent Double Irons, Double Cutter, Hollow and Straight,	10 inch, 1½ inch Cutters,	$5.00

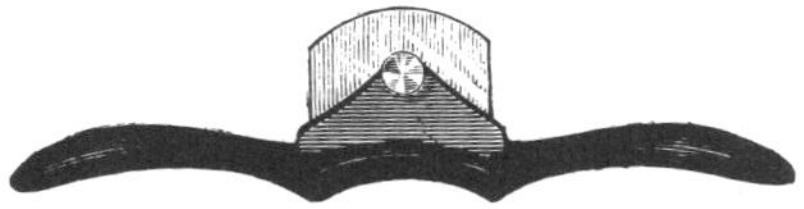

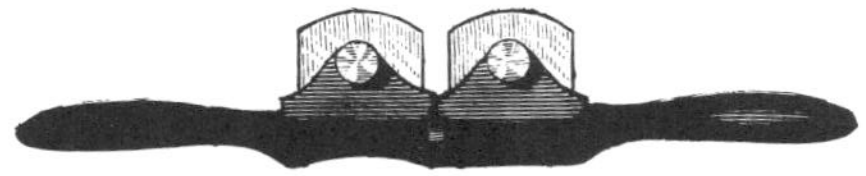

PATENT BOX AND SHIP SCRAPERS.

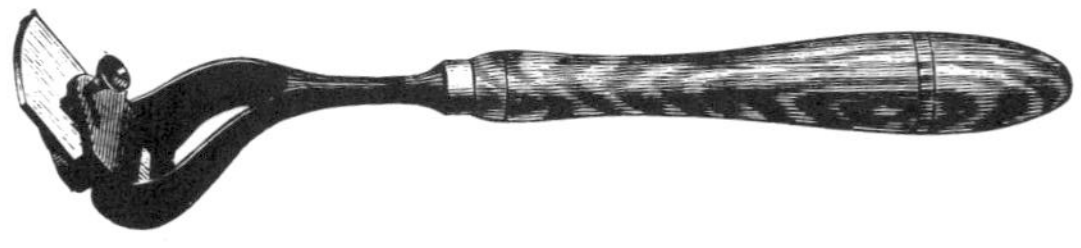

| 60, | Box Scrapers, | - | - | - | - | 2 inch, Steel Cutters, | $6.00 |
| 61, | Box Scrapers, | - | - | - | - | 1½ " " " | 5.50 |

1826   1830
H. CHAPIN.   H. CHAPIN'S SON.

H. CHAPIN'S SON'S
CATALOGUE OF 1882.

DISCOUNT SHEET.

Pine Meadow, Conn., July 2d. 1883.

Catalogue Page.		Discount Per Cent.
3-10	BOXWOOD RULES,	70 and 10
11-12	IVORY "	40 and 10
13-14	MISCELLANEOUS RULES,	60 and 10
15	BENCH PLANES, Common "Pearce,"	25
16-19	" " Extra and Premium,	20
20	" " Apple, Box and Rosewood,	20
15-21	" " with English Irons instead of American,	15
21	SHIP PLANES.	20
21	COOPER PLANES,	20
22	MISCELLANEOUS PLANES,	20
23-50	MOULDING PLANES,	15
51-55	GROOVING PLOWS,	15
56	CARRIAGE MAKER'S TOOLS,	15
57-58	GAUGES,	50 and 10
59-60	" Scholl's Patent,	50 and 10
61	" Marden's Patent,	50 and 10
62-63	PLUMBS AND LEVELS.—Non-Adjustable.	65 and 10
64-66	" " Patent Adjustable,	65 and 10
67-70	" " L. L. DAVIS' Pat. Adjustable,	60 and 10
71	POCKET LEVELS,	65 and 10
71	LEVEL GLASSES,	60 and 10
72-73	HAND SCREWS,	25 and 10
74	TURNING SAW FRAMES, AND SAWS,	25 and 10
75	" "	25 and 10
76	CHISEL HANDLES.	65 and 10
77	FILE AND AWL HANDLES,	65 and 10
78	PLANE HANDLES,	50 and 10
	SAW HANDLES,	50 and 10
	DOOR STOPS,	50 and 10
	" Rubber Tipped,	50 and 10
79	SPOKE SHAVES, Mosher's Patent,	50 and 10
	BOX SCRAPERS,	50 and 10
80	PLANE IRONS,	10 and 10
	PLANE STOPS.	10 and 10

TERMS: 30 days from date of shipment.

Cash Discount ON PLANES ONLY: 2 per cent. discount will be made for Cash, provided the invoice is paid on or before 10 days from date of shipment.

Invoices unpaid at the expiration of 30 days, sight draft will be made for full amount of invoice.

L.C. Stephens, died December 17, 1871. His obituary was published in the December 22 issue of the *Winsted Herald*.

"Pleasant Valley [Barkhamsted] Mr. Lorenzo C. Stephens, who for five or six weeks has been ill of typhoid fever, and of whose recovery no hopes were entertained for the last ten days of his life, passed very peacefully into the spirit land at about one o'clock p.m., on Sunday, December 17th, at the age of sixty-two years. Mr. Stephens was a man of fine feelings, of most liberal views, and in every thing fully up to the progress of the times. His remains followed by a large concourse of friends was conveyed to Riverton, where after appropriate services in the Episcopal Church, they were interred with Masonic honors."

On March 1, 1873 D.H. Stephens sent a letter to the hardware trade regarding his firm's position as to current discounts and depressed prices of rules then prevailing. (See Table I) The Standard Rule Co. was established at Farmington, Conn. (borough of Unionville) in 1872, replacing Belcher Brothers in 1873 for membership in the Rule Manufacturer's Association. By that date the firm J. & G. Walker of New York had also discontinued making rules. The five members of the Rule Manufacturer's Association were all located in Connecticut within a radius of 15 miles. In 1877 the members agreed to set production schedules and pooled sales according to the following allotments. (See Table II) Monthly reports were made to each concern by the other participating members through the acting secretary. The reported sales January 1 - June 30th with adjusting payments to the other firms is presented as Table III. Such price fixing, then widespread in the United States among many industries, was illegal after President Benjamin Harrison signed the Sherman Anti-Trust Act in 1890. While the list prices remained the same, the members agreed to changing discounts according to the times. (See Plate VII)

Table II

1877 Sales Quota Apportionment Among Rule Manufacturers

Firm	Per cent of Market
Stanley Rule & Level Co.	33.0
H. Chapin's Son	22.0
Stephens & Co.	22.00
Standard Rule Co.	15.0
Willis Thrall & Son	8.0

Table I

LETTER TO THE TRADE FROM STEPHENS & CO., RIVERTON, CONN., MARCH 1, 1873

Office of Stephens & Co.
Riverton, Conn., March 1, 1873

Gentlemen: Believing that the Trade will be likely to stock up at the present extremely low price of rules, and being in daily receipt of numerous letters of enquiry as to the greatest discounts we are offering, would say:

We have fixed upon the rate of sixty and ten off, although we are aware that rules can be bought at much less figure --- and lower than any printed quotations, newspaper or otherwise, we have seen - - - we intend to adhere to this price.

The responsibility of the present demoralized state of the rule trade does not rest upon us, for at equal prices we can at any time sell more goods than we produce, with but one travelling salesman, who is out but a small part of the time. These periodical "raids" upon the market are the work of parties who do not produce first class goods, and who every now and then are obliged to resort to this "cut and slash game" to get rid of surplus stocks, to the great disgust of the jobbing trade.

In future we shall have nothing to do with "combinations", but shall "stand upon or own bottom" and _trust to the merits of our goods which through any competition will be kept up to that well established standard which has given them so ready a sale_.

We are literally overrun with orders, and those friends who desire to place them, after the receipt of this circular, will please give us all the time possible for their execution.

The rule trade is a limited one, and we do not refer to the fact in any spirit of boasting, that by perserverance and a degree of mechanical skill, we have established a permanent and constantly increasing business second to no other, either in extent or reputation

We make nothing but _rules_ and do not intend to - knowing well as a rule the party who concentrates everything on a _speciality_, wins. Furthernore, we do not look for an advance for a long time. We shall expect to run upon the closest possible margin, and, in our opinion those merchants who overstock in anticipation of some immediate advances, will not realize them.

Stephens & Co.

Two Monthly Reports of Rule Sales during 1877 of Rule Manufacturers (See Table III, p.312)

A. S. UPSON, Pres't.   E. B. RIPLEY, Sec'y.   GEO. DUNHAM, Treas.

OFFICE OF THE
STANDARD RULE COMPANY,
MANUFACTURERS OF
BOXWOOD AND IVORY RULES.
PATENT PARTY-COLORED RULES, SPIRIT LEVELS, &C.

Unionville, Conn., *April 24, 1877*

H. Hopkins & Son
 Pine Meadow Ct.

Dear Sir

 Sales for March

Stanley Rule Level Co.	6,468.52
Stephens & Co.	5,985.33
H. Hopkins & Son	2,206.85
Willis Thrall & Son	201.50
Standard Rule Co.	533.57
	$15,193.77

are reports as follows.

Yours truly,
 E. B. Ripley, Sec'y.
 Stan. Rule Mfg. Asso.

310

A. S. UPSON, Pres't.   E. B. RIPLEY, Sec'y.   GEO. DUNHAM, Treas.
ESTABLISHED, 1833.
Office of WILLIS THRALL & SON,
DEALERS IN
HARDWARE;
MANUFACTURERS OF RULES, TRY SQUARES, BEVELS, &C., &C.
No. 10 CENTRAL ROW, HARTFORD, CONN.

Hartford, *Sept 22, 1877*

H. Shepard Esq.
 Secretary of Standard Rule
Co received yours of the 18th 1877
and of D. H. Stevens of Sept 22nd
1877. And I herewith send a
report of sales for month of Aug
1877 written as as follows

Stanley Rule & Level Co	6,559.63
H. Thompson & Son	2,707.90
D. H. Stephens	3,759.16
Standard Rule Co	650.03
	69.31
Willis Thrall & Son	$11,776.72

E B Thrall
 Sec'y

Plate VII – Announcements of Price Advances of Rules

Stephens & Co.,

MANUFACTURERS OF

U. S. Standard Boxwood and Ivory Rules

ALSO, EXCLUSIVE MANUFACTURERS OF

L. C. STEPHEN'S PATENT COMBINATION RULE.

Riverton, Conn., Oct 31st, 1884.

Gents:

We change our Discounts from this date to the following:

Boxwood Rules,	66⅔%	10% Cash.
Ivory "		} 55%
Miscellaneous,		
Combination,	60%	

Yours Respectfully,

STEPHENS & CO.

OFFICE OF

H. CHAPIN'S SON,

Pine Meadow, Conn., July 2d, 1883.

Gentlemen:

I enclose discounts, and you will please notice the reduced discount on

IVORY RULES.

The advanced cost of Ivory Stock has been so great during the year, necessitates this advance.

BOXWOOD RULES.

With the greatly improved and increased facilities, with double my former production, expect to be prompt in executing orders, and shall maintain the high standard that

CHAPIN'S RULES, PLANES, ETC.

has had for fifty-seven years.

Trusting you will favor me with a share of your orders, I am,

Yours Truly,

H. CHAPIN'S SON.

Table III - Report of Sales, Jan. 1 - June 30, 1877 by Rule Manufacturers.
[Note penalties for overselling quota charges to Stanley Rule & Level Co., Stephens & Co. and Standard Rule Co. (20%) and payments to H. Chapin's Son and Willis Thrall & Son (20% of shortage).]

Report of Sales Jan. 1 to June 30 inclusive 1877

1877	Stanley Rule & Level Co. 33%	H. Chapin's Son 22%	Stephens & Co. 22%	Standard Rule Co. 15%	Willis Thrall & Son 8%	Total
Jan & Feb	12,146.28	4037.24	4527.25	2308.67	351.61	23,371.05
Mar	6,468.52	2206.35	3783.33	583.51	201.56	13,190.77
Apl.	4,722.60	2736.95	2728.30	617.46	333.77	11,202.48
May	5,657.86	1728.87	2710.07	238.77	243.00	10,580.37
June	5,099.95	2301.38	2476.54	368.85	257.50	10,504.02
Total Sales	34,165.21	13,011.29	16,220.49	4,067.26	1,387.44	68,851.69
Share	22,721.06	15,147.37	15,147.37	10,327.75	5,508.14	68,851.69
Over	11,444.15		1,073.12			12,517.27
Short		2,136.08		6,260.49	4,120.70	12,517.27
20% on Over	2,288.83		214.62			2,503.45
20% on Shortage		427.21		1,252.10	824.14	2,503.45

Bridgeport Ct. August 2, 1877

H. Chapin's Son
Pine Meadow Ct.
Dear Sirs

Mr. Stephens report in this Am. Above fixed Statement showing $427.21 due to you by E. M. Chapin Treasurer of the Am. Rule Mfrs Assn payable according to Bylaw section 7 today from July 12, 1877

Yours truly
E. B. Ripley Secy.

From time to time E.M. Chapin received letters of inquiry as to whether his firm might be interesting in making and marketing a patented tool or some submitted design. This was particularly common for gauges and levels, which will be evident after reading Chapter X. Michael Garland submitted a broadside illustrating his patented plane-guide. (U.S. Pat. No. 106,808) (See Plate VIII) As this is not known to have been made at the Union Factory, apparently E.M. Chapin did not consider this design either worthwhile or profitable.

H. Chapin's Son prepared a price list for purchasing lumber for making planes and hand screws. (Plate IX) When H.L. James of Williamsburgh, Mass. closed up his firm January 1, 1878, he sold his plane stock to E.M. Chapin. (Plate X) A screw arm adjusting sash plane exists with the semi-circular imprint UNION FACTORY/Warranted, struck over H. James/Williamsburgh/Mass., suggesting that E.M. Chapin might have also purchased some finished stock from James for resale.[3]

Among the Chapin manuscript material in the collection at the Conn. Hist. Society are four sets of articles of agreement by the Plane Manufacturer's Union. These are dated: March 6, 1878; May 3, 1880; September 20, 1880 and December 22, 1885. Undoubtedly there were many earlier meetings and records, but these four are the only surviving in this collection. As previously mentioned in Chapter VI, price fixing among the principal wooden plane manufacturers is believed to have started about 1861, two years after the Rule Manufacturers' Association was formed. The Articles of Agreements adopted by the Plane Manufacturers' Union, December 22, 1885 are presented as Table IV. Of the four above mentioned surviving agreements this is the only to specify the apportionment of sales quota among the then five big firms (See Article 14, Table IV) as follows:

Auburn Tool Co.	24%
H. Chapin's Son	9%
Greenfield Tool Co.	7%
Ohio Tool Co.	32%
Sandusky Tool Co.	28%
	100%

It is assumed that these percentages were determined in proportion to the production capacities of these firms. Sometime between 1860 and 1865 H. Chapin's Sons had lost the lead and by the later date had decreased to fourth position. Sandusky Tool Co., founded in 1869, (See Vol. I, p. 224) had rapidly advanced to second on the list. By 1890 this firm was undoubtedly the largest wooden plane manufacturer in United States. However, it should be pointed out at the date of this 1885 agreement, the wooden plane market was a rapidly declining business in comparison to the expanding metal plane market.

An interesting agreement, adopted by the Plane Manufacturers' Union at their May 13, 1880 Meeting, concerned the marketing of seconds. "All 'culls' [seconds] to be sold at Auction and such to be stamped all our names or no stamp at all. A meeting of this Association to be held once every 3 months or oftener, if requested by any two Manufacturer Members of the Association."

The Products of Industry section of the Industrial 1880 US Census, recorded the H. Chapin's Son Factory as being capitalized at $50,000; employing 74 hands (59 male above 16 yrs.; 5 females above 15 yrs.; 4 children); 10 hours of work each day; average of $2.25 per day for skilled mechanic and $1.25 for ordinary labor; total wages paid during year $25,814; power from two water wheels, 13/14 ft. fall from a dam on Farmington River; $19,000 value of material and $90,000 value of product.

Plate VIII

Garland's Patented Improvement in Hand Planes

GARLAND'S IMPROVEMENT IN HAND PLANES!

This patent was allowed May 11th, 1870, and the invention relates to an attachment to the ordinary hand plane to assist the operator in securing a uniform square or bevel edge, without the assistance of a Try- or Bevel-Square. It can be set or adjusted to any degree, up to 45—right or left—and held by the quadrant attached to plane guide and passing through the spring attached to plane, as shown in cut.

The attachment may be detached at once by loosening the set-screws which hold the butt in place, and leave the plane free from obstruction to its ordinary uses.

The face of the plane is not interfered with in any manner whatever. It may be attached to several different kinds of planes with profit.

The undersigned would call the attention of Mechanics, Dealers in Tools and Tool Makers to this most valuable improvement.

Rights for Towns, Counties and States, together with all necessary information concerning the same can be had by applying to the patentee.

MICHAEL GARLAND.
West Eau Claire, Wis.

Plate IX

1870 Union Factory Plane Lumber Want List

Pine Meadow, Conn., Oct. 1871.

As I have frequent calls from parties having timber for sale; I would here state that I am in want of *only* the following kinds, and for which I will pay the annexed rates.

H. Chapin's Son.

FIRST QUALITY WHITE BEACH, SPLIT OUT.

Mouldings,	21 inches long,	2 by 4	.03
Jacks,	19 " "	3 1-2 " 3 1-2	.05 1-2
Fores,	25 " "	4 " 4	.13
Jointers,	31 " "	4 1-4 " 4 1-4	.18
Match,	15 " "	2 1-2 to 3 " 6 deep	.06

SAWED.

Mouldings,	21 inches long,	2 by 3 3-4	.03
Jacks,	19 " "	3 1-4 " 3 1-4	.05 1-2
Fores,	25 " "	3 3-4 " 3 3-4	.13
Jointers,	31 " "	4 " 4	.18
Match.	15 " "	2 1-2 to 3 " 6 deep	.06

HICKORY.

Bench Screws,	25 inches long,	4 in diameter,	.09
Hand "	25 " "	2 " "	.03
" "	20 " "	1 3-4 " "	.02
" "	16 " "	1 1-2 " "	.01

Hickory in 10 or 12 feet lengths, from 4 inches in diameter, upwards, per cord $7. to 9.

CHERRY LUMBER SAWED THROUGH AND THROUGH, 1 5-8 inches thick, per 1.000 feet, $33.00

APPLETREE, 4 inches in diameter and upward, per cord, $6. to 8.

Plate X - H.L. James' Bill to H. Chapin's Son for Plane Stock.
[Collection of the New Hartford Historical Society]

Williamsburgh, Mass., June 1ˢᵗ 1878

Mr H Chapin Son

Bought of H. L. James

Manufacturer of
Bench Planes, Moulding Tools, Tool Chests, Gauges,
PLANE, SAW AND CHISEL HANDLES, SAW BUCKS &c.

James celebrated premium polished bench planes.

With current rates Exchange on New York or Boston.

Terms ℀ 3 Can.

| 6390 | Stick Bush | 3½¢ | $222.95 |

The lot you sent under this date was short for Sweeth match, and all 14 inch, but I find on delivery that the balance from Christofield is some of it moulding 22 in which I had forgotten about. Tout is will make no difference. I send of a strike for this lot a long time ago.

1884 Feet Beech.
3223 Beech.

H. L. James.

Table IV - Articles of Agreement Adopted by the Plane Manufacturers at Auburn, New York, December 22, 1885. [Continued through page 320]

We the Subscribers mutually pledge ourselves and agree with each other to fully execute the following Articles in letter and spirit according to their true meaning and intent.

Art. 1. The officers of this Union shall be a President and Secretary.

Art. 2. The prices of the goods given in the catalogues issued by the several parties to this Union shall be uniform so far as they relate to goods embraced thereunder.

Art. 3. Parties making good different from those on the lists adopted by the Union of the same class or kind shall name the price at which they propose to list or sell them and submit the same to the Union for their approval or correction.

Art. 4. The terms and discounts upon the goods named shall be as follows:
Bench Planes of the first quality - twenty (20) percent
Bench Planes of the second quality - twenty five (25) percent
Fancy Planes of all kinds - fifteen (15) percent
Plane Irons - twenty (20) percent discount
Terms: Thirty days from date of invoive with a cash discount of two percent provided the invoice is paid on or before ten days from date of shipment
For invoices not so paid, sight draft is to be made thirty days from date of shipment for the full amount of such invoice.
To jobbing houses on the list as printed and such additions as may be mutually agreed upon at any of the meetings of this Union and placed upon record an additional discount of ten percent shall be made, with a further discount of seven percent in lieu of freight, and for cash, provided the invoice is paid on or before ten days from date of shipment; for invoices not so paid, sight drafts to be made at thirty days from date of shipment for the full amount of such invoices.
To all such jobbing house who at the end of any quarter of the calendar year shall certify that during the preceeding three months they have not sold any goods at less than the discounts on the printed sheets of the Union, a credit of 3% additional shall be allowed, but only on recipt of such statement and no allowance or drawback is to be made under any other circumstances.
All orders for goods shall be subject to the prices and terms ruling at date of shipment.
To California and Oregon trade only sixty days time may be allowed and discounts for cash corresponding with the above may be allowed if paid within thirty days of shipment - for invoices not so paid, drafts shall be made payable sixty days from date of shipment for the full amount of such invoice.
No invoice shall be dated in advance of shipment of goods.
No frieght shall be allowed to any customer.

Art. 5.   Planes may be sold on orders of syndicate buyers provided the orders be sent to the members of the Union with such direction that the goods shall be shipped direct to the customers of the syndicate buyer and billed to such customer at prices corresponding with his status as jobber or retailer, without commision or allowance to any party concerned

Art. 6.   Sales for export and consumption of goods in other countries except Canada may be made at the following rates of discount on satisfactory proof of actual exportation of goods by such evidence as will be satisfactory to the Union.
   Bench Plane of the first quality - forty five (45) percent
   Bench Planes of the second quality - fifty (50) percent
   Fancy Plane of all kinds - forty (40) percent discount
   Plane Irons at forty five(45) percent discount - from all double plane irons - forty (40) percent discpunt - from siggle plane irons - thirty (30) percent- from fillister, rabbet, match, and moulding irons, plow and match bits thirty five(35) percent.
   Terms - Thirty days from date of invoice with a cash discount of two percent provided the invoice is paid on or before ten days from date of shipment; for invoices not so paid, sight draft to be made thirty days from date of shipment for the full amount of such invoices.
   To insure the rates of discounts on any orders for export, such orders when sent shall include an exlicit statement that the goods ordered are intended for export and that the house sending the order pledges itself that such goods will be shipped to bona fide customers outside the United States.

Art. 7.   To parties in Canada and the Provinces who may order goods directly from any member of the Union, ten (10) percent in addition to the export prices may be given on planes.

Art. 8.   Parties who may buy goods ostensibly for export and subsequently sell or deliver such goods in the States or Territories shall be reported to all members of the Union and shall be precluded from purchasing any goods from any member of the Union thereafter.

Art. 9.   Any party of this Union may sell to any other party to the same at prices agreed upon between them, material or articles used in the manufacture of the goods included in its agreement. Such sales shall not be included in reports of sales. Any party may sell to manufacturers of planes outside this Union, plane irons at their regular export discounts. Such sales shall be regarded as export sales.

Art. 10.   Mr. Chapin is permitted to continue for the present and arrangement with Chas. M.Groskey for the sale of his planes at retailers dsicounts.

Art. 11.   Whenever goods have been received in exchange for others on sale of the same, the amount of such sale may be deducted, being specically explained.

Art. 12.   All goods shall be sold at the risk of the member selling and no deuction shall be allowed for uncllectable accounts.

Art. 13.   The parties to this agreement agree to keep full and accurate accounts of all goods heretofore named sold by them and to report to each of the other parties by the tenth day of each month the total amount of sales at both list and net prices made during the preceeding month and to whom sold.

Art. 14. The aggregate sales of the goods heretofore named shall be apportioned to each of the parties hereto as follows -
Auburn Tool Co. - twenty four (24) percent
H. Chapin's Son - nine (9) percent
Greenfield Tool Co. - seven (7) percent
Ohio Tool Co. - thirty two (32) percent
Sandusky Tool Co. - twenty eight (28) percent

Art. 15. Any of the parties hereto who may have sold a larger portion than the above named of the total amount of sales shall pay to the parties entitled to the same on the above basis - twenty five percent of the list price for all domestic sales, fifteen percent for all exports, except to Canada and ten percent for all exports to Canada. In estimating the surplus on which percentages are to be paid, the domsetic export and Canada sales shall be adjusted separately

Art. 16. Affirmation as to the correctness of statements of sales as aforesaid shall be made by each of the parties hereto and duly acknowledged before a Notary Public or other duly authorized officer and attached to such statement which shall show the amount of each sale and parties to whom sale was made, which affirmation shall be in the form agreed upon as follows -

State of _____ County SS
I _____ of the _____ Tool Co. of _____ State of _____ in compliance with the terms of an agreement made by and between the Auburn - Sandusky - Ohio and Greenfield Tool Companies and H. Chapin's Son on this ____ day of _____ A.D. 188_ in the city of _____ hereby affirm that I have made careful examination and being possessed of actual knowledge of the sales made and of the prices obtained by them and by those who are their agents or by them authorized in any way to sell for them or dispose of the goods made by them and that the said _____ Tool Company have not sold, bargained or otherwise disposed of any of the goods mentioned in said agreement at any greater discount or discounts or at less than the prices fixed by siad agreement nor have they or their agents or any person for them by any act direct or indirect or promise given or implied for the presnt or future done anything or agreed to do anything that has or will lessen or will result in lessening to any purchaser from them the cost or the price of any of the goods mentioned in said agreement below the prices agreed upn therein nor have they by indirection, commissions, prior agreements, drawback or in any manner violated the true intent, purpose, meaning and spirit of siad agreement in respect to said prices to purchasers or others or in respect to a full and true statement of sale as required by said agreement or otherwise howsoever - And that the statement of sales attached for the month of _____ AD 188_ is correct and embraces each and every disposition or sale made by them or their agents or any other persons from them of the goods named in the above mentioned agreement chargeable to business operations and sales of said month together with the names of the persons or firms to whom the goods were disposed during said month and the true amount of said goods shipped or otherwise at the list prices for said goods and also the net prices of same during said month to the best of his knowledge and belief.

Signed _____
Sworn to and subscribed before me this _____ day of _____ AD 188_
_____ Notary Public

This affidavit shall be attached to only one copy of the statement which copy will be forwarded to the Secretary. If the Secretary makes a statement for any party, he shall send a certified statement to the President.

Art. 17. The parties signing these articles severally pledge themselves that that they are not under any continuing contract or agreement - written, verbal or implied to furnishing goods to any party whatever at rates lower than those adopted by this Union.

Art. 18. No member of this union may have any agent for the sale of these goods.

Art. 19. The books, correspondence and papers relating to this business of each of the members of this Union shall be open to investigation, full and complete of either of the parties to this agreement or the authorized agent of either without previous notice.

Art. 20. It is mutually agreed that the prices to be charged for cases shall be as follows-
        Boxes to contian 30 Or 36 smooth   25¢
        Boxes to contian 30 or 36 jacks   50¢
        Boxes to contain 24 or 30 fores   60¢
        Boxes to contain 16 or 20 jointers 60¢
and boxes for other goods in proportion to the foregoing.
  No planes to be papered except fpr Pacific Coast trade or for export and panel plows and other fancy planes for customers where absolutely necessary and not otherwise.

Art. 21. If any or either of the parties hereto are by accident or from any cause prevented from furnishing sufficient of the aforesaid goods to fill their entire quota od sales in any one month to which they are entitiled, they shall not lose thereby any portion of such quota of slaes unless the amount of such delinquency shall amount to twenty percent of said quota in which case the party so failing shall not be entitled to any claim upon the surplus of sales made but the same shall be equally apportioned to the other parties hereto. If either of the parties hereto shall be unable to execute orders with reasonable promptness that shall at once notify each of the other parties hereto.

Art. 22. Meetings of the Union shall be held at the call of the Secretary at the request of any two members or by adjournment from time to time.

Art. 23. These articles shall be in force and bindery from Januray 1st 1885 to January 1st 1887.

Art. 24. These articles may be altered, annexed or repealed at any meeting, a majority of all the members concurring.

    We the undersigned hereby agree faithfully and fully to carry out in letter and spirit all and severally the provisions of the foregoing agreement.

    Witness our signatures hereto this twenty second day of December AD 1885 at Auburn, County of Cayuga, State of New York

        Greenfield tool Co. by *Gorham D. Williams*
        Ohio Tool Company   by *Alfred Thomas, Treas.*
        Sandusky Tool Company by *M. Gallup, Treas.*
        Auburn Tool Co. by *Geo. Casey, Pres.*
        H. Chapin's Son   *E. M. Chapin*

An advertisement from Ladd's Discount Book (New York, 1887) brought to attention some of the products at H. Chapin's Son. (Plate XI) The No. 57 four fold, two feet ivory rule bound in German silver is stamped E.M. Chapin. This is one of the few to bear this imprint, rather than the usual H. Chapin, which was continued on most rules and all planes through the tenure of the firm of H. Chapin's Son.

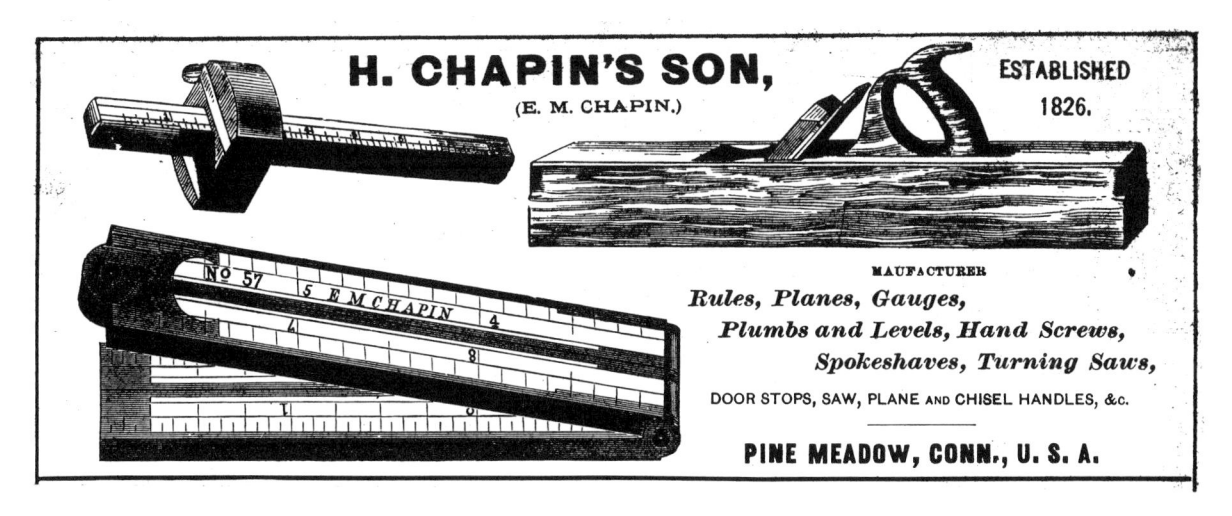

Plate XI - Advertisement in *Ladd's Discount Book*

The frontispiece to the *1882 H. Chapin's Son Catalogue* showed a sketch of the Union Factory at Pine Meadow. (Plate V) This print is signed Asher & Adams and was undoubtedly originally prepared for their *Pictorial Album of American Industry,* published in 1876. The sizes of the pages in this book was 18 in. x 24 in. The page describing H. Chapin's Son showed this illustration as well as those of several products offered by this firm. The text noted an abbreviated history of the firm and its accomplishments, intended for the general reader. Since the text was not documented, no information from this source has been reprinted in this study.

Notes - Chapter VIII

1. The *1870 Stanley Rule & Level Co. Catalogue* had 84 pages, but at least 12 pages in this were products made by Darling, Brown & Sharpe of Providence, R.I.
2. This Catalogue has been reprinted by Ken Roberts Publishing Co. [1978]
3. Collection of Joseph Dziadul.

Chapter IX

The Chapin Machine Company & Iron Planes

When Hermon Chapin transferred the Plane and Rule Shops to his sons, Edward and George, on July 1, 1865, he also deeded the Machine Shop, Blacksmith's Shop, Foundry and Old Brick Shop to his youngest son Philip.[1] The contents of the machine shop were recorded in Chapin's ledger. (See Table XV, Chapter VI)

Formerly these buildings and property had belonged to H.B. Kellogg & Co. After a fire in 1844, which destroyed the mill at the New Hartford Joint Stock Corporation, George Kellogg constructed a machine shop in which he manufactured cotton pickers. After his death, about 1845, Freeman Graham, a former apprentice to the Kelloggs, engaged in the manufacture of pistols, and also purchased the iron foundry from the heirs of Isaac Kellogg.[2] This enterprise failed in 1851 and Hermon Chapin acquired the property in 1852, continuing business there as Hermon Chapin & H.B. Kellogg & Co.

After acquiring his father's interests, Philip Chapin continued the line of machine products made by his predecessors. Among the products manufactured, according to an advertisement in 1868, were wool and cotton pickers, carding machines, presses, engine lathes, circular saw mills, plows, etc. (See Plate I) H.B. Kellogg sold his interest to Philip Chapin in 1866. In 1870 Philip organized this business as the Chapin Machine Co., he being president and principal stockholder.[3] (See Plate II) Among their products was an improved bolt header. (Plate III) A sketch of the office, machine shop, forge and foundry from a billhead is shown as Plate IV. The product line was expanded to include a domestic sewing machine, some of which was subcontracted. An indication of over-extension is evident from a letter from Pratt & Whitney Co. of Hartford, Conn., dated February 14, 1871:

> "We reply to yours of the 9th inst. that we estimate loss by means of reasons of non-completion of your order for sewing machine tools and fixtures @ $2500. We hope to have instructions to complete the tools and machines begun or know how the above losses in settlement of the account"

Plate V shows the above letterhead, but unfortunately the transcribed text was not reproducable. Products of the Chapin Machine Co. are noted on the two letterheads shown in Plate VI.

The Chapin Machine Co. obtained a loan of $25,000 from the Winsted Savings Bank on September 5, 1874 by mortgaging the property and equipment. The details of this mortgage are transcribed in Table I, which provides an excellent description of the equipment then in use at this shop. On February 7, 1877 Philip Chapin filed for bankrupcy in the United States Honorable District Court.[4] A new joint stock company, The Chapin Manufacturing Co., was then organized. However, soon after, this became insolvent. Edward Chapin acquired the deed to this property by auction at foreclosure on March 20, 1880.[5] Edward Chapin had lost considerable money on this venture, as he had countersigned several of the notes due the Winsted Savings Bank. The problem with Philip Chapin's management was two-fold. He neither had any training with machine shop practice nor previous business experience.

Plate I - Advertisements from *1868 CONNECTICUT BUSINESS DIRECTORY*
[Connecticut State Library, Hartford, Conn.]

---

266   CONNECTICUT BUSINESS DIRECTORY.

UNION FACTORY.
ESTABLISHED 1826.

E. M. CHAPIN.   G. W. CHAPIN.

H. CHAPIN'S SONS,
Manufacturers of

RULES, PLANES, GAUGES,
Hand Screws, Bench Screws, Levels, &c.

PINE MEADOW, CONN.

PHILIP E. CHAPIN,
Successor to HERMON CHAPIN and H. B. KELLOGG & CO.,

MANUFACTURER OF

KELLOGG'S
WOOL, COTTON AND SHODDY PICKERS,
CUSTOM CARDING MACHINES,

McCarthy's Long Staple Sea Island Cotton Gins, Bolt Headers,

PRESSES,
ENGINE LATHES, CIRCULAR SAW MILLS,

Saw Mill Dogs, Rose Water Wheels, Cider Mills, Plows, Castings, Mill Gearing, Shafting, Pulleys, etc., etc.

Pine Meadow,   Conn.

Plate V - Letterhead of Pratt & Whitney Company

F. A. PRATT, President.   A. WHITNEY, Superintendent.   M. STANNARD, Superintendent.
R. F. BLODGETT, Sec'y and Treas.   E. G. PARKHURST, Assistant Sup't.

Office of the Pratt & Whitney Company,
Manufacturers of First-Class Machinists' Tools, Sewing-Machine and Gun Machinery,
F. A. PRATT'S PATENT FRICTION CLUTCH FOR COUNTERSHAFTS, &C.,
M. STANNARD'S PATENT HYDRAULIC ENGINES AND ORGAN-BLOWING APPARATUS,
SPECIAL MACHINERY, &C.

Hartford, Conn., _____ 187_

Plate II - Stock Certificate of The Chapin Machine Company.
[Collection of the New Hartford Historical Society]

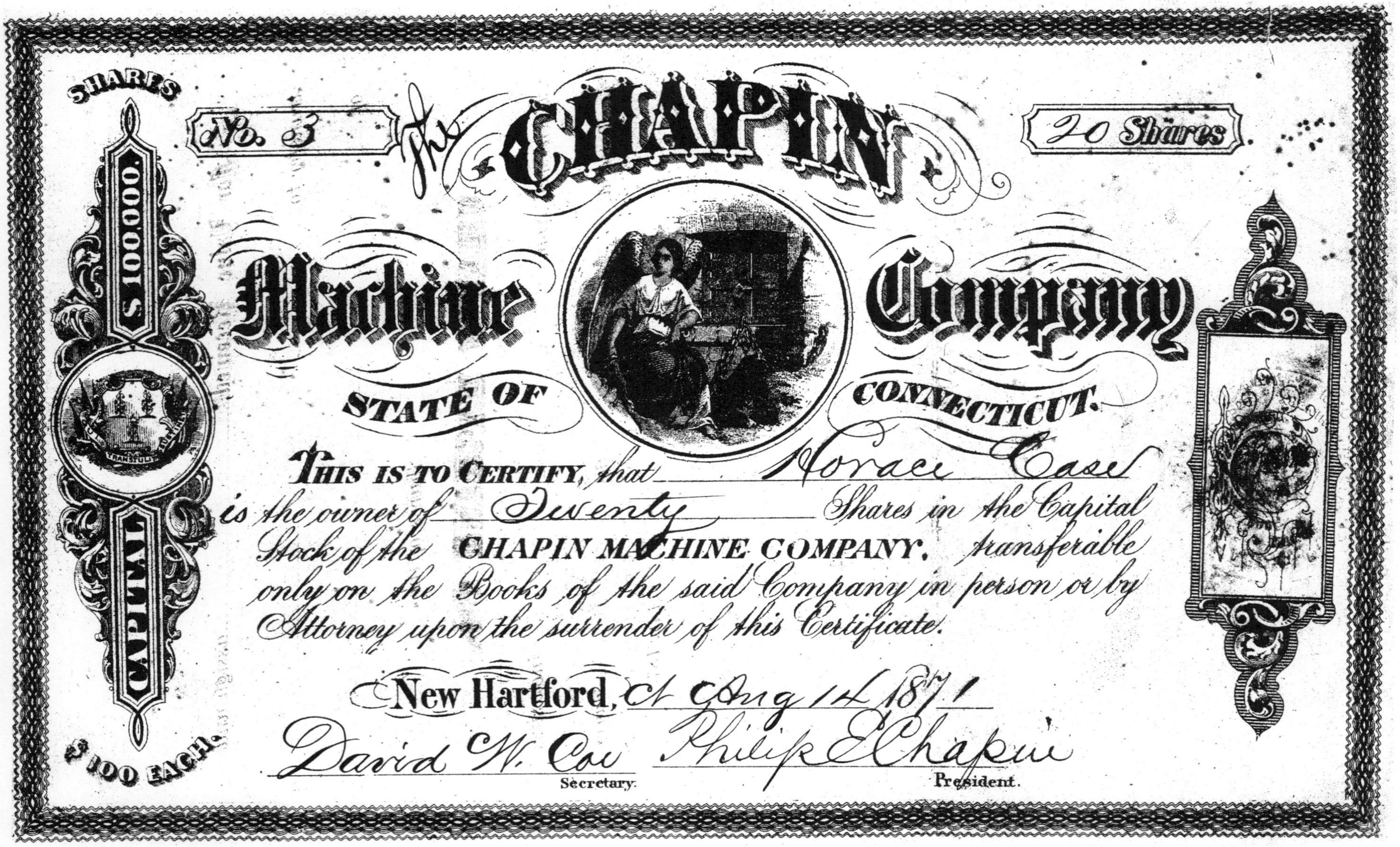

Plate III - Chapin's Improved Bolt Header

CHAPIN'S
Improved Bolt Header,
FOR HEADING CARRIAGE BOLTS.

This Machine is simple in its construction and can be run

Plate IV -   Sketch of Chapin Machine Company Factory.

Plate VI – Letterheads of the Chapin Machine Co. Noting Various Products.

Mortgage Loan of $25,000 to Chapin Machine Co. from Winsted Savings Bank
September 5, 1874 [New Hartford Land Records, Book 24, page 676]

To all People to whom these presents shall come, GREETING:

Know ye that the Chapin Machine Company, a corporation duly established and located in the town of New Hartofrd, County of Litchfield and State of Connecticut for consideration of Twenty Five Thousand Dollars received to its full satisfaction of the Winsted Savings Bank, a corporation located in Winsted, Connecticut, do give, grant, bargain, sell and confirm unto the said Winsted Savings Bank the following described parcel of Land and Mill privilege with Machine Shop, Foundry and Blacksmith Shop standing thereon, and Machinery, Special Tools, Water Wheels and main line shafting with pulleys therein situated in said New Hartford and bounded as follows; Easterly on the Farmington River, Southerly on D.B. Smith & Co. land, Westerly on land of D.B. Smith & Co. and land of P.E. Chapin, and Northerly on land of Philip E. Chapin, the said Northern boundry being six feet north of the north west corner of Brick Machine Shop and running East to a point six feet North of the Northeast corner of the Wheel House, thence east to Branch Canal, thence Southeast to a point eight feet North of the North east corner of the Blacksmith Shop, thence East to the River, with the right of passway to the Turnpike past the shop of Philip E. Chapin, known as the Kellogg Shop with the right of passway on south side of said lot, together with three sixteenths (3/16) of the Water Power, Dam and Canal, also one third part of Branch Canal and Reservoir with the right to enter upon and take water and repair the same, the Grantee paying, and doing its proportionate share of repairs, upon the same, together with the right of passway by the shop of H.Chapin's Son, together with all Patterns in Pattern Room, Pattern Flasks, Steam Boiler and Pipes, Trip Hammer, Tumbling Barrels, Forge and tools in Blacksmith Shop and the following described machinery:

One Large Planer
Two Crank Planers
Three N.H.Mfg.Co.Planers
One Large Pulley Lathe
One Eleven Feet Shafting Lathe
One Twenty Feet Shafting Lathe
Five six feet Lathes
Three nine feet Lathes
One Ten foot Lathe
One eleven feet Lathe
One five feet P.&W. Lathe
One six foot P.& W. Lathe
Seven four feet Lathes
One six foot Lathe
One tapping Lathe
One Profile Machine
One Brainard Milling Machine
Eight. P. & W. Milling Machines
Two P. & W. Screw Machines
One Pair of Rotary Shears
Two Drops
Two Presses
One Large N.H.Co.Drill Machine
Two P. & W. Drill Machines
Four C.M.Co.Drill Machines

One three spring Drill Machines
One centre Drill Lathe
Five Post Drill Machines
One Gear Cutter and Nut Tapper
Four Cutter Grinders
One Cylinder Milling Machine
One Bed Drilling Machine
One Portable Forge
One Band Saw
One Wood Turning Lathe
One Boring Machine
One Daniel's Planer
Two Turning Lathes
Two Saw Benches with Saws
All Benches and Vises
All Counter Shafts and Belting
Office Furniture in the Brick Machine Shop

Table I - Mortgage Loan by Chapin Machine Co. from Winsted Savings Bank. [continued on page 328]

[Table II - Continued from page 327]

It being the intent of said Company to Mortgage all Real Estate, Water Power, Machinery and Special Tools as security for the above loan, reference to the above property is here made to deed from P.E,Chapin to the Chapin Machine Co. bearing date July 1st,1870, recorded in Book 22, page 369 Town Records. To have and to hold the above granted and bargained premises with the appurtances thereof, unto the said Winsted Savings Bank and its assigns forever to them and their own proper use and behoaf. And also if the said Grantor does for itself, Executors, Administrators and Assigns covenant with said Savings Bank and its assigns that at and until the ensealing of these presents it is well sized of the premises as a good indefeasible estate in fee simple and have good right to bargain and sell the same is free of all incumbrances whatsoever. Except reserving such rights of way across said premises owned by other parties, also right of raceway to the Kellogg Property owned by Philip E. Chapin and furthermore the said Grantor does by these presents bind itself and its assigns forever to warrant and defend the above granted and bargained premises to the said Savings Bank and its assigns against all claims and demands whatsoever. Provided if said Chapin Machine Co. shall well and truly pay its five notes for the sum of Five Thousand each dated September 1874 payable to the order of Philip E. Chapin at the office of Winsted Savings Bank on demand with interest semiannually in advance and shall also repay all money paid by said Savings Bank for insurance of buildings on said premises, then this deed shall be void.

In witness whereof I have hereunto set my hand and seal the fifth day of September Anno Domini 1874, being hereto aothorized by vote of said Company at a Meeting legally held.

The Chapin Machine Co.
Philip E. Chapin, President

At a Meeting of the Directors of the Chapin Machine Co., legally held at their office in Pine Meadow, Ct., August 24th,1874 at 4 o'clock P.M. it was voted that Philip E. Chapin, President of said Company is authorized to borrow an amount not exceeding Twenty Five Thousand Dollars ($25,000) of the Winsted Savings Bank, Winsted, Conn. and to execute a Mortage of the real estate. Water Power, Machinery, Tools and any other property that can be included in a mortgage to said Saving Bank to secure payment to the same, and to do anything lawful acts to execute any papers that may be necessary in order to execute said loan.

E.M.Chapin, Secretary Protem

As previously noted in Chapter VIII an *Appendix* to the *1870 H. Chapin's Son Catalogue,* issued on October 1, 1872, called attention to the availability of iron planes. Iron planes had been manufactured in United States on a limited basis since the 1827 patent issued to Hazard Knowles.[6] (See Vol. I, p. 52) While numerous firms had offered a variety of metal planes, it was not until 1869 that Stanley Rule & Level Co. acquired Leonard Bailey's patents that such planes became popular. Their subsequent successful manufacturing and marketing resulted in extensive sales of metal planes. This marked the date of decline of wooden planes. The line of iron planes, formerly made by Bailey, Chaney & Co. of Boston (See Vol. I, 2nd edition, p. 208), with modifications of the adjusting screw, were first offered in the *1870 Stanley Rule & Level Co. Catalogue.*[8] This line of planes also included wood bottom planes with iron superstructure, now known as "transitional" planes.[9] Sustained successes were noted by Stanley Rule & Level Co., announcing their sales in their catalogues. (See Table II).

TABLE II

SALES OF BAILEY PLANES BY STANLEY RULE & LEVEL CO.
Noted in Catalogues and Price Lists

Year of Catalogue	Total Sales of Bailey Planes
1871 Supplement	6,500
1872	20,000
1874	80,000
1877	125,000
1879	175,000
1884	450,000
1888	900,000
1892	1,500,000
1898	3,000,000

Another line of metal planes, known as Perfect Metallic Planes, made by the Metallic Plane Co. of Auburn, N.Y., were introduced about 1870.[10] Apparently these were not marketed as successfully as those made by S.R. & L. Co. As early as 1870 this firm advertised for sales representatives — "Agents wanted EVERYWHERE to sell our planes." Apparently H. Chapin's Son were among agents for this line of planes, illustrating these on pages 20 & 21 of their 1874 catalogue, (See Chapter VIII), announcing that over "Fifty Thousand" of these planes had already been sold. Undoubtedly these were the iron planes to which they referred in their October 1872 Appendix to the 1870 catalogue. These illustrations in their 1874 catalogue were from the same cuts that appeared in a *Pocket Catalogue of the Metallic Plane Co.*[11] An 1878 brochure published by the Metallic Plane Co., announcing reduced prices is among the Chapin manuscript material at the Conn. Historical Society. (Plate VII)

Plate VII - 1878 Metallic Plane Co. Brochure
[Continued on Page 331]

1878.

REDUCED PRICE LIST
Metallic Plane Co.
AUBURN, N. Y.

Iron Planes, with Screw Adjustment and Moveable Throat.

No. 1, Smooth Plane, 8 in. long, 1¾ in cutter, - - Price each, $3 00
No. 2, Smooth Plane, 8 "   2   "   - - - " 3 25
No. 3, Smooth Plane, 8½ in. long, 2⅛ in cutter, - - - " 3 50
No. 4, Jack Plane, 15 in. long, 2⅛ in. cutter, - - - " 4 50
No. 5, Jointer Plane, 21 in. long, 2⅜ in cutter, - - - " 5 50

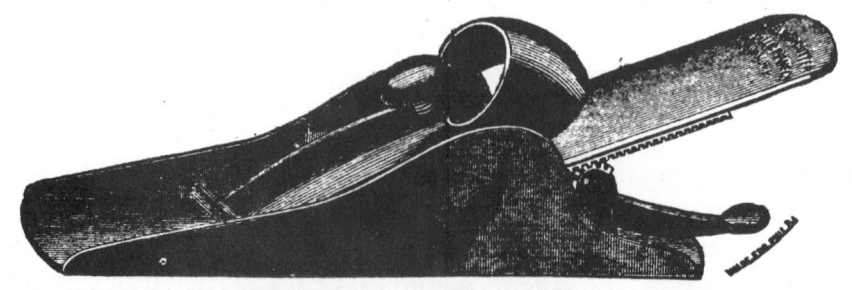

BLOCK PLANES.

No. 6, Block Plane, 6 in. long, 1 9-16 in. cutter, - - Price each, $ 70
No. 6½ " 5½ in. long, 1 9-16 in. cutter, - - " 70
No. 7, Block Plane, 6 in. long, 1 9-16 in. cutter, Adjustable Bit, " ~~1 10~~ 90.
No. 8, " 7½ in. long, 1¾ in. cutter, Handle and Knob and
   Adjustable Throat and Cutter, - - - " 1 50
No. 9, Block Plane, 8 in. long, 2 in cutter, Handle and Knob and
   Adjustable Throat and Cutter, - - - " 2 00

☞ Any of the Block Planes sent to any Address. post-paid, on receipt of list price.

Plate VII - 1878 Metallic Plane Co. Brochure
[Continued from Page 330]

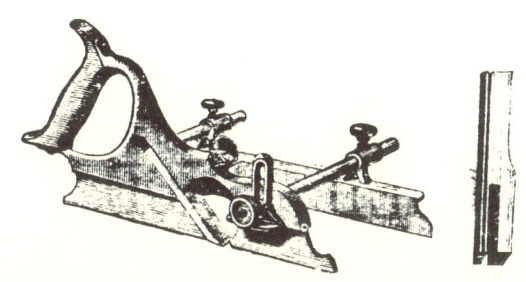

Combined Plow and Matching Plane.—$6.

This is a new and Perfect Tool of its class, combines both a Plow and Matching Plane, is cheaper than the wooden tools, and very much better. We supply a full set—eight Plow Bits and two Matching Irons all fitting the same stock. It is the BEST PLOW ever offered to our Mechanics.

Rabbett and Fillettster.—$4.

This is a beautifully working tool. By a moveable guide, or fence, any width can be cut up to two inches, and there is on each end a scale, by which to set the fence. It has a Spar and Stop, and will do the work of a full set of Rabbet Planes, and also of a Fillettster. It costs less than the same tools in wood.

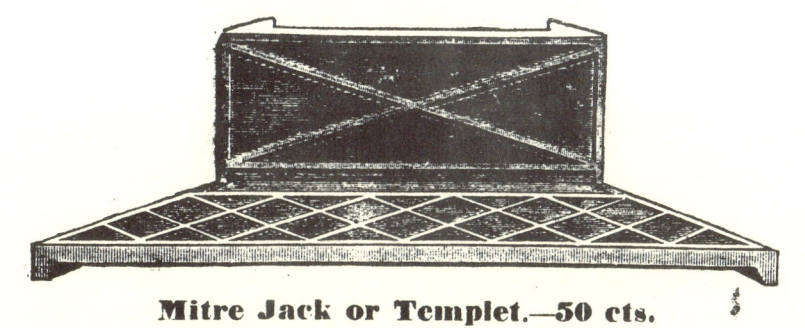

Mitre Jack or Templet.—50 cts.

This is a perfect and handy tool. Its angles are all exact and keep so. Every Wood-worker should have it. Indispensable for fitting Mouldings &c. ☞ Sent by mail, post-paid, on receipt of 50 cts.

Address E. G. STORKE, Business Manager,
AUBURN, N. Y.

A letter to H. Chapin's Son, dated January 11, 1876, soliciting a contract for an iron plane with a sketch of the proposed design by J. Pickersgill is transcribed in Table III. Undoubtedly E.M. Chapin received numerous similar requests.

Table III - Letter to E.M. Chapin from J. Pickersgill

```
                                    Box 3751 Post Office
                                    New York   11 Jan. 1876

H. Chapin's Son
Pine Meadow, Conn.

Dear Sir
            Your esteemed favor of 27 April 1875 with your Price
List and Illustrated Catalogue were duly received and would have
had earlier acknowledgement, but that during the fortnight which
elapsed from the date of my letter to the Hon'ble Henry L. James
and receipt of yours to me in reply thereto, negoiations had been
opened with a party who delayed action until it grew so late in
the season as to induce me to suspend further effort to get my
patent into operation until now.

            Allow me to remind you that my Bench Plane with a
semicircular bit is for both Iron and Wood.  It is simpler, easier
worked, and cost less to make than Bailey's of which the Stanley
Rule & Level Co. publish their sales on the 1st Oct. 1874 at over
80,000, and on the 1st April 1875 at over 90,000 Planes, making
an increase in their sales at the rate of 20,000 annually.

            The advantage gained by using planes having a semi-
circular bit arises from the fact that the bit requires little
pressure to hold it firmly in position in the stock, and conse-
quently can be easily regulated by the adjusting screw without
stopping to reset the bit.  Another advantage is that the bit
and clamping cap are out of the way, and do not obstruct the
passage of the shavings.

            You will much oblige me by candidly, and without
delay, informing me what kind of arrangement you would be willing
to make for the utilization of my Patent.  I would like to hear
from you as to how our respective interest would be made to
harmonize, and the extent to which you think sales of the Plane
can be effected.
                   I remain
                       Very respectfully,
                            J. Pickersgill
```

Illustration of Pickersgill Sem-circular Plane

Henry A. Foss of New Britain, Conn. was granted U.S. Patent No. 186,998, February 6, 1877 for an Improvement in Bench Planes. The drawing accompanying this patent is shown as Plate VIII. The brief in the *1877 U.S. Patent Gazette* stated:

> A very fine and delicate adjustment of the bit is had by means of a differential screw, one portion of which is connected with the bit, and the other with a stationary nut upon the other side of the plate which supports the bit. In combination with a body and bit of a bench-plane, a differential screw, one part working in connection with the bit, the other in a stationary nut, substantially as and for the purpose described."

This patent was assigned to Philip Chapin. Henry Foss came to Pine Meadow to superintend production of this plane at the Chapin Manufacturing Co. While there he was granted another plane patent, also assigned to Philip Chapin.[12]

A ten page pocket catalogue, *The Foss Patent Adjustable Plane,* was published in 1878 for Philip Chapin. (Plate IX) In all probability this project was financed by E.M. Chapin, as the Chapin Machine Co. went bankrupt. Apparently only a few of these planes were completed. An undated inventory made at the Chapin Manufacturing Co. listed several parts for making such planes, including patterns, tools and the license for the Foss patent, valued at $3000. (See Table IV)

The spokeshave illustrated in the brochure (Plate IX), referred to as the "Foss Iron Spokeshave" was actually patented by George D. Mosher of New Britain (U.S. Pat. No. 182,390) The notice of this in the *1882 H. Chapin's Son Catalogue* correctly referred to this as "Mosher's Patent Iron Spokeshave." (See Chapter VIII, p.79 of this catalogue) In all probability E.M. Chapin had paid Mosher a royalty fee for use of this patent. *The 1876 U.S. Patent Gazette* stated the following brief:

> "The knife is held in place and vertically adjustable by means of a clamp having a loop on its rear part and an inclined standard upon the body of the shave, between which the knife is fastened by a screw passing through the upper part of the clamp. The combination of a knife b, the clamp e, having the loop e', and the standard d, all as substantially described and for the purpose set forth." (See Sketch, Plate X)

About the time that Philip Chapin was experiencing these financial difficulties, the Stanley Rule & Level Co. received a Court judgment, June 21, 1878, that Leonard Bailey was infringing on patents held by them in the manufacture of his Victor plane.[13] (Plate XI)

The financial difficulties experienced in the failure of the Chapin Manufacturing Co. probably discouraged E.M. Chapin from investing further in metal planes. As pointed out in Chapter VIII, E.M. Chapin might have made use of Solon Rust's later patents which instead were used by Standard Rule Co. of Unionville, Conn.

After the failure of the Chapin Manufacturing Co., followed by the death of his first wife, Philip Chapin removed to Cleveland, Ohio. He remarried there and became general manager of the Cambria Iron Co. of Johnstown, Penn. He died in 1915, the only son of Hermon Chapin to live in the twentieth century.

334

Plate VIII -   Illustration of Foss Patented Iron Plane

H. A. FOSS.
BENCH-PLANE.

No. 186,998.　　　　　　　　　Patented Feb. 6, 1877.

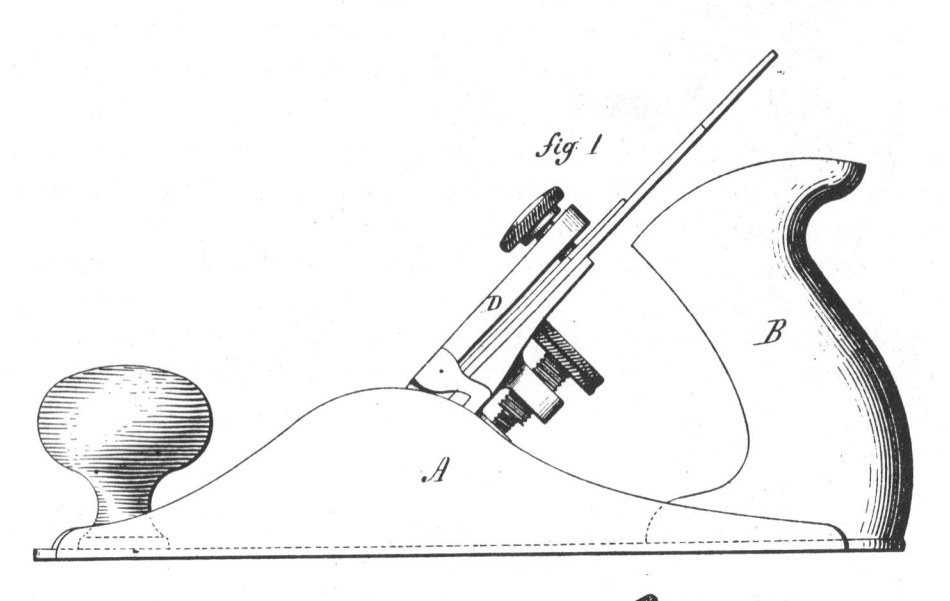

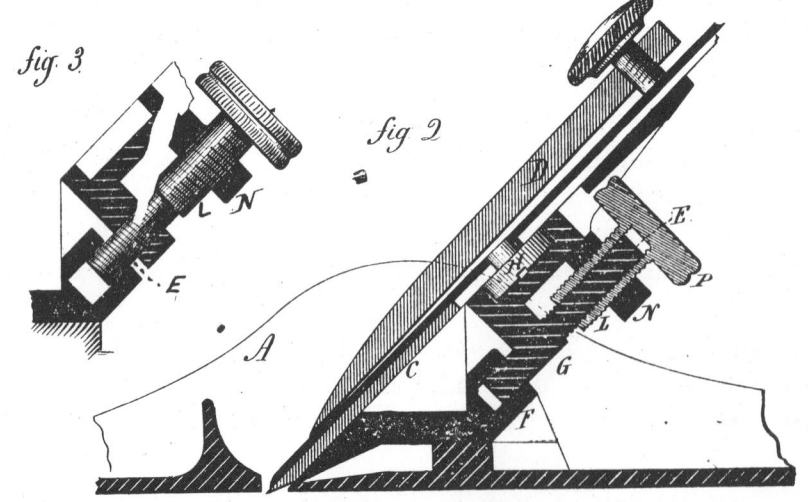

1879 Advertisement of Chapin Manufacturing Co. in *CONNECTICUT BUSINESS DIRECTORY*. [Collection of the Connecticut State Library]

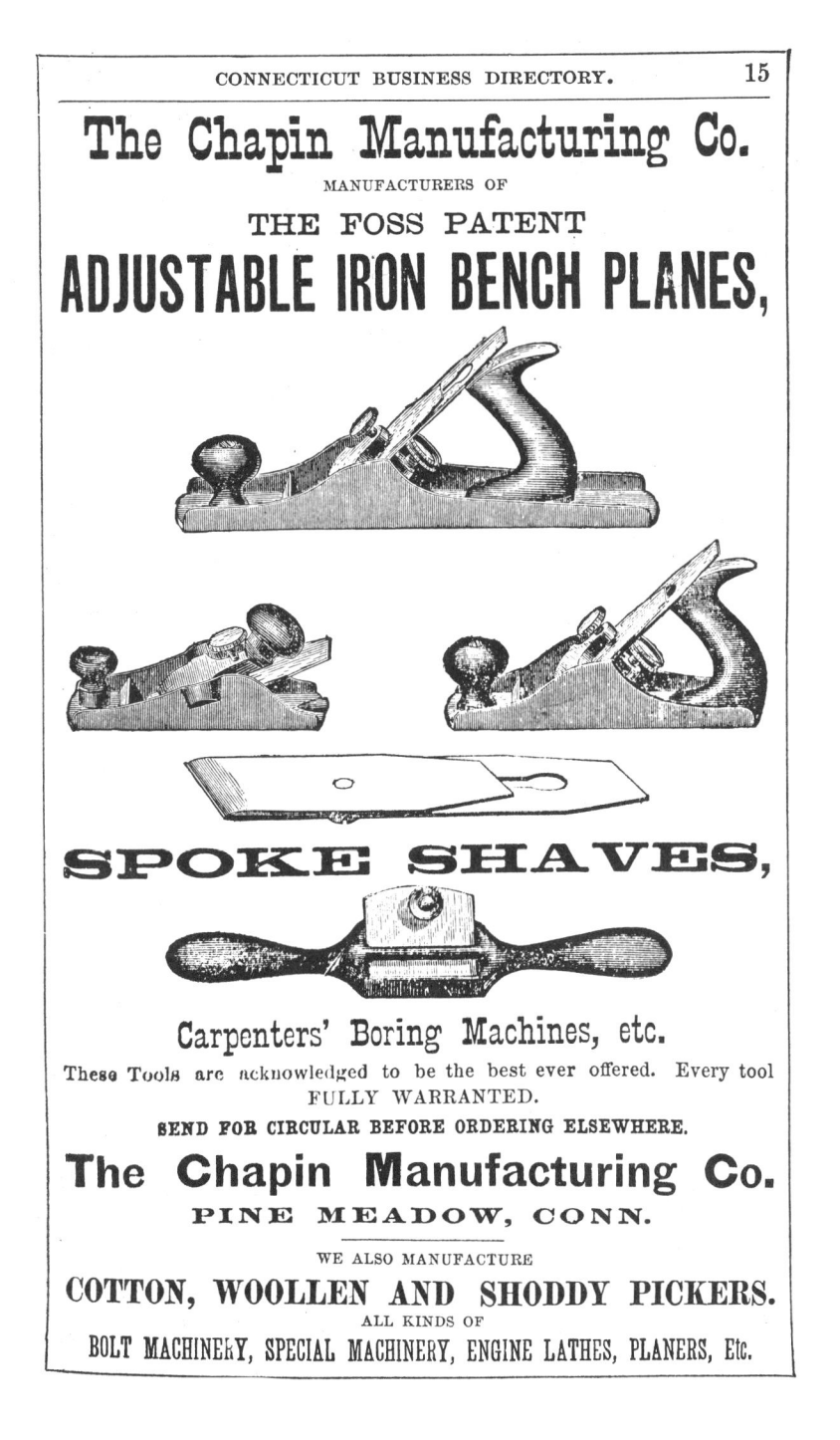

CONNECTICUT BUSINESS DIRECTORY. 15

The Chapin Manufacturing Co.

MANUFACTURERS OF

THE FOSS PATENT

ADJUSTABLE IRON BENCH PLANES,

SPOKE SHAVES,

Carpenters' Boring Machines, etc.

These Tools are acknowledged to be the best ever offered. Every tool FULLY WARRANTED.

SEND FOR CIRCULAR BEFORE ORDERING ELSEWHERE.

The Chapin Manufacturing Co.

PINE MEADOW, CONN.

WE ALSO MANUFACTURE

COTTON, WOOLLEN AND SHODDY PICKERS.

ALL KINDS OF

BOLT MACHINERY, SPECIAL MACHINERY, ENGINE LATHES, PLANERS, Etc.

Plate IX - Ten Page Pocket Catalogue Concerning Foss Patent Adjustable Iron Planes, etc. Manufactured by Philip Chapin, 1878. (Continued on pages 337 - 339)
[Collection of Connecticut Historical Society]

THE FOSS PATENT ADJUSTABLE IRON PLANES.

MANUFACTURED BY

PHILIP E. CHAPIN,

PINE MEADOW, CONN.

1878.

Reprinted by Ken Roberts Publishing Company with grateful acknowledgement to the Library of the Connecticut Historical Society for their permission. Sept. 1981

FOSS' IRON SPOKE-SHAVES.

No. 40. Raised Handle, 10½ inches in length, 2⅛ inch Cutter, per dozen, - - $2.00

No. 41. Raised Handle, 10½ inches in length, 2⅛ inch Cutter, round face to cut a convex, per dozen, - - - - 2.00

No. 42. Raised Handle, 10½ inches in length, 2⅛ inch Cutter, hollow face, per dozen, 2.00

No. 43. Double Cutter, 10½ inches in length, 1½ inch Cutter, one Cutter hollow and one straight, per dozen, - - - 3.00

Cutters for Spoke-shaves, per dozen, - - 1.00

Plate IX - (Continued from Page 336)

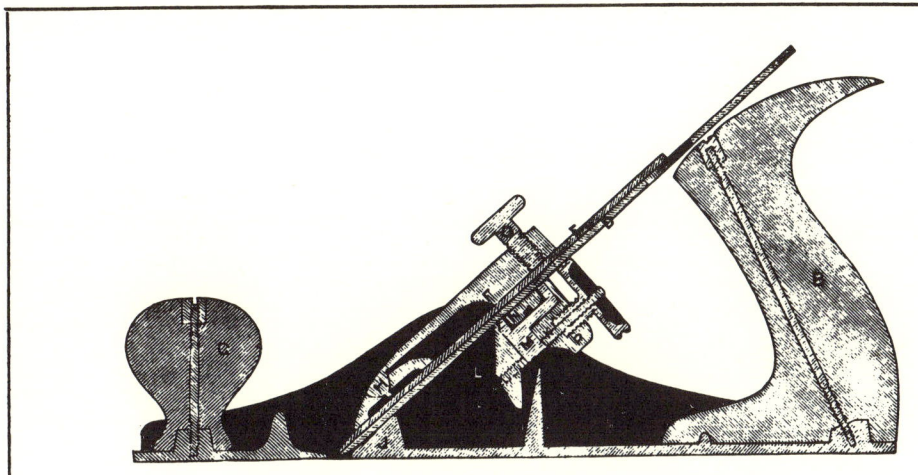

SECTIONAL VIEW OF THE FOSS PATENT PLANE.

FOSS' PATENT ADJUSTABLE
IRON BENCH PLANE.

The Cut on opposite page gives a sectional view of my Iron Smooth Plane.

The Bed A A is made in such a way that it cannot possibly warp, thereby insuring a perfectly straight face, a feature that is indispensable in a Bench Plane. The Handle B, and Knob C, are made of either wood or iron, to suit parties ordering; but unless iron is ordered, I prefer to put on wood, as I think wood is the best. It is easier to the hand while in constant use.

The Plane Iron D is made from the best English Cast Steel, and is tempered and ground by a process known only by us, and sharpened for immediate use before sent from the Factory. The Cap Iron E is also made from the best of steel, and is secured to the Plane Iron by an adjusting screw near the center.

The Cap F is in itself of great importance to a perfect Plane, and this improvement is controlled wholly by me. It is secured to the Plane by two ears or projections, one on each side, which is let into the sides A, and which act as a fulcrum, and is clamped by the thumb screw G. At the lower extremity of the cap is a joint H, which joint is a ball and socket, which is the fulcrum for the joint. The use of this joint is to insure a perfect bearing the whole width of the Plane Iron, thus preventing any possible chance for the Plane Iron chattering, which cannot be avoided in any other Plane made.

The seat J for the Plane Iron is cast on to the bed, which makes it as firm as solid iron can be, and is very broad, thus giving the Plane Iron a larger bearing than can be found in any other Plane. In most Planes this seat is a separate piece, and is secured to the bed piece with a screw, which is very liable to get loose and derange the working of the Plane.

In rear of the bit or Plane Iron D, and in a line substantially parallel thereto, is situated the adjustment for adjusting the Plane Iron to cut the shaving as coarse or fine as may be desired. One part, K, of the screw is arranged, its lower end supported in a suitable socket L, and with an arm M, extending toward the bit, and connected therewith through the cap screw N, so that the movement of the screw K will move the bit or Plane Iron accordingly. On to the part K, of the screw, the second tubular part O of the screw is set, threaded inside and out, the inside thread corresponding to the thread of the part K, and finer than the thread on the outside of the part O that is, so that there is a difference in the two threads (K being 24 threads to the inch, and O 18 threads to the inch). The part O is placed in a stationary nut P, and is provided with a suitable head by which it may be turned. The screw threads are both the same, that is, both right hand; therefore by turning the part O so as to run it downward, the part K will correspondingly run up into the part O, and the downward movement of the Plane Iron will be only the difference between the two threads, as for instance, the external thread of the part O, being 18 threads to the inch, and that of the part K, 24 threads to the inch; then a full revolution of part O would run that screw down one-eighteenth of an inch, and draw the part K up one twenty-fourth of an inch, and the bit would be moved 1-72d of an inch.

Every Plane is made interchangeable, so that when ordering any part or parts you can be sure of its fitting when you get it.

Any one having a Plane without an adjustment can order one and put it on without any trouble.

Plate IX - (Contined from Page 336)

FOSS' PATENT ADJUSTABLE PLANES.

We test every Plane at the factory, and see that every one is in perfect working order before sending out.

No mechanic should be without a complete set of The Foss Patent Planes. Every Plane warranted.

No. 0. Infant Plane, each, - - - - $0.25

No. 1. Block Plane, 6 inches in length, with Rosewood Knob and Handle, 1¾ inch Cutter, without Adjustment, - - .70

No. 2. Block Plane, 6 inches in length, Rosewood Knob and Handle, 1¾ inch Cutter, and with Nickel-Plated Adjustment, 1.00

No. 3. Block Plane, 6 inches in length, 1¾ inch Cutter, Adjustable Mouth, Rosewood Handle, without Adjustment, - 1.25

No. 4. Block Plane, 6 inches in length, 1¾ inch Cutter, Adjustable Mouth, Rosewood Handle, and Nickel-Plated Adjustment and Trimmings, - - - 1.50

No. 5. Smooth Plane, 7 inches in length, 1¾ inch Cutter, Rosewood Trimmings, without Adjustment, - - - $2.50

No. 6. Smooth Plane, 7 inches in length, 1¾ inch Cutter, Rosewood Trimmings, and with Nickel-Plated Adjustment, 3.00

No. 7. Smooth Plane, 8 inches in length, 1¾ inch Cutter, Rosewood Trimmings, without Adjustment, - - - 3.00

No. 8. Smooth Plane, 8 inches in length, 1¾ inch Cutter, Rosewood Trimmings, and Nickel-Plated Adjustment, - 3.50

No. 9. Smooth Plane, 9 inches in length, 2 inch Cutter, Rosewood Trimmings, without Adjustment, - - - 3.50

No. 10. Smooth Plane, 9 inches in length, 2 inch Cutter, Rosewood Trimmings, and Nickel-Plated Adjustment, - - 4.00

Plate IX - (Continued from Page 336)

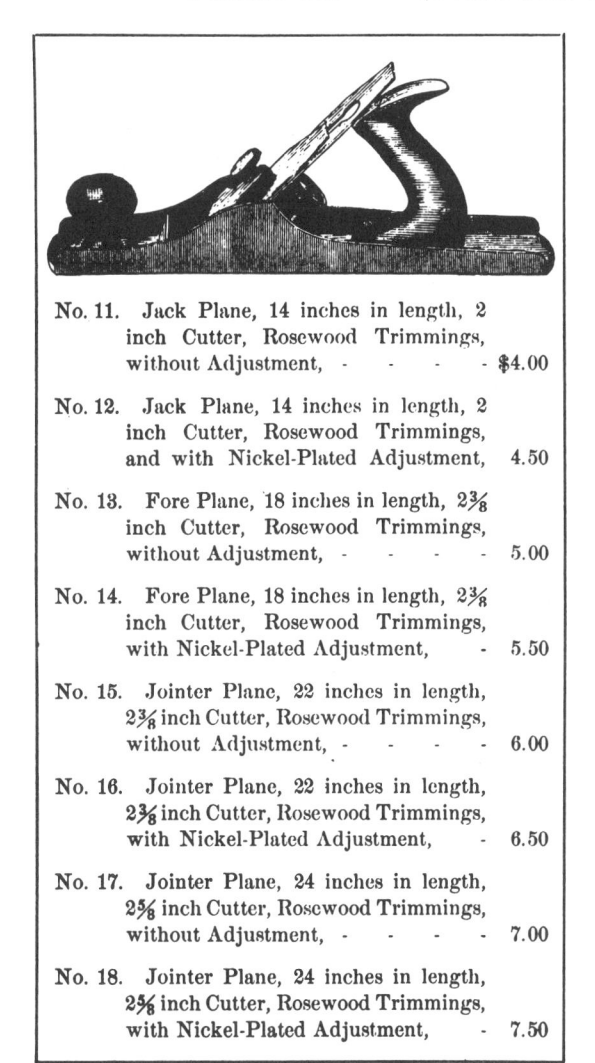

No. 11. Jack Plane, 14 inches in length, 2 inch Cutter, Rosewood Trimmings, without Adjustment, - - - - $4.00

No. 12. Jack Plane, 14 inches in length, 2 inch Cutter, Rosewood Trimmings, and with Nickel-Plated Adjustment, 4.50

No. 13. Fore Plane, 18 inches in length, 2⅜ inch Cutter, Rosewood Trimmings, without Adjustment, - - - 5.00

No. 14. Fore Plane, 18 inches in length, 2⅜ inch Cutter, Rosewood Trimmings, with Nickel-Plated Adjustment, 5.50

No. 15. Jointer Plane, 22 inches in length, 2⅜ inch Cutter, Rosewood Trimmings, without Adjustment, - - - 6.00

No. 16. Jointer Plane, 22 inches in length, 2⅜ inch Cutter, Rosewood Trimmings, with Nickel-Plated Adjustment, - 6.50

No. 17. Jointer Plane, 24 inches in length, 2⅝ inch Cutter, Rosewood Trimmings, without Adjustment, - - - 7.00

No. 18. Jointer Plane, 24 inches in length, 2⅝ inch Cutter, Rosewood Trimmings, with Nickel-Plated Adjustment, - 7.50

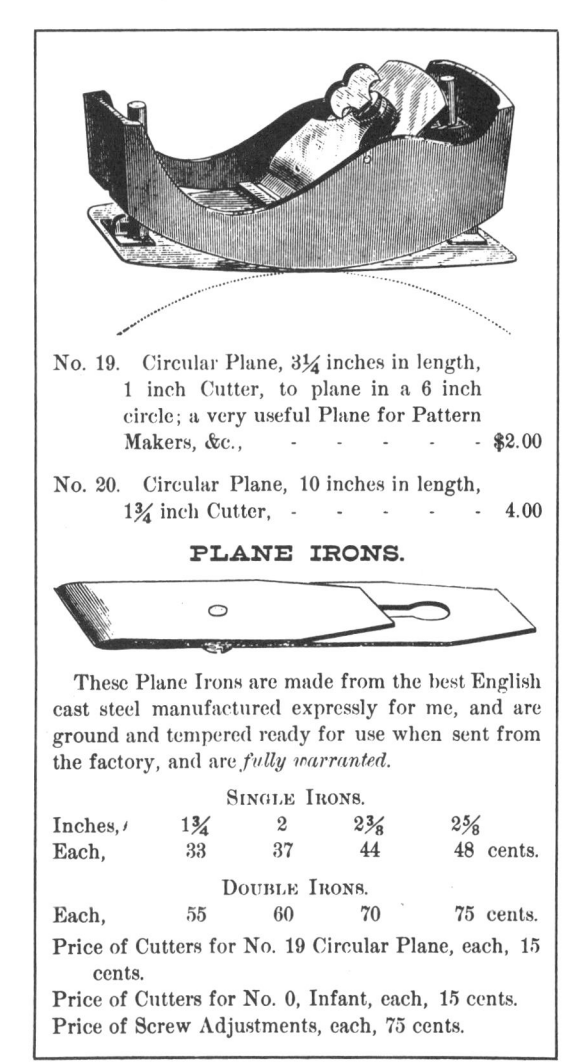

No. 19. Circular Plane, 3¼ inches in length, 1 inch Cutter, to plane in a 6 inch circle; a very useful Plane for Pattern Makers, &c., - - - - $2.00

No. 20. Circular Plane, 10 inches in length, 1¾ inch Cutter, - - - - 4.00

PLANE IRONS.

These Plane Irons are made from the best English cast steel manufactured expressly for me, and are ground and tempered ready for use when sent from the factory, and are *fully warranted*.

SINGLE IRONS.
Inches,	1¾	2	2⅜	2⅝
Each,	33	37	44	48 cents.

DOUBLE IRONS.
| Each, | 55 | 60 | 70 | 75 cents. |

Price of Cutters for No. 19 Circular Plane, each, 15 cents.
Price of Cutters for No. 0, Infant, each, 15 cents.
Price of Screw Adjustments, each, 75 cents.

IMPROVED BORING MACHINES.

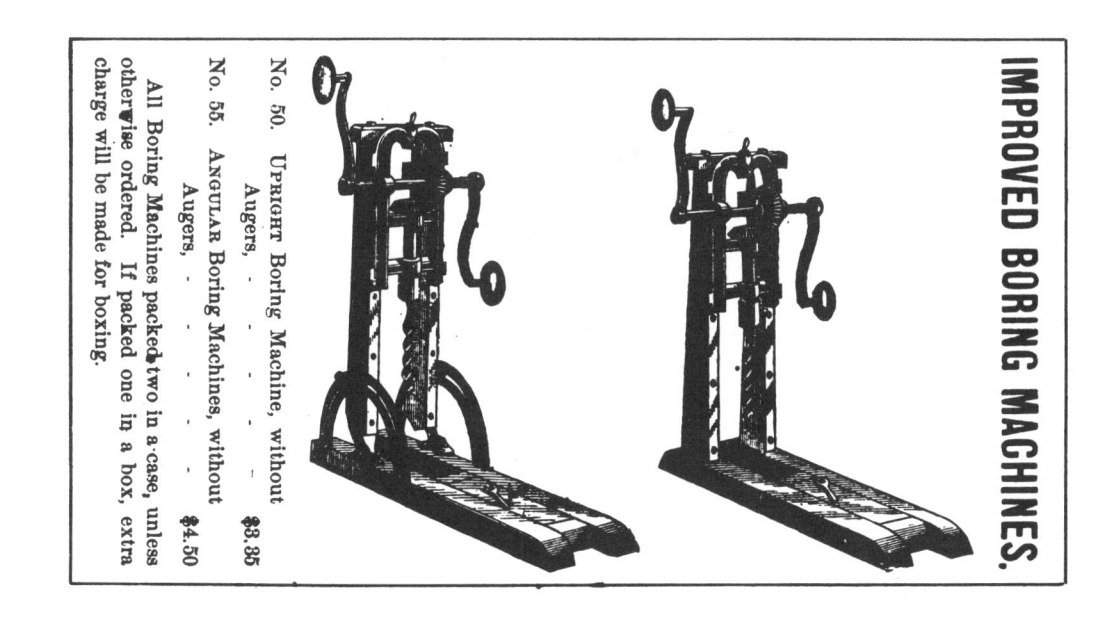

No. 50. Upright Boring Machine, without Augers, - - - $3.85

No. 55. Angular Boring Machines, without Augers, - - - $4.50

All Boring Machines packed two in a case, unless otherwise ordered. If packed one in a box, extra charge will be made for boxing.

Table IV - Inventory of Foss Patent Plane Parts

An undated inventory of the Chapin Manufacturing Co., believed to have been after the filing for bankrupcy, Feb. 5, 1877 of stock in process showed the following parts and products which were intended for H.Chapin's Son.

300 lbs. sheet steel for cutters	$45.00
900 Plane Handles	33.00
3000 Plane Handles partly finished	180.00
1000 #1 cutters	150.00
1200 #8 & #10 cutters	360.00
900 Infant Cutters	45.00
2000 spoke shave cutters	100.00
1200 Adjustments	120.00
1500 Thumb Screws	75.00
500 Jack Castings	75.00
48 doz. Spoke Shaves	48.00
36 #10 Smooth	72.00
30 #8 Smooth	52.50
4 #12 Jack	10.00
9 #2 Block	4.50
9 #4 Block	6.75
8 #1 Block	2.80
800 Plane Handles, Cocobola	80.00
800 Plane Knobs	25.00
Pattern & Tools for Foss Plane & LicenseFoss Pat. Plane	3000.00

[Document in Collection of New Hartford Historical Society]

Plate X - Geo. D. Mosher's Spokeshave Patent
[*U.S. Patent Gazette*, Sept. 19, 1876, p.479]

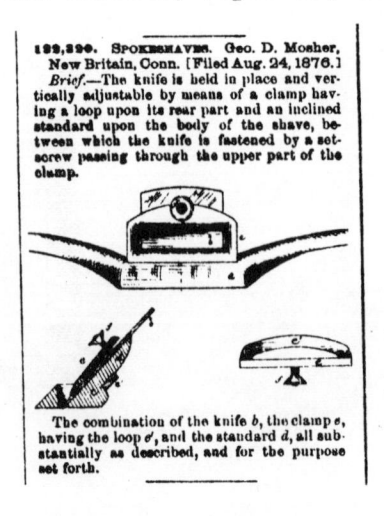

Plate XI - Announcement made by Stanley Rule & Level Co.
[Chapin Manuscript Files, CHS, Hartford, CT.]

The public will take notice, that on the 21st day of June 1878, Judge Shipman, filed an opinion in the Clerks Office of the United States Circuit Court, in which he decided that the Victor Plane, made by Leonard Bailey, of Hartford, Conn., is an infringement of the exclusive rights of the Stanley Rule & Level Company, to make and sell Planes under the Bailey re-issue of June 22d, 1875. The following is an extract from the opinion giving the Judges construction of the fourth claim of the Letters Patent under which the Stanley Rule & Level Company are acting, both in making Planes and prosecuting infringers.

"Construed in connection with the descriptive part of the specification and in view of the state of the Art, the fourth claim is for the combination, substantially as described of the cutter-iron and cap-iron adjustably united by a screw in the cap-iron to the plane iron, [being the ordinary compound plane iron,] and the lever operating by positive connection with the cap-iron, to adjust the cutting iron up and down between the same limits as those in which the cap-iron move."

We therefore caution the public against buying the Victor Plane, and all other Planes in which a compound plane iron is adjusted by a lever connected with the cap-iron, as we shall protect our rights against all who infringe by making, or selling, or using such Planes not manufactured by ourselves.

STANLEY RULE & LEVEL CO.

New Britain, July 2d, 1878.

Notes - Chapter IX

1. New Hartford Land Records, B.21, p. 252
2. *op. cit., History of Litchfield County*, p. 410
3. New Hartford Land Records, B.22, p. 369
4. *ibid*, B.23, p. 666
5. *ibid*, B.23, p. 559
6. *op. cit., Patented Transitional & Metallic Planes in America, 1827-1927*, pp.13-16
   pp. 13 - 16
7. K.D.Roberts, *1870 Stanley Rule & Level Co. Catalogue*, Documentary note
8. Reprinted by Ken Roberts Publishing Co., 1978
9. A transitional plane has a wooden sole and cast iron superstructure.
10. K.D and J.W. Roberts, *op. cit., New York Planemakers, etc.*, pp. 134-135
    See also, Note 6 above, pp. 170 - 177
11. Compare with Fig. 208, PP. 172 - 173, Note 6 above.
12. Note 6 above, p.70
13. *Leonard Bailey & Co. 1876 Catalogue*, Reprint by Ken Roberts Publishing Co., Documentary. See also Note 6 above, p. 271

Chapter X

Levels & Marking Gauges

Mass production of levels for the woodworking trades did not become common until the mid 19th century.[1] The bubble glass, consisting of a glass tube, containing alcohol and sealed an air bubble, known as a vial, was the heart of a level. Before levels could be economically manufactured, it was essential to develop sources of supply for such spirit glasses. John Staniford at Boston offered such a product. (See Plate I)

Plate I - John Staniford & Son, Plumb & Level Glass Manufacturers

JOHN STANIFORD & SON,
MANUFACTURERS OF
Plumb and Level GLASSES,
EAST CAMBRIDGE, MASS.

[JOHN STANIFORD.]   [JOHN W. STANIFORD]
(OVER.)

List of Prices.
[FEB. 1st, 1866.]

	Proved.	Unproved.
1 3-4 in. Per Gross,	$7 20	$6 00
2 in. " "	7 20	6 00
2 1-2 in. " "	7 65	6 45
3 in. " "	8 10	7 00
3 1-2 in. " "	9 00	7 85
4 in. " "	9 90	8 75
4 1-2 in. " "	10 80	9 50
Assorted from 3 to 4 1-2,	9 45	8 20

ALL ORDERS ADDRESSED
JOHN STANIFORD & SON
EAST CAMBRIDGE, MASS.
Or, to Mason Brothers, Boston,
Will receive immediate attention.

No. 18 WINTER STREET,
East Cambridge, Mass., July 1865.

Gents:

The undersigned would respectfully inform the Trade, that they have formed a Copartnership for carrying on the

MANUFACTURE OF PLUMB AND LEVEL GLASSES,
OF SUPERIOR QUALITY,

Such as have been manufactured for the last 30 years by the Senior Partner, which for accuracy, quality and workmanship they refer to the annexed Certificate of well-known manufacturers of Spirit Levels

JOHN STANIFORD & SON.

BOSTON, JULY 7, 1865.

This is to certify, that we have used JOHN STANIFORD'S LEVEL GLASSES in the Manufacture of our SPIRIT LEVELS, and found them to be of a very superior quality.

JOHN MULLIKEN.
JOHN W. STACKPOLE.

I fully endorse the above recommendation.

JOHN HARMON,
Successor to Mulliken & Stackpole.

Prices for Proved Glasses, $8.50 per Gross, nett Cash.
" " Unproved " 6.50 " " "

The most common woods used in making levels were cherry, mahogany and rosewood. In this application the requirements for wood are dimensional stability and resistance to wear. A finish was applied to produce a surface impervious to moisture.

The first firm in the state of Connecticut to manufacture levels on a large scale is believed to have been Hall & Knapp at New Britain. This concern was organized by Thomas Hall and Francis Knapp in 1852.[2] They incorporated in 1857.[3] On September 27, 1858 they merged with A. Stanley & Co., also of New Britain, thus forming the Stanley Rule & Level Co.[4] Their 1859 price list noted 22 varieties of wooden levels.[5] (17 mahogany; 4 rosewood and 1 cherry; and 4 metal)

L. & C.H. DeForest of Birmingham, Conn. listed 38 varieties of levels made from cherry, rosewood, mahogany or zebrawood and 22 of their "Patent Mosaic Spirit Levels" in their 1860 catalogue. (Plate II) Within this catalogue was stated:

"The attention of the Public is called to the 'Patent Mosaic Level. Each Level is composed of 100 to 500 pieces of wood of various kinds and colors, thus producing an article combining great beauty and utility, as the Level can neither warp or twist, and it is warranted ever to remain perfect."

Plate II - 1860 *L. & C.H. DeFOREST* Trade Catalogue
[Collection of Connecticut Historical Society]

PRICE LIST

OF

Joiners' Bench Planes,

MOULDING PLANES,

AND

SPIRIT LEVELS,

MANUFACTURED BY

L. & C. H. DeFOREST,

BIRMINGHAM, CONN.

NEW HAVEN:
J. H. BENHAM, PRINTER, COR. CHURCH AND CHAPEL STREETS.
1860.

It is not known the exact year that H. Chapin began to make levels. However it was sometime after 1853 and before 1858. The first dated catalogue to include levels is the 1858, which lists 26 bench and 2 pocket levels. (Plate III) What is believed to be an earlier undated catalogue, possibly 1857, noted 16 bench and one pocket level. (Plate IV) The earliest illustrations of H. Chapin's levels appeared in the *1869 Illustrated Catalogue and Price List of Hardware and Mechanics' Tools of Sargent & Co.*[6] These were the Nos. 290 and 297 Plumbs and Levels, which also appeared in the 1874 Chapin Price List. (See Chapter VII, pg. 61 of the 1874 Catalogue) The No. 290 was made from cherry, while the No. 297 was mahogany, furnished with machined cast brass angles (tips) on each corner and brass side castings (lips), adjacent to the spirit bubble. Both of these were also available after 1858 at slightly higher prices with a graduated adjustment to work at any elevation as Nos. 302 & 308. (see page 62 of 1882 Catalogue, Chapter VIII) The most expensive level was the No. 300 made from triple stock of laminated rosewood.

Plate III - Page 12 from 1858 Union Factory Price List

Plate IV - Page 12 from an Earlier Undated Union Factory Price List.

Plate III — H. CHAPIN'S PRICE LIST (Page 12)

Invoice No's	Hand and Bench Screws	Price per doz.
269	Bench Screws, Wrought Iron, Double Thread, 1 inch	15.00
270	do do do Collar, 1 inch	16.00
271	do do do 1⅛ inch	18.00
272	do do do Collar, 1⅛ inch	19.00

	Handles	
273	Jack Plane Handles	.85
274	Fore Plane Handles	1.45
275	Saw Handles	3.50
275½	do extra	4.00
276	Firmer Chisel Handles, Feruled, Hickory and Apple	.68
277	Paring do do do	.87
278	Socket, do do	.50
279	Auger Handles	.67

	Screw Drivers	
280	Screw Drivers, 4 inch	2.50
281	do 6 inch	3.00
282	do 8 inch	8.30
283	do 10 inch	4.10
284	do 12 inch	4.60

	Spirit Levels	
285	Level, to 12 inch	4.00
286	do to 18 inch	5.00
287	do to 28 inch	6.50
288	Plumb and Level, to 12 inch	6.50
289	do to 18 inch	7.50
290	do to 28 inch	9.50
291	do Tipped, to 12 inch	17.00
292	do do to 18 inch	18.00
293	do do to 28 inch	22.00
294	do do Triple Stock, to 28 inch	24.00
295	do do Mahogany, to 12 inch	22.00
296	do do do to 18 inch	24.00
297	do do do to 28 inch	28.00
298	do do do Triple Stock, to 28 inch	33.00
299	do do Rosewood, to 12 inch	32.00
300	do do do to 18 inch	35.00
301	do do do Triple Stock, to 28 inch	48.00
302	do Adjusting, to 12 inch	12.00
303	do do to 18 inch	18.00
304	do do to 28 inch	17.00
305	do do Tipped, to 12 inch	24.00
306	do do do to 18 inch	25.00
307	do do do to 28 inch	30.00
308	do do do Mahogany, to 12 inch	28.00
309	do do do do to 18 inch	30.00
310	do do do do to 28 inch	38.00
311	Pocket Levels	2.00
312	do with Brass Top	2.50

Plate IV — PRICE LIST (Page 12)

Invoice No's	Hand and Bench Screws	Price per doz.
269	Bench Screws, Wrought Iron, Double Thread, 1 inch	$15.00
270	do do do Collar, 1 inch	16.00
271	do do do 1⅛ inch	18.00
272	do do do Collar, 1⅛ inch	19.00

	Handles	
273	Jack Plane Handles	1.00
274	Fore Plane Handles	1.45
275	Saw Handles	3.00
276	Firmer Chisel Handles, Feruled, Hickory and Apple	.68
277	Paring do do do	.87
278	Socket, do do	.50
279	Auger Handles	.60

	Screw Drivers	
280	Screw Drivers, 4 inch	2.30
281	do 6 inch	2.75
282	do 8 inch	3.00
283	do 10 inch	3.75
284	do 12 inch	4.25

	Spirit Levels	
285	Level, to 12 inch	3.00
286	do to 18 inch	4.50
287	do to 28 inch	6.00
288	Plumb and Level, to 12 inch	5.50
289	do to 18 inch	7.00
290	do to 28 inch	8.50
291	do Tipped, two Side Views, to 12 inch	22.00
292	do do to 18 inch	24.00
293	do do to 28 inch	26.00
294	Plumb & Level, Tip'd with G S, Rose or Satinwood, to 12 inch	30.00
295	do do do to 18 inch	35.00
296	do do do to 28 inch	40.00
297	do Adjusting, to 28 inch	20.00
298	do Double, Adjusting, to 28 inch	22.50
299	do Tipped, Adjusting, to 28 inch	26.00
300	do Double, Tipped, Adjusting, to 28 inch	28.00
301	Pocket Level	2.00

Stanley Rule & Level Co. offered improved patented adjustable levels and plumbs in 1867.[7] Leonard Davis of Springfield, Mass. was granted two patents for adjusting levels, one in 1868 and one in 1871.[8] On October 16, 1877 Davis assigned one third of his interests in both of these patents to H. Chapin's Son. (See Plate V) These were illustrated in H. Chapin's Son's 1882 catalogue. (See pages 67 & 70, 1882 Catalogue, Chapter VIII)

From time to time E.M. Chapin received letters soliciting his interests in designs of tools Such was a letter from B.F. Neal of Waterbury, Conn., dated September 26, 1870:

> "...I have no model of my Level, but have made a hasty sectional sketch by which you can understand my invention [Plate VI] perfectly, which I enclose with a brief description. If you like it, I will tell you what arrangement I would like to make with you for its manufacture, but if you do not, will you please send it back to me and all will be alright..."

Apparently this unsolicited sketch was not returned to its owner, but it not believed that this feature was ever offered in any levels made by Chapin.

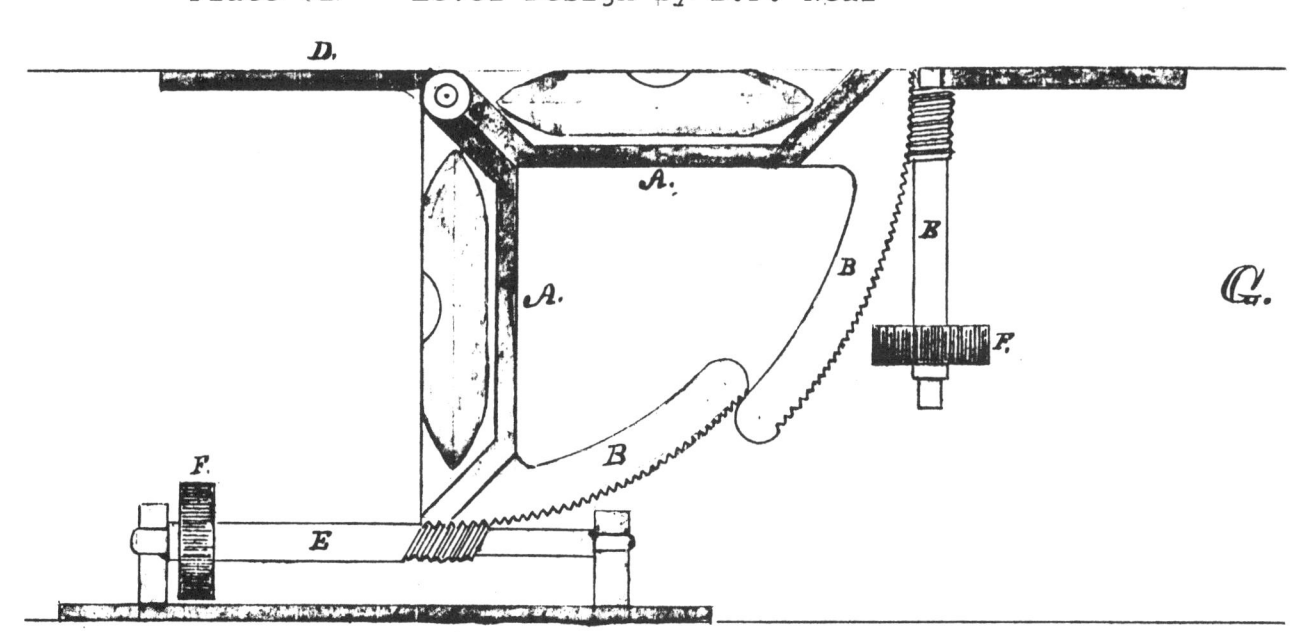

Plate VI - Level Design by B.F. Neal

Martin Wilcox of New Hartford, Conn. was granted U.S. Patent No. 178,354 on June 6, 1876 for "Improvement in Spirit Levels." This featured an adjustment device for the vial. This patent was assigned to H. Chapin's Son. Details of this arrangement are described and illustrated on page 64 of their 1882 Catalogue. (See Chapter VIII)

Another competitive firm manufacturing levels was Stratton Brothers of Greenfield, Mass.[9] Their U.S. Patent No. 100,413, dated March 1, 1870, was concerned with protection of the edges and corners of a level, inserting brass rods throughout the entire length and sides and a brass casting at each end. After this patent expired, both Stanley Rule and Level Co. and H. Chapin's Son copied this feature.[10] This was noted as "Chapin's Improved Brass Cornered Level," illustrated in Fig. 62 and also in a sketch from a Chapin catalogue. (Plate VII) This was available in cherry, mahogany and rosewood.

Levels were an important part of the products of various Chapin firms, continuing through the tenure of the Chapin-Stephens Co. A later detail, concerning the Voss patent aluminum level, will be described in Chapter 12.

Plate V - Leonard Davis Letter of Assignment of 1/3 Patent Rights to H. Chapin's Son
[Manuscript Material, Chapin Collection, Connecticut Historical Society] (Ms 6493)

Know all Men by these Presents That I, Leonard L. Davis of Springfield, Hampden Co. Mass. in consideration of one dollar and other consideration to me rendered and paid by H. Chapin's Son of New Hartford, State of Connecticut the receipt whereof is hereby acknowledged do hereby sell and assign to the said Chapin one undivided third part of the Letters Patent of the United States to me granted and severally entitled, dated and numbered as follows; to wit. Letters Patent for Improvement in Adjustable Spirit Levels dated March 17, 1868 and numbered 75,504 and Letters Patent for Improvement in Spirit Levels dated Nov. 21, 1871 numbered 121,088 together with all the rights in and to the inventions therein described and thereby secured. The same to be held and enjoyed by the said Chapin to the full end of the several terms for which said Letters Patent were respectively granted as fully and entirely, as the same would have been held and enjoyed by me if this assignment had not been made.

Witness my hand and seal this sixtieth day of October, A.D. 1877

In presence of

Noah D. Chaffee.

Leonard L. Davis.

Fig. 62 - Union Factory Levels. Bottom: 28 inch #306 Cherry, Graduated Adjusting, Brass-Lipped
Center: 28 " No.3 Rosewood, "Chapin's Improved Brass Corners" "
Top: 28 "   Solid Cherry,   "   "   "   "

Plate VII - Page 40, *CHAPIN-STEPHENS CO. CATALOGUE No. 114*

40   THE CHAPIN-STEPHENS CO., PINE MEADOW, CONN.

CHAPIN'S IMPROVED BRASS CORNERED
Extra Quality
PLUMBS AND LEVELS

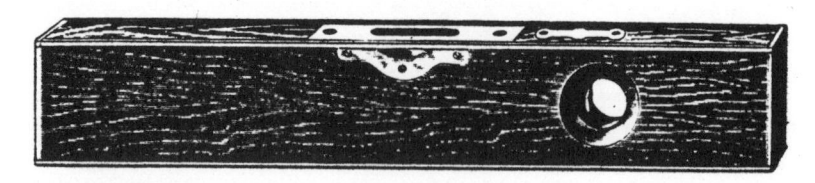

Patent Adjustable Plumbs and Levels, Brass Corners, Heavy Brass Top Plates and Ends, Brass Lipped Side Views.

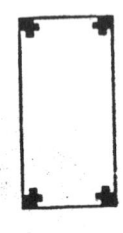

End view of our Brass Cornered Level, with tip removed, showing Solid Brass Corners Dovetailed into Wood.

No.
1. Solid Cherry, ... 18, 24, 26, 28, 30 inch
2. Solid Mahogany, ... 18, 24, 26, 28, 30 inch
3. Solid Rosewood, ... 18, 24, 26, 28, 30 inch

MACHINISTS' LEVELS

No. 10    No. 12
Extra Quality

10. Solid Rosewood Plumb and Level, Brass Corners, Heavy Brass Top, Plates and Ends, Brass Side Views, 8, 10, and 12 inch

12. Solid Rosewood Level (no Plumb), Extra Quality, Brass Corners, Heavy Brass Top Plate and Ends, Brass Side Views, Length, 6½ inches

All brass cornered Plumbs and Levels are highly polished the natural color of the wood.

[Reprinted by Ken Roberts Publishing Co.]

When Hermon Chapin first apprenticed to the firm of D. & M. Copeland in May 1822, the firm offered a line of "gages." (See Plate IV, Chapter I) Chapin's 1839 Price List noted five types of gauges: marking, cutting, mortise, panel and slitting, (Plate IV, page 8, 1839 Catalogue, Chapter III) A simple marking gauge had a single point at one end of a bar on which a sliding head was mounted. The head was fixed with a thumb screw or wedge. A mortise (spelled mortice, until 1862) gauge had two points on the same side; one fixed and the other on an adjustable slide. A panel gauge had a longer bar with a wider adjustable fence. A slitting gauge was similar to a panel gauge, except that a knife was mounted on the end of the bar, instead of a marking pin, and often had a handle on the fence.

As mentioned in Chapter VI, during the period 1856-1865 the Chapin firms may have purchased gauges from the firm R.H. Wheeler and their successor, Steele, Clark & Co. Title pages of these two firms' catalogues are shown as Plate VIII. The spelling "guages" in these two instances may have been an archaic spelling of gauge or a printer's error.

Christian Sholl of Mount Joy, Penn. was granted US Patent No. 41,867 on March 8, 1864 for "Improvement in Joiners Gages."[11] This consisted of a gauge the stem of which was comprised of three or four arms, each independently adjustable, and held by a single thumbscrew. The four arm version is illustrated on page 64 of the *1874 H. Chapin's Son Catalogue* (see Chapter VIII). The same cut was used in the 1869 Sargent & Co. catalogue, and reference is made to it being in the January 1869 H. Chapin's Son list in the June 1869 Discount List. This was offered through the *1897 H. Chapin's Son & Co. Catalogue* in both three and four bar designs in rosewood and mahogany. Both designs in rosewood are illustrated in Fig. 63.

John W. Butler of New Britain, Conn. was granted US Patent No. 134,729 on January 14, 1873 for "Improvement in Gages." He stated: — "In my improved gage the slide is made fast on the bar by simply rotating the slide partially in either direction." This design was based on a double wedge fitted within the slide, which ran in a groove on the bar, and became locked in turning the slide, the concave surface of the wedge being eccentric to the central hole in the slide. (See Plate IX) The terms of agreements with E.M. Chapin for using this patent are transcribed in Table I. Since Butler was from New Britain, he may have offered this design to Stanley Rule & Level Co. before H. Chapin's Son, This first appeared in the *1874 H. Chapin's Son Catalogue,* made in beech, applewood and rosewood in the forms of marking and mortise gauges. The Catalogue stated: — "These Gauges meet with universal approbation from the best mechanics, superior for its convenience in adjusting, so easily done by holding the Bar and turning the Head either way." Apparently these were not very successful, as this item was not listed in the *1882 H. Chapin's Son Catalogue.*

On April 16, 1872 John A. Marden, then of Veazie, Maine was granted US Patent No. 125,823 for "Improvement in Gages." On October 28, 1873 an agreement was signed between Marden and E.M. Chapin for the latter's use of this patent. (See Table II) Subsequently Marden wrote E.M. Chapin on December 12, 1873 (See Table III) and sent his description and drawings of this gauge. (See Plate X) Illustrations of this gauge are shown on page 61 of the *1882 H. Chapin's Son Catalogue* (See Chapter VIII) and in Fig. 64. This gauge must have been reasonably well received as it was continued through the *1902 Chapin-Stephens Catalogue,* but did not appear in the 1905 issue.

Another attempt to interest E.M. Chapin in a new product was W. A. Lee's letter of July 25, 1871 in an improved rule. (See Table IV) Apparently nothing further developed on this item.

Plate VIII - Price Lists of "GUAGES" [sic] R.H. Wheeler (left) & Steele, Clark & Co. (right)

RICHARD H. WHEELER

MANUFACTURER OF

GUAGES.

NEW HARTFORD, CONN.

SCREW-SLIDE MORTICE GUAGES.

No.					per doz.	
1	Common Beech			Ruled	$	94
2	"	"		"		1 00
3	"	"	Cutting		"	2 00
4	Appletree			"		1 50
5	Box or Rosewood, Brass Screws				"	2 75
6	"	"	"	Plated	"	5 00
7	Appletree Cutting				"	2 50
8	Best Mahogany or Appletree, Marking				"	4 00
9	"	"	"	Oval Head,	"	3 00
10	Beech Panel Ruled, Brass Screws				"	4 00
11	Appletree	"	"	"	"	5 00
12	Mahogany	"	"	Plated	"	10 00
13	Rosewood	"	"	"	"	15 00
14	Mahogany or Appletree, Thumb Slide				"	5 00
15	"	"	"	"	"	6 00
16	"	"	Screw Slide		"	7 00
17	Rose or Boxwood,		"	"	"	8 00
18	"	"	Brass Plated, Screw Slide,		"	13 00
19	"	"	Head & Bar Plated		"	15 00
20	"	"	"	"	"	11 00
21	"	"	"	"	"	10 00
22	Beech Slitting Handles,				"	9 00
23	"	"	Rollers		"	10 00

Terms, Cash on Delivery of Goods.

ALL GOODS DELIVERED AT COLLINSVILLE DEPOT.

HERALD PRINT, WINSTED, CONN.

PRICE LIST OF

GUAGES

MANUFACTURED BY

STEELE, CLARK & CO.,

NEW HARTFORD, CONN.

SUCCESSORS OF

R. H. WHEELER.

April 1, 1865.

Terms Cash on delivery of Goods. All Goods delivered at the Collinsville Depot. No charge for Boxes.

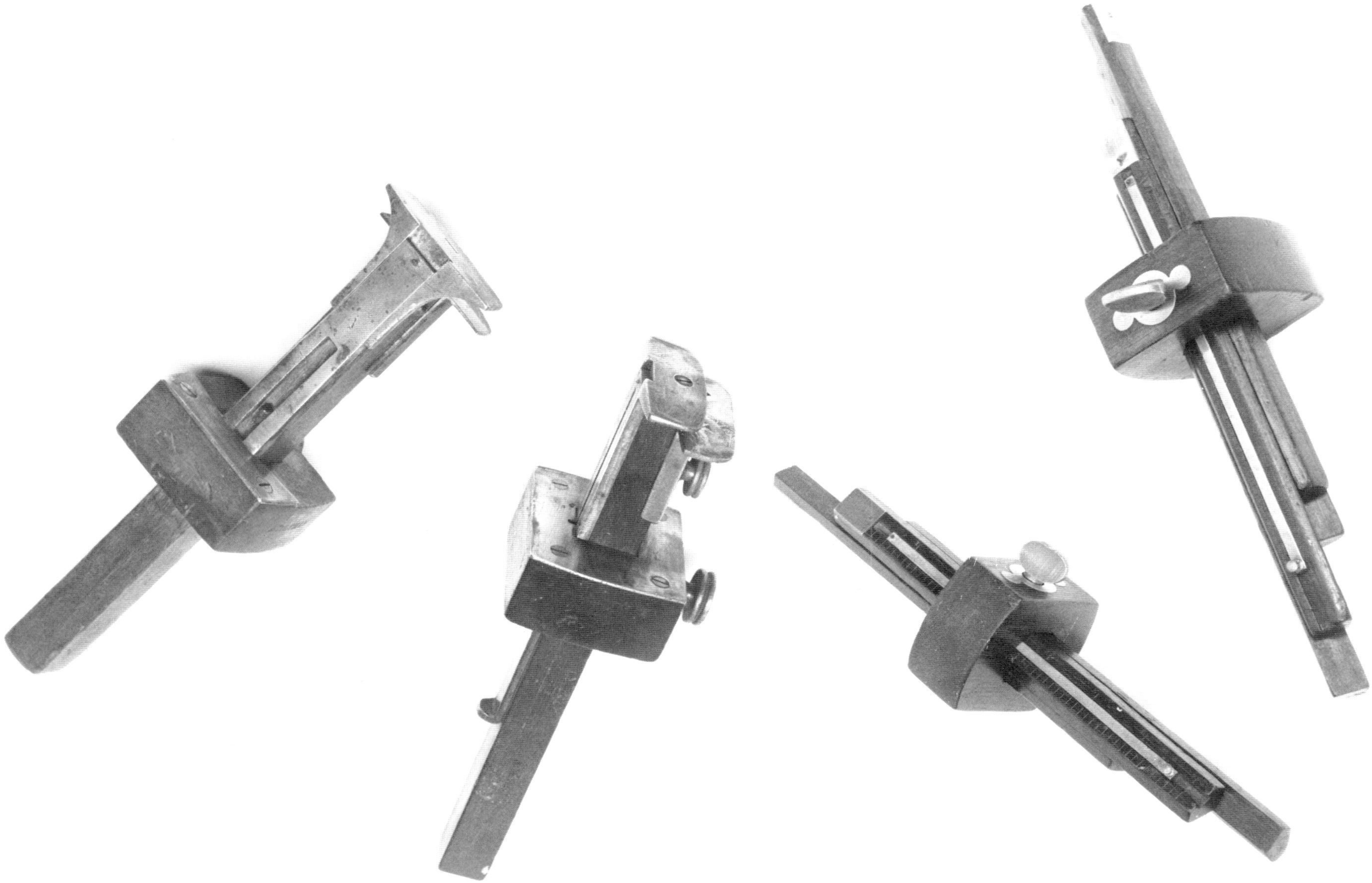

Fig. 63 - Marking Gauges Manufactured by E.M. Chapin's UNION FACTORY. Two by J.A. Marden's Patent (left); Two by C. Sholl's Patent (right); Upper right Four Slide Arms; Lower right Three Slide Arms.

Table I

AGREEMENT BETWEEN JOHN W. BUTLER AND E. M. CHAPIN, MARCH 31, 1873

This agreement made this 31st day of March AD 1873 between John W. Butler of New Britain, Connecticut, party of the first part, and Edw. M. Chapin of New Hartford, Conn., party of the second part, Witnesseth -

That whereas letters patent of the United States was on the 14th day of January AD 1873 granted to the sd. party of the first part for an Improvement in Carpenter's Gauges, which sd. patented article sd. party of the second part is desirous to make & sell, now therefore the parties have agreed as follows -

The party of the first part hereby gives to the party of the second part, the exclusive right to manufacture and sell sd. patented improvement to the end of the term of sd. patent - subject to the conditions hereafter named -

The party of the second part agrees to make full and true returns during the months of January, April, July & October in each quarter to the 1st day up to sd. months respectively of all the sd. Carpenter's Gauges sold by him in the three calandar months then last past, and if said party of the first part shall not be satisfied, in any respect with any such returns, then he shall have the right, either by himself or his attorney, to examine any and all the books of account of sd. party of the second part. concerning any items, charges, memorandums or information relative to the manufacture or sale of sd. patented Gauges, and upon request such, sd. party of the second part shall produce all such books for sd. examination.

The party of the second part agrees to pay the party of the first part a royalty of (5%), five per cent, upon the net sales of sd. Gauges sold by him, the whole of the sd. royalty for each quarterly term of three months as heretofore specified to be due and payable within fifteen days after the regular return day for that quarter, and sd. party of the second part agrees to pay the party of the first part at least twenty five dollars as sd. royalty, upon each of sd. quarterly terms, even though he should not sell enough of sd. patented Gauges to amount to that sum at the regular royalty of five per cent,

Upon failure of the party of the second part to make returns, or to make payment of license fees as herein provided, for thirty days after such returns or such payments are due respectively, then the party of the first part may terminate this license by serving a written notice to that effect upon the party of the second part, but sd. party of the second part shall not thereby be discharged from any liability to the party of the first part for any license fees due at the time up to the service of said notice.

The party of the first part hereby claims the payment of the sum of Twenty five dollars as expressed in article three for the three months ending June 30, 1873.

In witness whereof the above named parties hereunto set their hands & seals this day and year first above written.

John W. Butler
E. M. Chapin

353

Plate IX - Sketch of John Butler's Patented "GAGE" [sic]

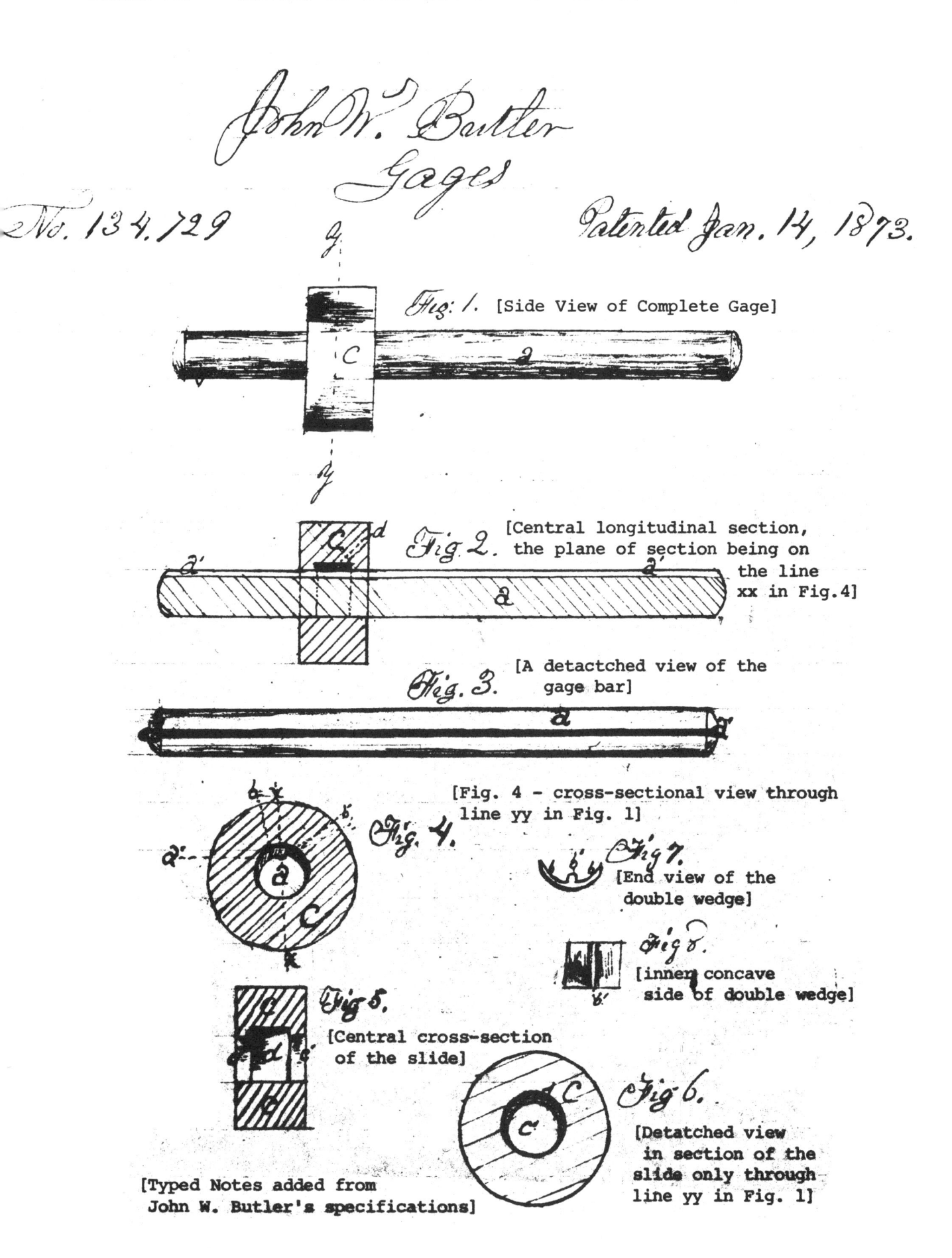

John W. Butler
Gages

No. 134,729   Patented Jan. 14, 1873.

Fig. 1. [Side View of Complete Gage]

Fig. 2. [Central longitudinal section, the plane of section being on the line xx in Fig. 4]

Fig. 3. [A detactched view of the gage bar]

[Fig. 4 - cross-sectional view through line yy in Fig. 1]

Fig. 4.

Fig. 7. [End view of the double wedge]

Fig. 8. [inner concave side of double wedge]

Fig. 5. [Central cross-section of the slide]

Fig. 6. [Detatched view in section of the slide only through line yy in Fig. 1]

[Typed Notes added from John W. Butler's specifications]

Table II

AGREEMENT BETWEEN JOHN A. MARDEN and E.M.CHAPIN, October 28, 1873

This agreement, made this 28th day of October AD 1873, between John A. Marden of So. Hadley Falls, Mass., party of the first part, and Edw. M. Chapin of New Hartford, Conn., party of the second part. Witnesseth: -

That whereas letters patent of the United States was on the 16th day of April AD 1872 granted to the said party of the first part for an improvement in Carpenter's Gauges, which sd. patent which sd. party of the second part is desirous to make and sell, now therefore the parties have agreed as follows, viz. -

The party of the first part hereby gives the party of the second part the exclusive right to manufacture and sell sd. patented improvement to the end of the term of sd. patent, subject to the conditions hereafter named.

The party of the second part agrees to make full and true returns during the months of January-April-July and October in each year to the 1st day of the month respectively of all sd. Carpenter's Gauges sold by him in the three calender months then last past, and if the said party of the first part shall not be satisfied in any respect with any such returns, then he shall have the right, either by himself or his attorney, to examine any and all of the Books of account of sd. party of the second part containing any items, charges, memoranda or information relating to the manufacture of sd. patented Gauge, and upon request, sd. party of the second part shall produce all such books for sd. examination.

The party of the second part agrees to pay the party of the first part a royalty of one dollar per dozen of all the sd. Gauges sold by him, the whole of sd. royalty for each quarterly term of three months as here before specified to as due and payable within fifteen days after the regular return day for that quarter.

Upon failure of party of the second part to make returns, or to make payment of fees as herin provided, for thirty days after such payments are due respectively, then the party of the first part may terninate this license by serving a written notice to that effect upon the party of the second part, but sd. party of the second part shall not thereby be discharged from any liability to the party of the first part for any license fees due at the time of the service of said notice.

In witness whereof the above named parties here under set their hands & seals this day
     J.A.MARDEN
     E.M.CHAPIN

Table III - Letter to E.M. Chapin from John Marden, Dec. 12, 1873

South Hadley Falls, Dec.12th 73

Mr. Chapin, dear sir,

 I hope you will excuse me for not attending to the bsiness before & I hope you will not neglect or delay, as I have done. I was sick when I was down there and have not been able since to attend to it.

I have made the drawings to engrave and the description as well as I can. As it is all together a new thing for me, I hope you will take it and correct the thing and put it over the road. I hope to hear from you soon and receive some of the Gauges.
        Yours truly,
          J.A. Marden

[Chapin Manuscript Collection, Connecticut Historical Society, Ms 64937]

Plate X - John Marden's Drawings and Description of His Patented Gauge
[See Table III]

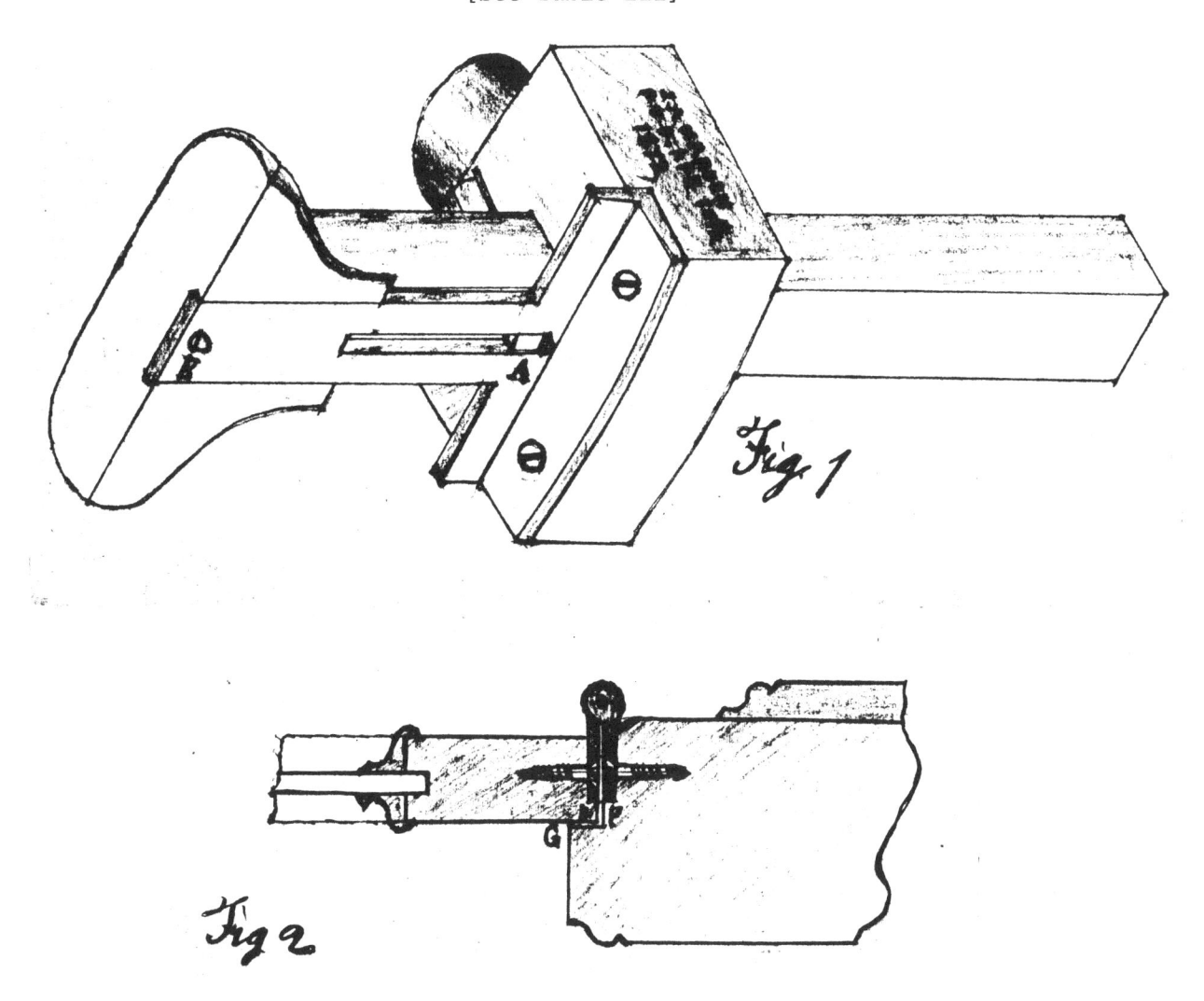

Fig. 1

Fig. 2

This Gauge is so constructed that it shall be set at one operation to mark the distance of the hinge from the jamb and to mark on the door the distance of the hinge from the corner of the door, and also to cut in the depth that it will be necessary to remove the wood to fit the hinge in flush with the edge of the door and the jamb.

In the accompanying drawing Fig. 1 is a perspective view of the Gauge. Fig. 2 is a section view of the hinging edge of the door, hinge and jamb.

    Spurr A Gauges the door as seen at B Fig. 2
    Spurr E Gauges the jamb as seen at F Fig. 2

It will be readily seen that the 2 spurss will always correspond, and no chance for mistake, the allowance being made in the make of the Gauge for a little play and room for the paint as seen at G Fig. 2.

This Gauge is adapted to doors up to any thickness from ½ to 3 inches.

In Gauging the door the Gauge must of course be used on the forward side of the door in shutting at the side that shuts against the jamb.

Table IV -   Letter and Sketch by Wm. J. Lee to E.M. Chapin

LeRoy, New York
July 25th, 1871

H. Chapin's Son
Dear Sirs,
    Yours of the 21st was duly received and in reply send you a rough sketch of "Improved Rule". It is so simple that I think it will do as well as "model". You can easily see by it (the sketch), if you think there is anything in it! If you think favourable and would like to engage in its Manufacture, I will have the Patent issued to you and me jointly and you can pay me what you think right. I know nothing about the business, so am willing you should decide what I should get as a royalty or how much and take it all. Mechnics (Carpenters) and they all say it is a good thing. I know in my trade "Tinsmith" I would not for the one I have take $5.00, if I could not get another. I have to take so many different bevils in Hot Air work for elbows and go back to shop and make them, with this I take a note of my different "Bevils", shut up my rules and can refer to it at Shop, no matter how many, before we had to nail Lath together to remember all we took. I have carried home 9 different Bevils in that way. You will see that all the extra expense will be the different tools to cut joints & mark the Circle at joint. Hoping to hear from you soon,

    I remain yours, respt. Wm. J. Lee

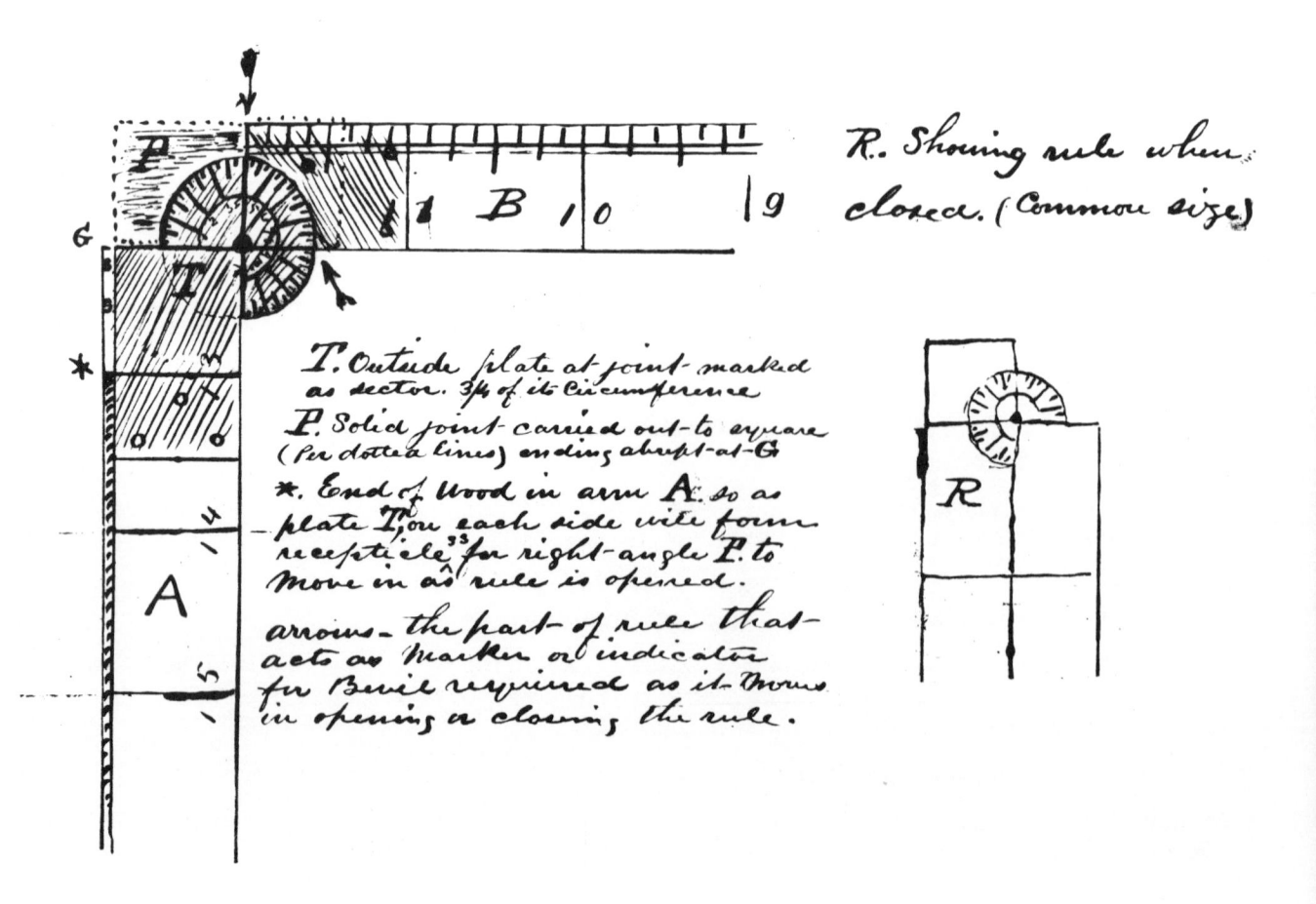

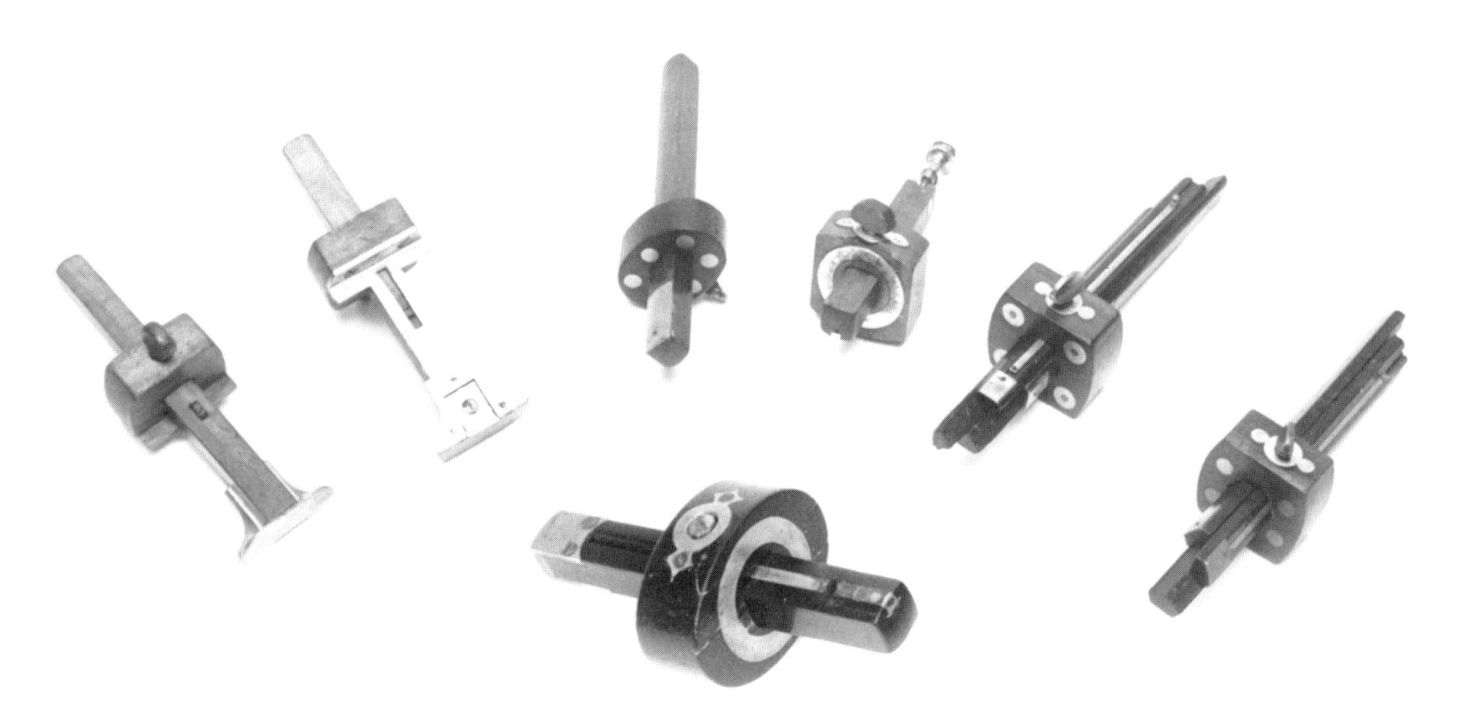

Fig. 64 — **Top**: Various Marking Gauges Manufactured at the Union Factory. Two at Left: Marden's Patent; Two at Center: Imprint of H.Chapin. Two at Right: Sholl's Patent. **Front Center**: Gauge with no Imprint, but believed to have been made in Great Britain. Possibly Union Factory copied this and thus manufactured design seen third from right at top.

Notes - Chapter X

1. Michael D. Kaufman, "Some 19th Century Massachusetts Level Makers" *Chronicle of EAIA,* Vol. 32, No.3, Sept.1979, p. 37

2. R.K Leavitt, *History of the Stanley Works,* [New Britain, CT, 1951], p.22

3. Secretary of State Records, State Capitol, Hartford, Conn.

4. *ibid,* This date is often erroneously listed as 1857.

5. Reprinted by Ken Roberts Publishing Co., May 1975

6. Collection of the Publisher

7. U.S. Patent No. 68,603 granted to Samuel N. Chapin and Augustus Stanley, Sept. 16, 1867; U.S. Patent No. 82,769 granted to J. A. Traut, assigned to Stanley Rule & Level Co., Oct. 6, 1868.

8. U.S. Patent No. 75,534, March 11, 1868; No. 121,088, Nov. 2, 1871

9. Details regarding the Stratton Brothers of Greenfield were published in *Catalogue No. 6, Mechanick's Workbench,* [Marion, Mass., Dec.1978], p. 8

10. This was first advertised by Stanley Rule & Level Co. in their 1892 Catalogue and by H. Chapin's Son Co. in their 1897 Catalogue.

11. The incorrect spelling SCHOLL appears in both the 1874 and 1882 catalogues of H. Chapin's Son.

Chapter XI

The Union Factory, 1832-1900

Edward Merrill Chapin, proprietor of H. Chapin's Son, died December 19, 1896, at the age of 63. His two sons, Hermon Mills Chapin (born September 17, 1866) and Frank Merrill Chapin (born June 28, 1869) were then respectively 30 and 28. An obituary, published in the local paper, referred to him as "one of Connecticut's prominent Masons."[1] This account also noted his long services as town treasurer, member of the General Assembly both in the State House and Senate, Director of the State Prison Board and the State Reformatory. Sixty of the firm's employees attended his funeral, publishing the following resolution.[2]

"Resolved by us the employees and exemployees of H. Chapin's Son that we recognize our grevious loss of a kind friend, a just and equitable employer and a true and honorable citizen."

A photograph of E.M. Chapin, taken when he was about 50 years old, is shown as Fig. 65.

[History of Litchfield County, Phila.,PA., 1881]

Fig. 65

No significant changes in products at the H. Chapin's Son firm appear to have occurred during the period from 1882 through the time of E.M. Chapin's death. A record of sales for the first quarter of each year during the period 1891-1897 is shown in Table I. The average was $24,315. Assuming sales were of the same magnitude for the remaining three quarters, the average annual sales would have been of the order of $100,000 per year. A comparative listing of wooden planes of the then largest four firms, published in 1891 in the *John H. Graham Illustrated Price List and Catalogue of Hardware Manufacturers* [New York, N.Y.] is reproduced as Plate I. At that date the Greenfield Tool Co. had discontinued and the Ohio Tool Co. was about to combine with the Auburn Tool Co.

TABLE I

TOTAL SALES AT H. CHAPIN'S SON DURING FIRST QUARTER
Jan. 1 - March 31 for years 1891 - 1897

Year	Amount of Sales
1891	$20,407.33
1892	26,978.23
1893	32,178.95
1894	22,116.54
1895	20,331.24
1896	26,199.69
1897	21,992.43
Average for these 7 years	24,315.

About this time a variation of the patent adjustable plow, No. 239-3/4, was offered by H. Chapin's Son. this had iron rods attached to the plane body, through which fixtures screwed to the fence slid. A central threaded metal rod regulated the distance between the fence and body. This plane is illustrated in Fig. 66. Since no Chapin catalogue is known to exist listing this version, it is difficult to date. However from the small number of such planes reported, this was probably made only for a short time.

"A rule composed of a wood body, ivory strips covering said body and strips...I have produced a rule that possesses all the advantages of a solid ivory rule, yet is much cheaper and far more lasting and durable, and one that presents a neat appearance, the hinge-plate of the intermediate sections being concealed by ivory strips."

H. Chapin's Son purchased an assignment of this patent from Hogarty for $500.[3] Since such a rule did not appear in the *1897 H. Chapin's Son Catalogue,* it would appear that this design was not significant. At that date rules were more significant items with H. Chapin's Son Co. from the viewpoint of sales than planes, which were then becoming obsolete by the superior iron planes then offered by numerous firms. In any event Michael Hogarty gained attention at the firm and soon became superintendent.

In the inventory and appraisal of E.M. Chapin's estate dated January 1, 1897, the Rule, Plane and Level Manufacturing Plane, including land, buildings, fixtures, water wheels, main line of shaftings, heating system, etc. was valued at $35,000. The inventory and appraisal of the machinery in this factory was valued slightly over $3000. (See Table II) These data provided an excellent record of the type of machinery then in use.

Table II - INVENTORY and APPRAISAL of MACHINERY in RULE
PLANE and LEVEL SHOP of E.M. CHAPIN's SON
January 1, 1897
[Prepared for the Estate of the late E.M. Chapin]

LEVEL PACKING ROOM	1 Gauging Machine	$75.00
	1 Marking Machine	175.00
PLANE ROOM	1 Pitman Planer	50.00
	1 Wedge Machine	5.00
	1 Sticking Machine & Cutters	25.00
	1 Combination Machine for Handles and Mortise, etc.	40.00
	1 Moulding Mortise Machine	10.00
	1 Band Saw	50.00
	1 Beating Machine	40.00
	1 Cheeking Machine	25.00
	1 Burring Machine	10.00
	1 Heading Machine	10.00
	1 Rounding Machine	10.00
	3 Splitting Saw Tables with Saws	50.00
	1 Drop	2.00
	1 Cornering Machine	3.00
	1 Sand Paper Drum	5.00
	1 Rounding Machine for Smooths	15.00
	2 Presses	30.00
	1 Pair Shears	5.00
	1 Rotary Pump	5.00
	1 Pair Rotary Shears	15.00
	1 Cornering Machine for Wedges	2.00
	1 Rotary Planer	10.00
OLD SAW ROOM	1 Large Saw Frame with Saws	25.00
	1 Grind Stone with Frame	3.00
	2 Emery Machines with Wheels	15.00
	1 Rotary Planer	8.00
BOX ROOM	1 Roughing Machine	10.00
	1 Matching Machine	10.00
	1 Planer for Lumber	40.00
	1 Grind Stone with Frame	3.00
	1 Wood Saw Cutting Machine	.50
	2 Saw Beds	25.00
WHEEL ROOM	1 Emery Grinder	3.00
	1 Rotary Pump	8.00
LEVEL ROOM	9 Counters and 49 Pulleys	51.80
	40 Belts, large and small	25.00
SAW ROOM	1 Hubbing Machine	15.00
	1 Jig Saw	15.00
	1 Horizontal Boring Machine	3.00
	1 Shaping Machine	2.00
	1 Mortise Machine	6.00
	1 Boring Machine	5.00
	3 Splitting Saw Tables	26.00
	1 Drop Saw Table	3.00
	1 Burring Machine	3.00

[continued on Page 361]

[Table II continued from page 360)

LEVEL ROOM [Attic]	1 Rotary Planer	$8.00	
	1 Drop Press	10.00	
CHAPIN MACHINE SHOP	1 Saw Table and Saws	5.00	
	1 Daniels Planer	12.00	
	1 Drill Press	10.00	
	4 Lathes for Skate Rools	60.00	
PACKING ROOM	1 Boring Lathe	15.00	
STUFF ROOM	4 Iron Saw Beds	120.00	
	2 Edging Machines	200.00	
	1 Edging and Siding Machine	20.00	
	5 Wicking Machines	85.00	
	1 Siding Machine	75.00	
	3 Tennoting Machines	15.00	
	1 Rotary Filing Machine	100.00	
	1 Blower	10.00	
	1 Crane	3.00	
RULE ROOM	11 Drill Lathes and Sockets	132.00	
	13 " " " " upright	195.00	
	14 " " " " somgle	140.00	
	2 Riveting Machines for Binding	50.00	
	5 Arching Machines	75.00	
	1 Beveling Machine	15.00	
	2 Cutting Machines for Tip Banding	40.00	
	1 Cropping Machine	8.00	
	9 Filing Machines	180.00	
	3 Splitting and Milling Machines	45.00	[for Tips]
	1 " " " "	20.00	[for Head Banding]
	1 Tennoting Machine for B'd Heads	20.00	
	1 Milling Machine for Tip B'nd'g	15.00	
	2 Machines for Letting Back Heads	30.00	
	2 Machines for Letting up Hollows	24.00	
	2 Machines for Milling	30.00	
	2 Machines for Tennoting Tips	30.00	
	2 Machines for Sawing Middle Plates	60.00	
	1 Riverting Press	25.00	
	1 Letting Back Machine for Middle Jts.	90.00	
	1 Milling Slide Machine	16.00	
	1 Rounding Butt Machine	15.00	
	2 Nicking Machine for Heads & Tips	32.00	

Total $3002.30

Plate I   362   (continued on Page 363)

John H. Graham & Co.

Comparative List of Planes.

Auburn Tool Comp'y.	Ohio Tool Comp'y	Chapin Tool Comp'y.	Sandusky Tool Comp'y.	DESCRIPTION.
1	1	104	1	Smooth Plane, Single Iron.
3	3	112	3	" " Double "
7	5	112½	5	" " " Iron, Solid Handle.
7½	5½	...	5½	Jack Handled Smooth Plane.
8	8	415	7	Boxwood Smooth, Double Iron.
9	12	105	10	Jack Plane, Single Iron.
10	13	...	11	" " " Bolted Handles.
11	14	105½	12	Razee Jack, " with Start.
12	15	113	13	Jack Plane, Double Iron.
14	16	...	14	" " " Bolted Handle.
16	17	113½	15	Razee Jack, " " with Start.
17	18	106	16	Fore Plane.
19	20	106½	18	Razee Fore Plane, Single Iron, Start.
20	21	114	19	Fore Plane, Double Iron.
22	22	...	20	Fore Plane, Double Iron, Bolted Handles.
24	23	114½	21	Razee Fore Plane, Double Iron, with Start.
26	24	107	22	Jointer Plane, Single Iron, with Start.
29	26	107½	24	Razee Jointer, " "
30	27	115	25	Jointer Plane, Double Iron.
35	28	...	26	" " " Bolted Handle.
37	29	115½	27	Razee Jointer, " with Start.
46	31A	431	38	Mitre Plane, Square, Single Iron.
47	31	432	38½	" Smooth Shape, Single Iron.
49	31¼	434	39	" " Double Iron.
51	119	160	149	Jack Rabbet, with Handles and 2 Cutters.
53	119	159	149	" with Handle on Side.
55	...	411	28	Applewood Smooth Plane, Double Iron.
56	...	412	30	" Jack " "
57	...	413	31	" Fore " "
57½	...	414	32	" Jointer " "
60	114	162	144	Raising Plane.
63	115	...	145	" with Screw Arm.
69	75	171	99	Board Match Plane, Twin or Separate.
70	76	172	100	" " Plated.
73	77	175	101	" " Solid Handle.
74	78	176	102	" " " Plated.
75	79	177	103	Plank Match Planes.
76	80	178	104	" " Plated.
80	82	181	106	" " Screw Arms.
81	84	182	106½	" " " Plated.
87	94	230	116	Panel Plow, Beech, 4 Irons, Wood Stop.
89	95	232	117	" Screw Stop, 8 Irons.
89½	96	233	118	" " Boxed Fence.
90	96½	234	119	" with Handle.
90½	97	235	120	" " Boxed Fence.
91	98	243	121	" Boxwood Arms.
92	100	236	123	" " with Handle.
93	99	244	122	" " Boxed Fence.
94	101	238	124	" " Handle Boxed, Fence.
95	102	245	130	Panel Plow, Box or Rosewood,
96	104	240½	132	" " Screw Stop with handle.
97	103	...	131	" " Ivory Tipped.
98	105	...	133	" " Screw Top Hdle, Iv'ry Tipped.
99	...	...	134	Panel Plow, Beech, Boxwood Arms.
100	109	...	137	" Ebony, with Handle Ivory Tipped.
101	...	...	143	" " Self-Regulating.
102	36	122	46	Astragals.
105	37	123	47	Side Bead, Single Boxed.
106	38	124	48	" Double "
107	39	125	49	" " " Dovetailed.
108	41	126	51	Centre Bend, " "
108	42	127	52	" Solid, " "
109	49	225	80	Cabinet Maker's Ogee.
113	...	130	52½	Torus Bead.

Plate I   363   (continued from Page 362)

113 CHAMBERS STREET, NEW YORK

COMPARATIVE LIST OF PLANES.—Continued.

Auburn Tool Comp'y.	Ohio Tool Comp'y.	Chapin Tool Comp'y.	Sandusky Tool Comp'y.	DESCRIPTION.
114	141	...	97	Door Moulding Plane, Boxed.
115	139¼	145	179	Door Plane, Screw Arm and Fence.
115	139¾	145	181	" " " and Ogee.
116	139½	145	180	" " " and Bevel.
117	51	146	65	Filletster, without Cutter.
118	52	147	66	" with "
119	53	148	67	" " " and Brass Side Stop.
120	54	149	68	" " " and Brass Side Stop, Boxed.
121	55	150	69	" " " and Brass Screws.
121½	56	150½	70	" " " B. S. Stop, Boxed and Fenced.
123	57	154	71	" " " " B.W. S. Arms, B. Screw Stop, Bxd.
124	58	154½	72	" " " " B.S.S. Box'd and Hdle.
125	140	207	96	Reverse Ogee and Square.
126	62½	206	82	Roman Reverse Ogees.
127	62	206	81	Reverse Ogee.
128	59	204	74	Ogee.
140	60	208	77	Grecian Ogee.
142	...	209	78	" and Bead.
144	61	209	79	" with Bevel and Fillet.
145	63	212	83	Grecian Ogee.
147	65	214	85	Grecian Ovolo and Bead.
150	64	214	84	" with Bevel or Fillet.
155	43½	219	54	Scotia, or Quarter Pound.
155½	43¼	217¾	54¾	Casing Moulding Plane, Fence, to work on edge.
156	43	219	53	Cove Planes.
157	44	220	55	Cove and Bead.
158	89	...	110	Nosings, Mouldings.
165	125	185	155	Sash Plane, One Iron, Bevel or Ovolo.
165	126	187	156	" Two Irons, "
165	127	191	157	" " " Boxed.
165	131	193	164	" Screw Arms, Self-Regulating, Bevel.
165	133	168	192	" Dovetailed Boxed, Bevel or Ovolo.
166	132	195	166	" Screw Arms, Self-Regulating, Bevel Boxed.
168	131½	193	165	" " " Gothic.
168	133½	192	169	" Dovetailed, Boxed, Bevel or Ovolo.
169	132½	195	167	" B'x'd, Gothic or Ogee, Screw Arm, Self-Reg.
174	45	202	56	Coping Plane, Double for Sash Plane.
176	47	138	60	Dado, Brass, Side Stop.
177	48	139	62	" Screw Stop.
180	72	163	92	Hollow and Round.
180	73	167	94	" "
181	116	157	146	Rabbet Planes, Skewed.
181	117	158	147	" Skew, with Cutter and Boxed.
181	120	155	150	" Square.
182	122	131	152	Reeding Planes.
183	123	161	151½	Side Rabbets, Right and Left.
184	124	...	153	Snipe Bills, Single.
185	136	168	175	Table Planes, with Gouge.
186	137	169	176	" " Dovetailed, Boxed.
187	138	170	177	" with Fence.
189	90	132	111	Nosing One Iron.
189	90½	134	112	" " with Handle.
189	91	133	113	" Two Irons.
189	92	133½	114	" " with Handle.
190	30	430	36	Tooth Plane, Single Iron.
192	34	436	44	Circular or Heel Plane, Single Iron.
193	35	437	45	" " Double Iron.
196	32	442	41	Gutter Plane.
198	32½	443	42	Pump Plane, for Chain Pumps.
199	29D	446	045½	Box Maker's Plane, Jack Shape, Razee, Single Iron.
200	...	446	45½	" " " " Double Iron.

John H. Graham Illustrated Price List and Catalogue of Hardware Manufacturers, [New York, 1891, pp. 48 & 49

Fig. 66 - Union Factory Patent Adjustable Plow No. 239-3/4 in Applewood
[Rare example with iron slide arms and iron adjusting screw]

According to the terms of E.M. Chapin's will ownership of H. Chapin's Son was divided into thirds among his wife, Mary, and his sons Hermon M. and Frank M. Chapin. The firm contiuned to be run by the executors of his estate, Rufus E. Holmes, an attorney of Winsted, and his eldest son, Hermon Chapin, until August 26, 1897, when a new firm, H. Chapin's Son Company was organized. (See Table III)

Table III ARTICLES OF ASSOCIATION OF THE H. CHAPIN'S SON COMPANY
[Published in New Hartford Tribune, August 26, 1897]
(Recorded in New Hartford Town Records Book 29, page 162)

The undersigned hereby associate as a Joint Stock Corporation, under the statute laws of the State of Connecticut, by articles of agreement as follows: -

ARTICLE I. The name by which the Corporation shall be known is the H. Chapin's Son Company.

ARTICLE II. The purpose for which it is constituted is to manufacture, buy, sell and deal in articles composed in whole or in part of metals, woods, ivory, or other material, to buy sell, hold or deal in Real Estate or other property, and generally to do all things incidental to said business.

ARTICLE III. The Corporatioh is to be located in Pine Meadow in the Town of New Hartford, County Litchfield and State of Connecticut.

ARTICLE IV. The amount of its Capital Stock is Sixty Thousand Dollars, divided into Six Hundred Shares of the par value of One Hundred Dollars each.

ARTICLE V. Each Subscriber to these Artilces agrees to take the number of shares of said Capital Stock annexed to his name, each share to be of the par value of One Hundred Dollars and to pay twenty percent there of in cash on the twenty-fifth day of August 1897, and the balance thereof in instalmnets as called for by the Directors.

Dated at Pine Meadow, Conn. this twenty-fifth day of August, 1897.

Hermon M. Chapin, Pine Meadow, Conn., Two Hundred Sixty-four Shares
Frank M. Chapin, Pine Meadow, Conn., Two Hundred Sixty Shares
S.M. Jones, Englewood, N.J., Twenty-five Shares
Charles M. Chapin, Bernardsville, N.J., Fifteen Shares
Coe Brass M'f'g Company, Torrington, Conn., Ten Shares
Rufus E. Holmes, Winsted, Conn., Twenty-one Shares

Rufus E. Holmes, President   Frank M. Chapin, Treasurer & Secretary

Plate II

A heading of an invoice listed the new officers of the firm. (Plate II) A new catalogue of 80 pages was issued September 1897. The title page of this is shown as Plate III and the index as Plate IV. The illustrations were made from the same cuts as used in the 1874 and 1872 catalogues. The discount sheet accompanying this catalogue, dated July 18, 1897, is shown as Plate V. The discount on planes noted on this list were the highest at any time since the prices were fixed, early in the 1860's. An advertisement published in *Wright's Catalogue of America's Greatest Manufacturers* [New York, N.Y., 1899, p. 44] illustrated some of the products offered by The H. Chapin's Son Co. (Plate VI)

The Statement of the Treasurer of the H. Chapin's Son Co., dated July 18, 1900, reported the financial affairs for the year ending July 1, 1900. (Table IV) This showed that a profit of about 10 percent on merchandise manufactured during the last year had been made. In consideration of the costs of labor and investment in the factory, this was not a particularly attractive return. However, it must be considered that this was now in a declining stage of business.

Table IV -

STATEMENT OF TREASURER OF THE H. CHAPIN'S SON CO.

July 18th, 1900.

Merchandise sold year ending July 1, 1900		$74,298.63
" on hand July 1, 1900		20,035.92
		$94,334.55
" on hand July 1, 1899		12,586.86
" manufactured year ending July 1, 1900		$81,747.69
Rents received		120.00
Machinery manufactured year ending July 1, 1900		350.00
Tools " " " " "		200.00
Paid for Labor	$43,236.05	
Insurance	840.70	
Repairs	457.13	
Interest	847.64	
Commissions	351.10	
Expenses	5,375.51	
Transportation	1,086.95	
Samples	21.15	
Timber	4,135.35	
Brass, Iron and Ivory	14,047.26	
Supplies	4,080.59	
Profits	7,938.26	
	$82,417.69	$82,417.69

A supplementary issue of the *New Hartford Tribune,* dated December 21, 1900 presented a brief historical account of the Chapin firms. A description of the factory stated: —

> "The plant as is now, consists of a building two stories high, about 300 feet long and 50 ft. deep. It is a frame building and has three wings extending in the rear. This is the working department. The office is located at the northern end of the main building, is of brick and three stories high. The well appointed offices are located on the ground floor and the floors above are used for storage...The entire plant is run by water power. The Farmington River is dammed just below the NY, NH and H. Railroad, and the water is carried from here to the mills by means of a commodius head race, known hereabouts as "the ditch." All of the buildings are heated by steam and lighted by gas throughout. The plant covers several acres of ground and in the rear of the main buildings are immense yards used for keeping the wood and lumber which is made up into products of the factory. About 100 hands are constantly employed and the number sometimes reaches 125."

A photograph of the office and front of the factory, taken about this time, and used on a "penny" post card, is shown as Fig. 67. Attention is directed to the Frontispiece, which shows a similar view, also taken about the same time, but included several of the employees.

An insight as to the working conditions at the Union Factory is provided between 1890 and 1900. (See Figs. 68-73) These illustrate various operations in the rule department.

The apparent wealth of the Chapin family after the Civil War is noted from their spectacular homes. The house built for Philip Chapin and his bride, Amilia Bushnell, in 1867 as a wedding present is shown in Fig. 74. Soon after Amilia Chapin died and Philip left Pine Meadow for Cleveland. Edward M. Chapin's stylish Victorian Gothic wood-frame house, built in 1871, is shown in Fig. 75. Both houses originally had similar interior arrangements, and though remodeled are presently standing at Pine Meadow.

Fig. 74 Former Philip Chapin House   Fig. 75 Former E.M. Chapin House
[*Report of the District Study Committee of the Town of New Hartford*, 1979
Courtesy of the New Hartford Historical Society]

Notes – Chapter XI

1. *New Hartford Tribune,* Vol. XVII, Dec. 25, 1896, p. 3
2. *ibid,* P. 3
3. New Hartford Land Records, B.29, p. 262

Plate III - Title Page to 1897 H. CHAPIN'S SON CO. CATALOGUE

PRICE LIST

and

Illustrated Catalogue

of

RULES, PLANES, GAUGES,

Moulding Planes, Grooving Plows, Plumbs and Levels, Door Stops, Hand Screws, Handles, Turning Saw Frames and Saws, C. Scholl's Patent Gauge, Marden's Patent Gauge, Plane Irons, Spoke Shaves, Etc., Etc.,

Manufactured by

THE H. CHAPIN'S SON CO.,

UNION FACTORY,

Established 1826.

R. E. HOLMES,	H. M. CHAPIN,	F. M. CHAPIN,
President.	*Vice-President.*	*Sec'y and Treasurer.*

PINE MEADOW, CONN., U. S. A.

September, 1897.

Plate IV - Index to *1897 H. CHAPIN'S SON CO. CATALOGUE*

INDEX.

	PAGE.
Astragals,	28
Awl Hafts,	77
Awl Handles,	77
Applewood Planes,	25
Boxwood Rules,	3 to 12
Board Measure,	9, 15
Bench Rules,	15
Board Sticks,	15
Bench Planes,	18 to 25
Boxwood Planes,	25
Bead Planes,	27 to 29
Caliper Rules, Boxwood,	10
" " Ivory,	14
Carriage Makers' Tools,	26
Coopers' Planes,	24
Cornice Planes,	54
Chisel Handles,	76
Dado Planes,	30
Door Stops,	78
Filletster Planes,	31
File Handles,	77
Gauges,	60 to 63
" Marking,	60
" Cutting,	61
" Panel,	61
" Mortise,	61
" Slitting,	61
" Scholl's Patent,	62
" Marden's Patent,	63
Gauging Rods,	16
Hollows and Rounds,	33 to 38
Hand Screws,	72
" " Beaded,	73
Ivory Rules,	13, 14
Level Glass,	71
Log Sticks,	15
Levels,	64, 71
Machinists' Levels,	70
Miscellaneous Rules,	15, 16

	PAGE.
Miscellaneous Planes,	24
Moulding Planes,	44 to 54
Match "	40
Nosing "	30
Ogee "	44 to 48
" Grecian Planes,	47, 48
Ovolo Planes,	49 to 51
" Grecian Planes,	49, 50
Planes, Common Bench,	18
" Extra "	19, 20
" Premium "	21, 22
" Without Irons,	23
" Panel,	31
Plows, Grooving,	55 to 59
" " Pat. Adjusting,	58, 59
Plumbs and Levels,	64 to 70
" " Pat. Adjustable,	66 to 68
Pocket Levels,	71
Plane Handles,	78
" Irons,	80
" Stops,	80
Rulers,	17
Rules,	3 to 16
Rabbet Planes,	32
Rosewood Planes,	25
Ship Carpenters' Bevels,	10
" Planes,	23
" Scrapers,	79
Slide Rules,	9
Sash Planes,	41 to 43
Saw Handles,	78
Spoke Shaves,	79
Stationers' Goods,	17
Table Planes,	39
Turning-Saw Frames,	74
" " and Saws,	75
Wantage Rods,	16
Yard Sticks,	15

Plate V – Discount Sheet to *1897 H. CHAPIN'S SON CO. CATALOGUE*

1826.
H. CHAPIN.

1860.
H. CHAPIN'S SON.

1897.

THE H. CHAPIN'S SON CO.

Catalogue of 1897.

DISCOUNT SHEET.

PINE MEADOW, CONN., U. S. A., SEPT. 1, 1897.

Catalogue Page.		Discount Per Cent.
3–12	BOXWOOD RULES,	80 and 10 10 10 10
13–14	IVORY "	50 and 10
15–16	MISCELLANEOUS RULES,	60 and 10 10
17	STATIONERS' RULERS,	10 and 10
18	BENCH PLANES, Common "Pearce,"	60
19–22	" " Extra and Premium,	55
19–25	" " With English Irons instead of American,	35
23	SHIP PLANES,	50
24	MISCELLANEOUS PLANES,	50
25	BENCH PLANES, Apple, Box and Rosewood,	35
26	CARRIAGE MAKERS' TOOLS,	25
27–54	MOULDING PLANES,	50
55–59	GROOVING PLOWS,	50
60–61	GAUGES,	60 and 10 10
62	" Scholl's Patent,	60 and 10
63	" Marden's Patent, for Door Hangers,	50 and 10
64–65	PLUMBS AND LEVELS,—Non-Adjustable,	75 and 10 10 10
66–68	" " " Patent Adjustable,	75 and 10 10 10
69	" " " Chapin' Imp. Brass Cornered,	50
70	" " " Machinists' Brass Cornered,	50
71	POCKET LEVELS,	70 and 10
71	LEVEL GLASSES,	70 and 10
72–73	HAND SCREWS,	40 and 10
74	TURNING SAW FRAMES,	30 and 10
75	" " " AND SAWS,	30 and 10
76	CHISEL HANDLES,	65 and 10
77	FILE AND AWL HANDLES,	65 and 10
78	PLANE HANDLES,	40 and 10
78	SAW HANDLES,	40 and 10
78	DOOR STOPS,	60 and 10
79	SPOKE SHAVES, Chapin's Improved,	50 and 10
79	BOX SCRAPERS,	50 and 10
80	PLANE IRONS,	40
80	PLANE STOPS,	20

NOTE:—Rules with Foreign graduation 10 and 5 per cent less discount than English.

TERMS:—30 days, no cash discount, or 2 % cash if paid in 10 days from date of invoice.

Invoices unpaid after 30 days from date, sight draft will be made.

Plate VI - Page 44 from *Wright's Catalogue of America's Greatest Manufacturers*

AMERICA'S GREATEST MANUFACTURERS.

Established 1826 by H. Chapin
1860 H. Chapin's Son, successor E. M. Chapin
1897 The H. Chapin's Son Co.

HOLLOWS AND ROUNDS

COMBINATION RULE AND GLASS CUTTER—Patented
Write for Descriptive Circulars of Combination Rule and Glass Cutter; also Patented Bound Rule.

MORTISE GAUGES

GROOVING PLOWS

THE H. CHAPIN'S SON CO.
UNION FACTORY

RULES...
Moulding Planes, Grooving Plows, Plumbs and Levels, Door Stops,

PLANES
Hand Screws, Handles, Turning Saw Frames and Saws, C. Scholl's

GAUGES
Patent Gauge, Marden's Patent Gauge

PATENTED

PATENTED

PINE MEADOW, CONN., U. S. A.

S Guiterman & Co., Ltd.
35-36 Aldermanbury, London, E. C. } London Agent

New York Agents { Surpless, Dunn & Co
55 Warren Street

MACHINISTS' LEVELS
SOLID ROSEWOOD

CHAPIN'S IMPROVED BRASS CORNERED, PATENT ADJUSTABLE PLUMBS AND LEVELS

Brass Corners, Heavy Brass Top Plates and Ends, Brass Lipped Side Views
Cherry, Rosewood and Mahogany

— 44 —

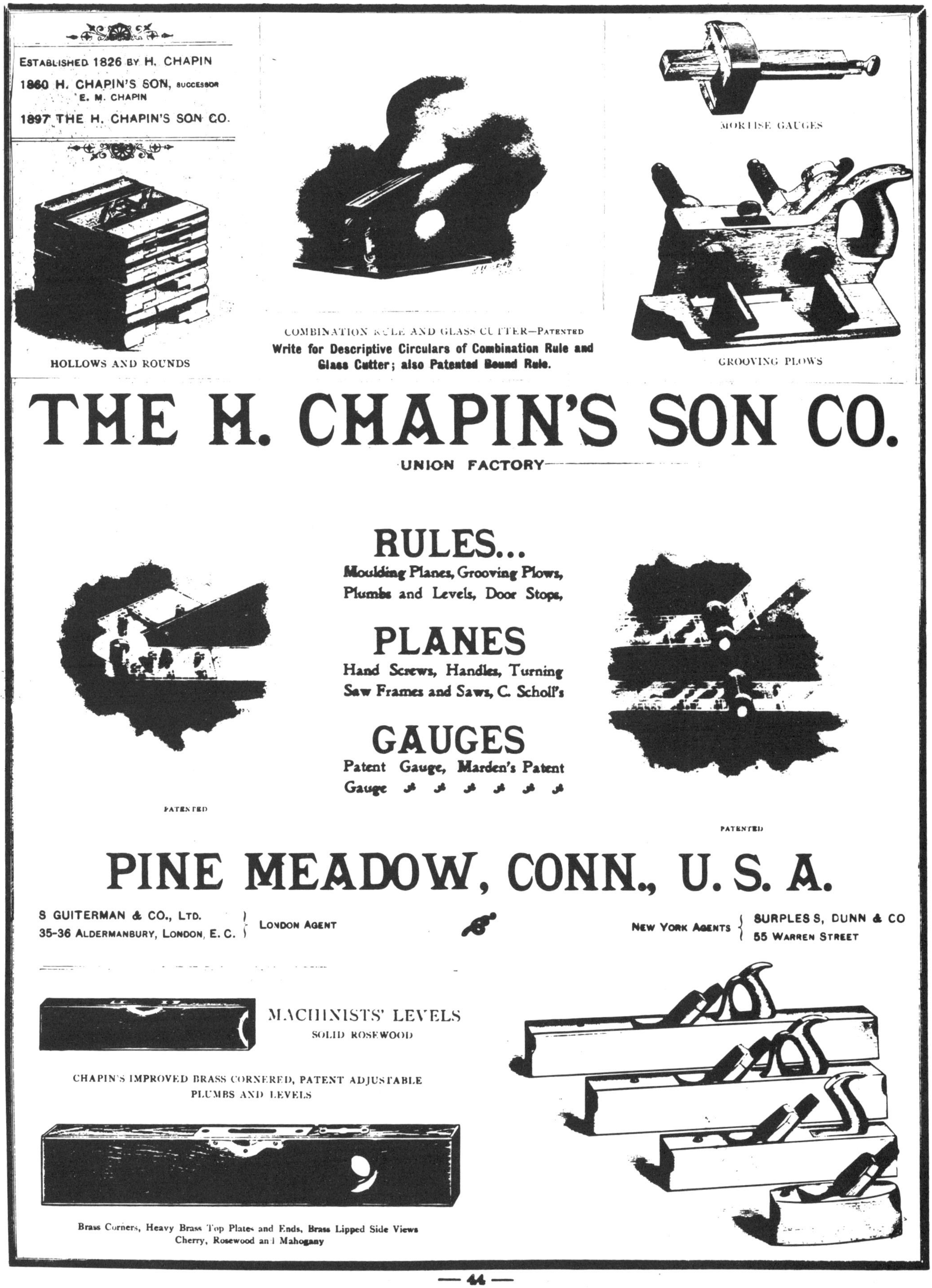

Fig. 68 - Union Factory Rule Shop, c.1890-1900; Preparing Stock

Fig. 69 - Union Factory Rule Shop, c.1890-1900; Making Rule Joints

Fig. 70 - Union Factory Rule Shop, c.1890-1900; Jointing Rules

Fig. 71 - Union Factory Rule Shop, c.1890-1900; Assembling and Finishing Rules

Fig. 72 - Union Factory Rule Shop, c.1890-1900: Varnishing Rules

Fig. 73 - Union Factory Level Shop, c.1890-1900; Machine for setting vials; In background one of E.M. Chapin's sons inspecting finished level.

375

Photograph 6138—The Chapin-Stephens Co., Pine Meadow, Ct.

Fig. 67 - Union Factory Postcard, c. 1901

Chapter XII

Chapin-Stephens Company, 1901-1929

A letter written January 14, 1970 by the late Harry Delos Stephens (b. 1890-d. 1972), son of Frank L. Stephens and grandson of Delos H. Stephens, noted some reminiscences during his youth at the Riverton factory of Stephens & Co.[1]

"Perhaps you remember that on top of the "el" of the old Hitchcock factory, there was a cupola which was glassed in on all four sides. The ivory was received, as I remember, from some New York importing company, It was, I believe, in slabs which were long and thick enough to be sawed into the pieces used for making folding rules. These pieces were rough sawed, a little oversize and resawed to the finished dimensions. The inlaid I made was the scrap edge from the individual sticks as they were cut from the rough cut sawed pieces. I well remember the smell of the ivory in the "saw room" when "Slim Hoskins" (boss of the saw room) was cutting ivory. The saws were very fine toothed, and had to be very sharp, run at high speeds and fed slowly in order not to burn the pieces, or crack them, ivory being quite brittle. The next step was to bleach it. This was done in the cupola. The sticks were built up like an open rail fence, around a square frame which consisted of a top and bottom piece and a long wooden screw in the top piece so that the ivory could be tightly clamped in 3 to 4 feet stacks. I used to go up in the cupola with Grampa and help him do the job. That is why I remember so much about the details.

At the time of which I speak I was nine or ten years old because we moved to New Hartford in 1901. Every evening, before bed time, Father went all through the factory and sometimes I went with him, he carried a kerosene lantern which threw shadows of our legs on the walls and floor and gave me sort of a spooky feeling. Often barefooted, I'd sometimes get small brass slivers in my feet and pop would stop and operate.

Power from both shops came from a waterwheel and I used to get a great thrill out of starting it. This was done by turning a large wheel, the shaft of which came up thru the floor. "Slim" supervised the operation, of course."

Among the problems that faced Delos H. Stephens at his Riverton firm of Stephens & Co. was that his only product was rules. At the turn of the 20th century he was 68, alone in his management and now faced with the new competition of the folding, flexible zig-zag rule. This new product had been introduced in America by the Stanley Rule & Level Co. in 1899.[2] His business had declined and he was heavily indebted to the point of facing foreclosure. On August 13, 1901 he appointed Rufus E. Holmes, then also president of H. Chapin's Son Co. to supervise and settle his deplorable financial affairs.

"...as my true and lawful attorney, for me and my name, to adjust, settle, and compromise any debts that I may owe, and any accounts, claims and demands subsisting against me...also to subscribe for me for capital stock of H. Chapin's Son Co....to the amount not in excess of twenty-five thousand dollars at its par value, and to pay for said stock with all my machinery, tools, merchandise and material in or connected with the manufacture of rules by me at said Riverton under the name of said Stephens & Company..."

The following day, August 14, a special meeting of the directors of the H. Chapin's Son Co. was held to consider continuance of J.J. Hogarty as plant superintendent and to increase the capital by $5,000 for the purpose of purchasing the business and assets of the Stephens & Co. of Riverton. (See Table I) The bill of sale by Delos Stephens to H. Chapin's Son Co. is transcribed as Table II and the list of goods exchanged in this transaction in Table III. This listing provided detailed data regarding the machinery and equipment then in use for manufacturing rules. The new firm of Chapin-Stephens Co. was incorporated October 1, 1901 in accordance with the resolution of the directors of H. Chapin's Son Co. (Table IV)

TABLE I

MINUTES of DIRECTORS MEETING H. CHAPIN'S SON CO.

A Meeting of the Directors of the H. Chapin's Son. Co. was held at the Office at 10 AM [August 14, 1901], pursuant to notice sent to each Director by mail.

Meeting called to order by President. Present: Rufus E. Holmes, Frank M. Chapin, Hermon M. Chapin and H. Wales Lines.

After discussion it was voted to pay M. J. Hagerty a salary of five hundred dollars per annum in lieu of sharing savings as provided in the old contract.

A recess was taken to 4:30 PM, the Meeting was again called to order and the following resoltions were offered and passed unaniously:

Resolved Subscribers to the increased Capital be called on to pay their subscription at once, and the same was done to the satisfaction of the Directors.

Resolved that the Bill of sale of the tools, machinery, supplies, stock, material, both finished and unfinished, book accounts, goodwill, &c., signed by Rufus Holmes, as attorney for Delos H. Stephens, be accepted in payment of said Stephens subscription to the increased Capital Stock and that the power of Attorney be placed on file.

Resolved that five thousand Dollars in money be placed in the hands of our President Rufus E. Holmes with which to complete the purchase of Mr. Stephens' Rule business and its appurtanences.

Resolved that the Secretary be and hereby is authorized to procure a seal for the Corporation under the new name as follows - The Chapin-Stephens Co., New Hartford, Conn.

Resolved that the Secretary be and is hereby authorized to procure a new book of Stock Certificates and transfers.

There being no further business the Meeting was then dissolved.   Attest

An announcement of the formation of the Chapin-Stephens Co. was made in *The Iron Age,* August 29, 1901. (See Table V) This related a brief history of the former firms, listed the Directors of the new firm and announced the New York sales office at 80 Chambers St. under the direction of V.P. Humason.

Table III (Continued through Page 381)

ARTICLES of RULE MANUFACTURE BELONGING TO STEPHENS & CO. SOLD to H. CHAPIN'S SON COMPANY August 14, 1901

SAW ROOM
- 1 Log Cut off Machine
- 1 Stabbing (Iron) Saw Machine
- 2 Slitting   "   Machines
- 1 Emery Grinder
- 4 Counter Shafts and Pulleys
- 1 lot of saws, 6 to 24 in. dia.
- 2 Filing Vises, saw sets, &c.
- 1 Grindstone and frame (wood)
- 1 Elevator
- 1 Stove
- 1 lot of Belting for above
-   Fire Pails

STUFF ROOM
- 2 Edging Machines
- 2 Surfacing   "
- 1 Yard Stick Planing Machine (4 arbor)
- 1 Iron Frame and cut off Machine
- 1 Grinding Machine (Double)
- 1 Vise, Jaws, cutters, etc.
- 5 Countershafts & 1 line Shaft
-   Belting, Pulleys & Small Tools
-   Fire Pails

RULE ROOM
2nd story
- 2 Upright Drills, frame & shafts
- 1 Frame with
- 2 Horizontal Drills
- 2 let back Machines
- 1 Milling & Cal. Rounding Machines
- 1 12 ft. Countershaft & belts
- 1 Double Frame, 12 ft. long, with
- 2 Countershafts
- 3 Horizontal drill lathes
- 1 Tip Machine
- 1 Milling Machine
- 1 Burring Machine
- 1 slide Machine
- 1 Milling Machine
- 1 Head let back & Milling Machine
- 1 Tip Miller & Saw Machine
- 1 Sawing Machine for Pat. Rules
- 1 Let back middle Jt. Machine
- 1 Milling Machine
- 1 Edge Plate & Sawing Machine
-   Pulleys, belts & tools for above

- 1 Roughing off Mach. for Iron pieces and Iron Frames
- 1 6 Spindle Radial Drilling Machine, belts, tools, etc.
- 2 Gang Drills on Iron Pedestals, belts, & counters.
- 2 Bench Drills for Pat. Rules

- 1 Old Pitman Filer
- 3 Horizonatl Drilling Machines on Iron Frams
- 3 Counters, belts & Pulleys

- 1 Big belt Filer - 36 files, counter, jacks & belts
- 1 extra set files for above

Table III (Continued)   379

RULE ROOM 2nd Story (continued)	1 Composite Mill on Iron Frame for filing tips,counter,belts 1 Big Head Filer on Iron Frame, 24 files, counter, belts 1 extra set of Files for above 8 Bench Vises, Re. Blocks and all tools, hammers,scrapers, drills and lot of clamps for Rule Making 1 Copper extinguisher for fire Fire Pails
3rd Story	1 Double 9 foot frames, 2 counters, belts & pulleys 1 Double closing pin machine 2 Middle Joint sawing machines 1 Tip splitter & milling machine 1 Horizontal drill lathe 1 Head let back & Milling machine 1 Riveting Machine 1 Small milling machine on iron bed 2 Composite Milling Machines on Iron beds for 41 heads & roughing off 1 Composite Milling Machine 1 Wire straightening machine & reel 1 Big Belt Filer, 2 sets of 36 files, iron legs 1 Wood Frame 4 x 6 with 3 tenoning machines,counters & belts 1 Automatic Pin Cutter, belts, counter & reel 4 Arching Presses 1 Toggle Joint Vise 1 Double frame 6 x 12 ft contianing nine machines as follows 5 Sawing & Nicking Machine 3 Double Horizontal Lathes, pulleys & Shafts 1 new one stored over office for middle joint pinning 1 Upright Lathe for 41 & 70 heads 1 Machine on Iron pedestal for nicking heads,pulley & shaft 1 6 Spindle radial drilling Machine,counter,drills & belts 2 Upright drills, iron bed & legs 1 " " on wood extension of same 7 Bench Vises A lot of hammers, cramps & small tools 1 Brass civered tumbling barrel, 12 x 6 in. 4 Fire Pails 1 Copper Extinguisher for fire
Joint Room	1 Large Power Press 1 Medium " " 1 Small " " 2 Foot Presses on Iron Legs 1 Punching Press (foot) on bench 1 Emery grinder with chuck & counter 1 Automatic Scraper on Iron bed & legs, counter 1 Drop Press 1 Power Press for Tips, Iron bed & legs 4 Joint drivers 1 Pin Cutter, Iron bed & legs

Table III (Continued)

Joint Room (continued)	1	Tumbling Barrel (wood) 15 x 22 in.
	1	Scraping Machine for broad wings
	1	Big Machine for rolling tips, iron bed & legs
	1	Frame of wood for cutting wings on slide
	3	Automatic Roll Lathes, Iron bed & legs
	1	Sawing Machine, iron bed & legs (for brass work)
	1	Automatic turning lathe for long rolls, iron bed & legs

On Wood frame 12 x 3
- 1 Healving Machine
- 1 Turning Lathe for 4½ rolls &c.
- 1 Milling Machine for middle plates
- 1 Countersinking Machine for Head Joints

- 1 Pair Large 3 ft. shears for brass
- 1 Iron Pedestal (nothing on it)
- 1 Pratt & Whitney Turret Lathe for long rolls, counter, etc.
- 8 Hand Scrapers for joint parts

- 144 Punches & dies for joints
- 1 Bench Vise

A lot of small tools for joint work, files, punches, dies, &c.

- 1 25 foot counter in this room

A lot of wood drawer-boxes for joint parts, pins, rolls, &c

Machine Shop
- 1 8 foot Planer with tools & counters &c.
- 1 8 foot Engine Lathe, chuck, tools, counters with index plate
- 1 Upright Drilling Machine, chucks & tools of all sorts with it
- 1 Shaping Machine & tools, wrenches, &c.
  A lot of reamers, mills &c to fit drill and lathe
- 1 Machine not in use - can be used for rule work, iron legs
- 1 Small Upright Drill for the smallest drills & fine work
- 1 Emery Grinder on Iron bed & legs
- 1 "   "   " Bench, used with water
- 1 Iron Bed 2½ ft x 12 in.
  A lot of bolts, screws &c for shop work
- 1 12 foot 1½ in. Iron Shaft
  A few boxes or parts of bars of fine tool steel
- 1 16 foot counter in this room and some short ones.
- 1 Grindstone on Wood Frame, 2 ft. dia., 3 in. face
- 1 Stove and all the fittings that belong to a small machine shop

Pattern Room
- 1 Iron Sawing Machine, bed & legs & several saws
- 1 Emery Grinder for sharpening fine saws
- 1 Hand Forge
  A lot of small tools for wood work
- 1 Big Hack Saw 2 foot blade 2 in. wide for blocking off Ivory Tusks

Desk Rule Room
- 1 Sawing Machine, iron legs & bed, 2 or 3 small saws
- 1 8 in. Composite Mill on Bench
- 1 Small cut-off sawing Machine for desk Rules
- 1 Gang of Drills of 7 for desk rule work, iron legs & bed
- 1 Riveting Machine for desk rule work, on iron legs & bed
- 1 Belting Machine, wood frame, for desk rules
- 1 Old Marking Machine (not now in use)
- 1 Wood Turning Lathe, some cutters & tools for desk rule work
- 1 Planer for Desk Rule Work on Iron Legs

Table III (concluded)

Room	Contents
Grinding Room	1 Pedestal Emery Grinder with wheels & fixtures for fine work, counter shaft
	1 Polishing Machine, iron bed & legs, some small tools
Marking Room (south side of road)	4 Marking Machines, iron bed & legs & Tools
	3 Large Stamping Machines on iron bed & legs
	2 Guaging Machines, Iron bed & legs
	11 Stamping & figuring machines on frame of wood, 15 x 3 feet
	7 Scaling & figuring Machines on bench
	1 Crank elevator
	1 Hand Guaging Machine
	2 Iron Slabs or beds for rule work, 2 ft by 1½ ft.
	1 Bench Vise
	Large lot of Small tools & fixtures used in this room
	Counter & belts over head in garret, stamps etc.
	1 Stamping Machine (hand) for Architects Rules
Room West of Marking Room	1 Large Spiral figure & Stamping Machine, iron legs & bed
	1 Yard Stick Guaging Machine, iron bed & legs
	4 Stamping & figure Machines on bench
	1 Grind Stone on wood frame
	2 polishing machines, wood frame, counters & belts
Varnishing Room	1 Pin Sticker
	1 Vise
	150 Varnish Frames
Blocking Room	Miscellaneous packs of wood & Iron for sand papering

Table II

BILL OF SALE - Delos H. Stephens to H. Chapin's Son Co.
August 14, 1901

Know all men by these presents:

That I, Delos H. Stephens. of the Town of Barkhamsted in Litchfield County and State of Connecticut, acting herein by my duly authorized attorney, Rufus E. Holmes, of the Town of Winsted in said County and State, for a valuable consideration [$5000], received to my full satisfaction of the H. Chapin's Son Company, a corporation located in the Town of New Hartford in said County and State, have bargained and sold, and do by these presents bargain and sell unto the said H. Chapin's Son Company the articles of personal property enumerated and described in the schedule hereto annexed, comprising the machinery, tools and implements, the goods in whole and in part manufactured, the raw materials for making such goods, the book accounts and other chases in action, and the goodwill pertaining to the business and plant for the manufacture of rules hitherto carried on and owned by me at Riverton in said Barkhamsted, under the name of Stephens & Company, and also everything in way of personal property belonging to said business and plant and not specifically enumerated in said schedule. And I do hereby agree to warrant and defend the aforesaid articles of personal property to the said H. Chapin's Son Company.

In witness whereof I hereunto subscribe my name and affix my seal by my attorney aforesaid this fourteenth day of August AD 1901.

Delos H. Stephens
by Rufus E. Holmes, atty.

Table IV

Incorporation of the Chapin-Stephens Co. Oct. 1, 1901
[Recorded New Hartford Land Records, B29, p39]

We hereby certify that at a Special Meeting of the Stock Holders of H. Chapins's Son Company, a joint stock corporation organized under the statute of the State of Connecticut, at their office at New Hartford on the 14th August 1901 the name of the said Company by a vote of stock holders, holding more than 50% of the whole stock, change to THE CHAPIN - STEPHENS COMPANY to take effect October 1, 1901.

Table V

"The Chapin-Stephens Company" From *THE IRON AGE,* Aug. 29, 1901

THE CHAPIN-STEPHENS COMPANY.

THE H. CHAPIN'S SON COMPANY, Pine Meadow, Conn., and Stephens & Co., Riverton, Conn., have joined forces, and the Riverton plant will be moved to Pine Meadow at once and established in the buildings of the Chapin Company. The two oldest Rule manufacturing concerns in the United States are thus brought together, making a very strong company with large capacity.

H. Chapin, the grandfather of the present members of the firm of that name, established the factory at Pine Meadow in 1826, when he began manufacturing a full line of Carpenters' Planes. This branch of the business is now being carried on on an extensive scale by the present company. A few years later Mr. Chapin added the manufacturing of Plumbs and Levels and some other minor lines, which are now made by the present company. In 1835 he began the manufacturing of Folding Carpenters' Rules. E. M. Chapin, who died in December, 1896, was closely identified with the business as his father's employee until the early 60's, when he became sole owner of the company, carrying on the same with success until the time of his death. E. M. Chapin's Sons, H. M. and F. M. Chapin, during their early school days were closely identified with the business during vacation time, and since 1885 H. M. Chapin has been identified with the business, and in the year 1889 F. M. Chapin also became connected with it.

In the year 1853 L. C. Stephens and his son, D. H. Stephens, started up at Pine Meadow manufacturing Rules under the firm name of L. C. Stephens & Co., where they did a successful business. They moved to New Hartford in 1859, and in 1861 adopted the style of Stephens & Co., which has been used ever since. They remained in New Hartford until 1864, when they moved further up the Farmington River and located at Riverton, where they have since been located. F. L. Stephens, son of D. H. Stephens, worked with his father and became familiar with the business. In 1876 he became permanently connected with the company and he has since been successfully identified with them.

This consolidation of interests will be known as the Chapin-Stephens Company after October 1 next. The *personnel* of the new company will doubtless be somewhat different from that of the present Chapin company. It is very probable that R. E. Holmes will continue to be president; H. M. Chapin, vice-president, and F. M. Chapin, treasurer, with F. L. Stephens as secretary. The present Board of Directors will probably be increased somewhat. The Chapin-Stephens Company will open a store at 80 Chambers street, New York, under the management of V. P. Humason, who is identified with the new company, and who has represented Stephens & Co. for the last 25 years.—*From The Iron Age, Aug. 29, 1901.*

A new illustrated catalogue and price list of products manufactured by Chapin-Stephens Co. was issued January 1, 1902. The title page of this is shown as Plate I and the index and discount sheet as Plate II. With exception of the few rules acquired from the former Stephens & Co., the goods offered in this were essentially the same as listed in the former *1897 H. Chapin's Son Co. Catalogue*. With the incorporation of Chapin-Stephens Co. it was necessary to adopt an new numbering system for rules. It was decided to use the same numbers followed by Stanley Rule & Level Co. A four-page brochure was published in January 1902 to relate the former numbers used by the previous firms with the new numbers. *The 1901 Sargent & Co. Catalogue* published a Comparative List of Rules made by the three firms Stanley Rule & Level Co., H. Chapin's Son Co. and Stephens & Co.[3] (Table VI) Since Sargent & Co. were selling rules manufactured by the Chapin firm, they used the same numbers. The *1902 Sargent & Co. Catalogue* published a new Comparative List of Rules (Table VII) which related the former H. Chapin's Son Co. numbers to the newly adopted Chapin-Stephens, as they continued to sell the latter firm's rules.[4]

Table VI - *1901 Sargent & Co. Catalogue* Comparative List of Rule Numbers

Comparative List of Rules.

Stanley	Stephens	Chapin	Stanley	Stephens	Chapin	Stanley	Stephens	Chapin	Stanley	Stephens	Chapin	Stanley	Stephens	Chapin
1	13	41	39	98½	76	54	49	19	65	71	2	78	...	38½
4	15	44	40	99¼	77	55	73	6	65½	72½	5	78½	63	32
5	17	45	41	111	83	56	74	7	66	32	84	81	66	36
12	14	48	42	31	85	57	75	9	66½	...	84¼	82	67	37
15	27	49	43½	...	90½	58	33	96	67	53	22	83	...	33
18	2	39	44	...	92	59	50	20	68	41	10	84	42¼	14
26	9	46	45	...	93	60	52	21	69	70	1	85	77	59
29	1	38	48	...	89	61	42	11	70	54	23	86	83	60
32	98	72	49	...	90¾	61½	44	11½	72	56	24	87	84	61
32½	99	73	50	112	98	62	42½	15	72½	54½	26	88	94	57
34	124	80	51	46	16	62½	42¾	15½	73	57	27	89	86	62
36	95	70	52	49¼	18	63	45	12	75	59	28	90	89	52
36½	100	70½	53	48	17	63½	44½	13	76	60	30	92	91	55
38	95½	74	53½	39	17½	64	72	3	77	61	31	92½	90½	54

Table VII - *1902 Sargent & Co. Catalogue* Revised List of Rule Numbers

[Revised List of January 1, 1902, Sargent & Co. Catalog, page 1122A]
Comparative List of Rules, Etc.
Old Numbers Compared with the New.

Old Nos.	New Nos.	Old Nos.	New Nos.	Old Nos.	New Nos.	Old Nos.	New Nos.	Old Nos.	New Nos.	Old Nos.	New Nos.	Old Nos.	New Nos.	Old Nos.	New Nos.	Old Nos.	New Nos.
1	69	15½	62½	27	73	37	82	50	6	63	94½	74	38	83½	67¼	90	43¼
2	65	16	51	28	75	38	29	51	16	64	95	74½	40¼	84	66	90½	43½
3	64	17	53	28½	75½	39	18	52	90	65	95½	75	40¾	84¼	66½	90¾	49
5	65½	17½	53½	29	76½	40	22	53	90½	66	95¾	76	39	84½	66¼	91	48¾
6	55	18	52	30	76	41	1	54	92½	67	97	77	40	84¾	66¾	91½	48¼
7	56	19	54	31	77	42	2	55	92	68	98½	77½	40½	85	42	92	44
9	57	20	59	32	78½	43	23	56	88½	69	99½	78	99¾	85¼	73¼	93	45
10	68	21	60	32½	78	44	3½	57	88	70	36	79	39½	85½	43	94	45¼
11	61	22	67	33	83	44½	4	58	91½	70¼	13½	80	34	85¾	77¼	94½	45½
11½	61½	23	70	33½	83½	45	5	59	85	70½	36½	81	35	86	46	95	58¾
12	63	23¼	61¼	34	79	46	26	59½	85½	70¾	13	81½	30	87	46½	96	58
13	63½	23½	70¼	34½	79½	47	27	60	86	71	14	82	33½	88	{ 47	96¼	58½
13½	53¾	24	72	34¾	79¾	48	12	60½	86½	71½	14½	82½	33		{ 47½	96½	94
14	84	25	72¼	35	79¼	49	15	61	87	72	32	83	41	89	48	97	41½
15	62	26	72½	36	81	49½	49½	62	89	73	32½	83¼	68¼	89½	48½	98	50

Plate I - Title Page to *1902 CHAPIN-STEPHENS CO. CATALOGUE*
[Collection of the Connecticut Historical Society]

ILLUSTRATED CATALOGUE

AND PRICE LIST OF

BOXWOOD AND IVORY RULES.

Miscellaneous Rules. Yard Sticks. Stephens' Patent Combination Rule, Square, Level, etc. School Rules. Desk Rules. Improved Desk Rules, etc.

PLUMBS AND LEVELS.

Non-Adjustable Levels. Patent Adjustable Levels. Chapin's Improved Brass Cornered Levels. Machinists' Brass Cornered Levels. Pocket Levels and Level Glasses.

PLANES.

Beechwood, Applewood, Boxwood and Rosewood. Common Bench Planes. Ship Planes. Moulding Planes. Grooving Planes. Miscellaneous Planes. Carriage Makers' Tools.

GAUGES.

Marking Gauges. Panel Gauges. Premium Gauges. Mortise Gauges. Cutting Gauges. Slitting Gauges. C. Scholl's Patent Gauges. Marden's Patent Gauges.

HAND SCREWS. BOX SCRAPERS. SPOKE SHAVES. CHISEL HANDLES. SAW HANDLES. FILE AND AWL HANDLES. PLANE IRONS. PLANE STOPS. DOOR STOPS. TURNING SAW FRAMES AND SAWS, etc.

MANUFACTURED BY

<u>1826.</u> **THE CHAPIN-STEPHENS CO.,** <u>1854.</u>

[UNION FACTORY, Established 1826.] PINE MEADOW, CONN., U. S. A.

January, 1902.

Plate IIA — Index to *1902 CHAPIN-STEPHENS CO. CATALOGUE*

INDEX.

	PAGE.
Astragals,	28
Awl Hafts,	71
" " Sewing,	71
" " Pegging,	71
Board Sticks,	15
Carriage Makers' Tools,	26
Door Stops,	73
Gauges,	55–58
" Marking,	55
" Cutting,	56
" Panel,	56
" Mortise,	56
" Slitting,	56
" Premium,	55
" Marden's Patent,	58
" Scholl's Patent,	57
Gauging Rods,	16
Hollows and Rounds,	33, 34
Hand Screws,	66
" " Beaded,	66
Handles,	69–73
" Brad Awl,	71
" Scratch Awl,	72
" Sewing Awl,	71
" Pegging Awl,	71
" Chisel,	69, 70
" Carving Tool,	72
" File,	70
" Plane,	73
" Saw,	73
" Screw-driver,	72
Levels,	59, 63–65
" Machinists'	64
" Pocket,	65
Level Glasses,	65
Log Sticks,	15
Planes,	18–49
" Base Moulding,	48
" Bead,	27–29
" Common Bench,	18
" Extra Bench,	19, 20
" Premium Bench,	21
" Without Irons,	23
" Applewood,	25
" Boxwood,	25
" Bead,	27–29
" Cooper,	24
" Cornice,	49
" Dado,	30
" Door,	31
" Filletster,	31
" Miscellaneous,	24
" Moulding,	39
" Match,	35
" Nosing,	30
" Ogee,	39, 41
" Ogee Grecian,	42, 43

	PAGE.
Planes, Ovolo,	46, 47
" Ovolo Grecian,	44, 45
" Raising,	32
" Rabbet,	32
" Reeding,	29
" Rosewood,	25
" Ship,	23
" Snipe Bills,	48
" Sash,	36, 37
" Sash Coping,	38
" Scotia's,	47
" Table,	34
Plane Irons,	75
Plane Stops,	75
Plows,	50–54
" Grooving,	50–52
" " Pat. Adjusting,	53
Plow Bits,	
Plumbs and Levels,	60–64
" " Adjustable,	60–62
" " Non-Adjustable,	60
" " Machinists',	64
" " Brass Cornered,	63–64
" " Masons' Adjustable,	61
" " " Non "	60
Rules,	3–16
" Architects' Boxwood,	7
" " Ivory,	14
" Boxwood,	3–12
" Board Measure,	9, 15
" Bench,	15
" Caliper, Boxwood,	10
" " Ivory,	14
" Carriage Makers'	12
" Ivory,	13, 14
" Miscellaneous,	15, 16
" Pocket,	3
" Slide,	7–10, 14
" { Stephens' Pat. Comb. Rule, Level, Square, etc., }	16
" Three Feet,	11
" Narrow, Boxwood,	4, 5
" Broad,	6, 7
" Extra Narrow, Boxwood,	5
Rulers,	17
" Desk, Plain,	17
" " Brass Edge,	17
" Stephens' Patent Grooved,	17
" School,	17
Ship Carpenters' Bevels,	10
Scrapers, Patent Box and Ship,	74
Spoke Shaves,	74
Stationers' Goods,	17
Turning Saw Frames,	67, 68
" " " and Saws,	68
Wantage Rods,	16
Yard Sticks,	15

Plate IIB – Discount Sheet Jan. 1, 1902 for *CHAPIN-STEPHENS CATALOGUE*

1826.
H. CHAPIN.

1854.
STEPHENS & CO.

1901.

THE CHAPIN-STEPHENS CO.,

Catalogue of 1902.

DISCOUNT SHEET.

PINE MEADOW, CONN., U. S. A., JAN. 1, 1902.

	Discount Per Cent.
BOXWOOD RULES,	60 and 10
IVORY "	35 and 10
MISCELLANEOUS RULES,	50 and 10
STEPHENS PAT. COMBINATION RULE, Level and Square,	55 and 10
STATIONERS' RULERS,	10
BENCH PLANES, Common "Pearce,"	50
" " Extra and Premium,	45
" " With English Irons instead of American,	35
SHIP PLANES,	40
MISCELLANEOUS PLANES,	40
BENCH PLANES, Apple, Box and Rosewood,	35
CARRIAGE MAKERS' TOOLS,	25
MOULDING PLANES,	40
GROOVING PLOWS,	40
GAUGES,	50 and 10
" Scholl's Patent,	50 and 10
" Marden's Patent, for Door Hangers,	50 and 10
PLUMBS AND LEVELS.—Non-Adjustable,	40 and 10
" " " Patent Adjustable,	40 and 10
" " " Chapin's Imp. Brass Cornered,	40 and 10
" " " Machinists' Brass Cornered,	40 and 10
POCKET LEVELS,	40 and 10
LEVEL GLASSES,	60 and 10
HAND SCREWS,	30
TURNING SAW FRAMES,	30 and 10
" " " AND SAWS,	30 and 10
CHISEL HANDLES,	65 and 10
FILE AND AWL HANDLES,	65 and 10
PLANE HANDLES,	40 and 10
SCREW DRIVER HANDLES,	40 and 10
SAW HANDLES,	40 and 10
CARVING TOOL HANDLES,	40 and 10
DOOR STOPS,	60 and 10
SPOKE SHAVES, Chapin's Improved,	50 and 10
BOX SCRAPERS,	50 and 10
PLANE IRONS,	30
PLANE STOPS,	20

NOTE: Rules with Foreign graduation 10 per cent less discount than English.

TERMS:—30 days, no cash discount, or 2 % cash if paid in 10 days from date of invoice. Invoices unpaid after 30 days from date, sight draft will be made.
Prices are subject to change without notice.

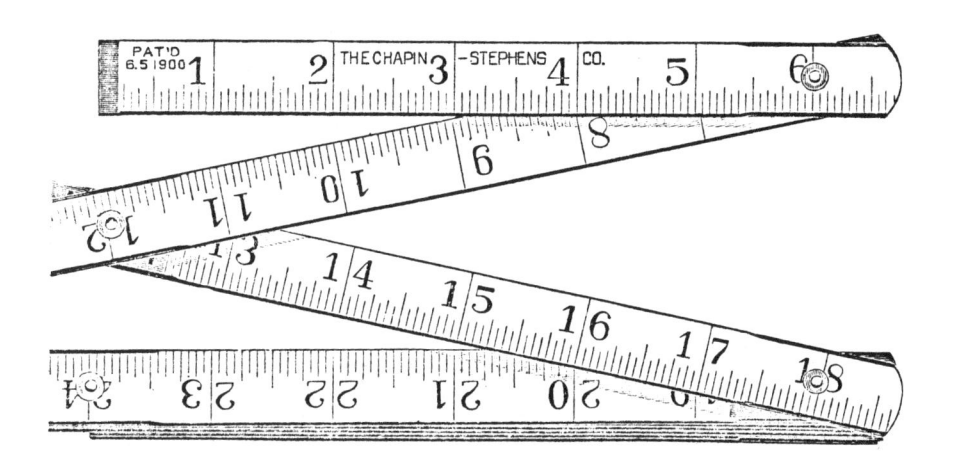

The next issue of a Chapin-Stephens Co. catalogue was published in 1905. The foreword to this 78 page catalogue is reproduced as Table VIII. At this date the New York offices were located at 9 to 15 Murray St. A new product illustrated and listed in this catalogue was the Flexifold Rule with riveted joints, similar to the increasingly popular Stanley Rule & Level Co.'s zig-zag. (See Plate III) A patent date of June 6, 1900 is noted on the illustration of this rule. These were available in yellow or white enamel in 2, 3, 4, 5, 6 and 8 feet sizes, graduated in 1/16 in. increments. Another new item offered in this catalogue was Wood's Patent Extension Sight Level. (Plate IV)

An article, noting the historical background and facilities of the firm, published in 1908 reported the New York Office was then located at 126 Chambers St. with John E. Humaston as manager.[5] He was the son of the late Virgil P. Humaston, who previous to his death in 1905, had served Stephens & Co. at New York for 25 years.

The Annual Report of the Chapin-Stephens Co., dated July 30, 1912 listed the same officers as noted in Table V.[6] However, the Annual Report filed January 15, 1913 noted Frank M. Chapin as president, Hermon M. Chapin as vice-president and treasurer and Frank L. Stephens as secretary and assistant treasurer.[7] Apparently Rufus Holmes had died sometime during 1912.

The next general catalogue published for the Chapin-Stephens Co. was their No. 114 of 84 pages.[8] The title page and index to this are shown as Plates V & VI. The frontispiece consisted of an artist's sketch of the factories. (Plate VII) The foreword noted the officers and solicitation for continued business. (Plate VIII) There were few changes from previous catalogues. A relatively new product, flexible rivet joint rule, previously called "flexifold" was listed as "Pearce."

Plate III -   Flexifold Rule Noted in *1905 CHAPIN-STEPHENS CATALOGUE*

THE CHAPIN-STEPHENS CO., PINE MEADOW, CONN.

FLEXIFOLD RULES,

With Riveted Joints.

Table VIII -   Foreword to *1905 CHAPIN-STEPHENS CO. CATALOGUE*

R.E. Holmes, President   F.L. Stephens, Secretary
H. M. Chapin, Vice-President   F.M. Chapin, Treasurer

In preparing this catalogue it has been our aim to make it as plain as possible for the buyer, and a careful study of its pages will give a good idea of the different styles of tools we make.

This factory established in 1826 has become well known to the trade. Our present Company was formed in 1901 by the consolidation of the plants of H. Chapin's Son Co. and Stephens & Co., the two oldest Manufacturers of Rules, Tools, Planes, etc. in the United States.

By utilizing the best features of the two old plants and improvements made, we have developed our facilities largely, and have one of the best equipped Factories in existence today for the production of these goods.

Many changes have been made in list prices since our last catalog was printed and we request all former lists be destroyed and goods ordered by this catalog only.

All goods made by us are warranted.

THE CHAPIN-STEVENS CO.

July 1, 1905   Pine Meadow, Conn.

Plate IV -   Wood's Patent Level as Note in *1905 CHAPIN-STEPHENS CATALOGUE*

EXTENSION SIGHT LEVELS.

WOOD'S PATENT.

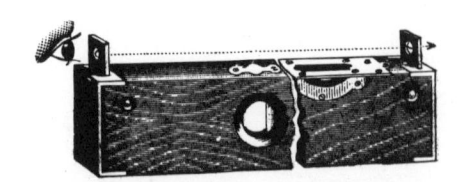

Sights Raised for Long Distance.

This improvement greatly enlarges the scope of the tool over the usual form of level, making it available for leveling lengths of 100 feet or more, and shorter lengths, without the cumbersome and unreliable straight edge commonly used with the ordinary level.

Sights Depressed for Ordinary Use.

Plate V - Title Page to *CHAPIN-STEPHENS CATALOGUE No. 114*

Rules
    Planes
        Gauges
            Plumbs and Levels
Hand Screws
    Handles
        Spoke Shaves
            Box Scrapers, Etc.

CATALOG
No. 114

THE CHAPIN-STEPHENS CO.
UNION FACTORY

FACTORIES AND GENERAL OFFICES
PINE MEADOW, CONN., U.S.A.

NEW YORK OFFICE
126 Chambers Street

[Reprinted by Ken Roberts Publishing Co., 1975]

Plate VI - Index to *CHAPIN-STEPHENS Co. CATALOGUE No. 114*

INDEX.

	PAGE
Awl Hafts,	78
" " Sewing,	78
" " Pegging,	78
Board Sticks,	27
Carriage Makers' Tools,	36
Gauges,	63-65
" Marking,	63
" Cutting,	64
" Panel,	65
" Mortise,	65
" Premium,	63-64
Gauging Rods,	27
Hollows and Rounds,	43-44
Hand Screws,	75
" " Beaded,	75
Handles,	76-82
" Brad Awl,	78
" Scratch Awl,	79
" Sewing Awl,	78
" Pegging Awl,	78
" Chisel,	76-77
" Carving Tool,	79
" File,	77
" Plane,	80
" Saw,	80-82
" Screw-driver,	79
" Wall Scraper,	82
Levels,	66-74
" Machinists',	72
" Pocket,	74
Level Glasses,	74
Log Sticks,	27
Planes,	28-62
" Applewood,	35
" Astragals,	37
" Base Moulding,	58
" Bead,	37-39
" Bench, Common,	28
" Bench, Extra,	29-30
" Bench, Premium,	31-32
" Boxwood,	35
" Cornice,	59
" Dado,	40
" Door,	41
" Filletster,	41
" Hollows and Rounds,	43-44
" Miscellaneous,	34
" Moulding,	49-59
" Match,	45
" Nosing,	40
" Ogee,	46-51
" Ogee Grecian,	52-53
" Ovolo,	46-48
" Ovolo Grecian,	54-55
" Rabbet,	42
" Raising,	43
" Reeding,	39
" Rosewood,	35
" Quarter Rounds,	56-57

	PAGE
Planes, Sash,	47
" Sash Coping,	48
" Scotia's,	57
" Ship,	33
" Snipe Bills,	58
" Table,	44
" Without Irons,	28
Plane Irons,	84
Plane Stops,	84
Plows,	60-62
" Grooving,	60-62
Plow Bits,	84
Plumbs and Levels,	66-73
" " " Adjustable,	69-70
" " " Extension Sights,	73
" " " Non-Adjust'le,	66-68
" " " Machinists',	72
" " " Brass Cornered	71-72
" " " Masons' Adjustable,	70
" " " Masons' Non-Adjustable,	70
Rules,	3-27
" Architects', Boxwood,	12
" " Ivory,	18
" Bench,	26
" Board Measure,	9
" Boxwood,	3-16
" Broad, Boxwood (2 feet),	7-8
" Broad, Boxwood (3 feet),	15
" Caliper, Boxwood,	13-14
" " Ivory,	19-20
" Carriage Makers',	16
" Extra Narrow, Boxwood,	11
" Flexifold,	22
" Ivory,	17-20
" Miscellaneous,	26-27
" Narrow, Boxwood, (2 Feet),	4-6
" " " (3 Feet),	15
" "Nearsite," Boxwood,	7
" "Pearce,"	23
" Pocket, Boxwood,	3
" " Ivory,	17
" Ship Carpenters' Bevels,	12
" Slide,	11
" Stephens' Pat. Comb. Rule, Level, Square, etc.,	21
" Window,	16
Rulers,	24-25
" Boxwood,	24
" Desk, Plain Edge,	24
" " Brass Edge,	24
" Stephens' Patent Grooved,	25
" School,	25
Sawdust, Boxwood,	85
Scrapers, Box,	83
Spoke Shaves,	83
Stationers' Goods,	24-25
Wantage Rods,	27
Yard Sticks,	26

Plate VII - Frontispiece to *CHAPIN-STEPHENS CATALOGUE No. 114*

Plate VIII - Foreword to *CHAPIN-STEPHENS CATALOGUE No. 114*

F. M. CHAPIN, *President.*

    H. M. CHAPIN, *Vice-President and Treasurer.*

        F. L. STEPHENS, *Secretary.*

Since our consolidation in 1901 of the plants of H. Chapin's Son Company, established in 1826, and Stephens & Company, established in 1854, we have reorganized nearly every department in our factory, moving some of them into new and larger quarters, so that now the combined capacity of our works has been more than doubled.

In making these betterments we have not for a moment lost sight of quality and finish, but rather when it has been possible for us to do so, we have improved same.

It is our purpose to continue to guarantee all goods of our manufacture as has been our practice since this business was established.

To our many customers throughout the civilized world we extend our thanks for the continued preference they have shown for our tools during the nearly ninety years of our existence, as is evidenced by the growing demand for same. We hope to continue to merit this appreciation shown us by the public.

THE CHAPIN-STEPHENS COMPANY,

PINE MEADOW, CONN.

Early in 1914, after publication of Catalogue No. 114, Chapin-Stephens Co. purchased Elmore Manufacturing Co. of West Hartford, Conn. This consisted of a line of diversified screw drivers; screw driver bits; snail, rose and flat countersinks; bit reamers; ice picks; awls; gimlets; tack pullers and machinist, cold and cape chisels. An addition to the factory at Pine Meadow was constructed to accommodate the machinery moved there from the previous location. A ceremony was held August 14, 1914 to dedicate the new addition. A record of this event was sealed in a cornerstone. (Table IX) The acquisition of Elmore products was a belated attempt to acquire a new line to supplement the decreasing demands for rules and wooden planes. Stanley Rule & Level Co. ten years previously in 1904 had acquired the lines of Hurwood screw drivers and chisels manufactured by the George E. Wood Co. of Plantsville, Conn.[9] Chapin-Stephens Co. issued a supplement to their No. 114 Catalogue to illustrate and price their new lines of screw drivers, etc.

Table IX

RECORD DICTATED by FRANK M. CHAPIN, PRESIDENT OF CHAPIN-STEPHENS CO., AUGUST 13, 1914, PLACED in CEMNET BLOCK in COMMEMORATION OF ERECTION of a PLANT ADDITION

To the one who opens this receptacle placed this day in a cement block showing the year in which the Polishing and Forge Shop in connection with our plane was built, to take care of the new business acquired by the purchase of the Elmore Tool Mfg. Co., as shown in the enclosed notice.

These buildings are being erected for us under contract by the H.Wales Lines Company of Meriden, Conn. Mr. Lines, the President of the Company, has recently passed his fiftieth anniversary of his connection with the building business in Meriden. He is one of the stockholders and a director of this Company, and father-in-law to the President of this Company, the writer of this letter.

This business was established here in 1826 by Hermon Chapin. In 1854 Stephens & Co. started their Rule Business here in Pine Meadow, later moved to New Hartford, then to Riverton. In 1901 Stephens & Co. were brought into consolidation with The H.Chapin's Son Co., which was then the name the firm was running under, that had been established by Hermon Chapin in July 1826, as referred to above. The Stephens learned the trade of Rule making from Hermon Chapin before starting into business for themselves, so that by this consolidation it was sort of coming back home with the business.

Hermon Chapin died in 1866 while on a visit at Savannah, Ga. His son, Edward M. Chapin, conducted the business under the name of H.Chapin's Son until the time of his death on Dec. 19, 1896. In 1897 the business was formed into a joint stock company under the name of H.Chapin's Son Co., as previously referred to.

The late Rufus E. Holmes of Winsted, Conn. was President, Hermon M. Chapin, Vice President and Frank M. Chapin, Secretary and Treasurer. At the consolidtion in 1901 the name was changed to the present name of The Chapin-Stephens Company. Frank L. Stephens succeeded to office of Secretary at that time. After the death of Mr. Holmes, Frank M. Chapin was made President, Hermon M. Chapin, Vice President and Treasuer and Frank L. Stephens, Secretary. These are the present officers of the Company. Said officers, together with H. Wales Lines of Meriden, Conn., Chas F. Brooker of Ansonia, Elisha J. Steele of Torrington, constitute the Board of Directors, there being a vacancy in the Board, owing to the recent death of William B. Chapin at his home in Washington, D.C. William B. Chapin was the son of Philip E. Chapin, the only living brother of the late Edward M. Chapin. At this writing Philip E. Chapin and wife are somewhere in Europe, as is also Charles M. Chapin, another grandson of Hermon Chapin, being a son of the late George W. Chapin. With Charles M. Chapin in Europe is his wife, daughter and son. Why it is particularly mentioned at this time that they are in Europe is because of the great European War, which is now going on with Austria and Germany at war against Servia, Russia, England and France. The Germans have been attempting to cross Belgium and have met with stiff resistance by the Belgians, who have kept the Germans back around the forts about Liege. At this time the Germans are occupying Liege but have not yet captured the forts, There are other engagements going on elsewhere, which one will have an opportunity to trace out in history when this communication is discovered and read.

Mr. Adolph Mischler is the foreman for the Lines Co. on this work. Our own boss carpenter is looking after the carpenter work on the job under Mr. Mischler. This is Mr. Edward Boudouin. Mr. Mischler is of German parentage and Mr. Boudouin of French parentage, but notwithstanding the difficulties on the other side they are getting on harmoniously in their work.

Woodrow Wilson is President of the United States, and at this time all America is sorrowing with him in his loss of Mrs. Wilson, who just passed away and was laid to rest Tuesday Aug.11th, at her home in Rome, Ga.

One might go on with interesting facts of this present time indefinitely, but the capacity of our receptacle is limited, so this communication must now be brought to a close.

This date block is being laid by Ellie Lines Chapin, youngest daugther of H. Wales Lines and wife of Frank M. Chapin.

~~~ CHAPIN'S ~~~
SOLID CHERRY LEVEL,

12 inch polished cherry level with handsome nickel plated top plate.

No. 100.   Packed one dozen in pasteboard box.
WRITE FOR PRICES.

THE H. CHAPIN'S SON CO., Pine Meadow, Conn.

Delos Hart Stephens, died May 5, 1919 at New Hartford. An obituary noted some interesting details of his life.[10]

"...he was educated at the Connecticut Literary Institute at Suffield and at a boys school in Perth Amboy, N.J. When a young man, he with his father, Lorenzo C. Stephens, entered the employ of Hermon Chapin of Pine Meadow, manufacturer of planes and rules. In 1854 Mr. Stephens and his father started the manufacture of boxwood and ivory rules on their own account in a building at Pine Meadow. In 1859 the business was moved into a shop built for them by Captain John Smith, for many years past occupied by the Standard Brush Co. and which was burned down about two years ago. Here they carried on the business until 1864 when Delos Stephens bought the factory at Riverton formerly used for making chairs, continuing the business alone, his father withdrawing from the firm, but representing it to the trade. Mr. Stephens continued the business at Riverton, retaining the firm name of Stephens & Co. until 1901 when it was consolidated as Chapin-Stephens Co. with the H. Chapin Son Co. of Pine Meadow. Mr. Stephens had a gift for invention and development of fine machinery which was a prime factor in the production of his goods. His aim was to produce the best rules that could be made and the reputation of his product proclaimed his success. During his 37 years of business life in Riverton he was active in the betterment for the village and did much by his example and aid for the welfare of the community..."

An engraving made from an artist's sketch of Delos Stephens, believed to have been made about 1880, when he was 38 years old is shown as Fig. 74.[11] He was 87 years old when he died.

Fig. 74 Delos Hart Stephens

[History of Litchfield County, Phila.,PA., 1881]

The next catalogue offered by the Chapin-Stephens Co. was their No. 122 on January 1, 1922. The foreword to this publication of 61 pages is shown as Plate IX. Their lines of rules, planes, levels and gauges were confined to the first 46 pages, which was a substantial reduction from the 84 pages of the No. 114 Catalogue. Pages 44-59 noted the new lines of Elmore products. No prices were listed in this catalogue, but these were sent out on separate printed lists.

On August 11, 1924 Chapin-Stephens Co. announced price reductions on planes and screw drivers. (Plate X) Again on October 1, 1925 plane prices were lowered. (Plate XI) A price list of six pages, issued on October 1, 1925, believed to have been the last general price list published by the firm, is reprinted as Plate XII. A brochure of four pages noting inexpensive products made by the Chapin-Stephens Co. suggested "some specialties for the 'Five and Ten Store Trade'." (Plate XIII)

Plate IX-A - Foreword to *Chapin-Stephens Catalogue No. 122*

TO OUR LEGION OF FRIENDS
IN THE CIVILIZED WORLD.

To our legion of friends in the civilized world we extend thanks for their continued preference shown for tools manufactured by this firm for the past ninety-five years. The ever growing demand for these tools is highly pleasing to us of the third generation and confirms our belief that quality of tools together with an effort to put a personal touch in all our dealings with the trade is the key note of this long continued service to the army of mechanics throughout the world.

We hope to continue to merit this confidence shown by the ever increasing buying public.

This catalogue cancels all previous editions.

Very truly yours,

THE CHAPIN-STEPHENS COMPANY.

Established July 1, 1826

Pine Meadow, Conn.,
Jan. 1, 1922.

Plate IX-B - Title Page to *CHAPIN-STEPHENS CO. Catalogue No. 122*

1826
H. CHAPIN
Union Factory

1854
STEPHENS & CO.

1901
THE CHAPIN-STEPHENS CO.
UNION FACTORY

RULES,
      PLANES,
           GAUGES,
                  PLUMBS & LEVELS,
HANDSCREWS,
      CHISEL HANDLES,
           FILE HANDLES,
                PLANE HANDLES,
SAW HANDLES,
      SCREW DRIVERS,
                  GIMLETS,
AWLS,
      PUNCHES,
           BITS,
                CHISELS, Etc.

FACTORIES AND GENERAL OFFICES
PINE MEADOW, CONN., U. S. A.

NEW YORK OFFICE
126 Chambers Street

[Collection of the Connecticut Historical Society]

COMBINATION RULE AND GLASS-CUTTER.

THE CHAPIN=STEPHENS CO
SUCCESSORS TO
PATENTED.

MADE BY

THE H. CHAPIN'S SON CO.,
MANUFACTURERS

Rules, Planes, Levels, Etc.,

PINE MEADOW, CONN., U. S. A.

OUR motto is "Advance."

Our life work is to advance.

Since we started in 1826 we have continued to advance.

Here we are again.

Yes, we have a winner this time.

Protected by letters patent, too.

And controlled by us.

Have you seen it?

Our combination rule and glass-cutter is just what you want.

Send us a trial order.

Haven't time to give full details here.

Cut on first page shows cutter in operation.

Cut on last page shows construction of same.

We carry these in stock fitted to our No. 11 and No. 23 rules.

Yes, we will put the cutter in any of our other rules for orders of ½ gross of one kind.

This cutter in our new, improved, bound or half-bound rule would make you a record-breaker for a seller.

If you want to please the trade, keep our glass-cutter rules in stock.

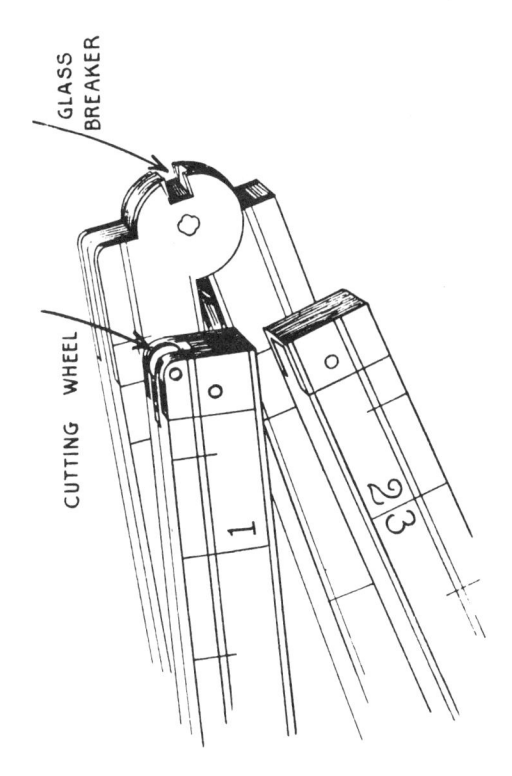

PATENTED.

MADE BY

THE H. CHAPIN'S SON CO.,
MANUFACTURERS

Rules, Planes, Levels, Etc.,

PINE MEADOW, CONN., U. S. A.

Why not order a sample gross with your next goods?

You will find they won't have time to get shop worn on your hands.

To use glass breaker in head joint, open notch full width, slip it over the glass, close rule and use as breaker.

A good, simple way to break glass is to slip same between the middle joints of rule when closed; hold firmly in hand and use as breaker.

We could claim many points of advantage for our glass-cutter rules, but prefer to let them speak for themselves.

We are constantly adding to and improving our entire line of goods.

With our recently increased facilities for turning out same we can give all orders prompt attention.

Plate IX-C - Unique Glass Cutter Rule. Originally manufactured by H. Chapin's Son Co., but continued by Chapin-Stephens Co.

Plate X - 1924 Announcement of Price Reduction by Chapin-Stephens Co.

ESTABLISHED
1826

THE CHAPIN – STEPHENS CO.
UNION   FACTORY

Pine Meadow, Conn.,
August 11, 1924.

Gentlemen:

Ninety-eight years in business should entitle us to your confidence and a fair share of your patronage in our several lines of high class Carpenters and Mechanics Tools.

New net prices are enclosed.

Boxwood, Ivory, Flexifold and Miscellaneous Rules remain the same.

Bench and Moulding Planes, Grooving Plows and Plane Irons are lower.

Gauges some styles remain the same and others show a slight advance. This is also the situation with Plumbs and Levels.

Pocket Levels, Level Glass, Hand Screws and Plane Handles remain the same.

Chisel and File Handles are reduced.

Saw Handles have advanced.

Screw Drivers are lowered. Also Cold Chisels.

We would suggest that you study these changes and let us have your orders at this time for shipments at once or later deliveries.

Yours respectfully,

THE CHAPIN-STEPHENS CO.

Plate XI - 1925 Announcement of Price Revisions by Chapin-Stephens Co.

ESTABLISHED
1826

THE CHAPIN -- STEPHENS CO.
UNION   FACTORY

Pine Meadow, Conn.,
October 1st, 1925.

Gentlemen:

July 1st, 1826, Hermon Chapin established a Plane Shop here in some of our present buildings under the name of H. Chapin Union Factory. Since that time the line has been added to by the manufacture of Rules, Levels, Hand Screws, Handles, Screw Drivers, etc. We are the oldest plane manufacturers in the States today.

At this time we are coming to you with quite a complete revision of our net prices on Planes and Plane Irons; net prices on other lines remaining the same.

It is our hope that we may continue to be favored with your orders for goods of our manufacture.

Your patronage is appreciated by us, so send in your orders, and in this way help us celebrate our approaching Centennial.

Yours respectfully,

THE CHAPIN-STEPHENS CO.

Plate XII - Net Price List, Oct. 1, 1925 for Catalog No. 122
[Continued through Page 405]

DR 1000

ESTABLISHED

1826

THE CHAPIN--STEPHENS CO.
UNION FACTORY

FACTORIES AND GENERAL OFFICES:

PINE MEADOW, CONN., U. S. A.

NEW YORK STORE: 126 CHAMBERS ST.

NET PRICE LIST

FOR

CATALOG No. 122

OCT. 1st, 1925

All prices F. O. B. Factory and subject to change without notice.

Terms:—Net 30 days or 2% for payment within 10 days from date of invoice.

[Collection of Connecticut Historical Society]

Plate XII - Net Price List, Oct. 1, 1925 for Catalog No. 122
[Continued from Page 400]

RULES

Pages 3-14 — BOXWOOD RULES

No.	Doz.	No.	Doz.	No.	Doz.	No.	Doz.
1	$8.40	36½	$5.21	63½	$2.87	73	$8.82
4	4.95	42	3.95	64	2.11	75	4.57
5	7.29	51	2.68	65	1.58	76	7.68
7	6.00	53	3.44	65½	4.21	76 C	12.74
12	4.40	53½	5.50	66¼	5.04	78½	9.15
12½	5.20	54	6.67	66½	4.33	79½	5.30
13	2.87	54 S	7.50	66¾	10.95	79¾	8.43
26	5.30	61	2.06	67	2.68	82	9.15
29	2.18	61½	2.25	68	1.50	83½	9.59
30	8.65	62	5.49	69	1.34	84	4.49
32	5.54	62 C	10.78	70	3.08	94	20.03
32½	7.95	62½	5.49	72	3.81	Right Hand Caliper Rules Add 50c Doz.	
36	3.60	63	2.73	72½	6.90		

Pages 15-16 — IVORY RULES

No.	Doz.	No.	Doz.	No.	Doz.	No.	Doz.	No.	Doz.
88	$11.03	40	$32.45	86	$47.25	87	$59.10	91½	$20.60
89	28.00	40½	17.65	86½	70.89	90	7.78	92	12.50

Page 17 — FLEXIFOLD RULES

Yellow

No.	Doz.	No.	Doz.
220	$1.00		
330	1.50	330 M	$1.50
440	2.00	440 M	2.00
550	2.50	550 M	2.50
660	3.00	660 M	3.00
880	4.00		

White

No.	Doz.	No.	Doz.
222	$1.10		
333	1.65	333 M	$1.65
444	2.20	444 M	2.20
555	2.75	555 M	2.75
666	3.30	666 M	3.30
888	4.40		

Page 18 — MISCELLANEOUS RULES

No.	Doz.	No.	Doz.	No.	Doz.	No.	Doz.
33	$1.98	34	$3.00	50	$4.18	80	$5.85
		41	2.86				

COMBINATION RULE, LEVEL & SQUARE. Page 14

No.	Doz.
.036	$24.00

DR 1000

For identification of Boxwood and Ivory Rules refer to Rule Number List, Plate VII, page 383 and 1874 H.Chapin's Son Catalogue Chapter VIII.

Plate XII - Net Price List, Oct. 1, 1925 for Catalog No. 122
[Continued from Page 400]

Pages 19-31 — PLANES

COMMON BENCH	PREMIUM	BEADS	RABBET PLANES	SASH
Single Irons	No. — Each	No. — Each	No. — Each	No. — Each
No. — Each	400 — $1.20	123	157	187 — $2.15
100 — $0.80	401 — 1.40	⅛ to ½ in. — $0.85	¼, ⅜ in. — $1.15	188 — 1.95
101 — .90	402 — 2.30	⅝ to ¾ in. — .95	½ to 1 in. — .70	189 — 1.50
102 — 1.60	403	⅞ to 1 in. — 1.10	1⅛, 1¼ in. — .75	191 — 1.80
103	26 in. — 2.40	1⅛ to 1¼ in. — 1.30	1⅜, 1½ in. — .80	192 — 2.60
24 in. — 1.70	28 in. — 2.60	1⅜ to 1½ in. — 1.50	1⅝, 1¾ in. — .95	195 — 3.00
26 in. — 1.70	404 — 1.70	124	1⅞, 2 in. — 1.00	196 — 3.30
28 in. — 1.80	405 — 2.05	⅛ to ½ in. — 1.00	159	200 — 1.25
30 in. — 2.00	406 — 2.50	⅝ to ¾ in. — 1.10	1 to 2 in. — 2.10	201 — 1.50
	407	⅞ to 1 in. — 1.25	160	MOULDING
Double Irons	26 in. — 2.90	1⅛ to 1¼ in. — 1.45	1¼ to 2 in. — 1.90	204
No. — Each	28 in. — 3.15	1½ in. — 1.65		⅜ to 1 in. — $1.00
108 — $1.00		126	Hollows and Rounds	1¼ to 1½ in. — 1.15
109 — 1.15		⅛ to ½ in. — 1.00		1¾, 2 in. — 1.30
109½ — 1.35	SHIP	⅝ to ¾ in. — 1.10	No. — Per Pr.	205
110 — 1.90		⅞ to 1 in. — 1.25		⅜ to 1 in. — 1.15
111	NOSING		167	1¼, 1½ in. — 1.30
24 in. — 2.00	No. — Each	No. — Each	2 to 12 — $1.60	1¾, 2 in. — 1.50
26 in. — 2.00		132	14 to 18 — 1.80	2¼ to 2½ in. — 1.75
28 in. — 2.15	423 — $1.15	½ to 1¼ in. — $1.25	20 to 24 — 2.00	206
30 in. — 2.40	424 — 1.35	1⅜ to 1½ in. — 1.50	26 to 30 — 2.30	¾ to 1 in. — 1.10
	425 — 2.15	1¾, 2 in. — 1.75		1¼ to 1½ in. — 1.25
EXTRA BENCH	426 — 2.35	133		1¾ to 2 in. — 1.50
Single Irons		½ to 1¼ in. — 1.60	MATCH PLANES	207
No. — Each	Miscellaneous	1⅜, 1½ in. — 1.85	No. — Each	⅜ to ⅝ in. — 1.10
104 — .90	No. — Each	1¾, 2 in. — 2.10		¾ to 1 in. — 1.25
105 — 1.00	430 — $1.60	DADOES	171	1¼ in. — 1.50
106 — 1.80	432 — 1.25	No. — Each	¼ in. — $3.50	1½ to 1¾ in. — 1.65
107	434 — 1.60	138 — $1.60	⅜ to 1 in. — 2.20	207½
24 in. — 1.90	446 — 1.40	139 — 2.20	172	⅜ to ⅝ in. — 1.15
26 in. — 1.90	447 — 1.35	FILLETSTERS	¼ in. — 4.25	¾ to 1 in. — 1.30
28 in. — 2.00	448 — 1.40	No. — Each	⅜ to 1 in. — 2.50	1¼ in. — 1.50
30 in. — 2.20		147 — $1.80	173 — Per Pr.	1½ in. — 1.75
Double Irons		148 — 2.00	¼ in. — 3.50	208
No. — Each		150 — 3.50	⅜ to 1 in. — 2.20	¾ to 1 in. — 1.10
112 — $1.10		151 — 5.00	1¼ to 1½ in. — 2.60	1¼, 1½ in. — 1.20
113 — 1.25	CARRIAGE MAKER'S TOOLS	RABBET PLANES	174	1¾, 2 in. — 1.50
113½ — 1.45		No. — Each	¼ in. — 4.25	209
114 — 2.10		155	⅜ to 1 in. — 2.50	⅜ to 1 in. — 1.30
114½ — 2.30	No. — Each	¼ in. — $1.80	1¼ to 1½ in. — 2.90	1¼, 1½ in. — 1.45
115	1 — $1.00	¼, ⅜ in. — $1.15	175	1¾, 2 in. — 1.75
24 in. — 2.20	2 — 1.25	½ to 1 in. — .70	¼ in. — 3.50	217
26 in. — 2.20	3 — 1.00	1⅛, 1¼ in. — .75	⅜ to 1 in. — 2.20	¼ to ⅝ in. — .95
28 in. — 2.35	4 — 1.25	1⅜, 1½ in. — .80	1¼ to 1½ in. — 2.60	¾ to 1 in. — 1.15
30 in. — 2.60	5 — 1.75	1¾ in. — .95	176	1¼, 1½ in. — 1.30
115½	6 — 2.00	2 in. — 1.00	¼ in. — 5.00	217½
24 in. — 2.40			⅜ to 1 in. — 3.30	⅜ to ⅝ in. — .95
26 in. — 2.40			1¼ to 1½ in. — 3.90	¾ to 1 in. — 1.15
28 in. — 2.55				1¼, 1½ in. — 1.30
30 in. — 2.80				217¾
				⅜ to ¾ in. — 1.50
				⅞, 1 in. — 1.65
				1¼, 1½ in. — 1.80
				PLOWS
				230 — $4.00
				231 — 4.35
				232 — 5.50
				233 — 5.85
				234 — 6.50
				236 — 7.75
				238 — 8.00

For Identification of Planes refer to 1874 H. Chapin's Son Catalogue in Chapter VIII.

Plate XII - Net Price List, Oct. 1, 1925 for Catalog No. 122
[Continued from Page 400]

Page 32 — PLANE IRONS

In.	Single Doz.	Cut Doz.	Double Doz.	In.	Single Doz.	Cut Doz.	Double Doz.
1½	$4.40	$4.40	$6.05	2⅛	$5.67	$5.67	$7.26
1⅝	4.95	4.95	6.60	2¼	6.05	6.05	7.70
1¾	4.95	4.95	6.60	2⅜	6.49	6.49	8.14
1⅞	5.23	5.23	6.88	2½	6.99	6.99	9.02
2	5.45	5.45	7.10	2⅝	7.87	7.87	9.90

Pages 33-35 — GAUGES

No.	Doz.	No.	Doz.	No.	Doz.	No.	Doz.	No.	Doz.	No.	Doz.
246	$0.73	249	$1.80	252	$4.80	255	$2.52	260	$7.20	271	$1.74
247	.90	250½	4.82	253	2.04	259	4.50	261	8.88	272	2.52
248	1.14	251	2.76	254	2.76	259½	6.00	262	10.44		

Pages 36-41 — LEVELS

Brass Cornered
No. 1 Cherry
Length	Each
18 in.	$1.99
24 in.	2.12
26 in.	2.26
28 in.	2.38
30 in.	2.51

No. 2 Mahogany
Length	Each
18 in.	$2.26
24 in.	2.38
26 in.	2.51
28 in.	2.64
30 in.	2.77

No. 3 Rosewood
Length	Each
18 in.	$3.15
24 in.	3.28
26 in.	3.40
28 in.	3.54
30 in.	3.67

Extension Sight
No.	Doz.
1½	$25.40

No. 10 Rosewood
Length	Each
8 in.	$1.18
10 in.	1.42
12 in.	1.54

No. 12 Rosewood
Length	Each
6½ in.	$0.65

MASON'S PLUMB RULE
No.	Doz.
35	$16.95
100 Oiled	$0.90
Pol.	1.15
102 Oiled	1.30
Pol.	1.65

Non-Adjustable
No.	Doz.
286	$4.35
287	5.75
289	6.40
289½	8.50
290	9.35
290½	12.05
292	9.90
293½	13.68

With Graduating Adjustment
No.	Doz.
304	$12.35
306	16.68

Pat. Adjustable
No.	Doz.
490½	$13.42
493½	14.95
494	19.63

With Graduating Adjustment
No.	Doz.
504	$16.42
506	20.15

POCKET LEVELS
No.	Doz.
311	$1.12
312	1.19

A new style Level has been added, small stock 2½"x1⅛".

No. 292 — Cherry, Polished, Arch Top Plate, side views, and Tipped. Assorted 12 to 18 inch.

Page 41 — LEVEL GLASSES

Plain

Inch	Doz.	Inch	Doz.	Inch	Doz.
1	$0.45	2	$0.60	3½	$0.75
1¼	.45	2¼	.60	4	.95
1½	.50	2½	.65	4½	1.00
1¾	.50	3	.70	Ass't'd 1½-3"	.70

With Two Silver Lines

Inch	Doz.	Inch	Doz.	Inch	Doz.
1	$0.50	2	$0.65	3½	$0.80
1¼	.50	2¼	.65	4	1.00
1½	.55	2½	.70	4½	1.05
1¾	.55	3	.75	Ass't'd 1½-3"	.75

For Identification of Numbers Refer to 1874 H. Chapin's Son Catalogue, Chapter VIII.

Plate XII - Net Price List, Oct. 1, 1926 for Catalog No. 122
[Continued from Page 400]

Page 42 — HAND SCREWS

No.	Doz.	No.	Doz.	No.	Doz.	No.	Doz.
800	$18.00	804	$11.40	808	$8.80	812	$4.35
801	15.75	805	10.80	809	6.00	813	3.60
802	14.40	806	10.00	810	5.55	814	2.85
803	13.50	807	9.40	811	5.10	815	2.40
						816	2.10

Pages 43-46 — HANDLES

PLANE

No.	Doz.
1	$0.96
2	1.68
3	1.68

SAW

No.	Doz.	No.	Doz.	No.	Doz.	No.	Doz.
5	$1.92	7	$6.24	10	$1.68	14	$1.20
6	2.04	8	2.16	11	2.04	16	2.28
6½	2.16	9	1.68	12	1.56		

CHISEL

No.	Gro.	No.	Gro.
361	$4.10	374	$1.85
362	3.88	376	1.85
368	3.08	377	3.30
369	2.77		

FILE

No.	Gro.
378	$2.05
379	2.26
380	1.65
381	1.87

AWL HAFT

No.	Gro.
388	$2.25

Pages 47-51 — SCREW DRIVERS

No.	Doz.	No.	Doz.	No.	Doz.	No.	Doz.	No.	Doz.
214		0400		1314		1415		1314B	$1.44
2½"	$1.14	2½"	$0.72	2½"	$1.44	2½"	$1.44	1405	2.16
3"	1.26	3"	.84	3"	1.68	3"	1.68	1409	2.64
4"	1.44	4"	.96	4"	2.04	4"	2.04	1412	3.72
5"	1.62	5"	1.08	5"	2.40	5"	2.40	1419	2.16
6"	1.80	6"	1.20	6"	2.88	6"	2.88		
8"	2.34	8"	1.56	8"	3.48	8"	3.48		
10"	2.82	10"	1.92	10"	4.32	10"	4.32		
12"	3.60	12"	2.28	12"	5.16	12"	5.16		
219		1213		1315		1416		1418	
2½"	.78	2½"	1.08	2½"	1.44	2½"	1.44	2½"	$2.64
3"	.90	3"	1.20	3"	1.68	3"	1.68	3½"	2.88
4"	1.02	4"	1.38	4"	2.04	4"	2.04	4½"	3.12
5"	1.14	5"	1.56	5"	2.40	5"	2.40	5¼"	3.72
6"	1.38	6"	1.74	6"	2.88	6"	2.88		
8"	1.62	8"	2.22	8"	3.48	8"	3.48		
10"	1.98	10"	2.82	10"	4.32	10"	4.32		
12"	2.34	12"	3.48	12"	5.16	12"	5.16		
400		1250		1414		1417		1428	
2½"	.72	2½"	.78	2½"	1.44	2½"	1.44		
3"	.78	3"	.90	3"	1.68	3"	1.68	3"	1.80
4"	.84	4"	1.02	4"	2.04	4"	2.04	4"	2.16
5"	.96	5"	1.14	5"	2.40	5"	2.40	5"	2.52
6"	1.08	6"	1.38	6"	2.88	6"	2.88	6"	3.00
8"	1.44	8"	1.62	8"	3.48	8"	3.48	8"	3.60
10"	1.80	10"	1.98	10"	4.32	10"	4.32	10"	4.44
12"	2.16	12"	2.34	12"	5.16	12"	5.16	12"	5.28

DR 1000

Plate XII - Net Price List, Oct. 1, 1925 for Catalog No. 122
[Concluded from Page 400]

Pages 52-59

SCREW DRIVER BITS		PUNCHES		COUNTERSINKS		AWLS	
No.	Doz.	No.	Doz.	No.	Doz.	No.	Doz.
15	$0.54	14	$0.84	001	$1.44	18	$1.62
35	.84	37	.60	002	1.80	1431	.84
010	.60	38	.66	04	1.20	1432	1.56
1421	.66	40	.72				

		40½	.72	ICE PICKS		TACK PULLERS	
		41	.78	No.	Doz.	No.	Doz.
DOUBLE END SCREW DRIVERS		1429	.78	1422	$1.56	10	$0.72
		1430	.78	1433	1.08		
		1431	.84			GIMLETS	

Size	Doz.	REAMERS		GIMLET BITS		No.	Doz.
5"	$0.60	No.	Doz.	No.	Doz.	5	$0.48
6"	.66	6	$1.68	80	$0.72	6	.60
8"	.72			87	.72	25	.60

CHISELS

COTTER PIN EXTRACTORS		No.	Doz.	No.	Doz.	No.	Doz.	No.	Doz.
Size	Doz.	1420		1424		1425		1426	
6"	$0.66	¼"	$0.96	Ass't'd		¼"	$0.96	⅜"	$0.90
7"	.78	5-16"	1.02	3 sizes	$0.96	5-16"	1.02	½"	1.08
		⅜"	1.14			⅜"	1.14	⅝"	1.44
		½"	1.32			½"	1.32	¾"	1.80
		⅝"	1.68			⅝"	1.68	⅞"	2.40
		¾"	2.04			¾"	2.04	1"	3.00
		⅞"	2.64			⅞"	2.64		
		1"	3.36			1"	3.36		

SPECIAL NOTICE

An extra charge of 5% will be made on invoices for goods shipped direct to dealers' customers.

Claims not allowed unless made within ten days from receipt of shipment.

Credits will not be given for goods returned without our permission.

Orders for special goods not subject to cancellation. Tools made to order will not be exchanged.

DR 1000

406

Plate XIII - Chapin-Stephens Co. Advertising Brochure
[Continued on Page 407]

SOME OF THE BEST SELLING
HARDWARE AND TOOL SPECIALTIES
FOR THE 5 AND 10 CENT TRADE.

SOME SPECIALTIES FOR THE FIVE

No. 68. Two-Thirds Size.

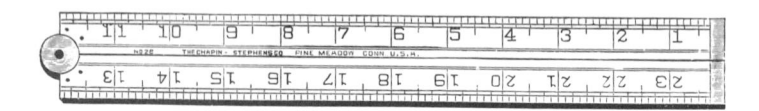

No. 29. One-Third Size.

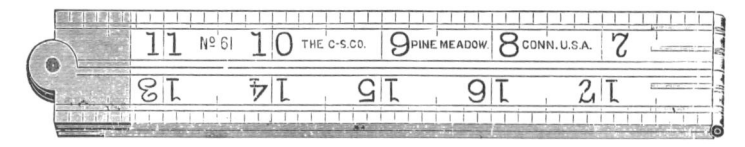

No. 61. One-Third Size.

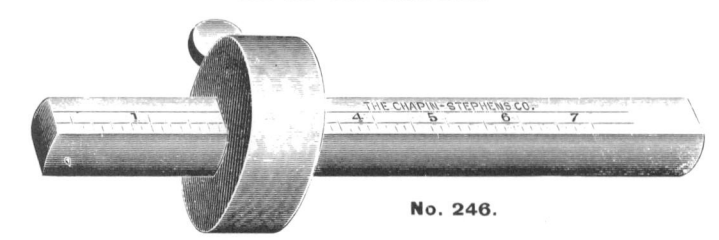

No. 246.

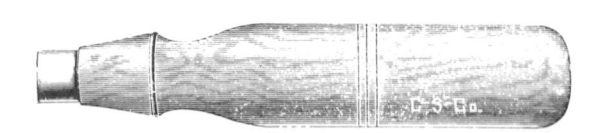

No. 362.

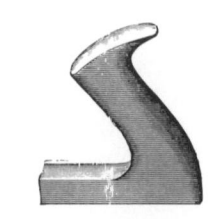

No. 374.

No. 1.

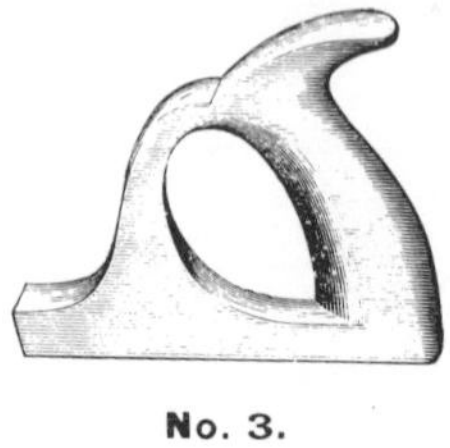

No. 3.

Plate XIII - Chapin-Stephens Co. Advertising Brochure
[Concluded from Page 406]

MANUFACTURED BY

THE CHAPIN-STEPHENS CO.
UNION FACTORY

NEW YORK STORE,
126 Chambers St.

PINE MEADOW, CONN., U. S. A.

AND TEN CENT STORE TRADE.

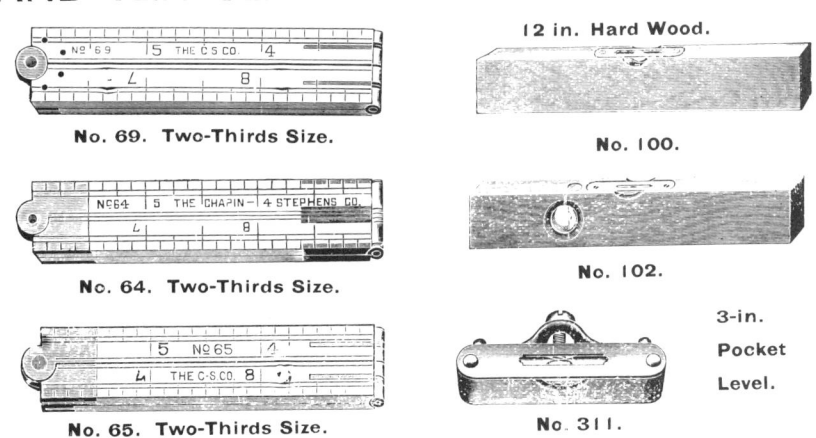

No. 69. Two-Thirds Size.

No. 64. Two-Thirds Size.

No. 65. Two-Thirds Size.

12 in. Hard Wood.
No. 100.

No. 102.

3-in. Pocket Level.
No. 311.

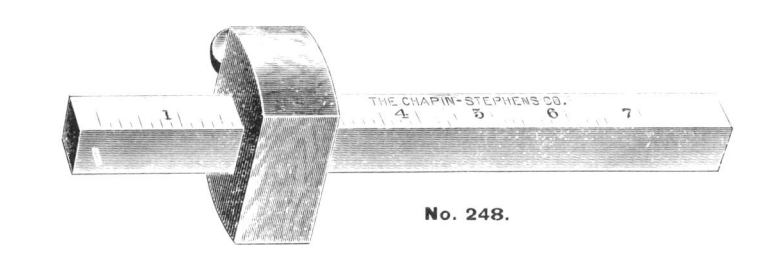

No. 248.

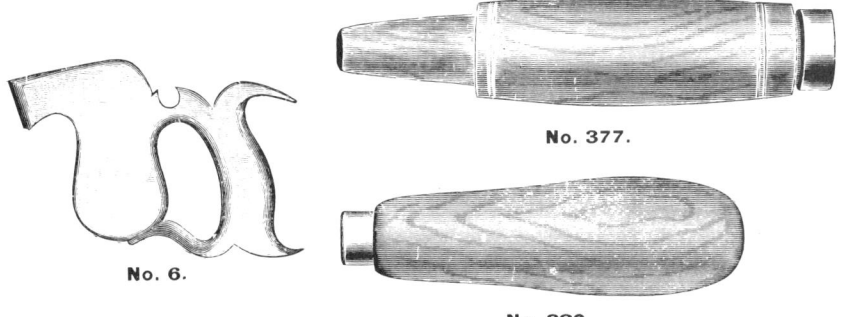

No. 6.

No. 377.

No. 380.

New York Store,
126 Chambers St.

THE CHAPIN-STEPHENS CO.
UNION FACTORY

PINE MEADOW, CONN., U. S. A.

Chapin-Stephens Co. was reorganized on January 1, 1926.[12] F. J. Damon of Torrington became president; Frank M. Chapin, vice-president; Harry Burgess of Torrington, secretary and treasurer; H.M. Chapin, assistant treasurer and W.F. Hoerle, assistant secretary, all of whom were directors, along with Thomas W. Bryant of Torrington. Frank L. Stephens left the firm in April. A.Z. Boyd succeeded John Humaston as New York agent, the agency there having moved to 126 Chambers St. Later, Fred J. Rudden, a sales representative at Chicago, became assistant secretary.

A new product, roller skates, was added in 1926 and advertised in a brochure commemorating the firms 100th Anniversary. (Plate XIV) The same year Vogel's patent rights for an aluminum spirit level were acquired. Page 41A was issued as a supplement to Catalogue 122. (Plate XV) P.H. Vogel Manufacturing Co. of New Britain was purchased and the machinery moved to New Hartford. Mr. Vogel went to Pine Meadow to superintend manufacturing this level at Chapin-Stephens Co. Photographs of this level are shown in Figs. 75 & 76, the later noting the three dates of Vogel's different patents.

Another item, believed to have been added about this time, was a unique, fancy square, having a level mounted in the face of the wooden leg. A photograph of this square, 15 in. x 7½ in., having a brass faced rosewood leg, is shown in Fig. 77.

On June 16, 1927 F. J. Damon, president of Chapin-Stephens Co., wrote a memorandum listing in detail the proposed contents for a new issue of a catalogue. "We suggest that only a sufficient quantity of catalogues be gotten out to take care of our requirements over a twelve months period...The size and shape of the new catalogue to conform to Catalogue No. 122." Whether this catalogue was ever issued is doubtful. While similar to the #122 there were some deletions of boxwood rule, the same ivory rules, and the complete line of planes in the proposed new catalogue.

Business was not good, both Frank and Herman Chapin were not in good health. On December 31, 1928 all the property, buildings and water power were sold to Stanley Works of New Britain. (Table X) At the time the firm was only a nuisance competitor to this industrial giant at New Britain in that Stanley Rule & Level Co. could not meet the low selling price that Chapin-Stephens Co. was then offering their rules. It was therefore expedient to buy Chapin-Stephens out and close up the firm. Stanley Works had done the same to Upson Nut rule and plane division at Unionville in 1922.[13]

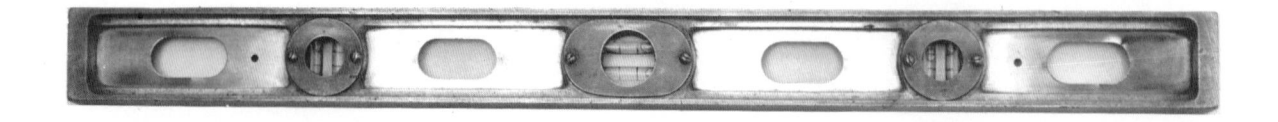

Fig. 75 - 28 inch Vogel's Patent Aluminum-Brass Level

Plate XV - Supplement to Catalog No. 122, Page 41A

THE CHAPIN-STEPHENS CO., PINE MEADOW, CONN. 41A

ALUMINUM BRASS SPIRIT LEVELS
VOGEL PATENTS

No. 100   12 x 2⅛ x ¾ Inch   Each $3.00 List

Open ends, aluminum rails, brass centers, three glass, one level and two plumbs

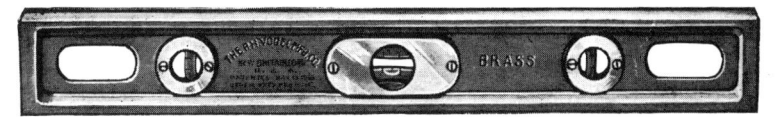

No. 200

No.		
200	18 x 2¼ x 1 Inch	Each $5.50 List
200	24 x 2¼ x 1 "	" 6.25 "
200	26 x 2¼ x 1 "	" 6.50 "
200	28 x 2¼ x 1 "	" 6.75 "
200	30 x 2¼ x 1 "	" 7.25 "

Closed ends, aluminum levels, brass centers, four glass, double level and two plumbs

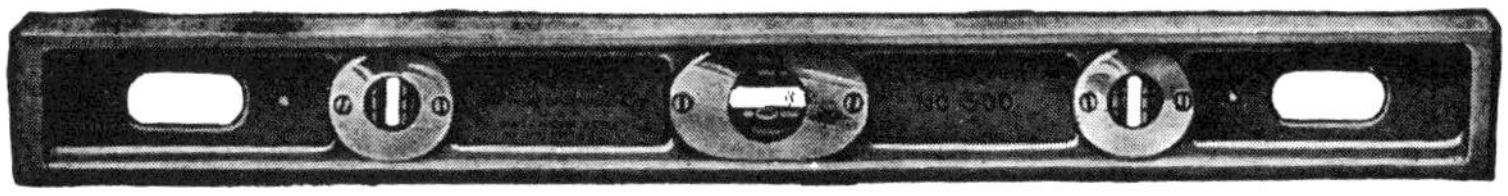

No. 300

300	18 x 2¼ x 1 Inch	Each $6.00 List
300	24 x 2¼ x 1 "	" 6.75 "
300	26 x 2¼ x 1 "	" 7.00 "
300	28 x 2¼ x 1 "	" 7.25 "
300	30 x 2¼ x 1 "	" 7.75 "

Closed ends, aluminum levels, brass centers, six glass, double level and two double plumbs

Brass Center

The Brass Center is 1-16 of an inch thick, has holes pierced on all four edges through which the Aluminum flows when cast, which rivets itself together so tight and solid that it makes the level indestructable and eliminates the possibility of warping.

VIALS AND CONTAINERS

The Vials are fluersine filled, marked with two lines and are fully tested before being put into the containers which are made from aluminum and fastened with brass machine screws and are adjustable. The florescent glass have been adopted for use in these levels on account of the improved visibility. To adjust Vials loosen the screws slightly, raise or lower the necessary end until bubble rests in the proper position, then tighten screws. If the Vials break, it is not necessary to send level to the factory for repairs. In sending for new containers with glass set in give number of level and state if it is for level or plumb. In ordering glass containers for level in number 200 state which one, as you will see by measuring that screw holes in one container is two and one-half inches apart and in the other three inches apart.

Each level is packed in individual pasteboard box.

These aluminum levels show superior workmanship and finish.

Supplement to Catalog No. 122 Page 41A.

Plate XIV - Roller Skate Brochure

MANUFACTURERS OF

RULES,
  PLANES,
    GAUGES,
      PLUMBS AND LEVELS,
HAND SCREWS,
  CHISEL HANDLES,
    FILE HANDLES,
      PLANE HANDLES,
SAW HANDLES,
  SCREW DRIVERS,
    SCREW DRIVER BITS,
      PUNCHES,
COUNTER SINKS,
  AWLS,
    ICE PICKS,
      TACK PULLERS,
GIMLETS,
  GIMLET BITS,
    COLD CHISELS,
      MACHINIST CHISELS.

THE CHAPIN--STEPHENS CO.
UNION FACTORY

PINE MEADOW, CONNECTICUT

Established July 1, 1826

1826   One-Hundredth Anniversary   1926

ROLLER SKATES

PRICE LIST No. 1

THE CHAPIN--STEPHENS CO.
UNION FACTORY

FACTORIES AND GENERAL OFFICES:

PINE MEADOW, CONN., U. S. A.

NEW YORK OFFICE: 151 CHAMBERS ST.

1826   One-Hundredth Anniversary   1926

ROLLER SKATES

For Boys and Girls

One Skate for All Sizes

BALL BEARING ROLLER SKATES

Fitted with Self Contained Steel Rolls.

No. 105

Tops, trucks, clamps, and stampings are made of the best cold rolled steel.

Adjustment is easily made and will hold.

Fitted with high grade web strap.

Extends from 8½ to 10¾ inches.

Packed 100 prs. in a Case.

Approximate weight 430 lbs.

PRICE OF PARTS

For No. 105 Skate

No.		Per Doz.
1	Outside Toe Clamp	$0.40
2	Inside Toe Clamp	.40
3	Toe Clamp Adjusting Screw	.15
4	Wheel Cone (all alike)	.15
5	Ball Case	.18
		Per Gross
6	3-16 in. Ball	.40
		Per Doz.
7	Axles for Self-Contained Rolls	.45
8	Axle Nut (all alike)	.12
9	Axle Nut D Washer (all alike)	.04
10	Dust Cap	.10
11	Adjustment Binding Bolt	.07
12	Adjustment Binding Bolt Nut	.07
13	Truck	.42
14	Toe Plate	.90
15	Heel Plate	.90
16	5-8 in. Web Strap	.84
17	Metal Back	1.00
		Per 100
18	Roll	10.00
		Per Doz.
19	Key (bright finish)	.25

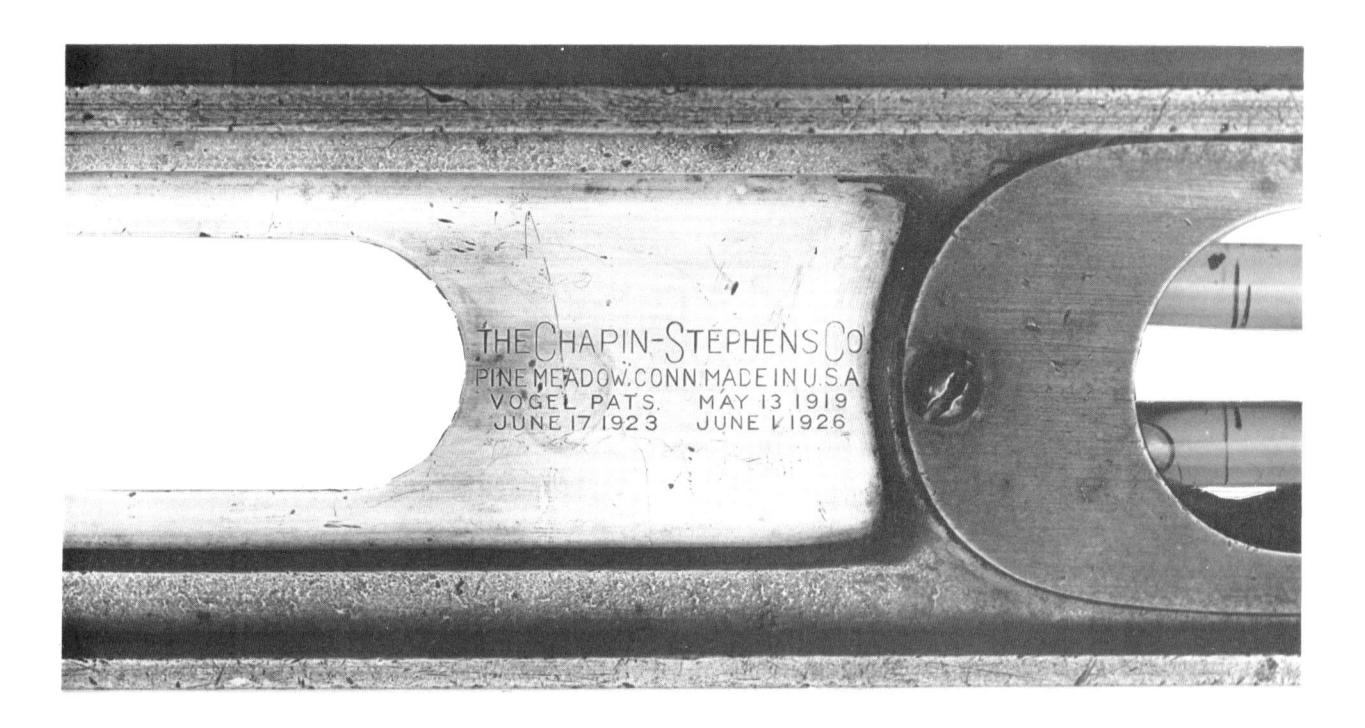

Fig. 76 - Patent Dates on Vogel Aluminum-Brass Level
[See Fig. 75 and Plate XV]

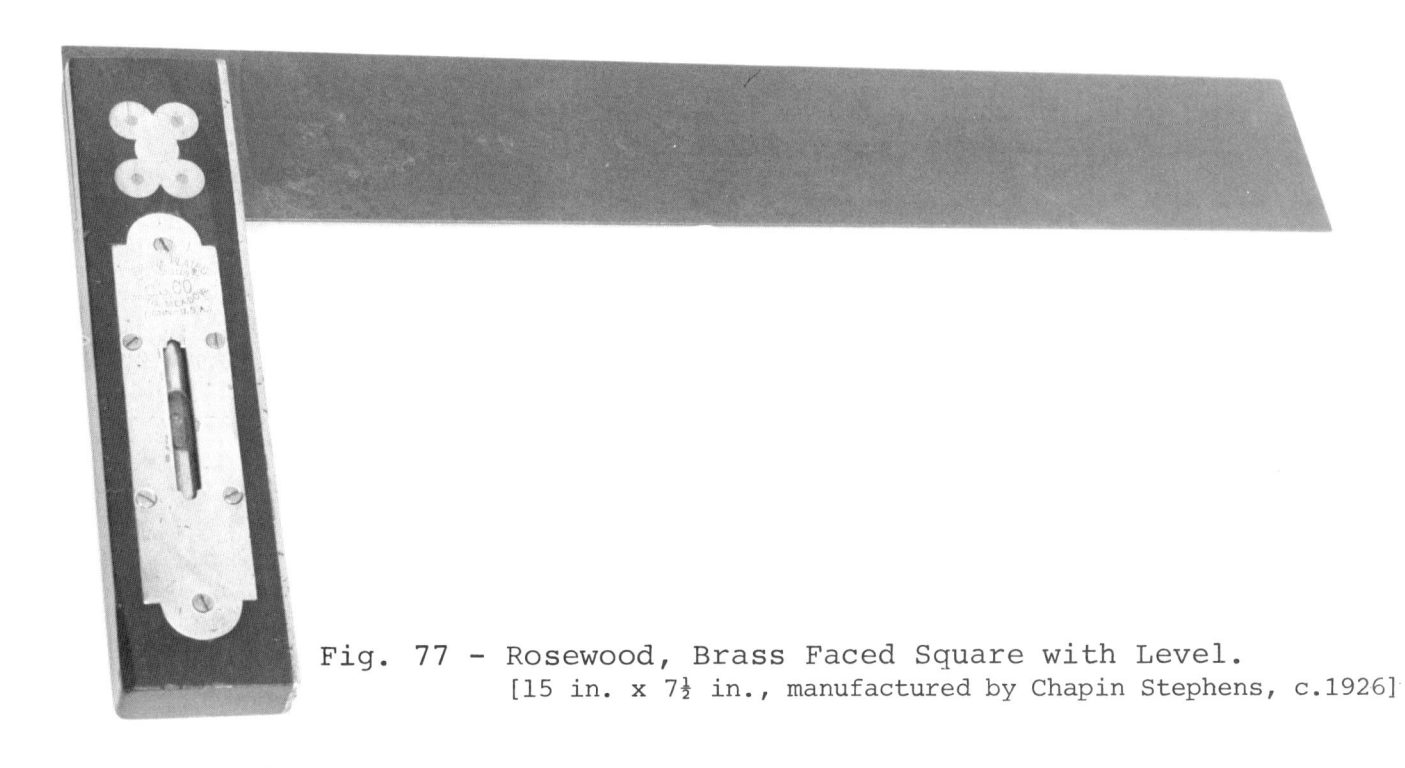

Fig. 77 - Rosewood, Brass Faced Square with Level.
[15 in. x 7½ in., manufactured by Chapin Stephens, c.1926]

Transcription of Letter by F. J. Rudden, Manager Chapin-Stephens Co.
Feb. 7, 1929

1826, H. CHAPIN   **1854, STEPHENS & CO.**
1901
THE CHAPIN-STEPHENS CO.
UNION FACTORY
MANUFACTURERS OF
RULES, PLANES, LEVELS, GAUGES,
SCREW DRIVERS, GIMLETS, PUNCHES, ETC.

FACTORIES AND GENERAL OFFICES
PINE MEADOW, CONN.

NEW YORK STORE
151 CHAMBERS ST.

F. J. DAMON, President
F. M. CHAPIN, Vice Pres.
H. F. BURGESS, Secy. & Treas.
H. M. CHAPIN, Asst. Treas.

151 CHAMBERS ST.
NEW YORK

PINE MEADOW, CONN.

Feb. 7th, 1929.

Gentlemen:- -

      Effective this date "The Chapin-Stephens Co." will discontinue the sale and manufacture of the following items: -

    Boxwood Rules   Hand Screws
    Wood Plumbs & Levels   Gauges
    Planes   Screw Drivers
    Aluminum Levels   Tack Pullers
    File Handles   Counter Sinks
             Chisel Handles

      Orders for discontinued items mentioned above will be accepted subject to prior sale until stock is exhausted.

      We will continue to manufacture and sell Carpenters Chisels, Hack Saw Frames and other lines of our manufacture not mentioned above, and we solicit your orders and inquiries.

      It is our intention to develop new lines as we find it possible and we will keep you posted both by letter and through the salesmen of the Union Hardware Company, who are our sales representatives.

      Anticipating a continuation of your business and requesting a further interest in our lines, we beg to remain

                           Very truly yours,
                           THE CHAPIN-STEPHENS CO.

                               F. J. Rudden
                               Manager

TABLE X

WARRANTY DEED - The CHAPIN-STEPHENS CO. to the STANLEY WORKS
[New Hartford Land Records, Vol. 38, pp. 305-306
Signed: Dec. 31, 1928; Recorded June 5, 1929]

TO ALL PEOPLE TO WHOM THESE PRESENTS SHALL COME - GREETING: Know Ye, that the Chapin-Stephens Company, a legal corporation organized and existing under the laws of the State of Connecticut, acting herein by F.J. Damon, its President hereto duly authorized, for the consideration of a valuable sum in dollars received to its full satisfaction of The Stanley Works, a legal corporation organized and existing under the laws of the State of Connecticut and located and doing business in the town of New Britain, County of Hartford and Stae of Connecticut does give, grant bargain, sell and confirm unto the said Stanley Works its successors and assigns, the following pieces or parcels of land, with all buildings thereon, situated in the town of New Hartford, in the village of Pine Meadow, in said County of Litchfield, namely:

1. The Rule, Plane and Level Factory Property
   [Reference Deed from Hermon Chapin to Edward M. and George W. Chapin, dated July 1, 1865, Book 21, page 263]
   [also by last will and testament of Edward M. Chapin, deceased, dated Aug. 25, 1897, Book 29, pages 159 & 160]

2. The Chapin Machine Co. Property
   [being the same premises conveyed. . . . Book 29, pages 537 & 538]

3. The Schott Property
   [Being the same premises conveyed. . . . Book 27, p. 264 April 9, 1903]

4. Tenements
   [pieces described . . . Book 29, pages 689 & 690]

5. Tenements
   [piece described . . . Book 31, page 370]

IN WITNESS WHEREOF, said Corporation has hereunto caused its name and corporate seal to be affixed by the hand of its President thereto duly authorized as aforesaid, this 31st day of December, 1928.

                            The Chapin-Stephens Company
                            By Frank J. Damon, its President

On February 7, 1929 F.J. Rudden, Manager of Sales at Chapin-Stephens informed the public that the firm had discontinued the manufacture of rules, planes, gauges and levels and was selling off all inventory stock. He solicited orders for chisels, presumably then being made by Union Hardware Co. of Torrington. After 103 years, trade at the Union Factory was finished. (See Page 412)

There were many circumstances that led to the closing of this prestigious firm, having tenure of over one hundred years. Their sales of principal products, plane and rules, had been on the decline since the end of the Civil War. Competition from other wooden plane manufacturers and new products from Stanley Rule & Level Co. after 1870 had seriously affected sales. Dependence on marketing their products by hardware, firms such as Sargent Co. at New York, rather than establishing their own sales offices at this important trade center had restricted promotional opportunities. The association with other rule and plane manufacturers in fixing prices and production quotas probably did more harm than good for future development. E.M. Chapin relied on continuation of sales of high quality wooden tools and trade as formerly developed by his father. In comparison Stanley Rule & Level had an aggressive approach to marketing and the development of new tools. The financial failure of Chapin Machine was undoubtedly a drain on E.M. Chapin's capital. Lacking experience in machine shop practice, the conservative E.M. Chapin probably had limited vision in the opportunities of fabricating tools made from metal. The third generation of Chapins managed the firm with pride and integrity, but their limited training in business and manufacturing practice stifled needed growth. Their selections of successor officers to manage the firm does not appear to have been beneficial or prudent.

Business failure in the tool business among wooden plane manufacturers was not confined to Chapin-Stephens Co. In fact they were the last surviving firm of the former big five. Greenfield Tool Co. was forced to close down after a fire in 1887. Auburn Tool Co. combined with Ohio Tool Co. in 1893 and discontinued manufacturing wooden planes before 1920. Sandusky Tool Co. sold out in 1926. On the plus side no one can question the high quality of goods produced during the 103 years: 1826-1929. Three generations of the Chapin family had been respected for their contributions to the development of the town. The firms and management had been a great asset to this community.

Notes - Chapter XII

1. Personal Communication with Mrs Kilburn K. Holt, sister of the late Harry D. Stephens, April 5, 1975
2. J.M. Burdick, *A Brief History of the Stanley Rule & Level Co.*, [New Britain, Conn., 1935], p. 2
3. Also see: K.D. Roberts, *Introduction to Rule Collecting*, [1983], p. 10
4. *ibid*, p. 6
5. Hardware Issue of *Weekly Implement Trade Journal*, [Kansas City, Mo., Mar. 1908]
6. New Hartford Land Records, B.32, p. 562
7. *ibid*, B.27, p. 717
8. Reprinted by Ken Roberts Publishing Co., March 1975
9. J.M. Burdick, *op. cit.*, [Note No. 2 above], p. 3
10. *Winsted Herald,* May 6, 1919
11. *op. cit, History of Litchfield County*
12. *Winsted Times,* September 23, 1926
13. See *Volume I,* Footnote No. 16, p. 222

Appendix

Fig. 78 - Wedge Gauges and Box

Appendix I
The Alfred G. Tovey Collection

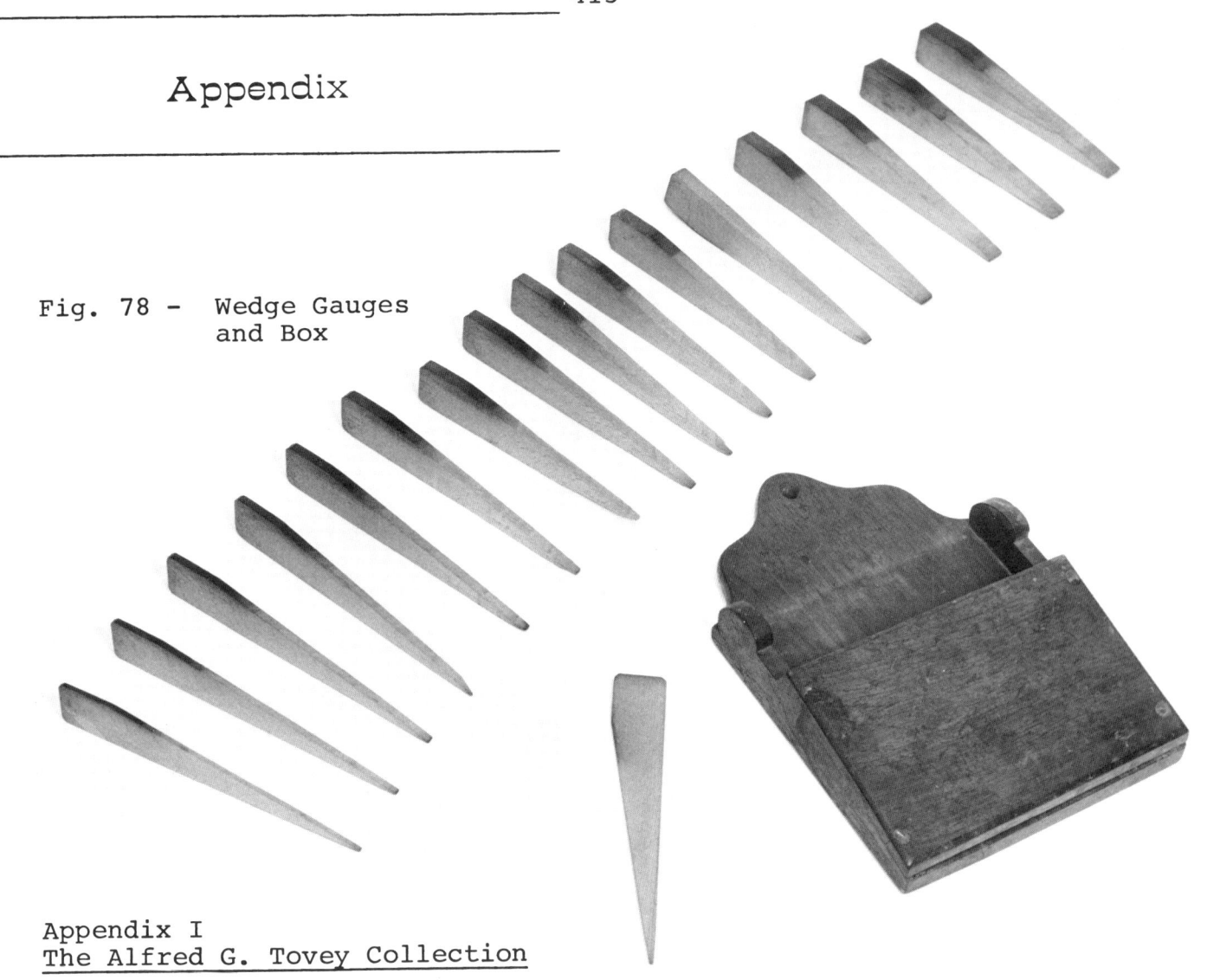

Alfred G. Tovey, believed to have been an apprenticed planemaker, emigrated from Bristol, England about 1880. He was employed at the Doscher Plane Co. at Saugatuck, Connecticut. He married a girl from Westport, and about the turn of the century changed employment to Chapin-Stephens Co. His wife became homesick and, not particularly enjoying New Hartford, convinced her husband to return to Westport. He continued making planes with the Doscher firm there until they closed down, shortly thereafter. Alfred Tovey died in 1943, age 88. Some of his planemaking tools survive and are illustrated in Figs. 78 - 81. The photograph above, Fig. 78, illustrates his wedge sizing gauges, Number 1 to 17, increasing in size in increments of 1/32 in. from 1/32 to 17/32 in. These enabled determination of stock size for the wedge, after cutting the throat of a moulding plane. Two views of his plane vise are shown in Figs. 79 & 80. This unique clamp was locked in a wood screw vise at the end of a work bench. The semi-circular lever opened and closed the jaws for gripping the plane. The opening could be adjusted. The lever straddled the iron screw of the bench vise, which allowed the clamp jaws to be opened and closed without removing from the bench vise. Two slide bars held the edge of the plane. Actually the plane was worked against these slide bars in a position opposite to that shown in Fig. 80. Fig. 81 shows his different marking patterns and templates for layout of smooth, moulding and skew rabbet planes.

416

Fig. 79 - Alfred G. Tovey's Plane Vise

Fig. 80 - Alfred G. Tovey's Plane Vise
[Note: Actually the plane should be set in the opposite position to permit working against the slide bars.]

Fig. 81 - Alfred G. Tovey's Templates and Patterns Used in His Planemaking

Appendix II - The Wolcott Collection at Colonial Williamsburg

At Colonial Williamsburg Foundation there are approximately 350 wooden planes in storage, originally from the collection of Stephen C. Wolcott. Mr. Wolcott lived within Gloucester County, Virgina, and was a founding member of Early American Industry Association, its first secretary, and first editor of the CHRONICLE. Upon his death, acting according to a bequest in his will, this collection of planes was turned over to Colonial Williamsburg in 1935. A note, dated May 2, 1935 to the curator at Colonial Williamsburg from Mrs. Wolcott indicated that:- "These planes were the model, or pattern planes used in a Connecticut plane factory long since gone out of existence".

A detailed study of these planes with Jay M. Gaynor, Curator of Mechanical Arts at this Institution, Edward Ingraham,III and me during April 1982 indicated that about 160 of these planes had been used for planemaking, and several had the imprint of H.Chapin/ Union Factory/Warranted. Approximately 100 of these were backing planes of reverse profiles to actual moulding planes. The other 60 were general purpose planes for performing compound work on the soles of planes, such as grooving for boxing a spline, shaping a fillet or bead, etc. During our two days of study we accomplished sorting these into similar groups as to intended use. It was apparent that some had been modified from conventional moulding planes to perform such special work. Figs. 82 - 86 illustrate 14 different planes from this collection, designated A - M. Those shown in Fig. 82(A-D), Fig. 83 (E-H), and Fig. 85 (M) are backing planes used for shaping planes of the opposite profile. Those shown in Fig. 84 were used for special work. The following table summarizes this data.

Figure Number	Plane Letter	Type of Plane	Number in Collection
82	A	Grecian OGee with Bevel	10
82	B	Reverse (back) OGee	4
82	C	Grecian Ovolo with Bevel	6
82	D	Quirk Ogee with Bevel	11
83	E	Bead	18
83	F	Astragal	6
83	G	Double Reed	6
83	H	Table Hollow	4 pair
85	I	Pair of Hollow & Rounds	18 pair
84	J	Beading for Compound Work	3
84	K	Astragal on Compound Work	7
84	L	Boxing on Compound Work	1
84	M	Rabbeting or Fillet Work	3

It is speculated that after Chapin-Stephens Co. was purchased by Stanley Rule & Level Co. in 1929, Mr. Wolcott may have inquired about the existence of such backing planes, etc. and purchased this group of planes. Incidentally, the term backing plane is used by W.J. Armour in his article in the Appendix to Chapter II. Present writers refer to such 18th Century planes as "mother planes". In my opinion such backing planes were used throughout the tenure of the wood moulding plane trade. The use of machine cutters, before electrically driven equipment was introduced, would have involved long set-up time for such short runs of 6 to 12 planes of a given size.

Future study of these planes in the Wolcott Collection may reveal further insights concerning wooden planemaking. Scholars with serious interests for studying this collection should contact Mr. J. M. Gaynor at Colonial Williamsburg Foundation to make an appointment.

420

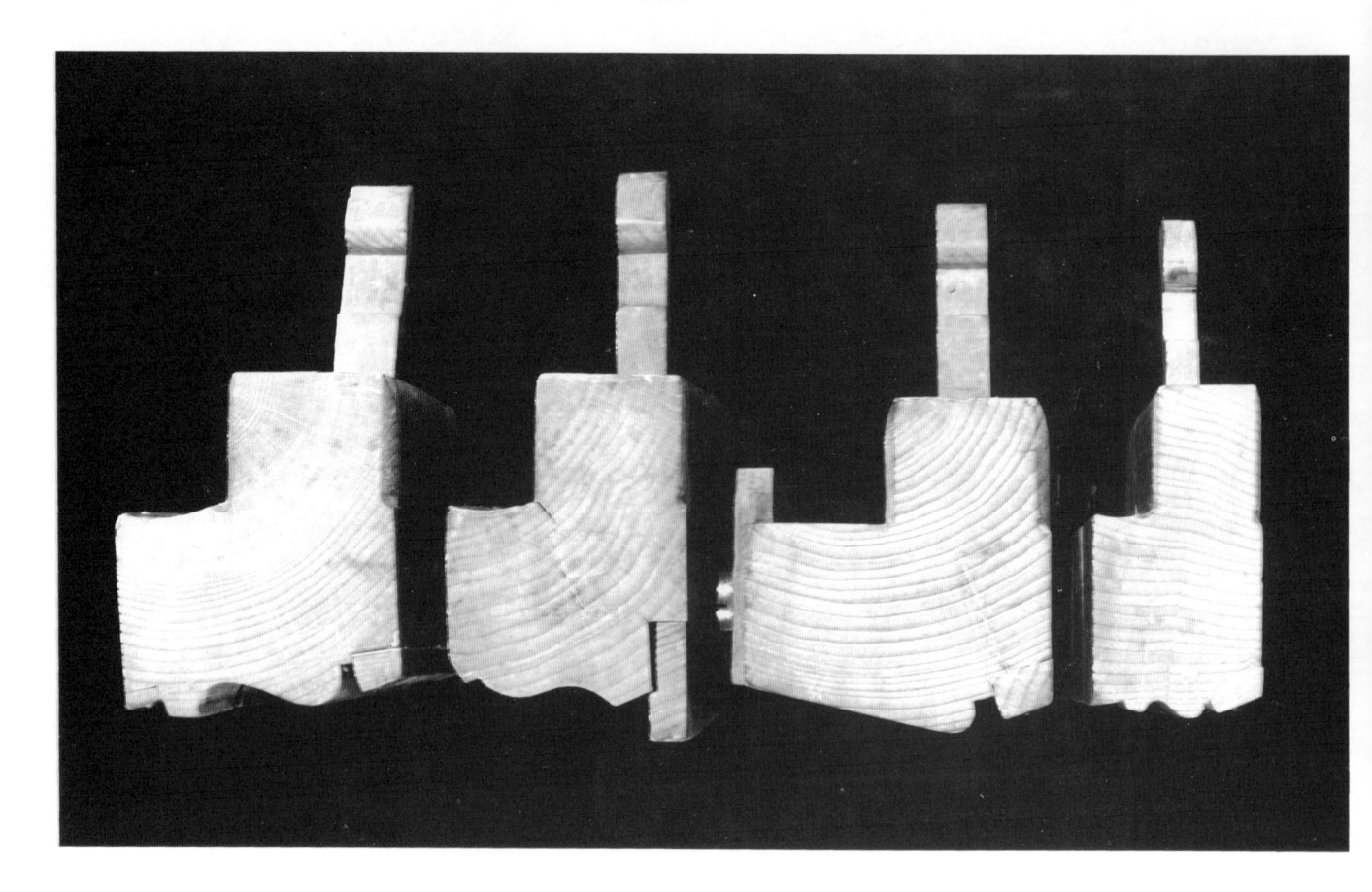

A. Grecian OGee   B. Reverse OGee   C. Grecian Ovolo   D. Quirk OGee
    with Bevel   with Bevel   with Bevel

Fig. 82 - Backing Planes from the Wolcott Collection
[Photograph Courtesy of Colonial Williamsburg Foundation]

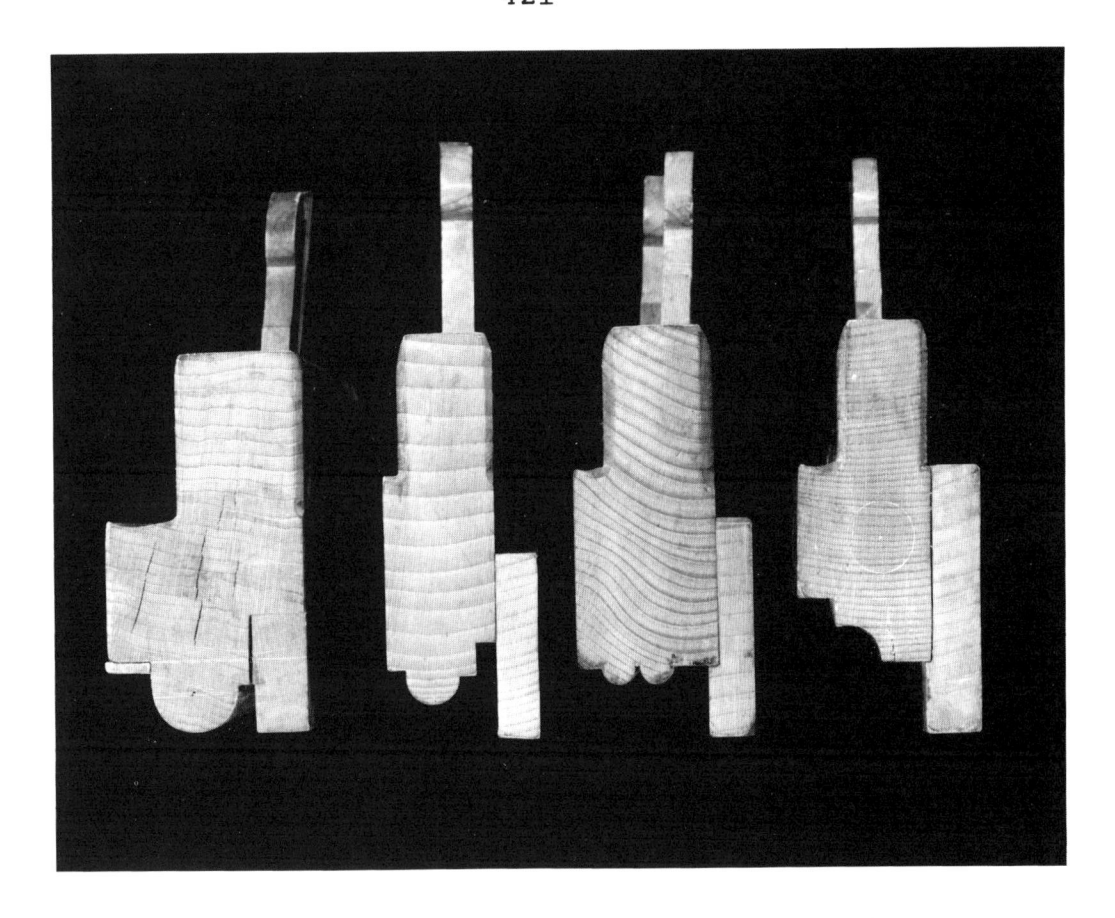

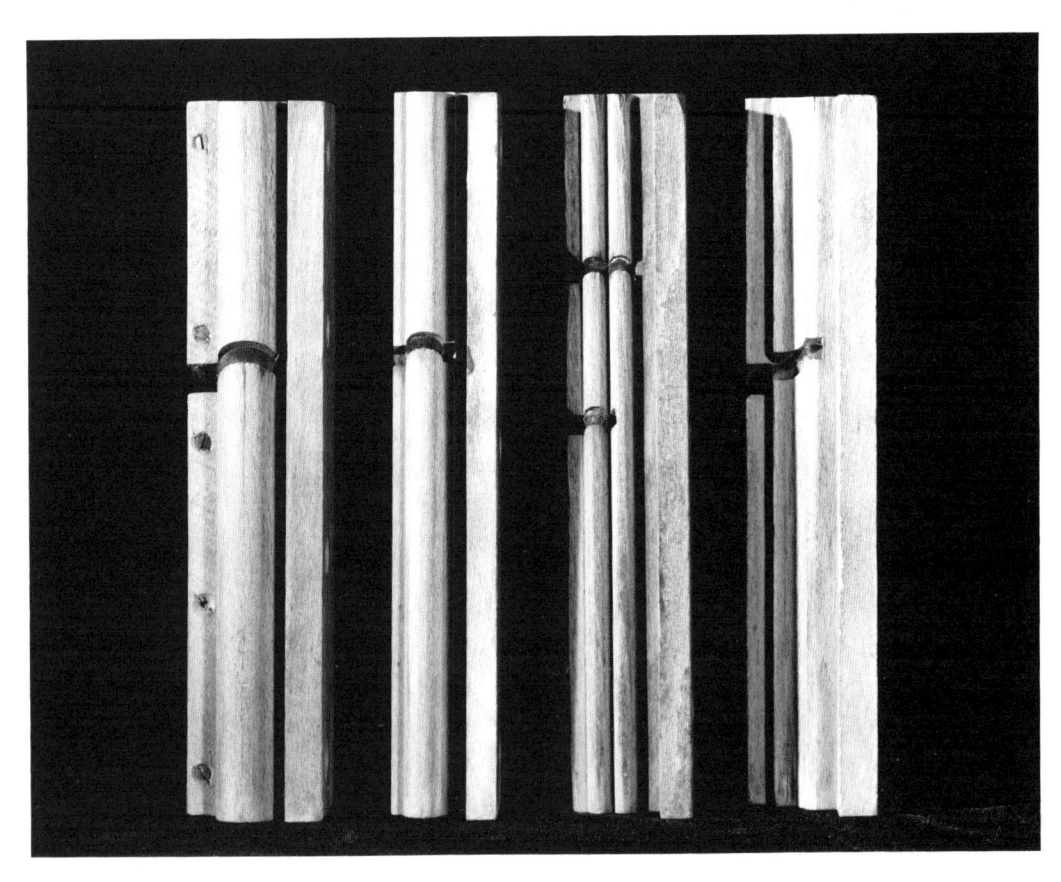

421

E. Bead   F. Astragal   G. Double Reed H. Table Hollow
Fig. 83 - Backing Planes from the Wolcott Collection
[Photograph Courtesy of Colonial Williamsburg Foundation]

422

J. Beading   K. Astragal   L. Boxing   M. Rabbet
Fig. 84 - General Purpose Plane for compound work in Wolcott Collection
[Photograph Courtesy of Colonial Williamsburg Foundation]

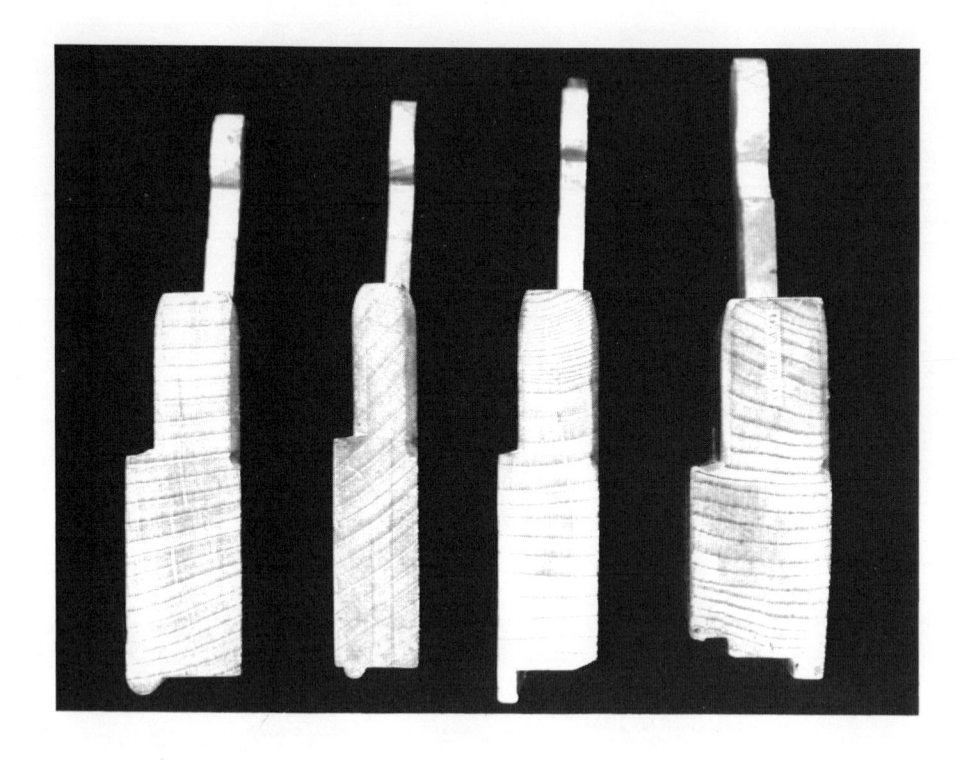

Fig. 85 - Pair of Hollow and Round Backing Planes in Wolcott Collection
[Photograph Courtesy of Colonial Williamsburg Foundation]

Fig. 86 - Backing Planes in the Wolcott Collection. Left Front: Grecian Ovolo (See Fig. 82-C) Left Rear: Double Iron Reeding Plane (See Fig. 83-H) Right: Astragal (See Fig. 83-F) [Photograph Courtesy of Colonial Williamsburg Foundation]

Appendix III - <u>The Chapin Collection of Planes</u>

As noted in the Preface, this collection has been assembled for study of planes made at the Union Factory, 1826 - 1929. Those persons who assisted me in this project have been cited in the Preface and I am indeed very grateful for their interests. Ultimately this collection will be donated to the Connecticut Historical Society, and it is hoped that future contributions make it more complete. The following photographs illustrate some of the planes, with additions of a few others not part of the collection, but pertinent to this study. Most of these types have been described in Volume I. However, following the captions in some cases commentary has been added. The Chapin Collection of planes, as it presently exists is shown in Figs. 88 - 89.

Fig. 87 - Union Factory No. 112 Smooth Plane with Added Whale-bone Handle.
[Collection of William White]

Fig. 88 - The Chapin Collection of Moulding Planes and Some Bench Planes.

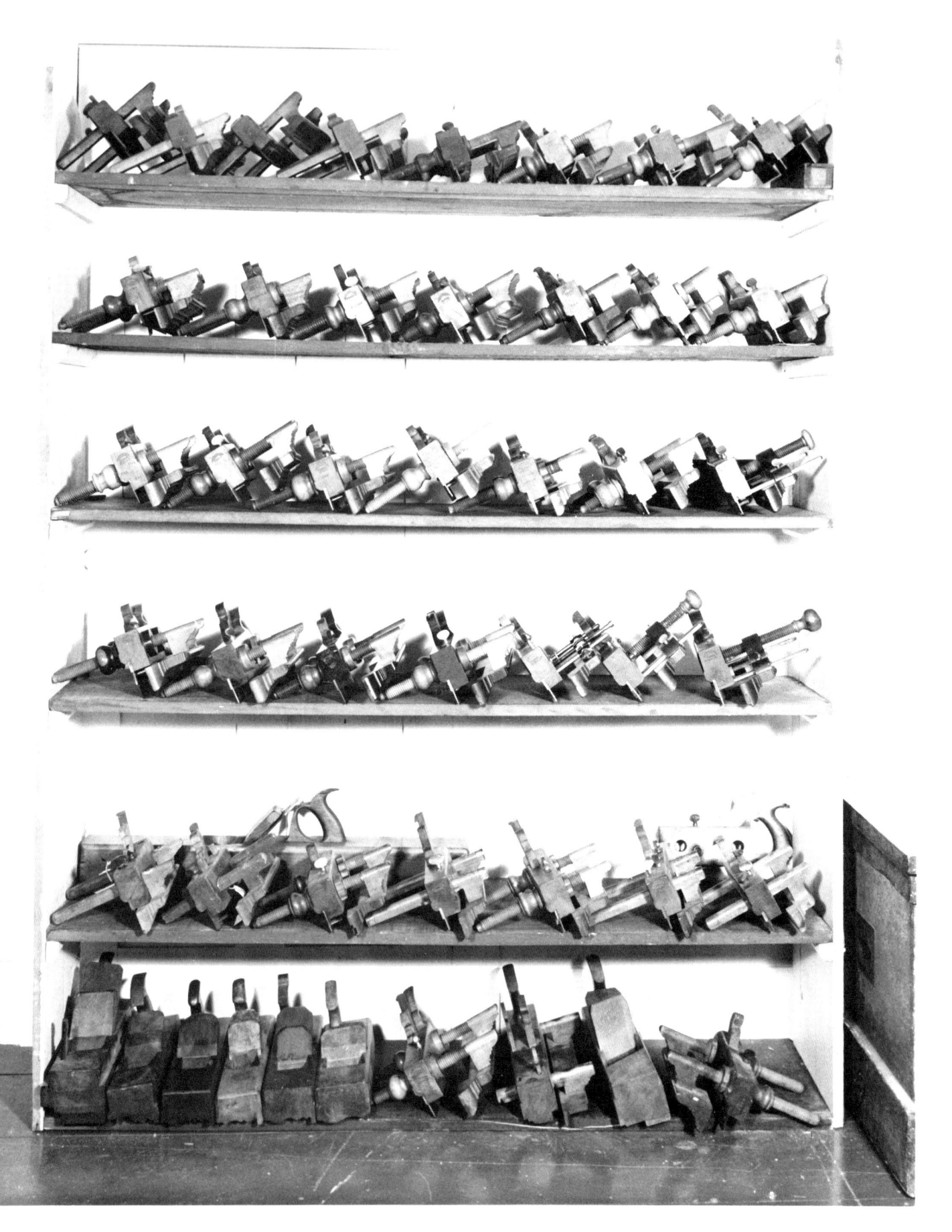

Fig. 89 -   The Chapin Collection of Plows and Special Bench Planes.

428

Fig. 90 - Extra Bench Planes (Double Iron, Best Cast Steel)
From Right to Left: #112 Smooth; #113 Jack; #114 Fore [18 in.]; #115 Jointer [26 in.]
These Union Factory Planes were the major part of the plane business, 1826 - 1929.

429

Fig. 91 — Union Factory Premium Bench Plane (extra Cast Steel Double Iron) with Bolted Handle and Start, #403 30 in. Long Jointer with No.1 Carriage Smooth Plane (4-3/8 in. length)
[Collection of Charles Watson]

Fig. 92 - Hollows & Rounds, Set of 9 Pair (even numbers #2 - #18)
          These were the conventional set from which almost any
          curved profile could be developed.

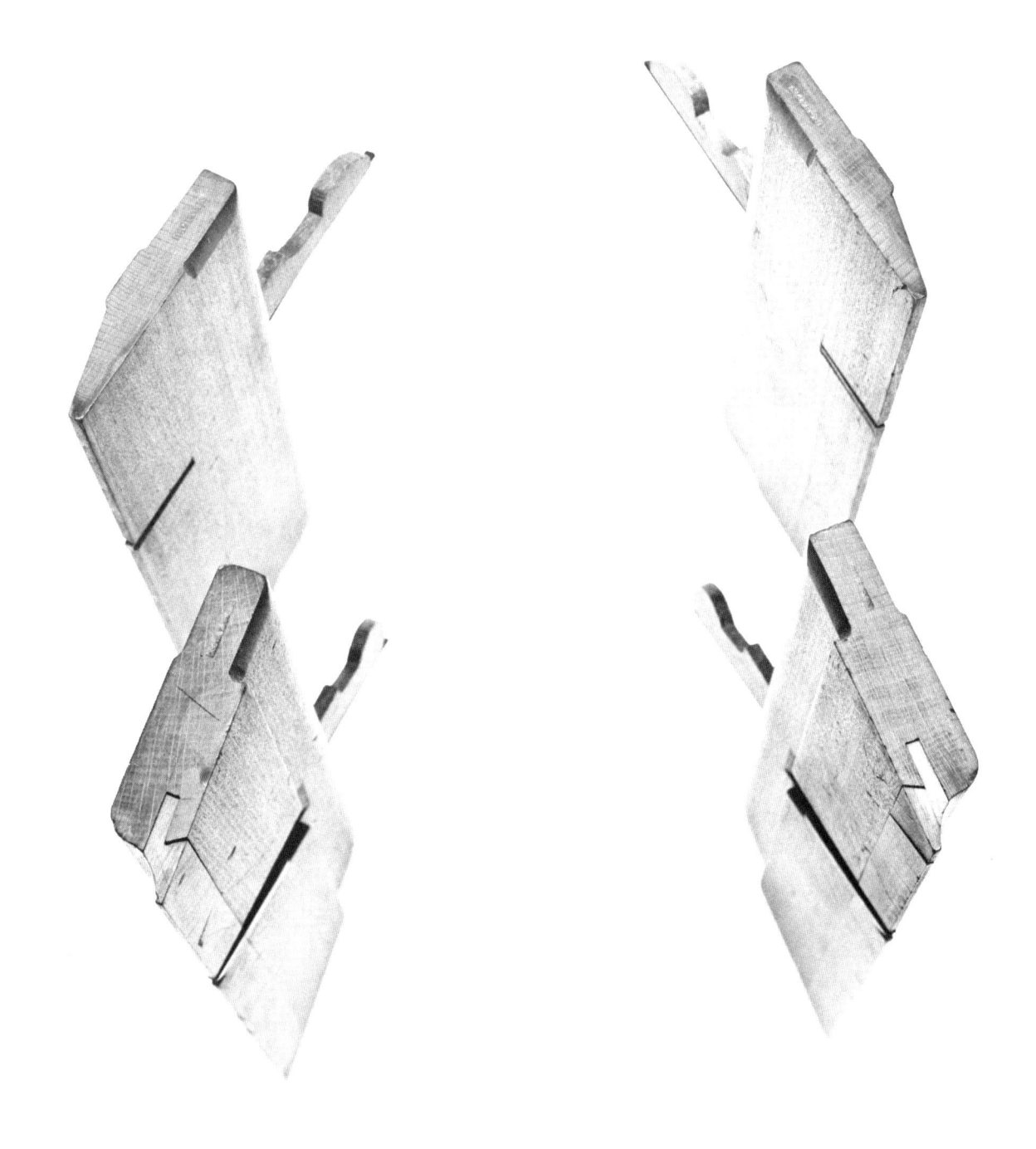

Fig. 93 -   #221½ Full Boxed Snipe Bills (used for trimming mouldings): Bottom
            #161 Pair of Side Rabbets   (used for trimming rabbet cuts): Top

Fig. 94 - Miscellaneous Handled Planes. Front: [left & right]: Single Iron Step or Nosing Planes Rear: [Right]: #113¼ Jack Razee Double Iron. [left]: 12 in. #440 Toy Jack converted into a Shooting Board Plane.

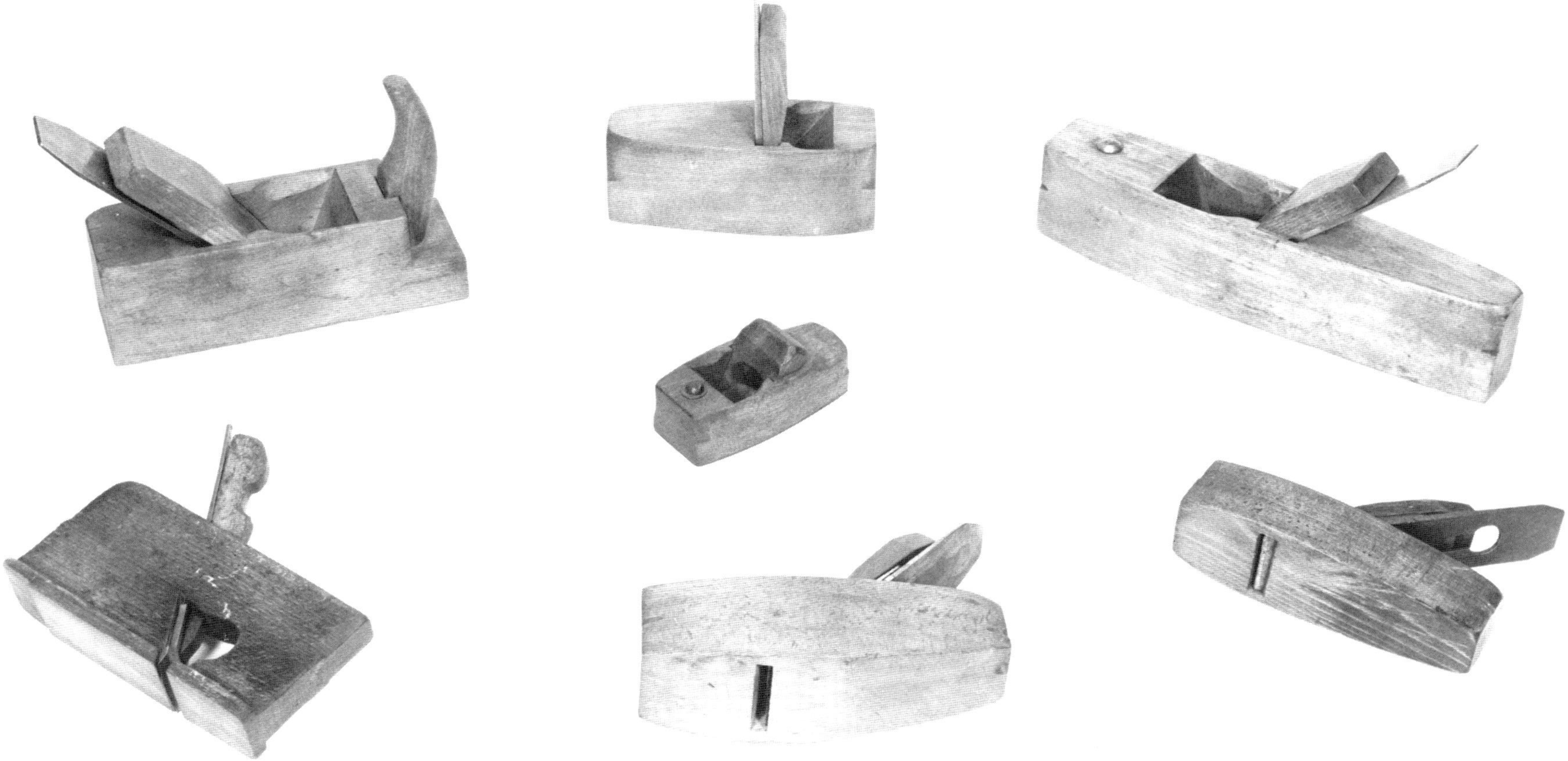

Fig. 95 - Miscellaneous Bench Planes. Front left: #5 Carriage Maker's T Rabbet; Front center: Smooth Plane converted into Compass or Rounding Plane; Front right: #439 Toy Smooth Plane; Center: #1 Carriage Maker's Plane; Rear left: #448 German Smooth or Bull Plane, double iron; Center rear: #430 Tooth Plane; Rear right: Double Iron Mitre Plane.

Fig. 96 - Handled Match Planes #173 [5/8", 3/4", 7/8" & 1"]

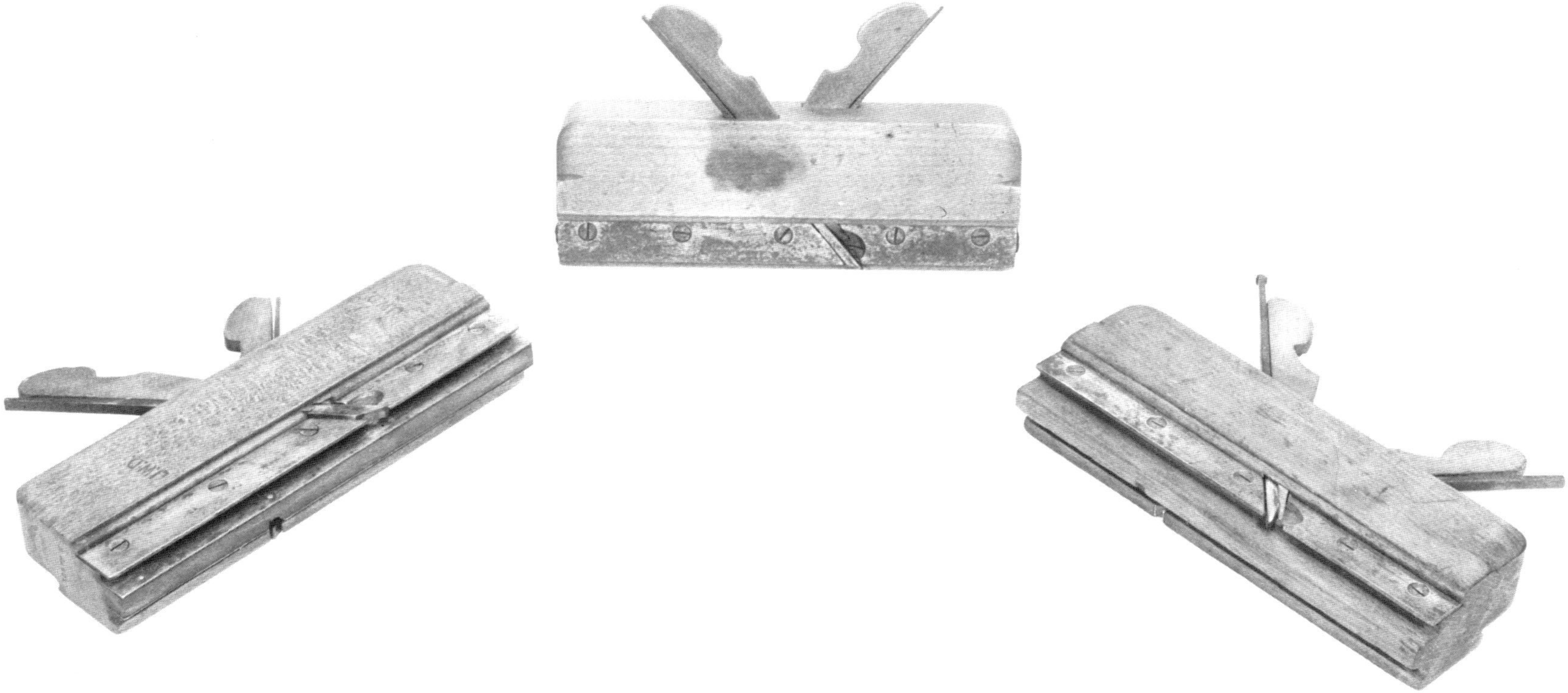

Fig. 97 - Double Iron, One Block, Match Planes #171 [5/8", 3/4", 7/8"]

Fig. 98 - Pair of Match Planes #181, Slide Arms with Wedge Locks

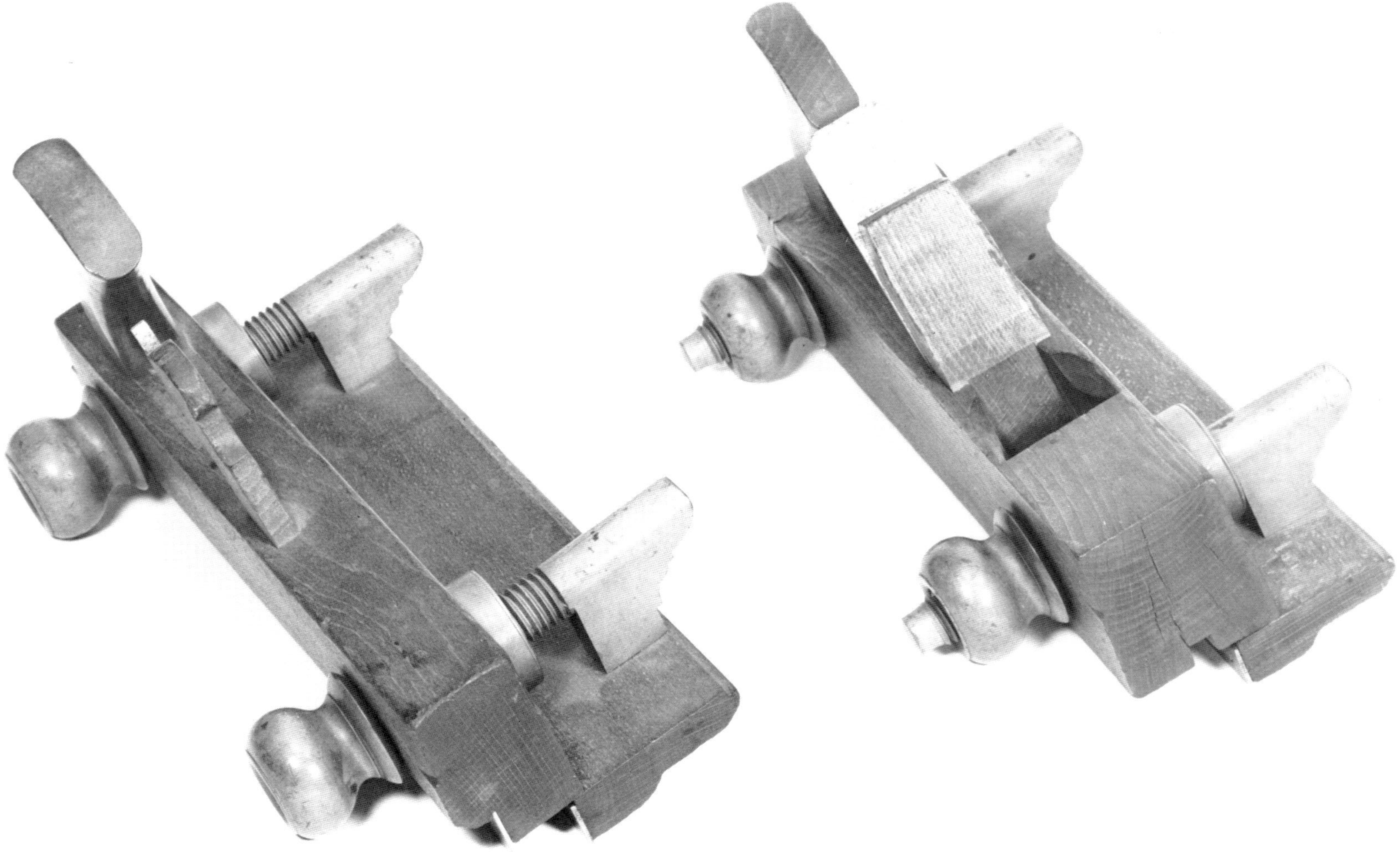

437

Fig. 99 - Pair of Match Planes with Boxwood Screw Arms and Plated Fence.

Fig. 100 - Set of 14 Bead Planes, Solid Boxed, except for 2 with Single Boxing
[From Right to Left: 1/8";3/16";1/4";5/16";3/8";7/16";1/2";5/8";3/4";7/8";1";1-1/8";1-1/4";1-3/8"]

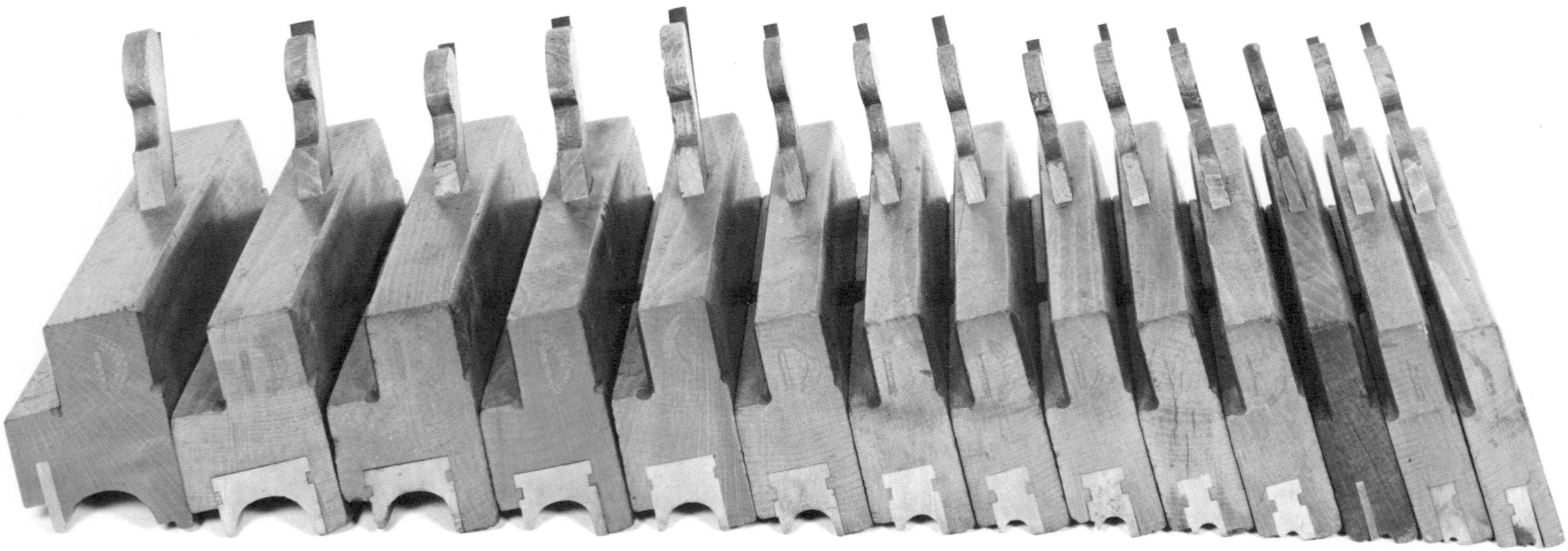

Fig. 101 — Dado Planes. Bottom Row: #137 Wood Stop; Second Row: #138 Brass Side Stop; Third Row: #139 Brass Screw Stop; Top: Handled with Screw Stop.

440

Fig. 102 - Set of 9 Reverse and Back OGee Moulding Planes #206
[From right to left: 1/2"; 5/8"; 3/4"; 7/8"; 1"; 1-1/4"; 1-1/2"; 1-3/4"- 2"]

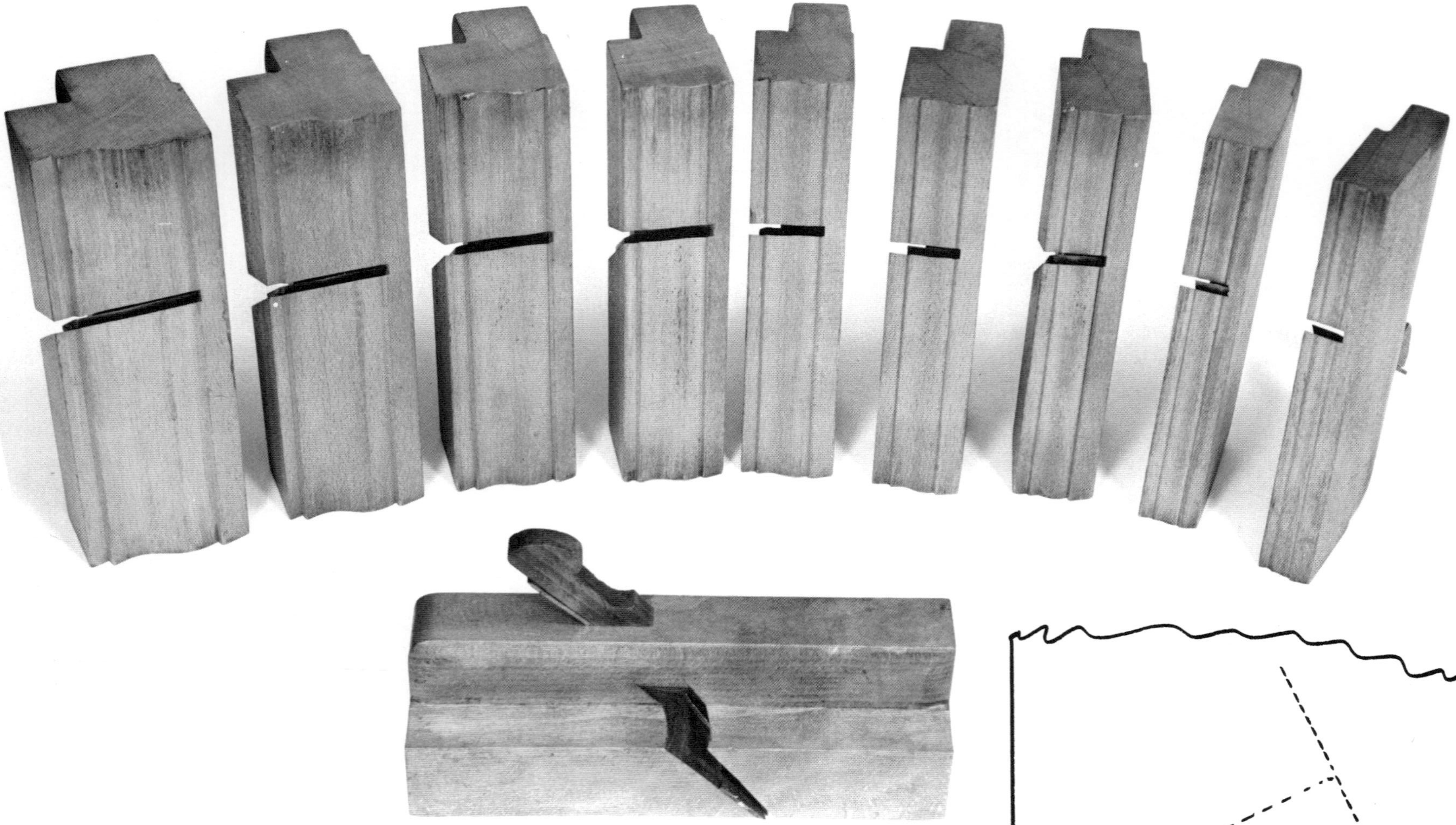

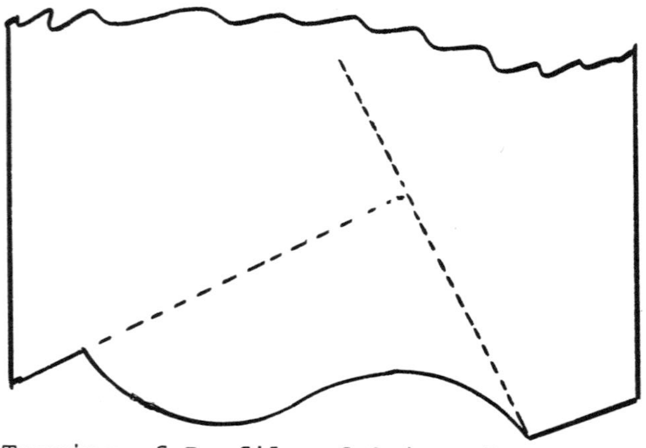

Tracing of Profile of 2 in. Plane and indicated Spring Line.

441

#223 Bed Moulding

No. 22 Base Moulding

Tracing of Profile of Planes Shown in Fig. 103

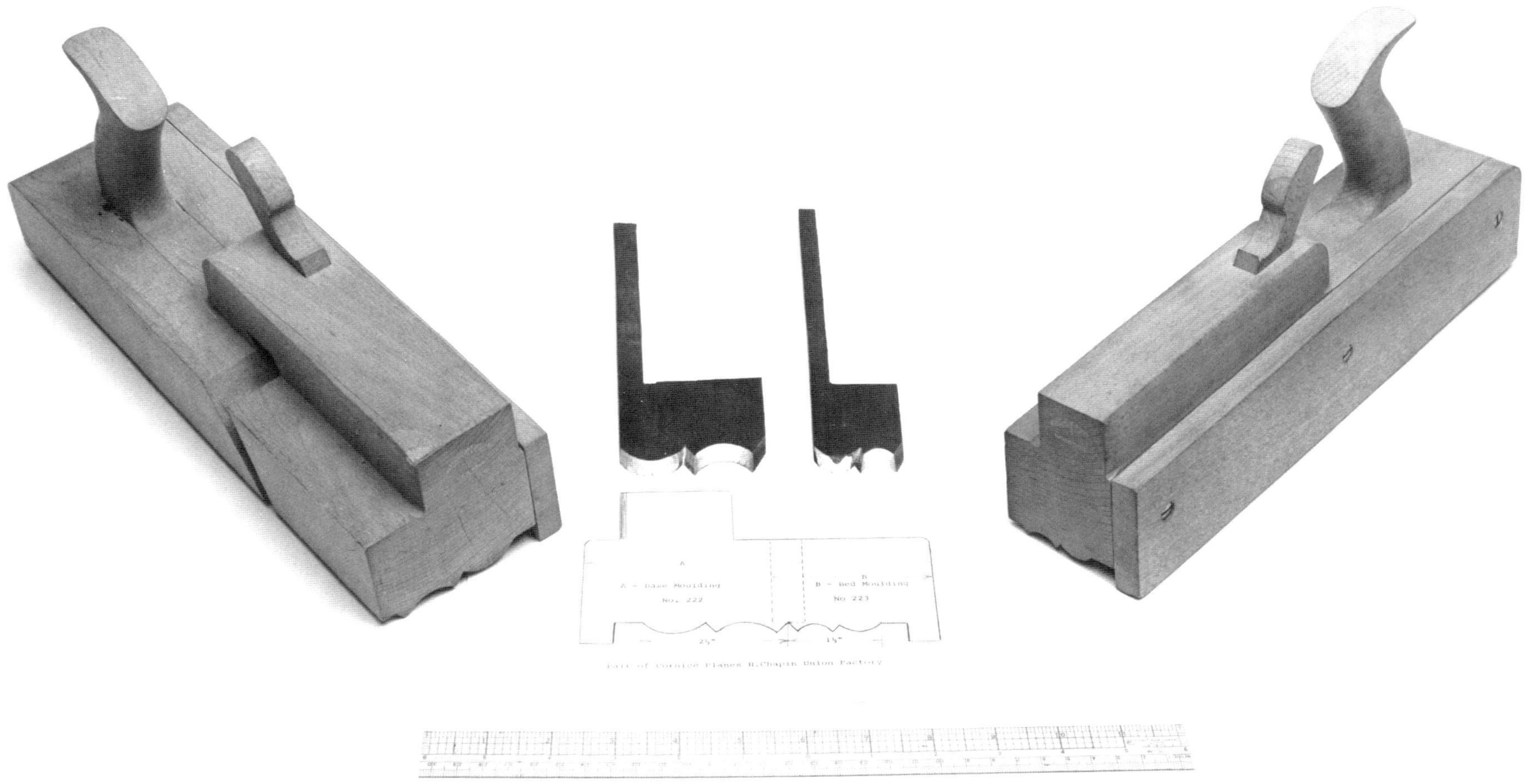

Fig. 103 - Pair of Base (#222) and Bed (#223) Handled Moulding Planes.
[See page 281 (page 49 *1874 H.Chapin's Son Catalogue*)]

Fig. 104 - Adjustable Sash Planes. Manually Adjustable; Screw Arm Self-Regulating; and Iron Screw Self-Regulating

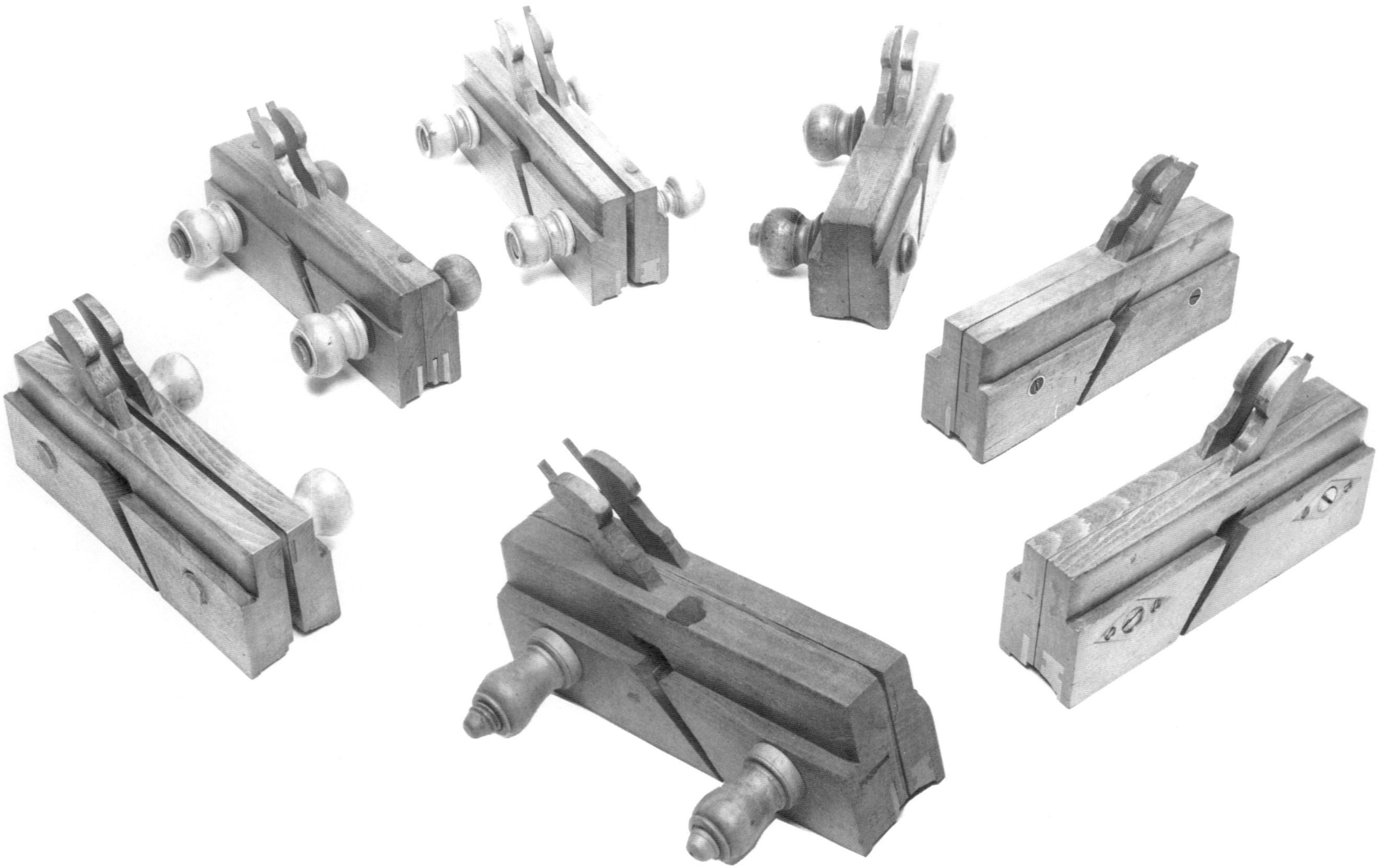

Fig. 105 — Screw Arm Filletster Planes. Upper left: Sash or Back Filletser No. 203 with Boxwood Arms; Front Center: No. 153, Dovetailed Boxed, Arranged with Brass Stops on Both Sides so it can be used as a Conventional or Back Filletster; Right" No. 154 Dovetailed Boxed with Brass Screw Stop.

Fig. 106 - No. 162 Raising Planes with Adjustable Side Stops.

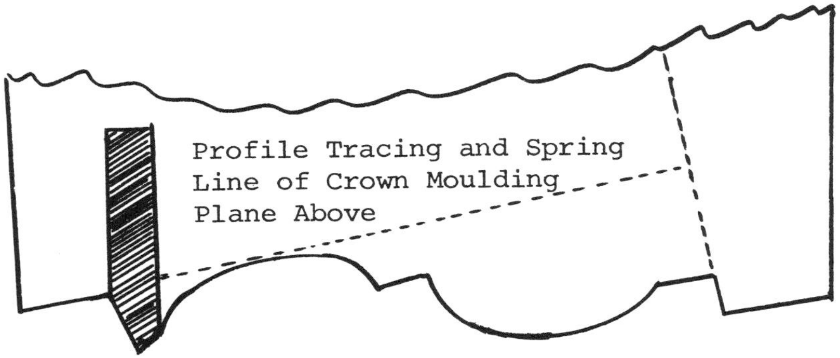

445

Profile of #225 Cabinet OGee Above

Profile Tracing and Spring Line of Crown Moulding Plane Above

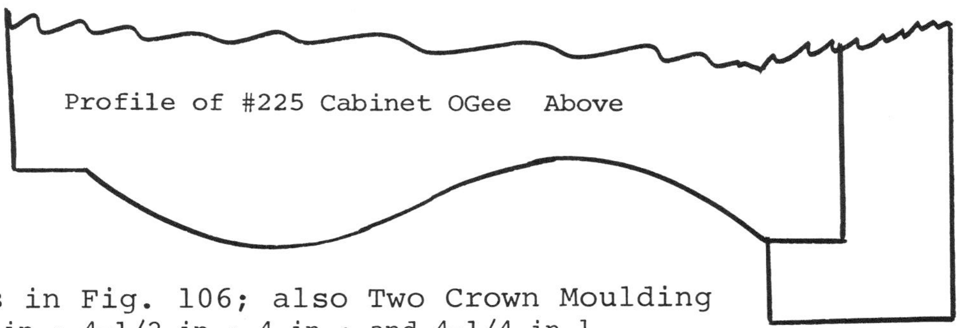

Fig. 107 - Soles of Two Raising Planes in Fig. 106; also Two Crown Moulding Planes [Widths: Left to Right: 4-3/4 in.; 4-1/2 in.; 4 in.; and 4-1/4 in.]

Fig. 108 - Front and Rear Views of M. Copeland 1 in. Grecian Ovolo Plane
Mint Condition Directly off the Shelf - Note Writing on Rear "Grecian
OGee with Bevel 87½ ¢" May have been made at Union Factory. c.1830

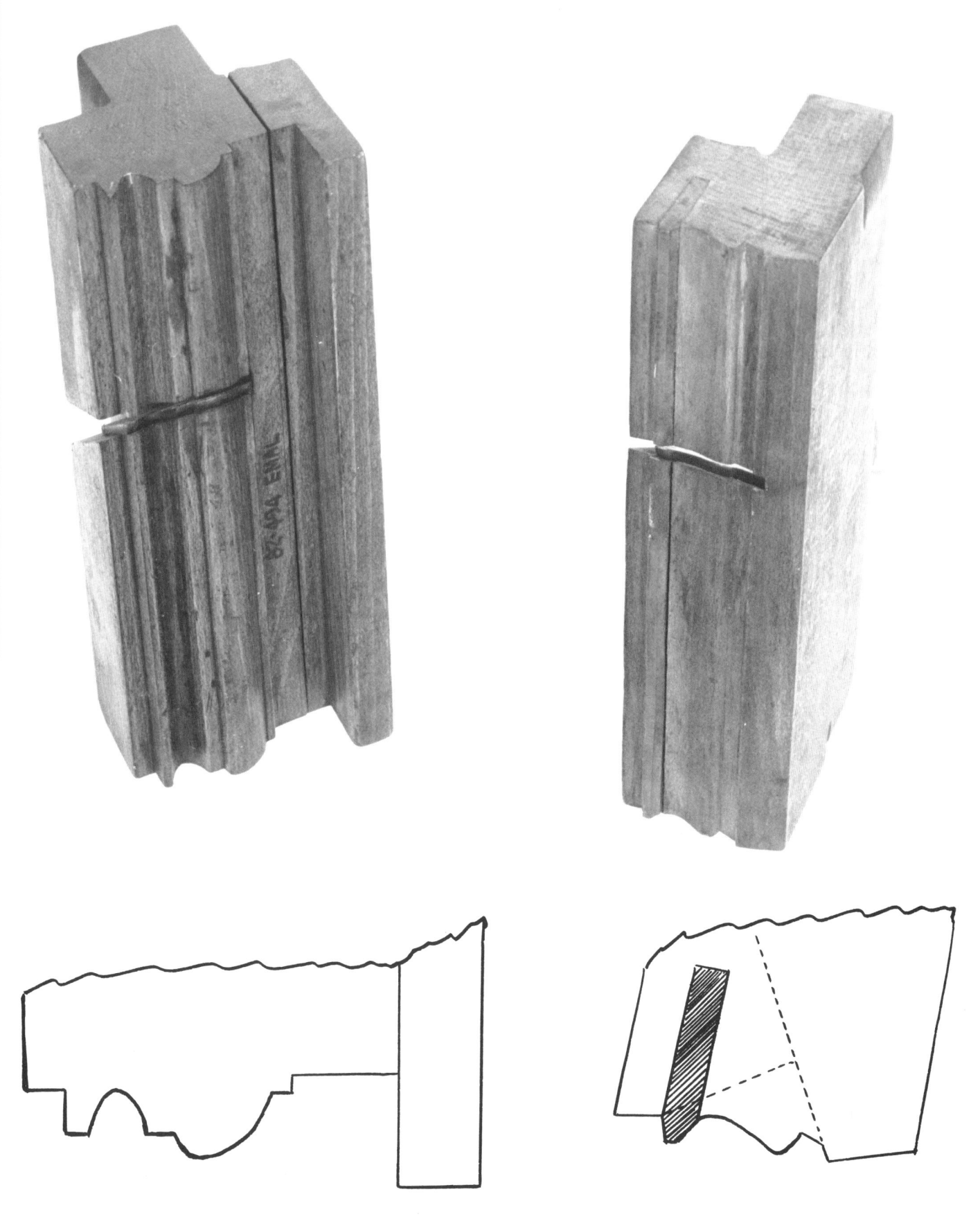

Fig. 109 - Two Early Union Factory Complex Moulding Planes.
Left: No. 4 [unidentified number] with attached fence, no spring.
Right: No. 160 1¼ in. Grecian OGee with Bevel. Tracing of
Profile indicatin Spring Line.

Fig. 110 - Miscellaneous Plows. Left to Right: P. Chapin, Baltimore; N. Chapin, Eagle Factory, [Westfield, Mass]; Willis Thrall & Son, Hartford [probably made at Union Factory]; #24 Solid Box First Rate Plow without Handle by H. Chapin. [P.Chapin Plane, Collection of Jim Hill]

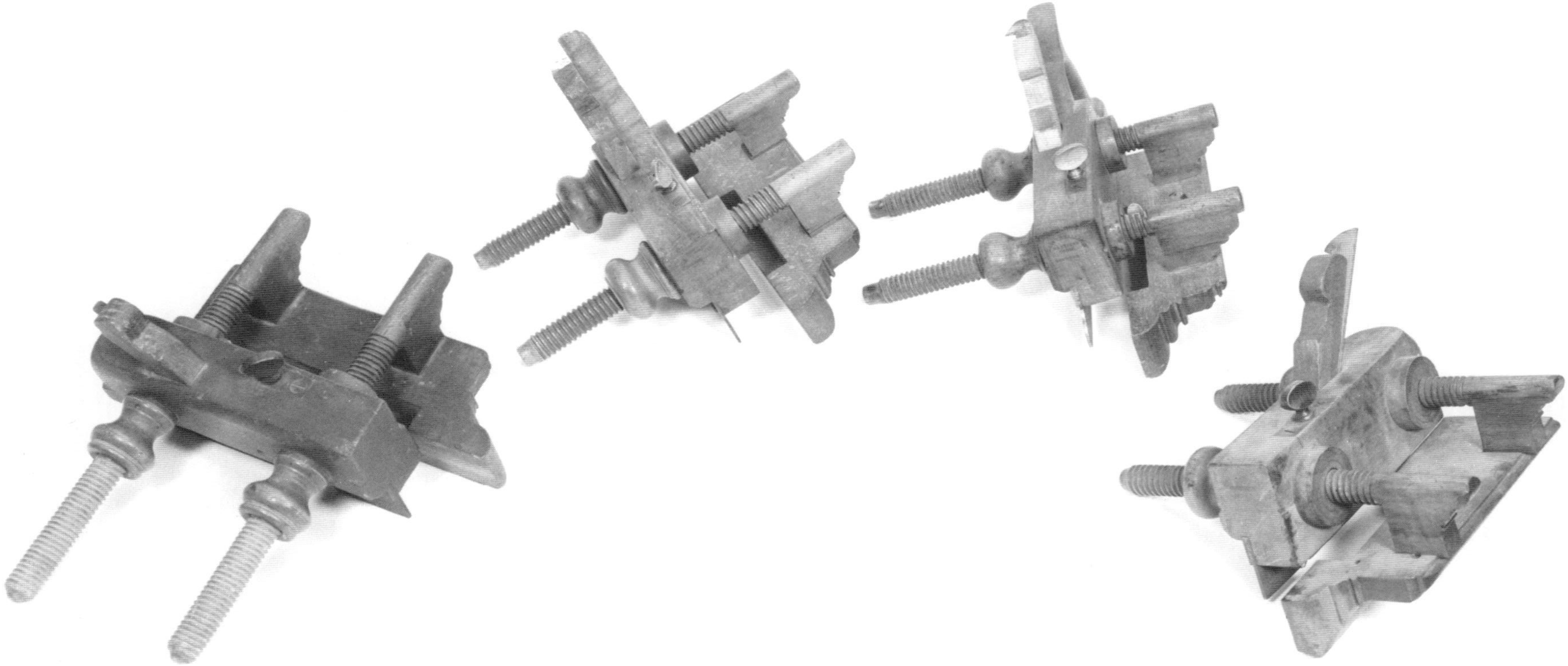

Fig. 111 - Union Factory Plows: Bottom: 1st. Rate Solid Boxwood with Rosewood [sap wood] Nuts and Lock Washers with overprint on Union Factory of "WAY & SHERMAN, N.York". Top: #238 2nd Rate, Screw Arm Plow with Dovetailed Boxed Fence.

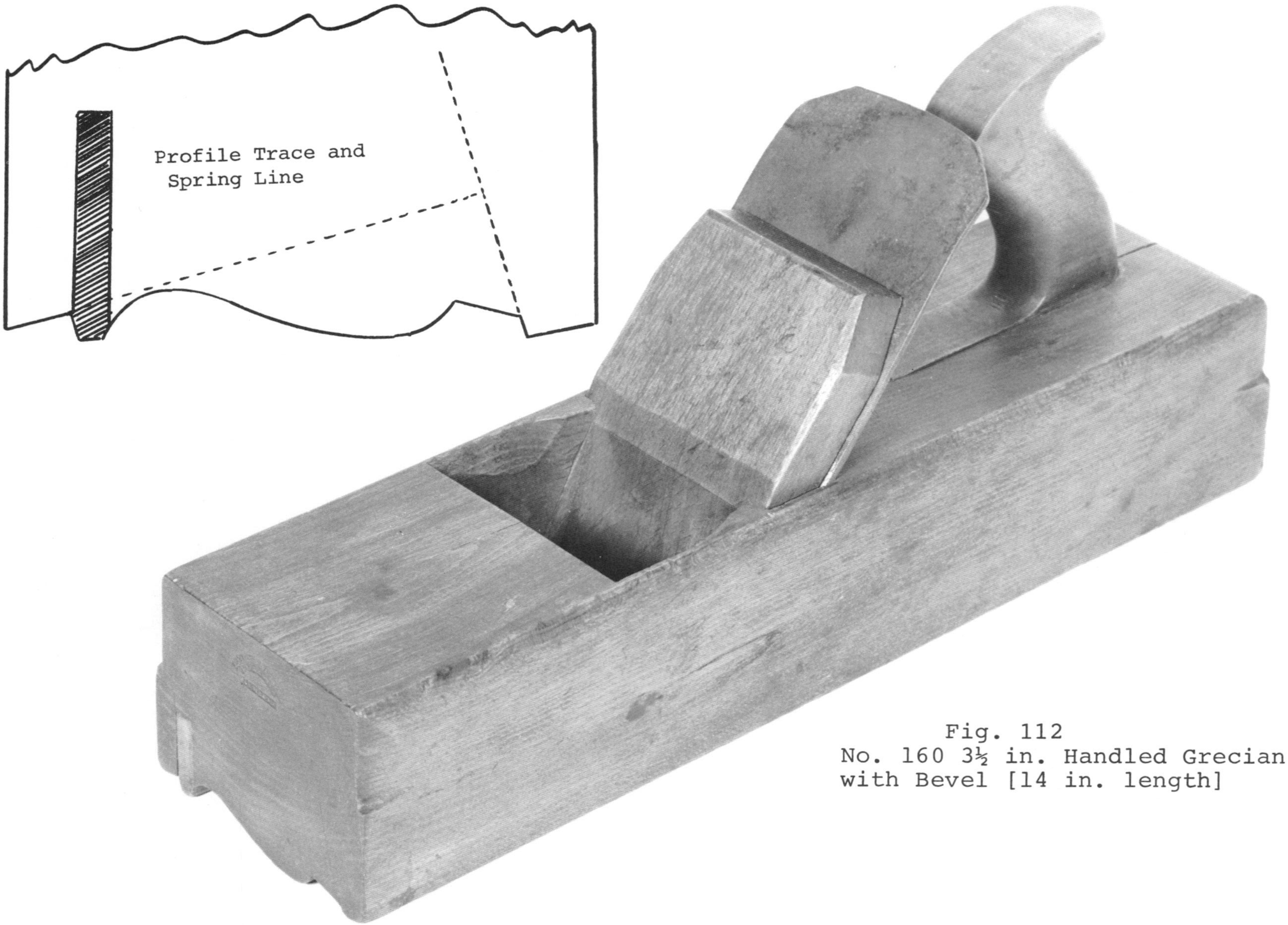

450

Fig. 112
No. 160 3½ in. Handled Grecian OGee with Bevel [14 in. length]

Profile Trace and Spring Line

Index

The Index is divided into two sections: I. Persons and II Subject Matter, covered in the twelve Chapters. The material in the Appendices is not indexed.

I. Persons

Armour, W.J.: 18, 52 - 66
Bolles, Franklin: 151, 152, 160, 169
Bolles, Henry: 12, 15
Brown, Henry: 80, 85, 93, 95, 99, 144
Butler, John: 253, 349, 352 - 354
Carter, Charles: 218, 223
Chapin, E.M.: 2, 6, 115, 116, 135, 136, 180, 187 - 190, 205 - 208, 217, 226, 227, 231 - 233, 328, 333, 345, 349, 352, 354, 356, 359, 360, 367, 382, 392, 414
Chapin, F.M.: 2, 365, 382, 387, 388, 391, 392, 400
Chapin, G.W.: 2, 115, 180, 187, 189, 205 - 208, 217
Chapin, Hermon: 1 - 3, 6, 12 - 17, 67, 70, 74 - 95, 97, 99, 100, 113 - 116, 135, 136, 138, 140 - 142, 144 - 158, 160, 162 - 166, 169, 172, 180, 187 - 189, 204 - 206, 222, 322, 344, 349, 382, 392
Chapin, H.M.: 2, 365, 382, 387, 388, 391, 392, 408
Chapin, Levi: 1, 95
Chapin, Nathaniel: 1, 95, 155
Chapin, Philip (I): 74, 75
Chapin, Philip E. (II): 2, 115, 135, 136, 180, 187, 189, 206, 207, 322, 328 - 333, 367
Chelor, Caesar: 45, 46
Clark, D.: 47
Clark, E.: 47
Copeland, Alfred: 67, 70
Copeland, D.: 3, 6, 9, 12 - 14, 17, 70, 73, 100, 108, 109
Copeland, D. & M.: 1, 3, 10, 11, 73, 100
Copeland, M.: 3, 9, 70, 73, 100, 108, 111
Copeland, M. & A.: 67, 70, 75
Davis, L.L.: 305, 306, 345, 346
DeForest, L.: 226, 228, 230, 343
Foss, Henry: 333 - 338, 331, 340
Fuller, Jo: 45, 47 - 50
Gardner, John: 22 - 28
Hitchcock, Lambert: 7, 180
Hogarty, Michael: 359, 377
Holmes, Rufus E.: 365, 381, 382, 387, 388
Ingraham, Edward: 29 - 50
Jones, Solomon: 158, 160, 189, 200
Kellogg, George: 12 - 14, 16, 70, 140, 141, 322
Kellogg, Isaac: 12 - 14, 16, 40, 140, 141, 322

Kennedy, Leonard: 7, 9, 10
Marden, John: 302, 349, 351, 354, 357
Merrill, Catherine: 6, 12, 143
Mosher, George D.: 307, 333, 340
Pearce, J.: 216
Nicholson, F.: 44, 46
Nicholson, J.: 46
Rust, Solon: 29, 113, 226, 227, 232 - 240, 242 - 253
Seymour, H.A.: 157, 158, 160, 161
Sholl, C.: 285, 349, 351, 357
Smith, Aaron: 45, 48, 49, 50
Stephens, Lorenzo: 113, 162 - 164, 167, 174, 308, 382
Stephens, Delos: 113, 162, 164, 180, 184, 308, 377, 378, 381, 382, 394
Stephens, F.L.: 388, 391, 392
Stratton Bros.: 345
Thrall, Willis: 158 - 160, 172, 183, 201, 308, 312
Vogel: 345, 408, 409, 411
Warner, William: 79, 80, 113
Wetherel, H.: 7, 8
Winship, William: 12, 15, 79, 93, 95

II. Subject Matter

Agreements with H.Chapin: 15, 70, 76 - 92, 99, 135, 144 - 145, 148 - 150, 153 - 157
Auburn Tool Co.: 88, 209, 212, 213, 313, 320, 359, 362, 363, 414
Baltimore Firms: 74
Barkhamsted: 7, 114, 146, 180, 184
Baldwin Tool Co.: 200, 202
Barton, D.R.: 188
Beech: 18, 44
Belcher Brothers: 151, 160, 162, 172, 183, 201, 216, 308
Birch: 44
Boxing: 69
Carriage Makers' Tools: 301
Chapin Machine Co.: 322, 324 - 327, 414
Chapin Manufacturing Co.: 322, 333, 335
Chapin-Stephens Co.: 160, 169, 174, 345, 375, 377, 382 - 384, 388 - 414
Collins Manufacturing Co.: 93 - 94
Copeland & Chapin: 2, 6, 12, 15 - 17
Copeland, D. & M.: 1 - 3
Cost Data: 100, 106, 107, 115, 118, 120 - 128
Discount Sheets (Union Factory): 205, 218, 224, 253, 254, 255, 258, 307, 366, 370, 386

Eagle Factory: 95, 96
English Planemaking: 43
Gauges: 105, 134, 189, 210, 211, 253, 284 - 287, 302, 349 - 357, 371, 403, 406, 407
Greenfield Tool Co.: 188, 226, 229, 313, 320, 349, 414
Hartford: 1, 7, 9, 16, 17, 322
H. Chapins & Sons: 2, 115, 135, 160, 180, 182, 183, 188, 189, 191, 203, 206, 226, 323
H. Chapin's Sons: 2, 160, 189, 201, 209, 210, 214, 216, 220, 221
H. Chapin's Son: 2, 160, 217, 241, 253 - 256, 297, 307, 311, 312, 320, 321, 329, 349, 358, 359, 362, 363
H. Chapin's Son & Co.: 2, 160, 365, 366, 368, 369, 371, 377, 378, 381, 391, 393, 394, 396
Howland & Co.: 209, 213
Iron Planes: 267, 329, 330 - 338, 340
Kiln Drying: 114, 214, 215
Levels: 134, 287, 288, 302 - 306, 342 - 348, 371, 374, 388, 393, 403, 408, 409, 411
L. Stephens & Co.: 160, 162, 165, 174
Metallic Plane Co.: 329 - 331
Middletown Tool Co.: 203
New Hartfrod: 1, 5, 7, 16, 17, 138 - 141, 144 - 158, 168, 180, 322, 367
Ohio Tool Co.: 188, 212, 216, 313, 320, 362, 363, 414
Pine Meadow: 5, 6, 67, 382
Phoenix Factory: 180, 184, 185
Planes -
    Bench: 11, 18, 28, 53 - 56, 80, 91, 103, 120, 212, 131, 182, 185, 195, 264 - 266, 268, 300, 402
    Filletster: 11, 64 - 66, 104, 122, 123, 126, 133, 182, 185, 196, 253, 402
    Moulding: 8 - 11, 29 - 50, 56 - 60, 63, 68, 84 - 87, 89, 96, 100, 104, 105, 108 - 112, 115, 121 - 126, 132, 182, 185, 196 - 198, 253, 269 - 282, 402
    Plow: 11, 61, 62, 67, 71 - 73, 79, 85, 105, 127, 133, 182, 185, 198, 226 - 233, 238 - 253, 282 - 284, 402
    Sash: 11, 96, 105, 126, 133, 182, 185, 198, 253, 276, 402
Plane Irons: 112, 168, 181, 182, 200, 024, 296, 403
Plane Lumber: 117, 181, 214, 222, 315, 316

Plane Machinery: 218, 223
Planemaking: 18 - 43, 52 - 66, 240, 242 - 249
Plane Manufacturers Association: 188, 313, 317 - 320
Plane Templates: 18 - 21, 57, 248
Rules: 10, 103, 130, 131, 151 - 179, 193, 194, 258 - 263, 300, 356, 359, 371 - 374, 387, 394, 401, 406 - 409
Rulemaking Machinery: 168, 170, 171, 179 180
Rule Manufacturers Association: 172 - 174, 183, 186, 188, 201, 216, 308, 310, 312, 378 - 381
Sandusky Tool Co.: 313, 320, 362, 363, 414
Sargent & Co.: 216, 218 - 221, 226, 344, 383
Spokeshaves: 307, 333, 336, 340
Stanley Rule & Level Co.: 158, 160, 162, 172, 174, 176, 183, 201, 216, 253, 308, 312, 329, 341, 343, 345, 349, 383, 390, 413, 414
Standard Rule Co.: 251, 308, 310, 333
Steele, Clark & Co.: 349, 350
Stephens & Co.: 160, 165, 166, 170, 171, 174, 180 - 183, 201, 216, 309, 311
Stephens, L. & Co.: 160, 162, 165, 174
Stephens Patent Combination Rule: 174 - 176
Trade Catalogues and Price Lists:
    D. & M. Copeland: 11, 100
    Union Factory:
        1839: 100 - 105
        1853: 102 - 105
        1858: 115, 119, 344
        1859: 129 - 174
        1861: 180, 183
        1862: 180
        1865: 189, 192 - 200, 209
        1874, 256 - 296, 344, 349
        1882, 297 - 307, 344, 349
    H.Chapin's Son & Co. 1897: 359, 368, 383
    Chapin-Stephens Co.:
    1902: 384 - 386
    No. 114: 387, 389, 391
    No. 122, 396
Union Factory: 12, 67 - 69, 71, 72, 74, 77, 95, 97, 100, 101, 113, 114, 116, 117, 129 - 134, 137, 140, 156, 169, 180 - 182, 189, 204, 205, 207, 210, 214, 217, 224, 226, 253, 254, 257, 297, 298, 315, 321, 323, 344, 347, 367, 368, 373, 375, 384
U.S. Census Data:
    1850: 113, 162
    1860: 174
    1870: 218